Audrey H. Nora MD

Genetic Concepts and Neoplasia

GENETIC CONCEPTS AND NEOPLASIA

*A Collection of Papers Presented at
the Twenty-Third Annual Symposium
on Fundamental Cancer Research,
1969*

*Published for
The University of Texas M. D. Anderson
Hospital and Tumor Institute at Houston,
Houston, Texas*

Baltimore
THE WILLIAMS & WILKINS COMPANY
1970

Dedicated to the Memory of
Theophilus Shickel Painter, Ph.D., Sc.D.
(1889–1969)

Acknowledgments

Members of the staff of The University of Texas M. D. Anderson Hospital and Tumor Institute at Houston acknowledge with appreciation the efforts of Dr. David E. Anderson, chairman of the 1969 symposium committee, and Dr. Jose M. Trujillo, vice-chairman, and of the following committee members: Drs. A. Clark Griffin, T. C. Hsu, Charles R. Shaw, Joseph G. Sinkovics, T. Elton Stubblefield, Walter J. Burdette, Russell W. Cumley, Robert B. Hurlbert, Mr. Joe E. Boyd, Jr., Mrs. Jane H. Brandenberger, and Miss Frances Goff. Acknowledgment is also made to Drs. Alexander G. Bearn, the late W. M. Court Brown, Boris Ephrussi, Hans F. Stich, H. Eldon Sutton, and K. Lemone Yielding, who graciously served as members of the advisory committee for this symposium. Judy A. Upton excellently served as secretary and coordinator for the chairman and committee.

Cosponsor of the symposium was The University of Texas Graduate School of Biomedical Sciences at Houston. Assistance and support also were provided by the American Cancer Society, Texas Division, and by grant R13 CA–11078–01 from the National Cancer Institute.

This symposium monograph was assembled and arranged for publication by the following members of the Publications Department at Anderson Hospital: Russell W. Cumley, Wendelyn White, and Joan McCay, assisted by Judith James, Barbara Gail Arnold, Lynda Burgner, Carol Dimopoulos, Janina Ely, Shirley Hartman, Judith Letteney, Lucinda Marinis, Nancy O'Dowd, Carol Thompson, and Kathleen Yacuzzo.

The volume was produced by Kathleen Yacuzzo under the direction of Joan McCay. Typesetting and printing were coordinated under the excellent supervision and cooperation of Mr. Claude Eads and Mr. Norman Purcell of The University of Texas Printing Division. The index was prepared by Lucinda Marinis under the direction of Wendelyn White and Joan McCay, with the consultation of Dr. David E. Anderson.

Table of Contents

Repair of Genetic Defects

Symposium Committee

Members   *Ex-Officio Members*

David E. Anderson, *Chairman*   Joe E. Boyd, Jr.

Jose M. Trujillo, *Vice-Chairman*   Jane H. Brandenberger

A. Clark Griffin   Walter J. Burdette

T. C. Hsu   Russell W. Cumley

Charles R. Shaw   Frances Goff

Joseph G. Sinkovics   Robert B. Hurlbert

T. Elton Stubblefield

Advisory Committee

Alexander G. Bearn, Professor and Chairman of the Department of Medicine, Cornell Medical Center, New York, New York

W. M. Court Brown (died December 16, 1968), Director, Medical Research Council's Clinical and Population Cytogenetics Research Unit, Western General Hospital, Edinburgh, Scotland

Boris Ephrussi, Professor and Director, Centre National de la Recherche Scientifique, Seine et Oise, France

Hans F. Stich, Chairman and Professor of Biology, Cancer Research Centre, University of British Columbia, Vancouver, British Columbia

H. Eldon Sutton, Professor of Zoology, The University of Texas at Austin, Austin, Texas

K. Lemone Yielding, Professor of Biochemistry and Chief, Laboratory of Molecular Biology, University of Alabama in Birmingham, Birmingham, Alabama

Session Chairmen

Alexander G. Bearn, Department of Medicine, Cornell Medical Center, New York, New York

D. G. Harnden, Department of Cancer Studies, Western General Hospital, Edinburgh, Scotland

T. C. Hsu, Department of Biology, The University of Texas M. D. Anderson Hospital and Tumor Institute at Houston, Houston, Texas

John W. Littlefield, Department of Pediatrics, Genetics Unit, Children's Service, Massachusetts General Hospital, Boston, Massachusetts

Hans F. Stich, Department of Biology, University of British Columbia, Vancouver, British Columbia

K. Lemone Yielding, Laboratory of Molecular Biology, University of Alabama in Birmingham, Birmingham, Alabama

Genetic Concepts and Neoplasia

Introduction

R. LEE CLARK, M.D.

President, The University of Texas M. D. Anderson Hospital and Tumor Institute at Houston, Houston, Texas

Meaningful cancer research is dependent upon selective information from various disciplines of biological and medical research. Only through the interaction and cooperative efforts of basic scientists and clinical researchers can we expect to answer the complex question of how neoplastic growth proceeds.

This eclectic approach, which integrates otherwise distant specialties, has proved highly productive in increasing our knowledge of cancer during the past three decades. However, keeping abreast of the general progress in related fields and maintaining an effective exchange of information between basic scientists and clinicians present tremendous problems to the specialist. For this reason, a Symposium on Fundamental Cancer Research was established at this institution at which various specialists gather annually to exchange ideas and information on the many aspects of cancer research. Each year, a subject is selected for exploration in detail by those scientists actively engaged in seeking new knowledge in this phase of research.

The symposium series is a major feature of the educational and research activities of The University of Texas M. D. Anderson Hospital and Tumor Institute at Houston. We make every effort to bring concepts of the various fields of basic life sciences to bear upon the problems encountered in the study of the neoplastic process. The proceedings of these symposia, published in monograph form, have not only brought the latest concepts of fundamental cancer research to the critical attention of oncologists, but have also contributed to the recorded knowledge of the life sciences.

The first symposium was held in 1946 and was attended almost entirely by investigators from Houston, Austin, and Galveston. The papers presented at the first six symposia covered diverse topics of general interest. However, enthusiasm for the meetings increased, and the programs were modified in 1952 so that each symposium now focuses on a single theme pertinent to the cancer problem. Gradually, the symposium series evolved from a small local meeting to a conference of international interest.

The subject of the 1968 symposium was "Exploitable Molecular Mechanisms and Neoplasia." The basic processes underlying the control of growth, differentiation, and tissue function and their relevance to malignant transformation and proliferation were studied in depth. This year's symposium topic, "Genetic Concepts and Neoplasia," is an extension of the 1968 theme.

The idea that cancer is caused by gene mutations is old, dating back to the earliest days of genetics; more recently it has received considerable attention. As early as 1866, Paul Broca reported the existence of a family genetically prone to neoplasia. All four daughters of a woman who died of breast carcinoma died of cancer—two of hepatomas and two of breast cancer. Ten of the 19 children in the third generation died of some type of neoplastic growth.

Beginning about 1870, the significance of chromosomes was recognized by cell biologists in Germany, including Flemming, Kolliken, Herwig, and Weismann. Their investigations led them to conclude that the chromosomes were the bearers of the hereditary determinants. About this same time, Miescher discovered nucleic acid. In the early years of the twentieth century, Cuénot (France), Tyzzer (United States), and Bateson (England) applied Mendel's genetic principles to animal studies, and in 1909, Johannsen of Denmark named the gene and distinguished between genotype and phenotype.

In 1914, Boveri (Germany) showed that tumors arise from abnormal chromosomal or chromatic complex developments and that the causes are varied. Numerous other scientists representing many nations have given us keys to the complex structure and function of genetic mechanisms; among them are 17 Nobel Prize recipients.

In 1933, Morgan (United States) received the Nobel Prize for his "discoveries concerning the function of the chromosome in the transmission of heredity." After extensive experimentation with *Drosophila* during the early 1900's, he not only furnished further proof of the Mendelian principles of heredity, but also introduced the concepts of "linkage" and "crossing-over."

In 1927, Müller (United States) demonstrated the first known instance of a physical agent which produced mutations when he revealed that the penetration of ionizing radiation into cells causes heritable mutations. The following year, Bauer (Germany) incorporated the gene mutation theory into the somatic mutation theory of cancer.

The deoxyribonucleic acid (DNA) composition of genes was demonstrated by Avery, MacLeod, and McCarty in 1944; and the basis of many modern studies on evolution of molecules which led to the understanding of inborn errors of metabolism originated with Pauling's demonstration of the molecular basis of genetic abnormalities in the hemoglobins of man. The beginning of modern biochemical genetics came with the work in the 1940's by Beadle and Tatum (United States), who demonstrated that each gene controls the production of one enzyme in the bread mold *Neurospora,* and by Lederberg and Tatum, who led the way in molecular genetics by reporting sexual recombination in the intestinal bacterium *Escherichia coli.*

In the 1950's, Ochoa (United States) paved the way for the unraveling of the genetic code with his demonstration that an enzyme isolated from a bacterium was capable of polymerizing the precursors of ribonucleic acid (RNA) in vitro; this led to the synthesis of the pure homopolynucleotides. In 1956, Kornberg (United States) isolated DNA polymerase, an enzyme capable of polymerizing the four deoxyribonucleosides and which operates inside and outside the cell. Watson of the United States and Crick and Wilkins of England constructed their now famous model of the structure of DNA which fit the known chemistry and biophysical characteristics of the molecule and made gene replication and action understandable.

The French scientists Lwoff, Jacob, and Monod studied lysogeny, or the relationship of viruses to genes, and its genetic significance during the 1950's. In 1960, their researches revealed an area for further investigation—the genetic control and intiation of disease as well as of the developmental processes during the entire life cycle from conception to advanced age. At the same time, the cell-free system for studying the incorporation of amino acids into polypeptides was developed, and Nirenberg, Ochoa and their collaborators were able to establish the genetic code (the "three-letter nucleotide words"). Khorana (United States) synthesized polynucleotides of known composition and order and provided essential code words for the elucidation of the genetic code. Meanwhile, Crick and Brenner (England) developed the theoreteical basis for the code.

In 1965, Holley (United States) defined the total structure of a transfer RNA molecule. Many other equally important contributions were made by dedicated scientists in many fields, all united by the common search for the secrets of the life process and its perpetuation in normal and disease states.

Today, we are still searching for the relationship of genetic mechanisms to carcinogenesis and are here to discuss the recent advances in genetic concepts with respect to cancer. We believe that future progress in understanding this disease will be based on detailed knowledge of the cellular genetic apparatus. We must determine whether the suspected cause of a neoplastic process is mutational, chromosomal, or viral. The program this year will explore the current state of knowledge in the following four primary areas: (1) disorders predisposing to cancer that have a genetic etiology of either abnormal genes or chromosomes, (2) interactions at both molecular and cellular levels between the genetic apparatus and exogenous agents, namely, radiation, chemicals, and viruses, (3) the exploitable potential of studies in somatic cell genetics in relation to neoplastic growth, and (4) conceptual advances in molecular biology involving the nature of gene repair. I am sure that the presentations by the eminent speakers and the discussions at this symposium will be most beneficial in contributing to our understanding of the role of the genetic apparatus in neoplasia. A better knowledge of cellular mechanisms should help us manage, and perhaps, ultimately, prevent cancer in man.

We sincerely regret that this year's recipient of the Bertner Foundation Award, Dr. Boris Ephrussi, was unable to attend the symposium and present his address. We are delighted, however, that Dr. Ephrussi received this award *in absentia* and has submitted his lecture for publication in this monograph. From 1934 to the present, Dr. Ephrussi has conducted studies which have resulted in some major advances in the science of genetics. These studies include observations on the biochemical mechanisms of gene action in *Drosophila*, the original utilization of organ transplantation in *Drosophila* which proved that genes control the chemical reactions in the body, and a somatic cell hybridization system which opened new areas of investigation for cancer researchers in their efforts to understand neoplastic and normal cell interactions. Investigators in cancer research are deeply indebted to this energetic man for his outstanding achievement in physiological genetics.

I am also pleased to announce two new awards in honor of men instrumental in the establishment and growth of The University of Texas M. D. Anderson Hospital and Tumor Institute at Houston. The Wilson Stuart Stone Memorial Award for Outstanding Fundamental Research Achievement in the Biomedical Sciences was recently founded to honor the late Wilson Stuart Stone of The University of Texas. Dr. Stone conducted important genetic studies on *Drosophila* and bacteria which contributed greatly to the growth of studies in the sciences of population genetics, mechanisms of genetic mutation, and radiation biology. He also was a leading influence in the development of The University of Texas as an outstanding center in the field of genetics and in establishing The University of Texas Graduate School of Biomedical Sciences at Houston. Of late, his primary goal was to interest promising young researchers in all aspects of the biomedical sciences to work with him and at The University of Texas. Accordingly, this award will be made at this symposium in future years to young scientists for research contributions during the immediate past five years in an area of biomedical science.

The second new award is the Anderson Award for Scientific Creativity and Teaching, which was established to honor distinguished scientists, not on an annual basis, but when deemed especially appropriate. The first recipient of this award is Dr. T. S. Painter. His outstanding research in cytogenetics has added much to our knowledge of both genetics and the neoplastic processes. He pioneered investigations of human chromosomes which later were to lead to crucial development in karyotypic studies. He first demonstrated the significance of the salivary gland chromosomes in *Drosophila* which now enable us to determine the cytological position of many genes. In 1942, he was the first man to point out the significance of the nucleolus in protein biosynthesis. Most recently, his investigations have involved heterochromatin and puffing in relation to RNA production and the transcription of the DNA message.

As most of you know, Dr. Painter served as President of The University of Texas System from 1944 to 1952; during this period, he was very influential in establishing the M. D. Anderson Hospital and Tumor Institute and gave me my opportunity, in 1946, to be the first full-time Director. Dr. Painter continues to work actively at the age of 80.*

The staff of The University of Texas M. D. Anderson Hospital and Tumor Institute at Houston wish to express their gratitude for the assistance of the following organizations in co-sponsoring this symposium: the American Cancer Society, Texas Division; the National Cancer Institute of the U.S. Public Health Service; and The University of Texas Graduate School of Biomedical Sciences at Houston.

* Dr. Painter died suddenly on October 5, 1969, at Fort Stockton, Texas, while returning to Austin from a hunting trip.

Bertner Foundation
Award Lecture

Somatic Hybridization as a Tool for the Study of Normal and Abnormal Growth and Differentiation

BORIS EPHRUSSI

Centre de Génétique Moléculaire, Gif-sur-Yvette, France

However strong one's belief in the importance of a chosen task, its recognition by one's peers always causes a great deal of personal satisfaction. It is therefore with deep gratitude that I accepted the great honor of the Bertner Foundation Award bestowed on me, at least in part, for the task I assigned to myself in 1960, that of proving that somatic hybridization, discovered by Barski and co-workers a few months earlier, can be forged into a tool for the genetic analysis of somatic cells.

Most of the conditions that would have to be fulfilled to that end were stated in a lecture I gave a year and a half later at the University of Michigan, a lecture in which I expressed a great deal of optimism as to the feasibility of the project. I must admit that this optimism was based on the rather shaky ground of our very first observations of the new phenomenon of somatic hybridization and of the properties of somatic hybrids. It is nevertheless now a fact that all of these conditions have been, at least in part, fulfilled and that somatic hybridization has become an effective tool for genetic analysis of somatic cells. Moreover, it is being used in all three areas of biological research which I listed, as follows, in the same lecture as the principal future beneficiaries of the new tool (Ephrussi and Sorieul, 1962):

"1. .... genetic analysis of somatic cells could, theoretically, replace experimental breeding and, if combined with tissue culture methods, would tremendously accelerate the genetic study of species where experimental breeding is slow or, like in man, impossible for other reasons.

"2. Genetic analysis of somatic cells is obviously necessary in the study of embryonic differentiation . . ., this fundamental and mysterious process . . ., which to be understood, must be studied on the very cells which are the seat of differentiation.

"3. .... genetic analysis of somatic cells could also be of great assistance in the study of the neoplastic process, in particular of virus-induced neoplasia and, more generally, in the study of cell-virus relationship."

What gives me even more satisfaction than the Bertner Foundation Award is that all three listed areas of biology are taking advantage today of the technique of somatic hybridization, that almost a whole session of this symposium will be devoted to work done with the tool I helped to forge, and the expectation that all three areas I listed will be represented in it. The latter is just a guess, however, because the deliberately noncommittal (not to say inscrutable) titles given a year ahead of time make it impossible to be sure.

Be this as it may, it will become obvious, I think, that my optimism was justified in the end, and that somatic hybridization represents today a powerful tool for the study of the genetic basis of a number of important biological phenomena.

Forging this new tool, however, took the combined efforts of many, and I would feel very unfair if I did not take this opportunity to acknowledge the role of at least those few who are responsible for the major steps in the development of the technique of somatic hybridization as we have it today. I shall do that in the course of a brief account of the history of somatic hybridization.

History of Somatic Hybridization

Strange as it seems, it appears timely to begin this account by recalling that the discovery of somatic hybridization was the work of a team of French workers led by Georges Barski. Although their first paper (Barski, Sorieul, and Cornefert, 1960) suggests that, in setting up mixed cultures of two mouse cell lines differing in cell morphology as well as in karyotype, Barski was looking for evidence of Pneumococcus-like transformation rather than for evidence of somatic hybridization, there is no doubt that these experiments first revealed the occurrence of cell hybrization. No search in the literature will prove that somatic hybridization was discovered in 1838 rather than in 1960, or in Oxford rather than in Villejuif, France (cf. Harris and Watkins, 1965; Harris, Watkins, Ford, and Schoefl, 1966).

It seems fair to say that the extension of Barski's results to numerous other pairs of mouse cell lines and the study of their karyotypes and phenotypes by a number of my co-workers and students—in particular, S. Sorieul, L. Scaletta, and Michihiro Yoshida—represented the second important step in the progress of somatic hybridization (reviewed by Ephrussi, Scaletta, Stenchever, and Yoshida, 1964), which stimulated members of other laboratories to join the ranks of cell hybridizers.

The third step in the progression of somatic hybridization was, in my opinion, the demonstration by Littlefield (1964) that the rare hybrids formed in most mixed cultures can be selected, with the help of drug resistance markers, in a manner analogous to that used in microbial genetics. (Littlefield's system is, in fact, an adaptation to mammalian cells of a selective system devised for bacteria by Szybalski, Szybalska, and Ragnie [1962].) Littlefield's original system, or his system as modified by Davidson and Ephrussi (1965), has permitted the isolation of many interesting new hybrids, and has shown the way for the use of "inborn errors of metabolism" as selective markers. These have recently been used by Siniscalco, Knowles, and Steplewski (1969) for the first successful crosses of diploid human cells.

The demonstration by Harris and Watkins (1965) that the incidence of fusion of cells of similar or different types and/or species can be tremendously increased by the action of ultraviolet-irradiated Sendai virus was an important step in the establishment of an alternative (or complement) to selection. It was proved shortly afterward by Yerganian and Nell (1966) and Coon and Weiss (1969) that, when properly handled, virus treatment can result in the formation of viable hybrids.

Harris and Watkins' 1965 observations on the formation of interspecific heterokaryons were also the stimulus which resulted in the isolation, by M. Weiss and myself, of the first spontaneous and viable interspecific hybrids (Ephrussi and Weiss, 1965) which, by the wealth of "inbuilt genetic markers" they contain (reviewed by Ephrussi and Weiss, 1967), proved to be unique for a variety of purposes, and they are now being used in a number of laboratories.

The last important step to be mentioned is the recent discovery by Weiss and Green (1967) of the rapid elimination of human chromosomes from human-mouse hybrids. The uses to which this phenomenon can be put in cancer research are illustrated in this volume (see Weiss, 1970, pages 456 to 476, this volume). I shall add only that the rapid loss of most human chromosomes permits, under appropriate circumstances, the localization of human genes on definite human chromosomes (Weiss and Green, 1967).

This is, as I see it, the list of those who, for their contributions to somatic cell hybridization, are entitled to a fair share of the great honor bestowed upon me. As for my own contribution, it consisted, I believe, mainly in the unwavering adherence to the principle, ascribed to Linus Pauling: "Don't let the facts interfere with the theory!"

Cellular or Molecular Approach?

Let us now turn from techniques to problems. I am, of course, refer-ring to those which are indicated in the title of my paper—the problems of normal and abnormal growth and differentiation. First, I will answer a question which, no doubt, is on the tips of many tongues: "Was not all this patient work I have described a waste of time? Can we not, at present, bypass the painstaking genetic analysis and seek the solution of the problems of cell differentiation and neoplasia by a direct attack at the molecular level?"

My own answer to this question is an emphatic no and it is, I am sure, sincerely shared by all those who are trying to explore the phe-nomena under consideration by means of somatic hybridization. My answer is no, neither because I wonder whether the mechanisms of the phenomena of normal and abnormal growth and differentiation must ultimately be described in molecular terms, nor because I deny the value of the information on these problems which, in fact, is being gained via the molecular approach. It is not because a differentiated cell of one tissue differs from a differentiated cell of another (or from its more or less remote precursors), and a neoplastic cell differs from its normal ancestor by a multiplicity of parameters, and because the nature of the complex interconnections between these numerous parameters is at the very heart of the problems. I believe that, because of the complexity of these inter-connections, the mechanisms of differentiation and neoplasia are, and for some time will be, more accessible to genetic analysis than to analysis of any other type.

Neoplastic Transformation

Undoubtedly, by far the simplest system at our disposal for the study of carcinogenesis is the exactly controllable and reproducible virus-induced neoplastic transformation of cells grown in vitro. This trans-formation, whether caused by ribonucleic acid- or deoxyribonucleic acid-containing oncogenic viruses, is characterized by multiple parameters which distinguish the transformed cells from their normal counterparts. Depending on the particular system, i.e., the kinds of interacting cells and viruses, all or most of the changes listed in Table 1 accompany the transformation.

In spite of the massive attack on the problem of viral oncogenesis which began with the establishment, in the late 1950's, of in vitro systems, the relationships between parameters 1 to 6 (Table 1) of virus-induced

TABLE 1. *Changes Accompanying Virus-Induced Transformation*

1. Modification of cell morphology
2. Increased incidence of chromosomal aberrations
3. Shortening of generation time, activation of cellular DNA synthesis
4. Acquisition of "permanence" or immortality
5. Loss of contact inhibition of cell movement and/or multiplication
6. Acquisition of several new antigens, in particular:
     a) Induced complement-fixing antigen (ICFA) or T-antigen
     b) Specific transplantation antigen (ITA)
7. Acquisition of neoplasticity as defined by the test of tumor production in immunologically compatible hosts

transformations and their bearing on neoplasticity (parameter 7) remain largely unknown. What is the role of the virus in the neoplastic transformation of the cell? Is the transformed state caused and maintained by the integration of the viral genome into the host's genetic machinery (*i.e.*, presumably the host's genome)? Or is the role of the virus limited to the induction in it of a heritable change? These fundamental questions remain unanswered even in the cases of the DNA viruses polyoma and, especially, SV40, which have attracted so much attention because of possible bearing on cancer in human beings.

As is well known, the greatest difficulty in answering these questions is that, until recently, there was no direct and unequivocal proof of the presence of the viral genome, or part thereof, in the cells transformed by these viruses. That is why, as soon as cell hybridization became possible, I undertook, with the late S. Sorieul, an experiment which I recalled as follows at the Nineteenth Annual Symposium on Fundamental Cancer Research:

"My own intervention in the polyoma problem goes back to the days when Vogt and Dulbecco (1960), from their early studies of the polyoma transformation, concluded that the role of the virus in the transformation of a normal cell into a neoplastic cell may consist either (1) in the integration of the viral genome (or of a part thereof) into the host cell genome, or (2) in the induction of a "cancer mutation" in the host cell. Stated in the genetic terms, the first hypothetical mechanism amounts to a gain of genetic material, the second one to a loss. With the advent of somatic hybridization, it became possible to test these alternatives, because they have the following corollaries. According to the first hypothesis, the hybrid between a polyoma transformed cell and a normal cell should be neoplastic; according to the second, it should be normal. We therefore undertook such crosses, and I shall give you the first results even though, by the time the hybrids were obtained, the reasoning which led to the experiments became obsolete as a result of the discovery of regulatory mechanisms" (Ephrussi, 1966).

Meanwhile, however, the discovery of the presence in cells transformed by polyoma and simian virus 40 (SV40) (to whatever mammalian species they belong) of virus-specific neoantigens ITA and T (unrelated to the viral antigens) was generally taken as a very strong indication, even proof, that they are coded by viral genes and, *mutatis mutandis*, that at least a part of the viral genome persists in the transformed cells (see, however, Huebner, 1967). The demonstration of the presence in these cells of an RNA species complementary to viral DNA (Benjamin, 1966) gave strong support to this conclusion, but the direct and final proof of the persistence of the whole SV40 genome in cells transformed by this virus was not provided until production of infectious virus was obtained by the use of the basic genetic device, *i.e.*, the combination of two cells possessing different genetic properties, namely, (Sendai virus-induced) fusion of SV40-transformed cells with susceptible indicator cells (Koprowski, Jensen, and Steplewski, 1967; Watkins and Dulbecco, 1967).

In retrospect, it is interesting to note that the argument of virus specificity, even though it led to the correct conclusion, was of dubious logic. Now, when the persistence of the viral genome in SV40-transformed cells is definitely established, the same argument is used to infer that the neoantigens are coded by viral genes. I shall consider these two points separately.

INTEGRATED VIRAL GENOMES

The now proved persistence, in the SV40-transformed cells, of the viral genome(s) and the likelihood of its integration into the genome of the cell (Weiss, Ephrussi, and Scaletta, 1968; Weiss, 1970, pages 456 to 476, this volume) make it highly probable that the viral genome is subject to a control basically similar to that which interferes with the full expression of the genes of temperate phage λ when it is integrated (as prophage) into the genome of *Escherichia coli*. Prophage contains all the genetic information needed for the formation of complete infectious phage, but its expression is checked by the action of a virus-specific protein, the repressor. The presence of the repressor renders the bacterium immune because the repressor interferes with the development of homo-immune superinfecting phages (*i.e.* phages recognizing the same repressor).

The facts (1) that viral coat proteins are not produced in SV40-

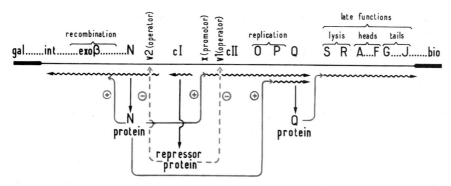

FIGURE 1. Provisional scheme of positive and negative regulation of transcription in the temperate bacteriophage λ. The upper (thin) line represents the genetic map of prophage λ inserted into the bacterial genome between genes gal and bio of *E. coli*. The transcription $(\sim\rightarrow)^x$ of most λ genes is positively controlled by the N protein. This is the case for: (1) The group of dispensable genes located to the left of N. (2) The segment x cII O P Q; in this case there is at least some transcription in the absence of the N product. This product, however, seems to be necessary for the full expression of the gene cluster. In addition, gene P can be switched on separately as a result of expression of N. (3) All the genes specifying late functions. Transcription of these genes is positively regulated by gene Q. The product of N is needed presumably for the expression of the late genes only because it activates Q. (The lengths of $\sim\rightarrow$ do not pretend to represent the actual sizes of the messenger RNA's, which are probably much shorter in most instances.) Positive regulation is symbolized by green arrows.

Any transcription, except for the region cI, can be blocked by the negative control (immunity) exerted by the product of cI (the λ repressor). This molecule interacts (red arrows) with two operators, thereby preventing transcription, to the left, of a unit of expression which includes N, and, to the right, of the cluster x cII O P Q. The other genes are blocked indirectly because the products of genes N and Q are absent. When these products are provided by heteroimmune superinfection, the prophage expresses gene P and all the late genes in spite of immunity.

transformed cells and (2) that these cells do not contain virus-specific thymidine kinase (an enzyme which apparently does operate in lytic infection) show that the genes specifying these proteins are, like the λ prophage genes, silenced in the persisting SV40 genome. Indeed, the presence in the transformed cells of a repressor interfering with the development of infectious SV40 recently has been directly demonstrated (Cassingena and Tournier, 1968). Thus, there must be more than an analogy between SV40-transformed cells and lysogenic bacteria, and it is worth recalling what is known about the organization and expression of the genetic material of λ.

The relative positions of many of the genes comprised in prophage λ (much more numerous than those comprised in the SV40 genome) are known. As can be seen in Figure 1, there is a remarkable correlation between their position within the prophage and their function. The genetic map of λ prophage looks very much like a programming tape of λ development. Furthermore, we are beginning to have a rather complete picture of the interactions which must occur for the full expression of the prophage's genetic information (which results in the production of infectious phage) and of the mechanism responsible for its repression. These interactions are also summarized in the schema of Figure 1. In brief, what it shows is that, in the bacterium lysogenic for λ, the transcription of almost all λ genes except cI is fully repressed by the product of this gene, the λ repressor (a protein). Repressor molecules interact with two operators, v1 and v2 (located on the two sides of cI) and thus prevent the transcription (negative control) of two units of expression— one of which includes gene N, the other the gene cluster x cII O P Q. The other genes (S to J) are blocked indirectly because their expression depends on the products of N and Q (positive control).

Induction of prophage development, achieved by various means, results from the inactivation of the repressor and thus permits the production of the product of N. This, in turn, sets into motion the different steps indicated by the green arrows (cf. Thomas, 1967; Dove, 1968). (For fuller explanation, see legend to Figure 1.)

This picture is impressive indeed. What I want to emphasize here, however, is the equally impressive fact that this picture was obtained almost exclusively by the use of genetic methodology as will be discussed later. Other disciplines (biochemistry, immunology) supplied only their techniques, and, generally played no more than a confirmatory role, and only exceptionally the role of arbiter in the choice of alternative hypotheses (as in the case of the protein versus RNA nature of the repressor).

ORIGIN OF VIRUS-INDUCED NEOANTIGENS

I shall return later to the techniques which microbial geneticists have used to gain the amazing amount of information of which I have given only the quintessence. Now, I wish to consider briefly the validity of the most important argument which has favored the idea of the presence of the viral genome in the transformed cells; it will be recalled that the latter was inferred from the virus specificity of neoantigens ITA and T. Yet, as recognized by Huebner in a paper written in 1965 (see also Rapp and Butel, 1970, pages 256 to 280, this volume),

> "The assumption that viral genes must be integrated within the cell genome in order to explain the persistence of such antigens [T-antigen] in replicating neoplastic cells is particularly subject to question for the following reason:
>
> "It must be assumed in the case of chemically and spontaneously induced neoplasms which often also develop new antigens (Old and Boyse, 1964; McBride and Wiener, 1964), that both the neoplastic state and the new antigens as well are the work of existing cell genes, *i.e.* the result of a kind of enforced somatic mutation or perhaps, more likely, de-repression of a normal gene.
>
> "It seems quite possible, therefore, that new expressions of existing cellular genes could also be responsible for at least some, if not most, of the antigenic and perhaps also of the neoplastic changes which occur after exposure to the DNA viruses under discussion" (Huebner, 1967).

The same *a priori* objection applies, of course, to the tumor-specific transplantation antigens, but here we have, in addition, the very suggestive evidence recently obtained by Pearson and Freeman (1968) that the polyoma virus-induced ITA (PYV-ITA) "might be determined largely by a derepressed embryonic cellular gene, rather than a viral gene and may be closely related to a naturally occurring embryonic antigen," the synthesis of which is apparently repressed in the adult. Evidence pointing to the participation of derepressed genes of the transformed cells in the production of PYV-ITA are cited by Pearson and Freeman. These facts should surprise no one for they have their equivalents in what is known as "conversion" of lysogenic bacteria, *i.e.*, the acquisition by the bacterium of new properties as a result of lysogenization. A classical example is the phage-specific modification of the "somatic" (lipopolysaccharide) O-antigens of *Salmonellae*. One such "conversion" (from the so-called Group E_1 to E_2, mediated by phage Σ^{15}) involves three biochemical changes in the polysaccharide moiety of the antigen. At least two of them are due to inhibition or repression in the lysogenized bacteria of enzymes specified by genes of the host whose normal expression is restored upon loss of the prophage (*cf.* Luria and Darnell, 1967).

In the present context it is relevant to notice that some *E. coli* phages (able, contrary to λ, to integrate anywhere in the host's genome) block, by the very fact of their insertion within a bacterial gene, the transcription of all genes belonging to the same bacterial operon which are distal to the insertion point (Jordan, Saedler, and Starlinger, 1968).

These facts are cited here—not so much as a reminder of the caution necessary in the assignment of definite functions to genes of oncogenic viruses, caution of which the enlightened (genetically minded) virologists are well aware—as a call for a change of emphasis, from the functions of the viral genes alone to the functions of the host cell as well. I do not think we shall understand the mechanism of virus-induced transformations so long as we have no knowledge of the role played in this process by the cellular genes. I think that two statements Dulbecco made several years ago are still valid, even though they seem to be often forgotten. One is:

> ". . . it is conceivable that the transformation is the consequence of a transient action of the virus and the persistence of the (viral) genes is purely a consequence of the fact that the cells were originally infected" (Dulbecco, 1964).

The other is the statement Dulbecco made in summing up the 1962 Cold Spring Harbor Symposium:

> "It seems most likely, and essentially necessary, that the mechanism of transformation involves an alteration of some genetic component of the cell, because the transformation appears to be hereditary and probably irreversible. Thus a knowledge of the genetic properties of the somatic cells is required before an intimate understanding of the process of transformation can be gained; extensive information on the genetics of these cells is therefore urgently needed" (Dulbecco, 1962).

If by "alteration of some genetic component" Dulbecco meant somatic mutation, then the only change in his statement to be made today results from the fact that, as is now known, stable cellular changes need not necessarily involve gene mutation, for epigenetic changes (i.e., changes in the functional state of the genome) can be clonally inherited also.

NEOANTIGENS OF SPONTANEOUS AND CARCINOGEN-INDUCED TUMORS

Emphasis, in future research, on the role of cellular genes finds further justification in the presence and nature of the neoantigens of some spontaneous and carcinogen-induced tumors. I refer in particular to (1) the neoantigens of some rat and mouse hepatomas which have been shown to occur normally during the embryonic life of these species but are absent in the adult liver (cf. Grabar, Stanislavski-Birencwajg, Oisgold, and Uriel, 1967); and (2) the so-called "carcinoembryonic antigens" which were first thought to be specific to human colonic tumors because they are undetectable in the colonic tissues of normal adults, but were recently found in the same tissues of fetuses (Gold and Freedman,

1965). There is little doubt in my mind that, in these cases, the reappearance of the embryonic antigens must be ascribed to derepression of previously "silent" cellular genes.

Even more striking, in this respect, are the cases of neoplasms which involve a change from the normal activity of a cell of a given tissue to that characteristic of cells of another tissue. This is observed, for example, in certain pulmonary tumors which secrete a hormone normally produced by the parathyroid gland (Sherwood, Potts, Melick, and Auerbach, 1966). We are concerned here with what cancerologists call "metaplasia" and the embryologists "transdetermination" (to be discussed further). Clearly, these neoplasms must be regarded as instances of breakdown of the normal developmental program or, as Markert put it in his lucid discussion, "Neoplasia: A Disease of Cell Differentiation," as cases of "normal gene activity . . . misprogrammed by epigenetic mechanisms to produce a neoplastic pattern of metabolism in which all of the individual components are normal" (Markert, 1968).

Considered from this angle, the problem of the mechanism of neoplasia merges with that of the mechanisms of normal development and differentiation and becomes inseparable from it. I shall, therefore, in the remainder of this lecture, try to give an outline both of the problems posed by the latter, as I see them, and in my opinion, of the way in which their solution should be approached.

Cellular Changes in Embryogeny

DETERMINATION AND DIFFERENTIATION

Ever since it became clear that, contrary to the speculations of early embryologists, every cell of an adult (higher) organism, whatever its specialization, contains the complete genetic information, the problem of cellular differentiation became one of the mechanism of the stable restriction of gene expression in the course of embryonic development. Two discoveries pointed the way to the reconciliation of two old and fundamental but apparently conflicting notions, the *genotype* of the classical geneticist and the *developmental potentiality* of the experimental embryologist. The first discovery showed that in unicellular organisms (especially the ciliated Protozoa), nuclei which are identical in genetic content can assume different functional states which are stable in vegetative reproduction (*cf.* Nanney, 1958); the second identified a new class of (regulatory) genes governing, in bacteria and bacteriophages, the expression of the structural genes which specify the primary structure of proteins (Jacob and Monod, 1961). Developmental potentiality of a cell lineage can now be equated with what Abercrombie (1967) proposes to call the *epigenotype*, *i.e.*, with that portion of the genome which, under appropriate conditions, can be expressed, while the rest of it remains silent. This formulation implies that what is so often spoken of, globally, as differentiation comprises, in reality, two different phenomena, namely (1) determination, the process which selects a particular segment of the genome which thereafter will be expressible (but not necessarily expressed) in a given cell lineage, to the exclusion of all others; (2) differentiation *sensu stricto*, *i.e.*, the process which results in the actual expression of the selected segment.

Two explanatory remarks are in order here. (1) I speak of determination as the selection of a particular segment of the genome, rather than of a gene, because, as justly emphasized by Grobstein (1966), a differentiated cell of a given type is characterized not simply by the synthesis of one particular characteristic product (enzymatic protein, hormone, *etc.*) but by a *set* of properties which make its "enzymatic profile" different from that of any other cell type. (2) The occurrence of correlated functional changes does not necessarily imply that the structural genes specifying the correlated functions (and thus defined as belonging to the same segment) are mechanically linked into a single operon-like unit; there can be functional rather than mechanical linkage. An example is the regulation by a single repressor of three noncontiguous operons concerned with the arginine pathway in *E. coli* (Jacoby and Gorini, 1969; Karlström and Gorini, 1969).

Although owing to the discoveries mentioned at the beginning of this section, the problem of developmental changes is now, in everybody's mind, a problem of regulation of gene activity, most current discusisons of the mechanisms involved are, in my opinion, regrettably and almost exclusively focused on the second, terminal phase of the process (differentiation in a strict sense) and on the question whether the regulatory mechanisms known to operate in bacteria can account for differentiation. It is, I think, worth keeping in mind that, as recalled above, we are concerned with two different processes which may, and in fact probably do, involve two different types of regulatory mechanisms. My own opinion at present is that (1) the "terminal" process of differentiation of a determined cell (and its oscillation in in vitro culture between the state of overt differentiation and that of an undifferentiated stem cell) may be based on rather simple factors similar to those operating in the induced biosynthesis of enzymes in bacteria; (2) determination, with its "mutual exclusion feature," which is so stable in higher organisms, probably involves a mechanism similar to that responsible for the inactivation (of most genes) of one of the X chromosomes in mammalian females (Lyon, 1961) which, in turn, may be similar to that which is responsible for the control of the expression of prophage λ. It will be recalled that, as described above (see page 16), prophage λ is a piece of genetic material which contains the complete information for its own programmed development; the expression of all this information is held in check by the action of a single repressor localized at only two points. As pointed out by Markert (1968), the occurrence of a single switch in the programmed development of higher organisms is testified to by the teratomas:

"[These] tumors are chaotic arrangements of many different cell types, frequently organized as functioning tissues. . . . Clearly, the neoplastic event in teratoma formation occurs at a very early stage in cell differentiation—in the primordial germ cell. The occurrence of a neoplastic event at this early stage, before the inception of any embryonic development, suggests the existence of a single basic common mechanism for programming genes. A defect in this postulated mechanism would produce the chaotic arrangement of tissues seen in teratomas but would not prevent normal differentiation of specific cell types once the initial defect had been passed. That is, specific programs for regulating gene function in highly differentiated cells can still develop in teratomas but the selection of a particular program appears uncontrolled and erratic. What this might mean in molecular terms is of course still completely unknown, but the biologic behavior of teratoma formation should provide useful clues in searching for biochemical mechanisms involved in the differentiation of normal cells" (Markert, 1968). (I regret that the author of these lines was not familiar with the monumental thesis of Brenda Finch (1968) aimed precisely at these objectives [preliminary report in Finch and Ephrussi, 1967]).

I shall not go on with theoretical considerations. In presenting them here, I wish only to emphasize that both neoplasia and normal development involve epigenetic changes and that the understanding of neoplasia will depend on as detailed a description of the regulatory mechanisms underlying determination and differentiation as that which has been obtained for the self-programmed development of prophage λ.

METHODS OF ANALYSIS

How has the sophisticated picture of regulation of phage development, represented in Figure 1, been obtained? Mostly by simple complementation experiments designed to establish whether diffusible substances produced by certain genes can bypass the block imposed by immunity on the expression of other genes in the *trans* position (introduced by heteroimmune infection).

A freely translated quotation from one of the principal authors of this beautiful work (Thomas, 1967) will explain the principle of the complementation technique which has served to establish all the green arrows shown in Figure 1:

"Assume that the expression of a gene, t, mediated by a diffusible substance, depends in turn on the expression of another gene, a, subject to the control of immunity. If we represent by + the success of the infection, *i.e.*, the lysis of the bacterium with release of numerous phages, the normal process can be schematized as follows:

$$\lambda \longrightarrow a \longrightarrow t \longrightarrow +. \quad (1)$$

"In the case of a lysogenic bacterium, whose prophage is designated as (λ), we shall have:

$$(\lambda) \longrightarrow\!\!\!\shortmid\!\!\! \cdots\cdots\cdots\cdots\cdots\cdots\cdots\cdots\longrightarrow \quad - \; . \quad (2)$$
immunity

"Function a will indeed not be expressed because of immunity and function t will not be expressed because it depends on the expression of a.

"If we infect a sensitive bacterium with a mutant defective for gene t (represented by λt^-), we shall have the following situation:

$$\lambda t^- \longrightarrow a \longrightarrow\!\!\!\shortmid\!\!\!\longrightarrow \cdots\cdots\cdots\longrightarrow \quad - \; . \quad (3)$$
mutation

"Suppose now that we infect with this same defective phage a bacterium lysogenized by a closely related heteroimmune prophage (λim_{434}) which carries no t defect, we shall then have:

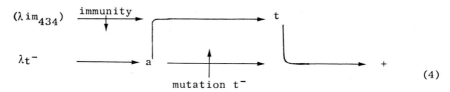

$$(4)$$

"Indeed, if the only reason for lack of expression of gene t of the prophage is the absence of substance a, and if the infection of sensitive bacteria with a t⁻ mutant is abortive only because of lack of substance t, then one may reasonably expect that the production of substance a by the super-infecting phage will permit the expression of gene t of the prophage, thus resulting in the release of phages of superinfecting type. . . .

"Summing up, if there are functions such as t, one may expect, at least in favorables cases, that infection of a lysogenic bacterium by a heteroimmune t⁻ defective phage will result in a normal release of phages of the superinfecting type:

It is the use of this simple method which has permitted the establishment of the regulatory circuits shown in Figure 1, and, more precisely, of the direct or indirect control of the expression of different λ genes by immunity and of their mutual dependence for expression.

I have chosen to describe the method used for the study of regulation of λ because λ probably represents the most completely analyzed piece of genetic material carrying the information for a set of correlated functions, and I wanted to show how the use of extremely simple techniques can disentangle a rather complicated series of relationships.

This done, I would like to emphasize two additional points. The first is that the elucidation of the control mechanisms regulating gene expression in bacteria—indeed the very demonstration of the existence of regulatory genes (Jacob and Monod, 1961)—was similarly achieved by the use of simple techniques, notably the study of dominance-recessiveness relationship in *cis* and *trans* heterozygotes, *i.e.*, in the F_1 of crosses of various mutants affecting the expression of few genes of the *lac* operon of *E. coli*. The same technique, used with phage mutants and combinations of mutants, established the red arrows of Figure 1.

The second point is that the technique of somatic hybridization, as it is today, permits similar studies of interactions (complementation, dominance relationships) between the genomes of practically any two mammalian cells. Hence, it can be usefully employed to begin the analysis of the mechanisms responsible for the establishment and maintenance of the differentiated state. In fact, some experiments have been performed to this end both in my own and in several other laboratories and have demonstrated the repression of differentiated functions in hybrids between cells which do perform such a function and cells which do not (reviewed by Davidson, 1969). These facts may be interpreted as evidence for the control of differentiated functions by diffusible regulator substances, but other interpretations are equally possible so long as the phenotypes of hybrids between two similarly differentiated cells have not been established. In any case, the limited results obtained thus far raise a number of new questions. To give one example: when a cell of a hamster melanoma, which synthesizes DOPA-oxydase and produces melanin in vitro, is crossed with a mouse fibroblast, the resulting hybrid produces no melanin; furthermore, evidence has been obtained that this is the result of the absence, in the hybrid cells, of dopa-oxydase, presumably owing to the negative control exercised by a diffusible regulator substance specified by the genome of the fibroblast (Davidson, Ephrussi, and Yamamoto, 1966). If we disregard the reservation made above concerning the validity of this interpretation and assume that it is correct, then the reported observations raise, among others, the following questions: (1) Are other functions of the "melanocyte-set" also repressed in the hybrid cells? (2) Does the "repression" of pigment formation in the hybrids require the continued presence of fibroblast genes, *i.e.*, are the genes which are responsible for melanin production active in the melanoma cell because of some stable change at the chromosomal level and only temporarily repressed in the hybrid? The first question can be solved by testing the hybrid cells for the presence of other "melanocyte functions"; the second hopefully can be answered by the study of hybrids between hamster or mouse melanoma cells and human fibroblasts. These hybrids will, most probably, be unpigmented also. If so, it will be easy to establish whether the pigment-forming process is resumed upon loss of the human chromosomes (which is rapid in human-mouse hybrids; see page 11) as it should if the "melanin-producing" (hamster or mouse) genes were only temporarily repressed in the hybrids.

Conclusion

The above examples were cited to show that the essential genetic operations whereby microbial geneticists have established the impressive picture of regulation of bacteriophage development (Figure 1) can now be performed on mammalian cells, and, *mutatis mutandis*, that the bottleneck in the genetic study of regulation in mammalian cells is no longer the lack of a genetic tool, but the paucity of mutant cell lines—the material to be explored by this tool. Bacterial and phage mutants are easy to come by, and this has enabled bacterial geneticists to accomplish an incredibly efficient job in a rather short time.

A comparable collection of mutant mammalian cells, which are difficult to obtain but which we must have if we are ever to understand the genetic basis of normal and neoplastic development, will not be obtained in the foreseeable future unless a collective effort is made. This indispensable collective effort obviously implies a corresponding financial effort. I am convinced that, if made, it would hold much more promise than an equally costly anticancer drug screening program.

ACKNOWLEDGMENTS

I wish to express my deep appreciation to Dr. René Thomas for stimulating discussions and for his help in designing Figure 1.

The work on cell hybridization in my laboratory has been supported by the National Science Foundation, the Centre National de la Recherche Scientifique, the Délégation Générale à la Recherche Scientifique et Technique, and the Jane Coffin Childs Memorial Fund for Medical Research.

REFERENCES

Abercrombie, M. 1967. "General Review of the Nature of Differentiation," *Cell Differentiation*, A. V. S. De Reuck and J. Knight, Eds. London, England: J. and A. Churchill, Ltd. Pp. 3–17.

Barski, G., S. Sorieul, and F. Cornefert. 1960. Production dans des (sic) Cultures In Vitro de Deux Souches Cellulaires en Association, de Cellules de Caractère "Hybride." *Comptes Rendus Hebdomadaires des Séances de l'Académie des Sciences série D (Sciences Naturelles)*, 251:1825–1827.

Benjamin, T. L. 1966. Virus-Specific RNA in Cells Productively Infected or Transformed by Polyoma Virus. *Journal of Molecular Biology*, 16:359–373.

Cassingena, R., and P. Tournier. 1968. Mise en Évidence d'un "Répresseur" Spécifique dans des Cellules d'Espèces Différentes Transformées par le Virus SV40. *Comptes Rendus Hebdomadaires des Séances de l'Académie des Sciences série D (Sciences Naturelles)*, 267:2251–2254.

Coon, H., and M. C. Weiss. 1969. A Quantitative Comparison of Formation of Spontaneous and Virus-Produced Viable Hybrids. *Proceedings of the National Academy of Sciences of the U.S.A.*, 62:852–859.

Davidson, R. L. 1969. "Regulation of Gene Expression in Somatic Cell Hybrids," *Recent Advances in Tissue Culture*, John Paul, Ed. (in press.)

Davidson, R. L., and B. Ephrussi. 1965. A Selective System for the Isolation of Hybrids Between L Cells and Normal Cells. *Nature*, 205:1170–1171.

Davidson, R. L., B. Ephrussi, and K. Yamamoto. 1966. Regulation of Pigment Synthesis in Mammalian Cells, as Studied by Somatic Hybridization. *Proceedings of the National Academy of Sciences of the U.S.A.*, 56:1437–1440.

Dove, W. F. 1968. The Genetics of the Lambdoid Phages. *Annual Review of Genetics*, 2:305–340.

Dulbecco, R. 1962. Basic Mechanisms in the Biology of Animal Viruses. *Cold Spring Harbor Symposia on Quantitative Biology*, 27:519–525.

———. 1964. Transformation of Cells In Vitro by DNA-Containing Viruses. *Journal of the American Medical Association*, 190:721–726.

Ephrussi, B. 1966. "Hybridization of Somatic Cells and Phenotypic Expression," *Developmental and Metabolic Control Mechanisms and Neoplasia* (The University of Texas M. D. Anderson Hospital and Tumor Institute, 19th Annual Symposium on Fundamental Cancer Research, 1965). Baltimore, Maryland: The Williams & Wilkins Co. Pp. 486–503.

Ephrussi, B., L. J. Scaletta, M. A. Stenchever, and M. C. Yoshida. 1964. "Hybridization of Somatic Cells In Vitro," *Cytogenetics of Cells in Culture* (Symposia of the International Society for Cell Biology), R. J. C. Harris, Ed., New York, New York, and London, England: Academic Press, Vol. 3. Pp. 13–25.

Ephrussi, B., and S. Sorieul. 1962. Mating of Somatic Cells In Vitro. *The University of Michigan Medical Bulletin*, 28:347–363.

Ephrussi, B., and M. C. Weiss. 1965. Interspecific Hybridization of Somatic Cells. *Proceedings of the National Academy of Sciences of the U.S.A.*, 53:1040–1042.

———. 1967. "Regulation of the Cell Cycle in Mammalian Cells: Inferences and Speculations Based on Observations of Interspecific Somatic Hybrids," *Control Mechanisms in Developmental Processes* (The Twenty-Sixth Symposium, The Society for Developmental Biology), Michael Locke, Ed. (*Developmental Biology*, Supplement 1). New York, New York, and London, England: Academic Press. Pp. 136–169.

Finch, B. W. 1968. *Multiple Potentialities of Clonal Cultures of Mouse Testicular Teratoma Cells: Their Retention During In Vitro Culture and Extinction upon Somatic Hybridization*. Ph.D. Dissertation. Western Reserve University, Cleveland, Ohio.

Finch, B. W., and B. Ephrussi. 1967. Retention of Multiple Developmental Potentialities by Cells of a Mouse Testicular Teratocarcinoma During Prolonged Culture In Vitro and Their Extinction upon Hybridization with Cells of Permanent Lines. *Proceedings of the National Academy of Sciences of the U.S.A.*, 57:615–621.

Gold, P., and S. O. Freedman. 1965. Specific Carcinoembryonic Antigens of the Human Digestive System. *Journal of Experimental Medicine*, 122:467–481.

Grabar, P., M. Stanislawski-Birencwajg, S. Oisgold, and J. Uriel. 1967. "Immunochemical and Enzymatic Studies on Chemically Induced Rat Liver Tumors," *Specific Tumour Antigens* (UICC Monograph Series), R. J. C. Harris, Ed. Copenhagen, Denmark: Munksgaard; and New York, New York: Medical Examination Publishing Co., Inc., Vol. 2. Pp. 20–30.

Grobstein, C. 1966. What We Do Not Know About Differentiation. *American Zoologist*, 6:89–95.

Harris, H., and J. F. Watkins. 1965. Hybrid Cells Derived From Mouse and Man: Artificial Heterokaryons of Mammalian Cells from Different Species. *Nature*, 205:640–646.

Harris, H., J. F. Watkins, C. E. Ford, and G. I. Schoefl. 1966. Artificial Heterokaryons of Animal Cells from Different Species. *Journal of Cell Science*, 1:1–30.

Huebner, R. J. 1967. "Non-Virion Neoantigens in Cells Infected with and Transformed by Viruses," *Specific Tumour Antigens* (UICC Monograph Series), R. J. C. Harris, Ed. Copenhagen, Denmark: Munksgaard; and New York, New York: Medical Examination Publishing Co., Inc., Vol. 2. Pp. 265–271.

Jacob, F., and J. Monod. 1961. Genetic Regulatory Mechanisms in the Synthesis of Proteins. *Journal of Molecular Biology*, 3:318–356.

Jacoby, G. A., and L. Gorini. 1969. A Unitary Account of the Repression Mechanism of Arginine Biosynthesis in *Escherichia coli*. I. The Genetic Evidence. *Journal of Molecular Biology*, 39:73–87.

Jordan, E., H. Saedler, and P. Starlinger. 1968. 0° and Strong-polar Mutations in the *Gal* Operon Are Insertions. *Molecular and General Genetics*, 102:353–363.

Karlström, O., and L. Gorini. 1969. A Unitary Account of the Repression Mechanism of Arginine Biosynthesis in *Escherichia coli*. II. Application to the Physiological Evidence. *Journal of Molecular Biology*, 39:89–94.

Koprowski, H., F. C. Jensen, and Z. Steplewski. 1967. Activation of Production of Infectious Tumor Virus SV40 in Heterokaryon Cultures. *Proceedings of the National Academy of Sciences of the U.S.A.*, 58:127–133.

Littlefield, J. W. 1964. Selection of Hybrids from Matings of Fibroblasts In Vitro and Their Presumed Recombinants. *Science*, 145:709–710.

Luria, S. E., and J. E. Darnell. 1967. *General Virology*. 2nd edition. New York, New York: John Wiley and Sons, Inc., 512 pp.

Lyon, M. F. 1961. Gene action in the X-Chromosome of the Mouse (*Mus musculus L.*). *Nature*, 190:372–373.

Markert, C. L. 1968. Neoplasia: A Disease of Cell Differentiation. *Cancer Research*, 28:1908–1914.

McBride, W. D., and A. Wiener. 1964. In Vitro Transformation of Hamster Kidney Cells by Human Adenovirus Type 12. *Proceedings of the Society for Experimental Biology and Medicine*, 115:870–874.

Nanney, D. L. 1958. Epigenetic Control Systems. *Proceedings of the National Academy of Sciences of the U.S.A.*, 44:712–717.

Old, L. J., and E. A. Boyse. 1964. Immunology of Experimental Tumors. *Annual Review of Medicine*, 15:167–186.

Pearson, G., and G. Freeman. 1968. Evidence Suggesting a Relationship Between Polyoma Virus-Induced Transplantation Antigen and Normal Embryonic Antigen. *Cancer Research*, 28:1665–1673.

Rapp, F., and J. S. Butel. 1970. "The Virus Genome and Transformation of Mammalian Cells," *Genetic Concepts and Neoplasia* (The University of Texas M. D. Anderson Hospital and Tumor Institute at Houston, 23rd Annual Symposium on Fundamental Cancer Research, 1969). Baltimore, Maryland: The Williams and Wilkins Co. Pp. 256–280.

Sherwood, L. M., J. T. Potts, Jr., R. A. Melick, and G. D. Auerbach. 1966. "Parathyroid Hormone Production by Bronchogenic Carcinomas" (Abstract), *Program of the Forty-Eighth Meeting of The Endocrine Society*. Philadelphia, Pennsylvania: J. B. Lippincott Co. Pp. 29.

Siniscalco, M., B. M. Knowles, and Z. Steplewski. 1969. "Hybridization of Human Diploid Strains Carrying X-Linked Mutants and Its Potentials for Studies of Somatic Cell Genetics," *Proceedings of the Wistar Institute Symposium on Heterospecific Genome Interaction*. Pp. 117–133.

Szybalski, W., E. H. Szybalska, and G. Ragnie. 1962. Genetic Studies with Human Cell Lines. *National Cancer Institute Monograph* No. 7:75–89.

Thomas, R. 1967. Le Contrôle du Développement chez les Bactériophages Tempérés. *Bulletin de la Société de Chimie Biologique*, 49:1463–1472.

Vogt, M., and R. Dulbecco. 1960. Virus-Cell Interaction with a Tumor-Producing Virus. *Proceedings of the National Academy of Sciences of the U.S.A.*, 46:365–370.

Watkins, J. F., and R. Dulbecco. 1967. Production of SV40 Virus in Heterokaryons of Transformed and Susceptible Cells. *Proceedings of the National Academy of Sciences of the U.S.A.*, 58:1396–1403.

Weiss, M. C. 1970. "Properties of Somatic Hybrid Cell Lines Between Mouse Cells and SV40-Transformed Human Cells," *Genetic Concepts and Neoplasia* (The University of Texas M. D. Anderson Hospital and Tumor Institute at Houston, 23rd Annual Symposium on Fundamental Cancer Research, 1969). Baltimore, Maryland: The Williams & Wilkins Co. Pp. 456–476.

Weiss, M. C., B. Ephrussi, and L. J. Scaletta. 1968. Loss of T-Antigen from Somatic Hybrids Between Mouse Cells and SV40-Transformed Human Cells. *Proceedings of the National Academy of Sciences of the U.S.A.*, 59:1132–1135.

Weiss, M. C., and H. Green. 1967. Human-Mouse Hybrid Cell Lines Containing Partial Complements of Human Chromosomes and Functioning Human Genes. *Proceedings of the National Academy of Sciences of the U.S.A.*, 58:1104–1111.

Yerganian, G., and M. Nell. 1966. Hybridization of Dwarf Hamster Cells by UV-Inactivated Sendai Virus. *Proceedings of the National Academy of Sciences of the U.S.A.*, 55:1066–1073.

Role of Genetic Change in Neoplasia

The Role of Genetic Change in Neoplasia— Constitutional Chromosome Abnormalities

D. G. HARNDEN*

Medical Research Council, Clinical and Population Cytogenetics Research Unit, Western General Hospital, Edinburgh, Scotland

There are several different ways in which it can be postulated that genetic change plays a role in neoplasia. In discussing the various topics raised in this session, it is important to keep the distinctions between these clearly in mind. They can be summarized as follows.

(1) *Variation in the genotype of the individual* could lead to (a) the inevitable development of neoplasia following particular epigenetic events; (b) an increased likelihood of a normal cell changing to a malignant cell, regardless of whether this involves further genetic change in the cell; or (c) failure of surveillance mechanisms, resulting from immunological deficiencies or cell contact phenomena.

(2) *Induced variation in the genotype of the cell* could be (a) modification of cellular genetic control mechanisms without any structural change in the deoxyribonucleic acid (DNA); (b) rearrangement of the existing genetic material which may or may not be evident as chromosome abnormality; or (c) structural change in the genetic material at the molecular level. Any one of these could predispose to the change from normal to malignant or might be the primary change itself.

(3) *Secondary genetic change at the cellular level*, although important in the progression of the neoplastic process, is different from the primary change, which may or may not have had a genetic basis.

These different types of genetic variation are, of course, not mutually exclusive. It is not unreasonable to postulate that a constitutional genetic variation could make the probability of a genetic change at the cellular level more likely, that this alteration predisposes the descendants of that cell to undergo further genetic change, and that all three steps are fundamental to the full development of a tumor.

In the present session, we will be concerned with asking the

---

* Present address: Department of Cancer Studies, Medical School, University of Birmingham, Birmingham, England.

simple fundamental question of whether genetic change plays a part in the initiation and development of neoplastic change, without delving too deeply into the underlying mechanisms. Dr. Miller (1970, see pages 78 to 84, this volume) and Dr. Anderson (1970, see pages 85 to 104, this volume) will discuss two different ways of determining whether the genetic constitution of the individual influences his liability to develop malignant disease: (1) one can examine syndromes with a known genetic basis to determine whether there is an unusual liability to malignant disease, and (2) attempts can be made to demonstrate that malignant disease, or at least a liability to develop malignant disease can be inherited.

In Edinburgh we have been concerned with one particular aspect of this problem for the past 10 years. We have been trying to determine whether patients with constitutional chromosome abnormalities have an unusual liability to develop cancer. In 1959, the Medical Research Council established in Edinburgh a Registry of Abnormal Karyotypes in which records would be kept of all persons found to have abnormal or mosaic chromosome constitutions (Court Brown *et al.*, 1964). The principal reason for establishing this registry was to determine morbidity and mortality patterns in people with an abnormal chromosome constitution, since it was already known that patients with Down's syndrome showed an unusual mortality from leukemia (Stewart, Webb, and Hewitt, 1958). The registry is now also used for a variety of other purposes, *e.g.* linkage studies. Although it was recognized that this project would take many years to produce results, the present situation with respect to morbidity and mortality from malignant disease is worth recording to illustrate how this project is building.

All types of constitutional chromosome abnormalities are recorded in the registry, with the specific exception of patients with trisomic Down's syndrome, since these are being dealt with adequately in other centers. The registry is divided into two parts: the first contains only cases in which the aberration is known to be familial, and the second contains the isolated cases. All abnormal cases are subject to an annual follow-up through the family doctor. The response rate is 95 per cent in any one year but the over-all loss from follow-up study during the first 10 years of the Registry's existence has been negligible. The kindred registry has a built-in control population, in that all first-degree relatives of the subjects with abnormal chromosome constitutions are also subject to annual follow-up. As a double check on the subjects developing cancer, the Cancer Registry of the South East of Scotland Regional Hospital Board has agreed to notify us of any registration of a malignancy in any of the karyotype registry cases.

A summary of the information on cancer cases in the karyotype registry is given in Table 1. It can be seen that when one omits those cases that were first studied because they were known to have malignant disease, the total number of cases of cancer is so far very small and does not merit detailed analysis. However, this study eventually will provide unbiased and objective evidence on whether constitutional chromosome aberrations predispose to malignant disease.

TABLE 1.   *Cancer Cases in the Medical Research Council's Registry of Abnormal Karyotypes in September 1968*

Chromosome constitution	Sex	No. of cases	No. of noncancer deaths	Number of cancer cases	
				Alive	Dead
Sex chromosome abnormalities	Male	400	18	4(3)*	8(5)
	Female	268	14	4(4)	1(0)
	True hermaphrodite	7	1	0	0
	Total	675	33	8(7)	9(5)
Familial autosome abnormalities	Male	150	4	0	0
	Female	147	0	9(3)	0
	Total	297	4	9(3)	0
Normal controls	Male	157	4	0	2
	Female	164	1	2	0
	Total	321	5	2	2
Nonfamilial autosome abnormalities	Male	35	9	0	0
	Female	25	14	1(1)	0
	Total	60	23	1(1)	0

* In parentheses are the cases who were ascertained first because they had cancer.

Another approach to the same problem is to determine the frequency of constitutional chromosome abnormalities in patients with cancer. Until recently, figures have not been available for the frequency of such abnormalities in the general population; however, recent surveys carried out on adult populations (Court Brown, 1967) and on newborn populations (Sergovich, 1968; Waltzer, Breau, and Gerald, 1969; Ratcliffe et al., 1970) allow a rough estimate of this frequency to be made so that a consideration of their frequency in patients with cancer becomes meaningful.

A study of this type is now in progress in Edinburgh; during the first year, 1,149 patients were studied (Harnden, Langlands, McBeath, O'Riordan, and Faed, 1969). Those studied were new admissions to the Department of Radiotherapy, Western General Hospital, Edinburgh, with

TABLE 2. *Cancer Patients with a Constitutional Chromosome Abnormality*
(Total Studied 1,149)

Type of malignancy	Age	Sex	Chromosome constitution
Lymphosarcoma	57	Female	45, D/D translocation
Carcinoma of the lung	59	Male	46, Pericentric inversion C
Carcinoma of the mouth	60	Male	47, Additional abnormal chromosome
Carcinoma of the cervix	52	Female	47, XXX
Carcinoma of the breast	32	Female	45, D/D translocation
Carcinoma of the breast	69	Female	46/47, Mosaic for additional abnormal chromosome
Lymphosarcoma	67	Male	46, Pericentric inversion Y
Carcinoma of the ovary	72	Female	46, 2/C translocation

a diagnosis of malignant disease. Although the patients studied represent a broad spectrum of types of malignant disease, there is a bias in favor of neoplasms normally treated by radiotherapy. For example, carcinoma of the gastrointestinal tract (with the exception of the esophagus) is grossly underrepresented. Chromosome preparations were made from lymphocytes cultured from samples of peripheral blood. Two cells were counted routinely from each subject, but more cells were examined in cases of doubt.

Eight patients were discovered to have a constitutional chromosome abnormality (Table 2), however, the number of patients is still too small to draw any firm conclusions. The finding of one XXX female is in keeping with the estimated frequency in normal populations, and the frequency of autosome aberrations is similar to that reported by Court Brown (1967) in a collection of different groups of adults who were studied for reasons other than a suspected autosome abnormality. The frequency of autosome abnormalities is thus slightly higher than the most recently reported figures on surveys of newborn babies, but little weight can be put on this fact, since considerable variation occurs between different surveys. This study indicates that there is no major over-all increase in the number of patients with constitutional chromosome aberrations in a heterogeneous population of subjects with malignant disease, although the possibility of a small increase still exists. The study is continuing, however, but emphasis in the future is likely to be concentrated on the problem of whether specific types of malignant disease are associated with constitutional chromosome aberrations.

ACKNOWLEDGMENTS

The work described in this paper is the result of a combined effort by many people, some of them on the staff of the Medical Research Council's Clinical and Population Cytogenetics Research Unit and some outside the Unit. In particular, I would like to record that the major stimulus and much of the direction of these projects came from the late Professor W. M. Court Brown.

REFERENCES

Anderson, D. E. 1970. "Genetic Varieties of Neoplasia," *Genetic Concepts and Neoplasia* (The University of Texas M. D. Anderson Hospital and Tumor Institute at Houston, 23rd Annual Symposium on Fundamental Cancer Research, 1969). Baltimore, Maryland: The Williams & Wilkins Co. Pp. 85–104.

Court Brown, W. M. 1967. *Human Population Cytogenetics.* Amsterdam, The Netherlands: North Holland Publishing Co. Pp. 16–17.

Court Brown, W. M., D. G. Harnden, P. A. Jacobs, N. Maclean, and D. J. Mantle. 1964. *Abnormalities of the Sex Chromosome Complement in Man.* (Medical Research Council Special Report Series No. 305). London, England: Her Majesty's Stationery Office, 239 pp.

Harnden, D. G., A. O. Langlands, S. McBeath, M. O'Riordan, and M. J. W. Faed. 1969. The Frequency of Constitutional Chromosome Abnormalities in Patients with Neoplastic Disease. *European Journal of Cancer*, 5:605–614.

Miller, R. W. 1970. "The Association Between Congenital Malformations and Cancer," *Genetic Concepts and Neoplasia* (The University of Texas M. D. Anderson Hospital and Tumor Institute at Houston, 23rd Annual Symposium on Fundamental Cancer Research, 1969). Baltimore, Maryland: The Williams & Wilkins Co. Pp. 78–84.

Ratcliffe, S., A. Stewart, M. Melville, P. Jacobs, and A. J. Keay. 1970. Chromosome Studies on 3500 Newborn Male Infants. *Lancet*, 1:121–122.

Sergovich, F. R. 1968. Chromosome Studies in Unselected Neonates. *Program and Abstracts: The American Society of Human Genetics* (October 10–13, 1968, Austin, Texas). P. 33.

Stewart, A., J. Webb, and D. Hewitt. 1958. A Survey of Childhood Malignancies. *British Medical Journal*, 1: 1495–1508.

Waltzer, S., G. Breau, and P. S. Gerald. 1969. A Chromosome Survey of 2,400 Normal Newborn Infants. *Journal of Pediatrics*, 74: 438–448.

Cytogenetic Studies on Human Tumors and Premalignant Lesions: The Emergence of Aneuploid Cell Lines and Their Relationship to the Process of Malignant Transformation in Man

N. B. ATKIN

Department of Cancer Research, Mount Vernon Hospital, Northwood, Middlesex, England

Although it has long been known that chromosome changes are of common occurrence in cancer cells, the nature of the association between aneuploidy and malignancy remains obscure. The idea that chromosome changes are always epiphenomena occurring subsequent to, and therefore not directly related to, the initial malignant change has been based largely on the observation that experimental tumors often have normal chromosome complements, at least in the early stages.

The ultimate goal in cancer research is an understanding of all the aspects of malignant transformation in man which, it is now realized, is often an extended process, with a histologically definable stage which may last many years before invasion and metastasis occur. In the light of recent cytogenetic findings on invasive tumors and, where available for study, preinvasive lesions, it now seems apparent that chromosome changes are intimately concerned with the development of the great majority of tumors in human beings. The important concept of clonal evolution (Ford and Clarke, 1963; Berger, 1965; Lejeune, 1965; De Grouchy, 1966) has provided a model relating the karyotype changes to the process of malignant transformation. Present evidence supports the view that this concept, based on observations of leukemia, is of general applicability to malignant disease in man.

The main objective of this paper is to put present findings on the chromosome complements of human tumor cells and premalignant lesions into some sort of perspective, in the hope that light may be shed on the evolutionary pathways leading to the aneuploidy which characterizes most cancers.

Malignant Tumors as Clones of Aneuploid Cells

Apart from acute leukemias, particularly the myeloid and monocytic varieties (Sandberg, Ishihara, Kikuchi, and Crosswhite, 1964; Lampert and Gauger, 1968), and childhood cancers (Cox, 1968), both of which quite frequently have diploid chromosome complements, malignant disease in man is generally characterized by varied and usually complex chromosome changes. With few exceptions, all malignant tumors from the common sites in adults that have been studied have presented changes which frequently include the appearance of one or more marker chromosomes, as well as the loss or, more often, gain of variable numbers of normal chromosomes.

With the improved techniques now available, the chromosomes of cancer cells in metaphase can be arranged as karyotypes, thus providing some indication of chromosome changes, although it is seldom possible to determine precisely what changes have occurred. However, a consistent finding is the similarity in the karyotypes derived from any single sample of tumor tissue which, contrasted with the variability from tumor to tumor, establishes the clonal relationship between the cells and leads to the important conclusion that the cells have arisen from a single chromosomally abnormal cell. Other more readily obtained cytogenetic data, including observations on the deoxyribonucleic acid (DNA) content and sex chromatin status of interphase cells, likewise generally support the single clone hypothesis. Evidence which does not support this concept is mostly of a negative character; thus, poor chromosome spreading and the presence of broken metaphases may leave doubt as to the existence of a clonal relationship between the cells. It is our experience that wherever a detailed analysis of a number of metaphases is possible, for example in a small series of cervical carcinomas (Atkin, Baker, and Wilson, 1967; Atkin, 1967a), a close relationship between the karyotypes is clearly evident.

HOW MUCH VARIATION EXISTS WITHIN EACH CLONE?

The question of the amount of variation to be found within each tumor cell population might, for instance, be related to the behavioral pattern of the tumor. However, for technical reasons, it is often difficult to assess the precise degree of variation (apart from that resulting from polyploidization), just as it has been in the past in the case of normal somatic tissues. A subpopulation of polyploid derivatives is commonly found in tumors; sometimes, however, the polyploids outnumber the cells of the lower ploidy line from which they were apparently derived (Atkin, 1967a). It seems probable that there is a degree of minor variation in karyotype which is large compared with the high degree of constancy found in normal tissues, but not as large as chromosome counts and karyotype analyses sometimes suggest (mainly because of the presence of broken metaphases in the chromosome preparations). A recent analysis of DNA data on interphase cells from 119 malignant tumors (Atkin, 1969b) has shown that an average of 50 per cent of the cells which fell within ± 35 per cent of the main mode were, in fact, within ± 5 per cent of the mode.

A COMPARISON OF DIFFERENT REGIONS OF THE SAME TUMOR, AND OF RECURRENCES WITH THE PRIMARY TUMOR

Having established the generalization that the malignant cells in any given sample of solid tumor tissue usually belong to a single clone, it is clearly desirable to extend the studies to include a comparison of different tumor regions. Data obtained in my laboratory on the karyotypes of cells in samples of tissue from different regions of the same untreated primary tumor and its metastases usually, but not always, show consistency. Findings suggest the further generalization that malignant tumors consist of one, two, or some other small number of clones. Some examples will be cited.

My colleague, Miss Marion Baker, is comparing the karyotypes in preparations from different regions of 17 cancers of the large bowel; two to six separate regions of each primary tumor are being studied. Although this study is not yet complete, there seems to be consistency within each tumor with two exceptions: one tumor has a near-diploid line in one region and a related near-tetraploid line in another, and the other shows apparently unrelated karyotypes having 41–42 and 68 chromosomes in regions which are histologically dissimilar.

From a similar study on 20 ovarian carcinomas (Atkin, Robinson, and Baker, 1969), it again appears that different regions of each primary tumor and its metastases generally but not always belong to the same clone. One exception was found: two regions of a primary cystadenocarcinoma showed different karyotypes. A giant marker chromosome was present in one region but not the other, and, although both regions were hypodiploid, there were differences in the numbers of chromosomes in the normal groups; also, a marker of about the size of a B-group chromosome was present in both regions, but length measurements suggested that this was, in fact, a different marker in the two parts. Whether the two cell lines arose independently from diploid cells or shared a common lineage at some stage therefore cannot be determined from the available evidence.

An opportunity for extensive assessment of the cells in squash preparations and histologic sections from different regions of a colonic carcinoma was provided by the presence of triple sex chromatin, a rather rare phenomenon, in the interphase cells. While most regions showed the triple sex chromatin pattern, double sex chromatin was present in a small area which histologically was of a more differentiated type (Atkin, 1967c).

Similarly, extensive DNA and sex chromatin data on a variety of human tumors show conformity in most instances between different regions of a tumor, whether obtained on the same or different occasions. As an example, the modal DNA value of a carcinoma of the breast was equivalent to the unusually high chromosome number of 125 chromosomes in both the primary tumor and a regional lymph node metastasis. There may, however, be a tendency in near-diploid tumors for polyploid derivatives, rather than cells having the basic chromosome complement, to give rise to metastases; this is apparent from DNA data on near-diploid carcinomas of the breast where the primary tumor may be near-diploid and the metastases near-tetraploid (Rabotti, 1959; Meek, 1961). A similar situation was found by Miss Marion Baker in a carcinoma of the cecum; her karyotype studies showed a hypodiploid line in the primary tumor and a related hypotetraploid line in a lymph node metastasis.

There is as yet little information comparing the karyotypes of recurrent tumors with those of corresponding primary tumors; Conen and Erkman (1968) have, however, observed an "identical chromosome abnormality" in a meningeal sarcoma and a recurrence of the same tumor excised after an interval of six months.

We may conclude that tumors can be monoclonal, diclonal, *etc.* Tumors consisting of multiple clones may represent a fusion of more than one tumor; this conclusion is supported by our observation that regions having different karyotypes may show differences in their histologic appearances. It is obvious that where differences are found between a primary tumor and its metastasis (or recurrence), the possibility that the latter has arisen from a part of the primary tumor with a karyotype different from that studied should be borne in mind.

Common Features of the Karyotypes of Different Tumors

MARKER CHROMOSOMES

The high frequency of marker chromosomes suggests that the

TABLE 1. *Incidence of Marker Chromosomes in 15 Carcinomas of the Cervix Uteri, 27 Carcinomas of the Corpus Uteri, and 20 Carcinomas of the Ovary*

		No. of tumors or tumor regions[*]		
		Carcinoma of the cervix uteri	Carcinoma of the corpus uteri	Carcinoma of the ovary
Marker chromosome(s) present	At least 1 giant marker (larger than the normal chromosomes)	4	7	13
	No giant marker	7	3	7
No marker chromosomes		4	17	1

[*] Different karyotypes were found in two regions of one ovarian carcinoma (see text).

majority of malignant tumors have undergone structural chromosome rearrangements, especially since it appears likely that many abnormal chromosomes at present go unrecognized as such because they resemble normal chromosomes.

Although the Philadelphia chromosome in patients with chronic myeloid leukemia remains the only abnormal chromosome which is highly specific for a particular form of malignant disease, it has been noted that ovarian (Lejeune and Berger, 1966) and testicular (Martineau, 1966; Galton, Benirschke, Baker, and Atkin, 1966; Rigby, 1968) tumors frequently show similar, though not identical, large markers. In a series of 20 ovarian carcinomas presently under study, we have found large markers (at least as long as the B-group chromosomes) in all but one (Atkin, Robinson, and Baker, 1969). In 13 of these tumors, one or more of the markers were longer than the longest normal chromosome. A different situation has been found in carcinomas at other sites. Table 1 summarizes our present findings on the incidence of marker chromosomes in ovarian, cervical, and endometrial carcinomas. The incidence of marker chromosomes at these sites clearly varies, although the reason for this is obscure. However, whereas in 15 of the ovarian tumors only the metastases were studied, the primary tumors were studied at the other sites. The ovarian carcinomas therefore may not constitute a comparable series, if the liability of tumors at this site to metastasize is related to the presence or absence of marker chromosomes. A possible relationship between a low degree of malignancy and the presence of minimal changes without marker chromosomes in some endometrial carcinomas will be considered later.

The findings suggest that certain chromosomes may be specifically involved in structural rearrangements in some types of tumor. However, one can do no more than speculate, since usually there is little or no indication of the origin of the markers in any given case. Often, the strongest statement that can be made is, for instance, that a large marker is probably derived at least in part from a particular large chromosome, where one is found to be missing.

Several other examples of possible specific chromosome changes in certain types of malignancy have been reported. The frequent occurrence of large markers of similar but not identical appearance in Waldenström's macroglobulinemia is well documented (Kanzow, Lange, Niederalt, and Gropp, 1967). It has been suggested that reticuloses are characterized by changes involving an E17 or E18 chromosome (Spiers and Baikie, 1968), and an acrocentric chromosome intermediate in size between the D- and G-group chromosomes was seen in at least three of seven carcinomas of the colon (Lubs and Kotler, 1967).

CHANGES IN CHROMOSOME NUMBER

Different tumors, even though from the same site and of similar histologic type, usually present varied chromosome changes which encompass a wide range of modal chromosome numbers. Nevertheless, certain ploidy levels tend to be favored. Information on the approximate modal chromosome number of a tumor can be obtained readily by microspectrophotometry of Feulgen-stained interphase cells (Atkin, 1964, 1966). A comparison of series of cervical, endometrial, and large bowel carcinomas (Figure 1) shows that, while the cervical tumors present a bimodal distribution with almost equal numbers of near-diploid and near-tetraploid tumors, the endometrial and large bowel tumors, though they cover a similar range, tend to congregate in the near-diploid and hyper-triploid regions, respectively.

The significance of the differences in the distribution of the modal DNA values of these tumors is not clear. The presence of near-diploid and near-tetraploid modes in the distribution of the cervical and endometrial carcinomas suggests that the tumors in the higher modal range have undergone a chromosome doubling at some stage. Squamous cell carcinomas of the cervix in the hypotetraploid range have been found to show a relatively favorable prognosis (Atkin, 1966), and thus may be of a comparatively low grade of malignancy. The relationship between ploidy level and prognosis of cervical carcinomas seems to be independent of the relationship between histologic grade (degree of differentiation)

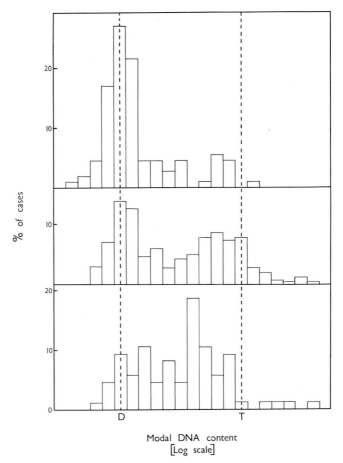

FIGURE 1. Modal DNA values of 111 carcinomas of the corpus uteri (top), 392 squamous cell carcinomas of the cervix uteri (middle) and 85 carcinomas of the large bowel (bottom). D and T signify diploid and tetraploid (epithelial) levels, respectively.

and prognosis (Atkin, 1964). Among endometrial carcinomas, however, the near-diploid tumors appear to have the more favorable prognosis. This will be considered in relation to karyotype changes of these tumors.

THE DISTRIBUTION OF CHROMOSOMES IN THE "NORMAL" GROUPS

It has previously been noted (Levan, 1966; Steenis, 1966) that malignant tumors in man tend to have relatively few chromosomes in

TABLE 2. *Average Values for the Proportions of Chromosomes in the Various Groups,
Expressed as a Percentage of the Proportions Present in Diploid Cells*

	Chromosome groups (per cent)										Average no. of marker chromosomes per tumor
	A1	A2	A3	B	C	D	E16	E17/18	F	G	
12 Carcinomas of the cervix uteri	97	110	148	75	106	70	110	98	104	75	1.5
5 Carcinomas of the large bowel (female)	86	108	136	74	110	97	100	116	86	90	1.2
6 Carcinomas of the large bowel (male)	92	92	96	81	107	92	126	77	105	80	0.8
20 Carcinomas of the ovary	74	90	109	62	113	69	94		108	85	2.5

the D- and G-groups. We have recently confirmed this on a series of 10
cervical carcinomas and 14 malignant tumors from other sites (Atkin and
Baker, 1969). On the average, each of these groups had only about 75 per
cent of the number of chromosomes expected on the basis of the total
number of chromosomes in the karyotype; there was some variation
from tumor to tumor, and in some of the tumors the expected number
was exceeded in one, but not both, groups. In the same series of tumors,
it was noted that the proportion of B-group chromosomes was below the
expected value in every instance, and again averaged about 75 per cent
of the latter. It may be, therefore, that chromosomes in these groups are
preferentially lost or involved in structural rearrangements. However,
one possible reason for a change in the proportion of the chromosomes in
the different groups is the inclusion of abnormal chromosomes, at present
indistinguishable from normal chromosomes, in one or more groups.
Whatever the precise nature of the changes, a tendency toward a shift in
the relative numbers of chromosomes in the various groups, independent
of the total number of chromosomes per karyotype, is a feature of cancers
in human beings (Table 2). In general, this tendency is toward the presence of relatively more chromosomes with centrally, rather than distally,
placed centromeres.

Pathways Leading to the Abnormal Karyotypes in Malignant Tumors

The presence of the same marker in a population of tumor cells indicates their origin from a single cell; however, tumor cells generally present many common changes which may have occurred either coincidentally or sequentially. The developing malignant cell line therefore may represent a succession of clones, each new clone adding to the sum total of chromosome changes. The clearest indication of a sequence of clones ("clonal evolution") in malignant disease in man has been obtained from studies on chronic myeloid leukemia in which changes occurring at the time of acute transformation are superimposed on the change or changes present in the chronic stage. The Philadelphia chromosome is highly specific for chronic myeloid leukemia and is usually the only abnormality present in the chronic stage. The additional changes which accompany or perhaps presage acute transformation vary from case to case, but it is of some interest that an identical pattern involving the loss of an E17 or E18 chromosome and acquisition of a metacentric marker has recently been observed in 11 of 24 cases in which the process of clonal evolution was studied (De Grouchy *et al.*, 1968).

Although beset with technical difficulties, the elucidation of the stages in the development of the aneuploidy found in solid tumors, and of the precise relationship of these stages to the histologic and behavioral stages of malignant transformation, now becomes of prime importance. Little can be inferred directly from the complex karyotypes of cancer cells regarding possible steps in their development, but, in some instances, the cytogenetic data suggest that there have been at least two stages. The observation that markers in near-tetraploid tumors are usually present in duplicate thus suggests that they were originally present in a near-diploid line which later doubled its chromosome complement; however, the presence of an odd number of chromosomes in one or more of the normal groups in the same tumors indicates that changes must have occurred after any chromosomal doubling (Figure 2). Where, as is common, a number of different but closely related karyotypes are found in a tumor, their pattern of interrelationship may suggest directions in which the cells are evolving, provided that technical factors (*i.e.*, artifactual chromosome loss) can be ruled out as a cause of the variation (Baker, 1968).

Where a dicentric or ring marker chromosome is repeatedly seen in the metaphases of a tumor, its incidence is nevertheless often low (*e.g.* 25 per cent), suggesting that such markers tend to be lost from the cell line without detriment to the line (Atkin, Baker, and Wilson, 1967; Atkin, 1967a).

In relation to the occurrence of structural chromosome rearrangements, it is of interest that breaks are not uncommon in tumor cells; these

FIGURE 2a. Karyotype of a representative metaphase from a poorly differentiated squamous cell carcinoma of the cervix uteri in a 51-yr-old patient. There are 71 chromosomes; note duplicated marker (M) and odd numbers of chromosomes in some groups (see text).

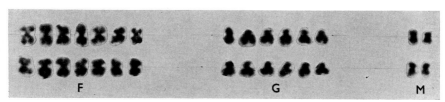

FIGURE 2b. Partial karyotype of a metaphase from the same tumor shown in Figure 2a; there are 142 chromosomes.

may range from isolated chromatid breaks to multiple fragmentation ("pulverization") of the chromosomes. Occasionally, multiple fragmentation is seen in one of two prophases or metaphases whose close proximity suggests that they are contained in a single cell. If viable, such cells might give rise to progeny which show the "double minute" phenomenon (multiple double chromatin fragments) described in childhood tumors (Cox, Yuncken, and Spriggs, 1965) and occasionally seen in tumors of adults.

EVIDENCE RELATING TO THE EVOLUTION OF THE ABNORMAL KARYOTYPES
OF MALIGNANT CELLS AT SPECIFIC SITES

When considering the hypothesis that malignancy is the result of a series of chromosome changes, perhaps occurring over a long period of time, the first possibility that comes to mind is that the initial chromosome abnormality might be congenital. An association between congenital chromosome anomalies and leukemia and other forms of cancer is well-known and will not be pursued here. Present evidence suggests that only a minority of cases of cancer are associated with a congenital chromosome anomaly; however, the possibility that a cancer patient might have an unsuspected chromosome anomaly should always be kept in mind. Two cases may be cited. The first, a man of 71 with an esophageal carcinoma, was found to have sex chromatin in both normal and malignant cells, and proved to have Klinefelter's syndrome with an XXY sex chromosome complement (Atkin and Baker, 1965a). The second patient, who presented with an endometrial carcinoma, showed double sex chromatin in the normal cervical epithelial cells; on further investigation, it appeared that this patient had an XO/XX/XXX mosaicism (Atkin, 1967b).

There is now good evidence that chromosome abnormalities are commonly found in premalignant lesions at at least two sites: the cervix uteri and large bowel. This presents an opportunity for comparison of the karyotypes of premalignant and malignant lesions at each of these sites; such comparison might provide evidence of the occurrence of chromosome changes related to the change from a preinvasive to an invasive state.

CHROMOSOME CHANGES IN PRENEOPLASTIC LESIONS OF THE CERVIX UTERI
IN COMPARISON WITH CERVICAL CARCINOMAS

In comparing chromosome changes in our cervical carcinoma series with the available karyotypes of premalignant lesions of the cervix described or illustrated by other authors, we have noted that, while some premalignant lesions yield cells with high chromosome numbers, others have near-diploid karyotypes which commonly show evidence of having undergone less complex chromosome changes than invasive tumors with similar chromosome numbers. However, premalignant lesions as a whole do not appear to show the same tendency toward a relative deficiency of acrocentric chromosomes (the G-group chromosomes, in fact, show on the average a slight relative excess); and though there was a deficiency of B-group chromosomes, this was not as great as for the invasive tumors

(Atkin and Baker, 1969). In contrast, a carcinoma in situ showing evidence of early stromal invasion (studied previously by us [Atkin and Baker, 1965b; Atkin and Baker, 1966]) was markedly deficient in both D- and G-group chromosomes (Atkin and Baker, 1969). A giant marker chromosome, seen in a high proportion of the metaphases in the chromosome preparations from this lesion, indicated the presence of a clone. The presence of chromosome protusions seen in dividing cells in histologic sections of the cone biopsy specimen (Atkin and Brandão, 1968) provided further evidence that cells having a large marker were widespread throughout the lesion.

DNA measurements on interphase cells from preinvasive cervical lesions (Atkin, 1969a) are compatible with the presence of clones which, as in the case of invasive tumors of the cervix, have chromosome complements which vary from case to case over a wide range. In each of the in situ carcinomas studied, the data suggested the presence of a single clone. The technique used involved the preparation of a suspension of cells from the surface of the lesion; only cells which remained in groups were measured. In each of two cervical dysplasias and in one of three carcinomas in situ with early stromal invasion, more than one clone appeared to be present. Of course, with this technique only clones which differ fairly widely in their modal chromosome number can be distinguished from one another. Nevertheless, over-all findings suggested a picture similar to that seen in invasive tumors. The cells were just as closely grouped around a modal value. The main difference appears to be that the presence of two or more clones is a common feature of preinvasive lesions, at least at the time when the change to an invasive lesion is occurring.

ADENOMATOUS POLYPS OF THE COLON AND RECTUM

Carcinomas of the large bowel may arise in polyps, and adenomatous polyps of the colon have recently been shown to present an increasing incidence of carcinoma in situ and invasive carcinoma with increasing diameter of the polyp (Culp, 1967). It is therefore of interest that chromosome changes appear common in polyps requiring surgical interference (*i.e.*, they have given rise to symptoms) or which are removed coincidentally with a carcinoma of the large bowel (Lubs and Clark, 1963; Lubs and Kotler, 1967; Enterline and Arvan, 1967; Atkin and Baker, in prep.). The chromosome changes may involve slight deviations from diploidy, such as the acquisition of a C-group chromosome. The acrocentric chromosomes do not appear preferentially involved in these changes, nor do the

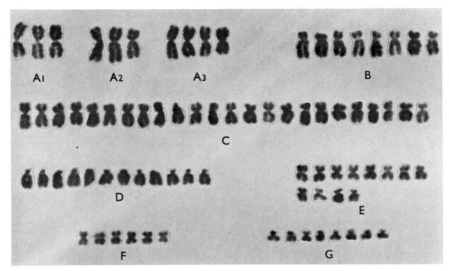

FIGURE 3. Karyotype of a representative metaphase with 80 chromosomes from an adenomatous polyp of the rectum in a 67-yr-old female.

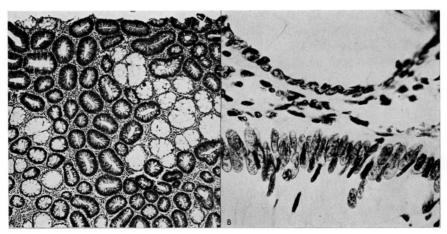

FIGURE 4. Histologic section of a benign adenomatous polyp of the colon removed from a 57-yr-old man who also had a colonic carcinoma. Two types of epithelium are seen, one of which (b, lower part of picture) has large nuclei, in agreement with the DNA data which suggested the presence of a hypotetraploid clone. Hematoxylin and eosin: a, reduced from ×285; b, reduced from ×1150.

occasional polyps which yield metaphases with high chromosome numbers seem to show the same tendency towards a relative reduction in the number of B-, D-, and G-group chromosomes shown by carcinomas (Figure 3) (Atkin and Baker, 1969). Figure 4 shows a histologic section of a benign polyp of the colon removed from a 57-year-old man who also had a colonic carcinoma. DNA measurements were compatible with a diploid or near-diploid chromosome complement in some regions and a hypotetraploid complement in others. The histologic section clearly shows the presence of two types of epithelium, one of which has large cells, in conformity with the DNA data which suggest that the lesion is in part composed of a clone of hypotetraploid cells.

CHROMOSOME ABNORMALITIES WITH EVIDENCE OF CLONE FORMATION AT OTHER SITES

There is, at present, only a limited amount of information on the karyotypes of known or possible premalignant lesions of other organs and tissues. Hydatidiform moles and choriocarcinomas have been studied by Makino, Sasaki, and Fukuschima (1965). We have recently reviewed their chromosome findings (Atkin and Baker, 1969): hydatidiform moles may yield cells with abnormal karyotypes; these cells, however, do not seem to show the tendency towards a reduction in the relative number of acrocentric and B-group chromosomes that is shown by the choriocarcinomas.

Caprio, Nespolo, and Bonadonna (1966) have found a significant proportion of cells with 47 chromosomes in a culture of a lymph node which, on histologic examination, showed nonspecific lymphadenopathy, possibly of viral origin; the extra chromosome was a small acrocentric of a size similar to or slightly smaller than the G-group chromosomes. A blood culture from the patient showed no chromosome abnormality. A similar case studied in this laboratory (Baker, 1969) showed the presence of one to three minute chromosomes in most of the metaphases in direct preparations and short-term cultures; some metaphases with minute chromosomes also showed an extra D-group chromosome. The patient was a 36-year-old male Pakistani with possible viral lymphadenopathy; again, no chromosome abnormality was found in a blood culture. One may speculate that, in view of the apparently localized chromosome abnormality, the lymphadenopathy in these two cases represented an early stage in the development of a malignant reticulosis.

Evidence for the presence of aneuploid clones has been obtained from chromosome studies on cultures of skin fibroblasts from a patient who had undergone radiotherapy for a carcinoma of the lung (Engel, Flexner, Engel-de Montmollin, and Frank, 1964), and after a test dose of X rays to the forearm (Visfeldt, 1966), as well as from cultured periph-eral blood from four of 133 patients who had received radiotherapy for ankylosing spondylitis or Thorotrast for cerebral angiography (Court Brown, Buckton, and Langlands, 1967). Socolow, Engel, Mantooth, and Stanbury (1964) found pseudodiploid karyotypes in cultures of a micro-follicular adenoma of the thyroid from a 54-year-old male who had received X-ray therapy for acne of the face and neck when in his teens; analysis of 10 metaphases showed some variation in the form of the ab-normal chromosomes from cell to cell.

AUTOIMMUNE DISEASE AND MALIGNANCY

An association between autoimmune disease and some types of malignancy is well established, and possible interrelationships between immunologic mechanisms, neoplasia, and chromosome abnormalities have recently been discussed by Fialkow (1967). There is some evidence linking autoimmune disease with chromosome abnormalities. In particu-lar, Hashimoto's disease, which may predispose to thyroid carcinoma (Dailey, Lindsay, and Skahen, 1955), has been seen in cases of gonadal dysgenesis with isochromosome-X (Fialkow, 1966). An interesting ques-tion is whether there may be an association between an acquired chromo-some anomaly, with localized clonal proliferation, and autoimmune disease. We have some evidence suggesting the occurrence of abnormal clones in the thyroid gland in cases of Hashimoto's disease, although this at present leaves unsettled the question of the cell type involved (e.g., whether epithelial or lymphocytic). The presence of cells with 47 chro-mosomes, including an extra C-group chromosome, in short-term cultures of thyroid tissue from a patient with Hashimoto's disease has been briefly reported (Atkin and Baker, 1965a). Unfortunately, it was not possible to examine the chromosomes in this patient's peripheral blood lymphocytes or skin fibroblasts. Of 13 cases (all female) that we have studied in direct chromosome preparations or short-term cultures of thyroid tissue, seven have yielded satisfactory preparations. Four of these had hyperdiploid cells, mostly with 47 chromosomes. Blood cultures have been done in two of the cases with abnormalities but reveal only normal karyotypes. In the first abnormal case studied (Atkin and Baker, 1965a), it now appears that about 60 per cent of 171 metaphases counted are hyperdiploid. While the majority of these have 47 chromosomes (those analyzed showing a C-trisomy), eight cells have 48 chromosomes and four have 75; those

TABLE 3. *Summary of Findings on 11 Near-Diploid Carcinomas of the Corpus Uteri*

Tumor no.	Degree of differ-entiation	Extent of myometrial invasion at hysterectomy	Karyotype (the chromosome number and changes from diploidy are indicated)
1	G	None	47 (+ C)
2	G	None	47 (+ C)
3	G	None	47 (+ D)
4	G	Up to ⅓rd thickness	47 (+ C)
5*	G†	Up to ⅓rd thickness	47 (+ C + F + marker — A2 — E16)
6	M	⅓rd to ⅔rds thickness	47 (+ C)
7	M	⅓rd to ⅔rds thickness	49 (+ 3C)
8	G	⅓rd to ⅔rds thickness	46 (+ G — E16)
9	P	Over ⅔rds thickness	46 (Dq-)
10	P	Over ⅔rds thickness (Metastases in pelvic lymph nodes)	46 (38 Metaphases apparently diploid; 2 had a marker in place of a B group chromosome)
11	P	(No hysterectomy)	47 (+ C)

These data were accumulated by Miss Marion C. Baker.
* Subsequently developed secondary tumor in colon.
† Adenoacanthoma.
Abbreviations: G, good; M, moderate; P, poor.

with 75 chromosomes show similar if not identical karyotypes.

Preliminary results obtained by Miss Marion Baker on the more recent cases show that there is some variation in the abnormal karyotypes within each case, and the thesis that Hashimoto's disease is associated with local clonal proliferation, while receiving some support from our findings, cannot yet be substantiated.

CHROMOSOME CHANGES IN CARCINOMA OF THE CORPUS UTERI

As already noted, the majority of carcinomas of the corpus uteri of an unselected series assessed by microspectrophotometry were near-diploid, the prognosis being significantly worse for the minority of tumors with high modal DNA values. There is, therefore, a relationship between chromosome number and prognosis which may be at least partly dependent upon a relationship between chromosome number and differentiation; all the well-differentiated tumors in our series were near-diploid, and more of the poorly differentiated tumors fell in the triploid or tetraploid region than in the diploid region. Nevertheless, follow-up results suggest that, within both the moderately and poorly differentiated groups, the near-diploid tumors have a relatively favorable prognosis.

When karyotype studies are made on the near-diploid tumors, however, it is apparent that there are significant differences between tumors of the corpus uteri and tumors with similar chromosome numbers at other sites such as the cervix uteri and large bowel. Small chromosome changes, such as the presence of a single extra chromosome, appear to be common among tumors of the corpus (Baker, 1968). It is well-known that carcinomas of the corpus often have a good prognosis and it has been suggested that those that are confined to the endometrium might, in fact, be classified as in situ carcinomas (Koss and Durfee, 1961). It seems possible, therefore, that the relatively benign characteristics of some tumors of the corpus which most histopathologists would classify as carcinomas may be related to the presence of minimal chromosome changes in their karyotypes. This is supported by the histopathologic findings on 11 near-diploid tumors, 10 of which were removed at hysterectomy (Table 3).

Conclusions

It is clear from the available cytogenetic data that human tumor cell populations are clonal in nature; we suggest that some tumors consist of a single clone, others of two or even more clones. Karyotype changes, though extremely variable, show certain common features: the presence of marker chromosomes and a tendency towards relatively few chromosomes with distally placed centromeres (fewer B-, D-, and G-group chromosomes and more A3, C-group, and E16 chromosomes). Apart from the Philadelphia chromosome, no specific marker has yet been demonstrated in cancer in man. Perhaps further data, processed by computer as in the study by Gofman, Minkler, and Tandy (1967), will confirm these authors' suggestion that a relative excess of E16 chromosomal material or a change in balance within the karyotype, such as between the E16 and G-group chromosomes, plays an essential role.

The future will undoubtedly bring the improvements in technique which will enable better assessment of the chromosome changes in each tumor and facilitate the accumulation of the substantially greater volume of data which is needed. In particular the difficulties of chromosome analysis of premalignant lesions, where only small amounts of tissue are available for study or where, as in many benign tumors, the mitotic activity is low, will probably have to be tackled by the use of culture techniques designed to augment the number of available metaphases. Studies in which cultures were employed have recently provided evidence of aneuploidy in a cystadenoma of the ovary (Fraccaro et al., 1968) and a series of meningiomas (Zang and Singer, 1967).

Already the data suggest that it may be possible to distinguish between a premalignant and an invasive lesion on the basis of the chromosome changes. This might have practical value if the emergence of a new clone with the ability to invade and metastasize in fact anticipates histologic evidence of invasion; the potential of the lesion could then be determined before it actually begins to invade. It is also evident from findings on carcinoma of the corpus uteri that chromosome data may help to clarify the status of tumors that histopathologists are at present unable to classify with certainty.

Chromosome studies on tumors and premalignant lesions from human beings support the concept of malignancy as the result of a series of random or stochastic events, rather than as a determinative process (Burnet, 1968), and indicate that in most tumors some of these mutational events (though not necessarily the first) involve chromosome changes. Those tumors that have normal chromosome complements may arise in a different way. Burch (1963) has suggested that oncogenic viruses often play a causal part in cancer in the young but only rarely in adults; perhaps this may have some relevance to the frequency with which childhood cancers have normal karyotypes.

It seems that, from the point of view of cancer control, at least as much attention should be paid to factors (of an immunologic nature or otherwise) which may, for a time, hold in check the developing malignant cell line as is paid to possible initiating agents such as viruses. Chromosome studies may help in the definition and recognition of the stages preceding that in which complete autonomy is achieved.

ACKNOWLEDGMENTS

The author wishes to thank Miss Marion C. Baker for the use of unpublished data and for reading and discussing the manuscript, Mrs. M. Mason for help in preparing the figures, and Mrs. B. J. Langdon for secretarial services. The work described in this report was supported by a grant from the British Empire Cancer Campaign for Research.

REFERENCES

Atkin, N. B. 1964. Nuclear Size in Carcinoma of the Cervix: Its Relation to DNA Content and to Prognosis. *Cancer*, 17:1391–1399.

———. 1966. The Influence of Nuclear Size and Chromosome Complement on Prognosis of Carcinoma of the Cervix. *Proceedings of the Royal Society of Medicine*, 59:979–982.

————. 1967a. A Carcinoma of the Cervix Uteri with Hypodiploid and Hypotetraploid Stem-Lines. *European Journal of Cancer*, 3:289–291.

————. 1967b. Sex Chromatin in Cervical Smears. *Acta cytologica*, 11:435–436.

————. 1967c. Triple Sex Chromatin, and Other Sex Chromatin Anomalies, in Tumours of Females. *The British Journal of Cancer*, 21:40–47.

————. 1969a. Early Cervical Neoplasia: The Use of Microspectrophotometry. *Obstetrical and Gynecological Survey*, 24:793–804.

————. 1969b. Perimodal Variation of DNA Values of Normal and Malignant Cells. *Acta cytologica*, 13:270–273.

Atkin, N. B., and M. C. Baker. 1965a. Chromosome Abnormalities, Neoplasia, and Autoimmune Disease. *Lancet*, 1:820–821.

————. 1965b. Chromosomes in Carcinoma of the Cervix. *British Medical Journal*, 1:522–523.

————. 1966. Chromosome Abnormalities as Primary Events in Human Malignant Disease: Evidence from Marker Chromosomes. *Journal of the National Cancer Institute*, 36:539–557.

————. 1969. Possible Differences Between the Karyotypes of Preinvasive Lesions and Malignant Tumours. *The British Journal of Cancer*, 23:329–336.

————. Chromosome Abnormalities in Polyps and Carcinomas of the Large Bowel. (in preparation.)

Atkin, N. B., M. C. Baker, and S. Wilson. 1967. Stem-Line Karyotypes of 4 Carcinomas of the Cervix Uteri. *American Journal of Obstetrics and Gynecology*, 99:506–514.

Atkin, N. B., and H. J. S. Brandão. 1968. Evidence for the Presence of a Large Marker Chromosome in Histological Sections of a Carcinoma In Situ of the Cervix Uteri. *Journal of Obstetrics and Gynaecology of the British Commonwealth*, 75:211–214.

Atkin, N. B., R. L. Robinson, and M. C. Baker. 1969. Karyotype Changes in Carcinoma of the Ovary. (in preparation.)

Baker, M. C. 1968. A Chromosome Study of Seven Near-Diploid Carcinomas of the Corpus Uteri. *The British Journal of Cancer*, 22:683–695.

————. 1969. Chromosome Studies on a Case of Lymphadenopathy of Possible Viral Origin. (in preparation.)

Berger, R. 1965. Chromosomes et Leucémies Humaines. La Notion d'Évolution Clonale. *Annales de Génétique*, 8:70–82.

Burch, P. R. J. 1963. Carcinogenesis and Cancer Prevention. *Nature*, 197:1145–1151.

Burnet, F. M. 1968. A Modern Basis for Pathology. *Lancet*, 1:1383–1387.

Caprio, G., A. Nespolo, and G. Bonadonna. 1966. Anomalie Cromosomiche in un Linfonodo non Neoplastico. *Tumori*, 52:433–441.

Conen, P. E., and B. Erkman. 1968. Chromosome Studies in Tumours and Leukemia. *Canadian Medical Association Journal*, 99:348–353.

Court Brown, W. M., K. E. Buckton, and A. O. Langlands. 1967. The Identification of Lymphocyte Clones, with Chromosome Structural Aberrations, in Irradiated Men and Women. *International Journal of Radiation and Biology*, 13:155–168.

Cox, D. 1968. Chromosome Studies in 12 Solid Tumours from Children. *The British Journal of Cancer*, 22:402–414.

Cox, D., C. Yuncken, and A. Spriggs. 1965. Minute Chromatin Bodies in Malignant Tumours of Childhood. *Lancet*, 2:55–58.

Culp, C. E. 1967. New Studies of the Colonic Polyp and Cancer. *Surgical Clinics of North America*, 47:955–960.

Dailey, M. E., S. Lindsay, and R. Skahen. 1955. Relation of Thyroid Neoplasms to Hashimoto Disease of the Thyroid Gland. *A.M.A. Archives of Surgery*, 70:291–297.

De Grouchy, J. 1966. Aberrations Chromosomiques et Processus Malins. *Annales de Génétique*, 9:55–57.

De Grouchy, J., C. de Nava, J. Feingold, G. Bilski-Pasquier, and J. Bousser. 1968. Onze Observations d'un Modele Precis d'Evolution Caryotypique au Cours de la Leucemie Myeloide Chronique. *European Journal of Cancer*, 4:481–492.

Engel, E., J. M. Flexner, M. L. Engel-de Montmollin, and H. E. Frank. 1964. Blood and Skin Chromosomal Alterations of a Clonal Type in a Leukemic Man Previously Irradiated for a Lung Carcinoma. *Cytogenetics*, 3:228–251.

Enterline, H. T., and D. A. Arvan. 1967. Chromosome Constitution of Adenoma and Adenocarcinoma of the Colon. *Cancer*, 20:1746–1759.

Fialkow, P. J. 1966. Autoimmunity and Chromosomal Aberrations. *The American Journal of Human Genetics*, 18:93–108.

————. 1967. "Immunologic" Oncogenesis. *Blood, The Journal of Hematology*, 30: 388–394.

Ford, C. E., and C. M. Clarke. 1963. Cytogenetic Evidence of Clonal Proliferation in Primary Reticular Neoplasms. *Canadian Cancer Conference*, 5:129–146.

Fraccaro, M., A. Mannini, L. Tiepolo, M. Gerli, and C. Zara. 1968. Karyotypic Clonal Evolution in a Cystic Adenoma of the Ovary. *Lancet*, 1:613–614.

Galton, M., K. Benirschke, M. C. Baker, and N. B. Atkin. 1966. Chromosomes of Testicular Teratomas. *Cytogenetics*, 5:261–275.

Gofman, J. W., J. L. Minkler, and R. K. Tandy. 1967. *A Specific Common Chromosomal Pathway for the Origin of Human Malignancy*. Livermore, California: University of California, 77 pp.

Kanzow, U., B. Lange, G. Niederalt, and A. Gropp. 1967. Chromonomenuntersuchungen bei Paraproteinämien. *Klinische Wochenschrift*, 45:1076–1084.

Koss, L. G., and G. R. Durfee. 1961. "Proliferative Disorders and Tumors of the Endometrium," *Diagnostic Cytology and Its Histopathologic Bases*. Philadelphia: J. B. Lippincott Co. Pp. 135–151.

Lampert, F., and J. U. Gauger. 1968. Chromosomen der Zellen der Akuten Leukämie in Kindesalter. *Klinische Wochenschrift*, 46:882–888.

Lejeune, J. 1965. "Leucémies et Cancers," *Les Chromosomes Humaines*, R. Turpin and J. Lejeune, Eds. Paris, France: Gauthier-Villars. Pp. 181–215.

Lejeune, J., and R. Berger. 1966. Sur une Méthode de Recherche d'un Variant Commun des Tumeurs de l'Ovaire. *Compte Rendus Hebdomadaires des Séances de l'Academie Sciences série D (Sciences Naturelles)*, 262:1885–1887.

Levan, A. 1966. Non-Random Representation of Chromosome Types in Human Tumor Stemlines. *Hereditas*, 55:28–38.

Lubs, H. A., and R. Clark. 1963. The Chromosome Complement of Human Solid Tumors. *New England Journal of Medicine*, 268:907–911.

Lubs, H. A., and S. Kotler. 1967. The Prognostic Significance of Chromosome Abnormalities in Colon Tumors. *Annals of Internal Medicine*, 67:328–336.

Makino, S., M. S. Sasaki, and T. Fukuschima. 1965. Cytological Studies of Tumors. XLI. Chromosomal Instability in Human Chorionic Lesions. *Okajimas Folia Anatomica Japonica*, 40:439–465.

Martineau, M. 1966. A Similar Marker Chromosome in Testicular Tumours. *Lancet*, 1:839–842.

Meek, E. S. 1961. The Cellular Distribution of DNA in Primary and Secondary Growths of Human Breast Cancer. *Journal of Pathology and Bacteriology*, 82: 167–176.

Rabotti, G. 1959. Ploidy of Primary and Metastatic Human Tumours. *Nature*, 183: 1276–1277.

Rigby, C. C. 1968. Chromosome Studies in Ten Testicular Tumours. *The British Journal of Cancer*, 22:480–485.

Sandberg, A. A., T. Ishihara, Y. Kikuchi, and L. H. Crosswhite. 1964. Chromosomal Differences Among the Acute Leukemias. *Annals of the New York Academy of Sciences*, 113:663–716.

Socolow, E. L., E. Engel, L. Mantooth, and J. B. Stanbury. 1964. Chromosomes of Human Thyroid Tumors. *Cytogenetics*, 3:394–413.

Spiers, A. S. D., and A. G. Baikie. 1968. Cytogenetic Studies in the Malignant Lymphomas and Related Neoplasms. *Cancer*, 22:193–217.

Steenis, H. van. 1966. Chromosomes and Cancer. *Nature*, 209:819–821.

Visfeldt, J. 1966. Clone Formation in Tissue Culture. *Acta pathologica et microbiologica scandinavica*, 68:305–312.

Zang, K. D., and H. Singer. 1967. Chromosomal Constitution of Meningiomas. *Nature*, 216:84–85.

Ionizing Radiation and Tumor Production

E. B. LEWIS

Division of Biology, California Institute of Technology,
Pasadena, California

Ionizing radiation has long been a promising agent for studying the mechanism of cancer induction. The dose of radiation delivered to a given tissue can usually be determined with much greater precision than can the dose of a chemical agent. By varying the radiation dose, or dose rate, while holding other factors constant, and then measuring the yield of malignant conditions, the investigator can hope to quantitate the kinetics of the cancer induction process. To be sure, there are many obstacles. For example, to assay for malignancy after exposure of somatic cells to radiation is much more difficult than to assay for chromosomal or gene damage after exposure of germ cells to radiation. Doses as low as several hundred rads, when delivered to the organism acutely, may not only kill large numbers of somatic cells but may disrupt the immunological and hormonal systems in such a way as to modify the yield of malignancies in a complex manner.

I would like to review the current status of our knowledge of dose-response relationships for radiation carcinogenesis in man, and to present some new data on cancer of the blood-forming organs in physicians. At the outset, it should be stressed that one cannot expect with data on human beings to have the degree of precision which can be achieved with data based on animal experiments. In addition, because of inherent differences in such factors as life-span or susceptibility of tissues to cancer induction, it will often be difficult to extrapolate from animal studies to man. Moreover, the detection of malignancies, especially at low doses of radiation, often requires careful examination of thousands of individuals over long time periods. This can sometimes be done more easily and more economically with human beings than with animals. Finally, the baselines for kinetic studies are the spontaneous frequencies of specific types of cancer. These frequencies are often known with a greater degree of accuracy for human than for animal populations.

Review of Dose-Response Relationships

LEUKEMIA

Populations Receiving Relatively High Doses of Radiation

Court Brown and Doll (1957) were the first to point out that if the relationship between incidence of induced leukemia and radiation dose is linear, then, on the basis of their data, one rad to the spinal marrow increases the incidence of this disease by about one case per million persons per year; in other words, the probability of leukemia per rad to the spinal marrow per year is about 1×10^{-6}. This estimate, however, applied to adult males who suffered from ankylosing spondylitis and who received fractionated, partial body irradiations yielding total mean spinal marrow doses of 400 rads or more. Nevertheless, an estimate of the corresponding probability of leukemia, derived from a population of Japanese atomic bomb explosion survivors, turned out to be in good agreement, probably within a factor of two or three, with that from the spondylitic series (Lewis, 1957). Furthermore, the incidence of leukemia in persons in the zone from 1,500 to 2,000 meters from the hypocenter was significantly higher, statistically, than in those in the "control" zone lying beyond 2,000 meters. However, the average absorbed dose of those in the 1,500- to 2,000-meter zone was unlikely to have been more than about 50 rems. These conclusions were deduced from an analysis of the combined data of Hiroshima and Nagasaki for the period January 1948 to September 1955 (Lewis, 1957).

A review will not be given here of numerous other studies of leukemia risks after relatively heavy exposures of children and adults to ionizing radiation. A particularly comprehensive review is that of Wald, Thoma, and Broun (1962). One of the few studies of any magnitude which failed to demonstrate a significant increase in leukemia following heavy exposure to radiation is a recent prospective study by Hutchison (1968) of women who had received radiation therapy for cervical cancer and who were followed in a group of clinics scattered throughout Europe and the United States. Yet, the observed number of cases was small (four), and Hutchison concluded that "for patients at risk in the interval four to eight years after exposure, a fivefold increased risk could be excluded, but a fourfold increase remained possible."

Populations Receiving Relatively Low Doses of Radiation

That absorbed doses well below 50 rads might suffice to induce leukemia first became evident from results of case-control studies of

Stewart, Webb, and Hewitt (1958) for children in England and Wales who had been irradiated in utero. Their findings were fully confirmed by MacMahon (1962), who analyzed a population of 734,243 children in the northeastern United States for the years 1947 to 1954. From an analysis of all such retrospective and prospective studies reported by 1961, including those which failed to find a positive association with exposure, MacMahon (1962) showed that the results of every study were compatible with a relative risk factor of 1.4 for the influence of maternal abdominal irradiation on subsequent development of leukemia in the child during the first 10 years of life. Most estimates would place the averaged absorbed dose to the fetus from such irradiation at 1 or 2 rads.

In a three-state study of childhood leukemias, Graham et al. (1966) not only found relative leukemia risk factors for in utero irradiations similar to those found in MacMahon's study, but as the result of inquiry into parental preconceptional exposures, Graham and colleagues also discovered an elevated leukemia risk in children whose mothers had received this latter type of exposure. This latter finding, which is compatible with the hypothesis of Stewart (1961) that some childhood leukemias arise as the result of prezygotic mutational or nondisjunctional events, may prove to be of great significance for understanding the etiology of leukemia. It is reminiscent of the elevated risk of mongolism associated with preconceptional maternal irradiation detected in the recent studies of Sigler, Lilienfeld, Cohen and Westlake (1965) and of Uchida, Holunga, and Lawler (1968), but not, however, in the studies of Carter, Evans, and Stewart (1961) or of Schull and Neel (1962).

That the relatively low absorbed doses received by adults in diagnostic irradiation of the trunk (chest and abdomen) may be leukemogenic is suggested by the results of a British study (Stewart, Pennybacker, and Barber, 1962), which confirmed and extended earlier results of a Danish study (Faber 1957; Faber, Andreasen, and Uhrbrand, 1958). Both groups of investigators exploited a finding which was most clearly evident in the series of irradiated spondylitic patients studied by Court-Brown (sic) and Doll (1957), namely, that the incidence of chronic lymphocytic leukemia was not markedly increased, if at all, whereas, the incidence of other common forms of adult leukemia, primarily the acute and chronic granulocytic types, was dramatically increased. Faber and co-workers and Stewart and her colleagues therefore compared the histories of diagnostic and therapeutic irradiations given to patients with these latter radiation types of leukemia and to patients with lymphocytic leukemia (or, in the Stewart series, lymphocytic leukemia and lymphosarcoma). Other control groups were also used. Both therapeutic and diagnostic procedures were more common in the radiation histories of the acute and granulocytic series of patients than in the lymphocytic series of patients or in other control groups. Stewart and her colleagues, on the basis of a study of leukemia patients older than 20 years of age selected during the years 1958 to 1960, concluded that "about 8% of leukemias other than the lymphatic leukemias were caused by diagnostic x-rays, and a further 3.6% by therapeutic x-rays." Gunz and Atkinson (1964) failed to find evidence associating higher leukemia risk with prior diagnostic radiation exposures in a similar study made in New Zealand; however, their results are still compatible with the risks found in the Danish and British series.

In a recent report of a prospective study of leukemia arising after radioiodine and/or surgical therapy for hyperthyroidism, Saenger, Thoma, and Tompkins (1968) found a significantly higher mortality from leukemia than would have been expected on the basis of mortality rates from this disease in the general population. These investigators are inclined to favor the hypothesis that hyperthyroidism per se increases the risk of leukemia since a higher mortality rate from leukemia was found in both ^{131}I-treated patients and those treated surgically. Judgment must be withheld until the pattern of frequencies of other neoplasms related to leukemia, such as lymphosarcoma, has been reported in this series of patients.

The earlier studies of Pochin (1960) and of Werner, Gittelsohn, and Brill (1961) called attention to the excess of cases of the radiation type following radioiodine therapy for hyperthyroidism. This excess may be caused, in part at least, by an artifact arising from the exclusion of cases prevalent in the patients at the time of irradiation. The prevalent cases, or those present at the time of therapy, tended, of course, to be of the chronic types; there is, therefore, a deficit of chronic lymphocytic types in the incident cases, or those which arise after therapy.

Some Factors Affecting the Dose-Response Relationship

It was noted some years ago that the probability of leukemia per individual per rad may not be constant for an indefinite period beyond the initial time of irradiation (Lewis, 1957). MacMahon (1962) estimates that the elevated risk of leukemia peaks at five to seven years after in utero irradiation and may be exhausted by age eight. There is evidence that the increased risk of leukemia in older individuals extends over longer periods of time, *i.e.*, up to 15 years and perhaps longer in the case of Japanese survivors of the atomic bomb explosion (Bizzozero, Johnson, and Ciocco, 1966), but the risk probably declines after 10 to 15 years, as judged by the experience of both the Japanese survivors and the irradiated spondylitic patients (Court Brown and Doll, 1965).

It was also pointed out some years ago (Lewis, 1957) that there are likely to be individual differences in susceptibility to radiation-induced leukemia, just as there are to spontaneous leukemia. "The indication of a linear relationship between dose of radiation and incidence of leukemia implies that there are some individuals in whom a single radiation-induced event (perhaps a gene mutation) suffices to produce leukemia. There may, however, be other individuals in whom two or more such events would be required before leukemia would be manifested. Thus, the values of the probability of leukemia per individual per rad per year . . . apply to the average individual in a given population, but do not necessarily apply equally to each and every individual in that population" (Lewis, 1957). That the age of the individual may be an important variable is evident from several studies. Doll (1962) analyzed the observed relationships between age and sensitivity to radiation-induced leukemia in spondylitic patients and atom bomb survivors. He showed that sensitivity to radiation-induced leukemogenesis tends to have an age dependence like that seen in the natural incidence of the disease.

The probability of leukemia per rad per year appears to be higher, perhaps by a factor of 10 to 20, following irradiation of a fetus (assuming an average dose from pelvimetry of 1 to 2 rads) than following irradiation of children, for example. However, as already noted, the duration of the elevated risk following the time of irradiation is evidently less, by a factor of at least two, for a fetus than it is for children or adults. The well-known childhood peak in leukemia mortality (approximately 70 deaths per million per year between ages three and five in white children) (Fraumeni and Miller, 1967) may be a reflection of the special sensitivity of the fetus to whatever leukemogenic factors are involved in determining the natural incidence of the disease. High fetal sensitivity to radiation-induced leukemogenesis may therefore be another example of Doll's rule.

OTHER TYPES OF CANCER

Simpson, Hempelmann, and Fuller (1955) compared children given partial body irradiation in infancy for an enlarged thymus condition with untreated siblings. This study provided the first evidence that doses of only a few hundred rads applied in infancy suffice to increase significantly the incidence not only of leukemia but also of thyroid tumors and benign bone tumors. Further follow-up of these children and of others has been done by Pifer *et al.* (1963), and more recently by Hempelmann *et al.* (1967). The risk of leukemia from such irradiation appears to have disappeared by age 20: however, the risk of developing other malignancies or benign tumors has tended to remain elevated beyond this age. Hempelmann (1968), in a review of a variety of groups of children receiving various kinds of thyroid exposure to ionizing radiation, concluded that if there is a threshold dose for the induction of thyroid nodules, it is below 20 rads. Risk estimates for thyroid carcinoma, however, are based on so few cases that they are to be regarded as provisional. Beach and Dolphin (1962) estimate that the risk is one or two cases per million persons per rad yer year averaged over a 20-year period following irradiation in infancy.

In the aforementioned studies of Stewart, Webb, and Hewitt (1958) and of MacMahon (1962), irradiation of the fetus was shown to be associated with an elevated risk of the child developing not only leukemia, but a variety of other childhood cancers as well. The relative risk factor for all such other cancers combined was 1.4, or the same as that found for leukemia (MacMahon, 1962).

Three recent studies indicate that the incidence of breast cancer and of lung cancer (Wanebo, Johnson, Sato, and Thorslund, 1968a, 1968b) and of thyroid cancer (Wood *et al.*, 1969) are significantly elevated in Japanese atom bomb survivors who were within zones of heavy irradiation (0 to 1,500 meters from the hypocenter).

Court Brown and Doll (1965) have reported a further follow-up of their series of irradiated spondylitic patients; they found significantly elevated death rates, not only from leukemia, but also from other cancers of organs in or near the radiation fields. For a period of 10 to 15 years following irradiation, the leukemia death rates in these patients averaged roughly 10 times the expected rates before declining to nearly normal levels. For at least 20 years after irradiation, death rates from other cancers of heavily irradiated organs have gradually increased to a level between two and three times the normal death rates.

There is increasing evidence that radiation exposure is associated with proportionately higher mortality rates from leukemia than from other neoplasms of the lymphatic and hematopoietic systems (LHS neoplasms). LHS neoplasms are defined here as those diseases which are given the code rubrics 200 through 205 in the Sixth and Seventh Revisions of the *Manual of the International Statistical Classification of Disease, Injuries, and Causes of Death* (1948, 1957). These neoplasms are comprised of lymphosarcoma (200), Hodgkin's disease (201), lymphoma (202), multiple myeloma (203), leukemia (204), and mycosis fungoides (205).

Court Brown and Doll (1965) showed that the ratio of observed to expected deaths from leukemia in patients therapeutically irradiated for spondylitis was approximately nine (based on 60 deaths occurring over a 20-year follow-up period) compared to a ratio of approximately two (based on 11 deaths) for observed to expected deaths from other LHS neoplasms. Studies of Japanese survivors of atomic bomb radiations show that the prevalence of LHS neoplasms other than leukemia, as measured at autopsy, is increased in heavily exposed survivors, as compared to that in lightly exposed or unexposed control groups (Anderson and Ishida, 1964). However, the increase in prevalence is proportionately much less for such neoplasms than it is for leukemia. The studies of American radiologists discussed below are consistent with these findings. However, mortality from leukemia is relatively much less in radiologists than it is in the heavily exposed Japanese or spondylitic populations.

Chronic Occupational Exposure to Radiation

Groups of healthy individuals who receive relatively low doses of radiation from chronic occupational exposure provide an excellent opportunity to assess cancer risks in the sense that such individuals should experience less cellular destruction and less disturbance to their hormonal and immunological systems than individuals who receive radiation for therapeutic reasons. Radiologists and other medical specialists exposed to radiation provide such occupational groups and the class of all medical specialists not using radiation, or using it on a limited basis, provides one kind of control group. Moreover, for the parent population, namely U.S. white males, death rates by cause are well defined. The principal difficulties in studying occupationally exposed groups stem from uncertainties about the actual absorbed dose levels. In the future, the frequency of chromosomal rearrangements scored in marrow and peripheral blood by standardized methods may serve as a valuable, if crude, biological dosimeter for assessing the accumulative exposure dose (see Court Brown, Buckton, and McLean, 1965).

Dublin and Spiegelman (1948) showed that for the years 1938 to 1942, age-specific mortality rates for physicians listed as specialists in radiology were lower than the corresponding rates for all physicians but somewhat higher than the corresponding rates for the class of all medical specialists. Seltser and Sartwell (1965) studied a longer time period and compared members of a radiological society with members of two other major specialty societies, one of pathologists and one of ophthalmologists and otolaryngologists. They found that mortality rates were highest in the radiologists; however, they noted that the opthalmologists and oto-laryngologists appear to have exceptionally low mortality rates.

That American radiologists appeared to experience more deaths from leukemia than would be expected was one of the first observations indicating the carcinogenic effect of chronic exposure to ionizing radiation (March, 1944). Dublin and Spiegelman (1948) were the first to take account of marked differences in age composition between the class of all radiologists and that of specialists. After correcting for such age differences, these investigators showed that leukemia mortality was significantly elevated in radiologists during the 5-year period investigated, 1938 to 1942.

An excessive number of deaths from leukemia relative to the number expected on the basis of U.S. white male age-specific rates has been shown in radiologists certified by the American Board of Radiology for a more recent time period, namely, the 14-year period from 1948 to 1961 (Lewis, 1963). In this study, it was shown that the excessive mortality from leukemia is unlikely to have been solely the result of better medical diagnosis of the disease in radiologists than in the general population. The operation of such a differential diagnostic factor might have been expected to elevate deaths from the various types of leukemia and from the related LHS neoplasms in the same relative proportions with which these diseases are observed in the general population. Instead, the excessive number of deaths from leukemia in radiologists was confined to leukemias of the radiation type and, although there was an excess of deaths among the lymphomas, the excess was not statistically significant. However, in the case of multiple myeloma, a statistically significant excess of deaths was observed; five deaths from this disease were observed whereas only 1.01 was expected on the basis of U.S. white male rates. Pohl (1960) reported three cases of multiple myeloma occurring among medical personnel after occupational exposure to radiation. The reported fourfold increase in prevalence of multiple myeloma found at autopsy in individuals who had been heavily exposed at Hiroshima appears to be based upon only one case (Anderson and Ishida, 1964).

To what extent can the percentage of all deaths from LHS neoplasms attributed to leukemia be used as an indicator of leukemogenic factors operating on a population? It has seemed desirable to explore this question in other groups of medical specialists who might experience considerable occupational exposure to radiation, although presumably less than that experienced by radiologists. To establish a baseline for such studies, it becomes imperative to determine the pattern of frequency of LHS neoplasms in the class of all medical specialists.

LEUKEMIA AND RELATED DISEASES IN PHYSICIANS

In order to study the pattern of LHS neoplasms in groups of physicians, death certificates were sought for all physicians whose obituary notices in the *Journal of the American Medical Association* reported under cause of death either an LHS neoplasm or certain related diseases, namely the following or their synonyms: polycythemia, myeloid metaplasia, and anemias, including aplastic anemia. Death certificates were also sought for every physician who was listed in the obituary notices as having been a diplomate of the American Boards of Radiology (ABR), Dermatology (ABD), or Urology (ABU).

The limited scope of the present study prevented making a search for death certificates for physicians who were diplomates of American Specialty Boards other than ABR, ABD, and ABU. Previous experience gained in determining causes of deaths occurring in Board-certified radiologists (Lewis, 1963) showed that some deaths from LHS neoplasms occurred in which the *Journal* notice either failed to mention cause of death or, as in a few cases, ascribed death to an ill-defined cause such as cancer or uremia. Therefore, to obtain a more nearly complete compilation of deaths from LHS neoplasms in other specialty groups, a third procedure was followed. Death certificates were sought for all persons for whom the *Journal* notice specified such specialty boards but either failed to mention cause of death or ascribed death to one of the following ill-defined categories: uremia, sarcoma, carcinoma, or malignancy. For deaths occurring from ages 35 to 74, there were 1,187 entries of this type in the 17-year period of the study (1948 to 1964). A search for copies of the death records in these cases yielded 1,169 death certificates, comprising 1,045 for which the *Journal* notice mentioned no cause and 107 for which the cause was listed as cancer and 17 as uremia. This supplementary procedure identified in the other specialty groups 16 leukemia deaths, 16 deaths from lymphomas, one death from aplastic anemia, and none from multiple myeloma.

These procedures for locating death certificates of physicians who died in the 1948 to 1964 period at ages 35 through 74 are expected to yield virtually complete coverage of deaths from LHS neoplasms in the three specialty boards, ABR, ABD, and ABU. For the remaining specialty boards, it is estimated from experience gained in studying the ABR, ABD, and ABU groups that about five (and not more than 30) more deaths from LHS neoplasms may have occurred. Although the *Journal* notice sometimes reports the immediate rather than the underlying cause of death, this occurs rarely in the case of LHS neoplasms, so far as can be judged by the ABR, ABD, and ABU groups.

A few deaths were traced for which the *Journal* notice failed to mention certification by a specialty board. Such deaths were located by tracing the names of specialists listed in the 1950 edition of the *Directory of Medical Specialists* but omitted from one or more later editions. Editions of this *Directory* were also used as the source for validating the information on specialty contained in the *Journal* notice.

The follow-up of the class of all physicians not listed as diplomates of American Specialty Boards is the least complete, since no effort was made to locate death certificates in those instances in which no cause or an ill-defined cause of death was reported in the obituary notices. Since seven of 79 deaths from LHS neoplasms in the ABR, ABD, and ABU groups had either no cause or an ill-defined cause cited in the *Journal* notice, it may be roughly estimated that the coverage of deaths from LHS neoplasms in all physicians other than Board-certified specialists is roughly 90 per cent, if a proportionate degree of reporting of cause in *Journal* notices occurred in such physicians.

Simple tabulations of the number of deaths from specific LHS neoplasms would be meaningless for comparative purposes, since the different study populations do not have the same composition with respect to age, and since the degree of ascertainment of deaths varies in the different groups as noted above. Moreover, the actual age composition is not known with sufficient accuracy to justify calculation of death rates for either nonspecialty or specialty groups, except for Board-certified radiologists for the years 1948 to 1961 (Lewis, 1963). It is therefore necessary to make age- and year-specific adjustments before making any comparisons of populations. It is believed that the following procedure adequately achieves these adjustments. An expected number of deaths from leukemia, for example, was calculated by assuming that the group of physicians would experience the same age- and year-specific proportions of deaths from this cause among all deaths from LHS neoplasms as would all U.S. white males. That is, for each of the eight five-year age intervals from 35 to 74 years, and for each of the 17 years of the study period, such proportions were calculated. In other words, the number of leukemia deaths (International code rubric 204) in U.S. white males divided by the number of all deaths ascribed to LHS neoplasms in such males (code rubics 200 through 205) were calculated from published sources of data. The resultant 8×17 matrix was then identically multiplied by a corresponding matrix containing in each cell the observed number of deaths from all LHS neoplasms in the population of physicians under study. Summation of all cells yielded the expected number of deaths from leukemia for the study period. A comparison of observed with expected numbers of deaths calculated in this way is shown in Table 1. In making similar calculations for multiple myeloma, unpublished data on deaths from this cause in U.S. white males for years 1949 through 1962 were made available by the National Center for Health Statistics. Deaths from multiple myeloma for the year 1949 were assumed applicable to the year 1948, those for 1962 were assumed applicable to the years 1963 and 1964.

TABLE 1. *Comparisons of Observed and Expected Numbers of Deaths from LHS Neoplasms in Specified Groups of Physicians Who Died at Ages 35 through 74 During the 17-Year Period, 1948 to 1964**

		Number of deaths							
Study Population		Leukemia		Multiple myeloma		Lymphomas†		All LHS neoplasms	
		No.	%	No.	%	No.	%	No.	%
American Board specialists	Observed	89	49.7	23	12.9	67	37.4	179	100.0
	Expected	77.0	43.0	20.1	11.2	81.9	45.8	179.0	100.0
All other physicians (M.D.'s)	Observed	187	51.0	43	11.7	137	37.3	367	100.0
	Expected	163.6	44.6	42.3	11.5	161.1	43.9	367.0	100.0

* Expected numbers of deaths from a stated cause are relative, being based upon the number of deaths that would have occurred had the physician group experienced the same age-specific and year-specific proportions of deaths from that cause among deaths from all LHS neoplasms as did the U.S. white male population.

The estimated percentage of follow-up of all deaths that may have occurred from LHS neoplasms is 97 per cent for the American Board specialists and 90 per cent for the group of all other U.S. physicians.

† Lymphosarcoma, Hodgkin's disease, and lymphoma.

Abbreviation: LHS, lymphatic and hematopoietic systems.

It is evident that observed percentages of deaths from the three major groupings of LHS neoplasms, *i.e.* leukemia (code rubric 204), multiple myeloma (203), and other lymphomas (200 to 202), are not greatly different from expected percentages. (No deaths from the rare mycosis fungoides [code rubric 205] were recorded in any of the series). In both the class of specialists and the class of physicians not belonging to a specialty there were proportionately more deaths from leukemia than expected. The presumption that this reflects occupational exposure to radiation can be tested readily, however, only for the specialists.

The excess number of deaths from leukemia in the class of all American Board specialists can be attributed, in part at least, to an excess of deaths from this cause in the three major specialty groups ABR, ABD, and ABU. The breakdown of LHS neoplasms, as well as of the two related diseases aplastic anemia and polycythemia vera, in these specialty groups is shown in Table 2.

TABLE 2. *Observed Numbers of Deaths of Physicians who were Diplomates of Specified American Specialty Boards and for Whom the Underlying Cause of Death as Stated on the Death Certificate was One of the Specified Hematological Diseases**

Underlying cause of death	American Board of Radiology	American Board of Dermatology	American Board of Urology
Leukemia	13(5)†	6(2)	7
Multiple myeloma	5	1	1
Lymphomas‡	7	0	1
Aplastic anemia	5	0	1
Polycythemia vera	0	1(1)	0
Total	30(5)	8(3)	10

* The tabulation includes only deaths occurring at ages 35 through 74 for the 17-year period, 1948 to 1964.

† Numbers in parentheses indicate additional deaths which are nonvalid for statistical purposes since the specified hematological disease was listed on the death certificate as a contributory, rather than as the underlying cause of death.

‡ Lymphosarcoma, Hodgkin's disease, and lymphoma.

In the case of ABR specialists, it was shown (Lewis, 1963) that the observed numbers of deaths from leukemia and multiple myeloma for the years 1948 to 1961 exceeded the expected numbers at statistically significant levels. U.S. white male age- and year-specific death rates were used as a basis for calculation. On the basis of preliminary estimates of the age composition of the living population of dermatologists at risk during each year of the 1948 to 1964 study period, the observed number of deaths from leukemia in this group significantly exceeds the expected number calculated on the basis of U.S. white male age-specific death rates for this disease. Judgment must be withheld on whether the death rate for leukemia is significantly elevated in the case of urologists, however, until the age composition of the living population at risk is evaluated.

It is of interest that Dublin and Spiegelman (1948), in a study of mortality rates during the five-year period 1938 to 1942, called attention to a possibly elevated risk of death from leukemia in a population of full-time specialists in dermatology. These investigators did not single out urologists as a separate group of specialists and therefore their study did not present estimates of risk in such individuals.

A clear indication of excessive mortality from leukemia, relative to mortality from all causes of death, is evident for dermatologists and urologists, as well as radiologists. This is shown in Table 3, where the observed number of deaths from leukemia in each five-year age group is compared with an expected number calculated on the assumption that the specialty group experienced the same proportion of deaths from leukemia among deaths from all causes as did U.S. white males. In the ABD group, the ratio of observed deaths from leukemia to expected deaths calculated in this way was 6:1.4; in the ABU group, the corresponding ratio was 7:1.91.

The 26 observed deaths from leukemia in the ABR, ABD, and ABU groups were ascribed to a variety of types, but chronic lymphocytic leukemia was not mentioned in any case as the underlying cause of death. Two deaths in the ABR group were ascribed simply to "leukemia," one death in the ABD group to "lymphatic leukemia" (chronicity unspecified), and one death in the ABU group to "chronic leukemia" (cell type unspecified). Aside from these possible instances of chronic lymphocytic leukemia, the preponderance of radiation types of leukemia in these specialty groups is supporting evidence for the conclusion that the excessive number of deaths from leukemia in the ABD, ABU, and ABR groups is the result, at least in part, of occupational exposure to ionizing radiation. Finally, additional supporting evidence is provided by the relative rarity of deaths from lymphomas in these specialty groups in relation to deaths from leukemia, as shown in Table 2. Thus, for populations with approximately the same age composition as these specialty groups, the ratio of leukemia to lymphoma deaths is expected to be about 1 to 1 (cf. 43.0 per cent leukemias to 45.8 per cent lymphomas expected in the group of all Board specialists; or 44.6 per cent to 43.9 per cent in the group of all other physicians) (Table 1). In fact, the ratio was 13:7 for radiologists, 6:0 for dermatologists, and 7:1 for urologists.

Summary

The probability of a tumor per unit dose of radiation per year seems closely dependent on age, so far as can be estimated from a review of studies of radiation-induced carcinogenesis in man. The average value of this probability for leukemia is on the order of one to two cases of this disease per million persons per rad to the marrow per year during childhood and early adult life in white populations (or, apparently, during all ages in Japanese populations). The value, however, is estimated to be 10 to 20 cases per million per rad per year during fetal stages in white populations. It may be inferred from Doll's analysis (1962) that this

TABLE 3. *Comparison of Observed and Expected Numbers of Deaths from Leukemia Occurring at Ages 35 through 74 in a 17-Year Period from 1948 through 1964 Among Diplomates of Specified American Specialty Boards*

Age interval (yr.)	American Board of Radiology			American Board of Dermatology			American Board of Urology		
	All deaths†	Leukemia deaths Obs.	Exp.	All deaths†	Leukemia deaths Obs.	Exp.	All deaths†	Leukemia deaths Obs.	Exp.
35–39	17	1	0.21	5	2	0.06	4	2	0.05
40–44	26	1	0.25	13	1	0.14	13	1	0.14
45–49	50	1	0.39	16	0	0.14	19	1	0.16
50–54	54	1	0.39	17	0	0.13	27	1	0.21
55–59	102	2(1)‡	0.70	30	0	0.22	39	0	0.28
60–64	78	2(1)	0.55	37	1	0.28	50	1	0.38
65–69	105	2(2)	0.76	25	1	0.19	48	0	0.36
70–74	98	3(1)	0.66	33	1(2)	0.24	46	1	0.33
Totals	530	13(5)	3.91	176	6(2)	1.40	246	7	1.91

* Expected deaths are those which would have occurred had the same age- and year-specific proportions of deaths from leukemia among deaths from all causes which characterized the U.S. white male population been applicable to the specialist population.

† This column contains the observed number of deaths in the specialty group from all causes, including leukemia.

‡ The numbers shown in parentheses are additional deaths from leukemia which are nonvalid for statistical purposes since leukemia was listed on the death certificate as a contributory, rather than as the underlying cause of death.

Abbreviations: Obs., observed; Exp., expected.

value may re reached again, or exceeded, at least in white males, over 60 years of age. These estimated values of the probability of leukemia are apparently applicable for only eight to 10 years if irradiation is given during the fetal stage, but may apply for 10 to 20 years if irradiation is given at any time after birth.

New data are presented which define the pattern of mortality from LHS (lymphatic and hematopoietic system) neoplasms in groups of medical specialists and other physicians. Three groups of specialists, radiologists, dermatologists, and urologists, have a remarkably aberrant pattern of such neoplasms; *i.e.* a disproportionately large number of leukemia deaths (and possibly multiple myeloma deaths, as well) occur in relation to deaths from lymphomas. In the case of radiologists and dermatologists, at least, it is likely that this aberrant pattern is the result of occupational exposure to radiation.

ACKNOWLEDGMENTS

The National Center of Health Statistics kindly made available mortality data on multiple myeloma for the years 1949 through 1962. The cooperation of public health personnel in vital statistics offices in each of the 50 states in supplying copies of death records is gratefully acknowledged. I am also indebted to Ruth Erickson, Pamela Lewis and Hugh H. Lewis for technical assistance. This work was aided in part by an institutional grant from the American Cancer Society and from the Michael Strieby Fund.

REFERENCES

Anderson, R. E., and K. Ishida. 1964. Malignant Lymphoma in Survivors of the Atomic Bomb in Hiroshima. *Annals of Internal Medicine*, 61:853–862.

Beach, S. A., and G. W. Dolphin. 1962. A Study of the Relationship Between X-Ray Dose Delivered to the Thyroids of Children and the Subsequent Development of Malignant Tumors. *Physics in Medicine and Biology*, 6:583–598.

Bizzozero, O. J., Jr., K. G. Johnson, and A. Ciocco, with the collaboration of T. Hoshino, T. Itoga, S. Toyoda, and S. Kawasaki. 1966. Radiation-Related Leukemia in Hiroshima and Nagasaki 1946–1964. I. Distribution, Incidence and Appearance Time. *New England Journal of Medicine*, 274:1095–1101.

Carter, C. O., K. A. Evans, and A. M. Stewart. 1961. Maternal Radiation and Down's Syndrome (Mongolism). *Lancet*, 2:1042.

Court Brown, W. M., K. E. Buckton, and A. S. McLean. 1965. Quantitative Studies of Chromosome Aberrations in Man Following Acute and Chronic Exposure to X Rays and Gamma Rays. *Lancet*, 1:1239–1241.

Court-Brown (*sic*), W. M., and R. Doll. 1957. *Leukaemia and Aplastic Anaemia in Patients Irradiated for Ankylosing Spondylitis* (Medical Research Council, Special Report Series No. 295). London, England: Her Majesty's Stationery Office, 135 pp.

————. 1965. Mortality from Cancer and Other Causes After Radiotherapy for Ankylosing Spondylitis. *British Medical Journal*, 2:1327–1332.

Directory of Medical Specialists. 1951. Chicago, Illinois: A. N. Marquis Co. Vol. 5, 1694 pp.

Doll, R. 1962. II. Age Differences in Susceptibility to Carcinogenesis in Man. *British Journal of Radiology*, 35:31–36.

Dublin, L. I., and M. Spiegelman. 1948. Mortality of Medical Specialists, 1938–1942. *Journal of the American Medical Association*, 137:1519–1524.

Faber, M. 1957. "Radiation-Induced Leukaemia in Denmark," *Advances in Radiobiology* (Proceedings of the Fifth International Conference on Radiobiology held in Stockholm on 15th–19th August, 1956), G. C. de Hevesy, A. G. Forssberg, and J. D. Abbatt, Eds. Springfield, Illinois: Charles C Thomas. Pp. 397–404.

Faber, M., E. Andreasen, and H. Uhrbrand. 1958. "Further Studies on Irradiation-Induced Leukaemia in Denmark," *Transactions of the Sixth Congress of the European Society of Haematology*, A. Videbaek, Ed. Basel, Switzerland, and New York, New York: S. Karger. Part 2. Pp. S211–S213.

Fraumeni, J. F., Jr., and R. W. Miller. 1967. Epidemiology of Human Leukemia: Recent Observations. *Journal of the National Cancer Institute*, 38:593–605.

Graham, S., M. L. Levin, A. M. Lilienfeld, L. M. Schuman, R. Gibson, J. E. Dowd, and L. Hempelmann. 1966. "Preconception, Intrauterine, and Postnatal Irradiation as Related to Leukemia," *Epidemiological Approaches to the Study of Cancer and Other Chronic Diseases* (National Cancer Institute Monograph 19), W. Haenszel, Ed. Bethesda, Maryland: U.S. Department of Health, Education and Welfare, Public Health Service, National Cancer Institute. Pp. 347–371.

Gunz, F. W., and H. R. Atkinson. 1964. Medical Radiations and Leukemia: Retrospective Survey. *British Medical Journal*, 1:389–393.

Hempelmann, L. H. 1968. Risk of Thyroid Neoplasms after Irradiation in Childhood. *Science*, 160:159–163.

Hempelmann, L. H., J. W. Piper, G. J. Burke, R. Terry, and W. R. Ames. 1967. Neoplasms in Persons Treated with X-Rays in Infancy for Thymic Enlargement. A Report of the Third Follow-up Survey. *Journal of the National Cancer Institute*, 38:317–341.

Hutchison, G. 1968. Leukemia in Patients with Cancer of the Cervix Uteri Treated with Radiation. A Report Covering the First Five Years of an International Study. *Journal of the National Cancer Institute*, 40:951–982.

Lewis, E. B. 1957. Leukemia and Ionizing Radiation. *Science*, 125:965–972.

———. 1963. Leukemia, Multiple Myeloma and Aplastic Anemia in American Radiologists. *Science*, 142:1492–1494.

MacMahon, B. 1962. Prenatal X-Ray Exposure and Childhood Cancer. *Journal of the National Cancer Institute*, 28:1173–1191.

Manual of the International Statistical Classification of Diseases, Injuries, and Causes of Death (International Committee for the Preparation of the Decennial Revision of International Lists of Diseases and Causes of Death, 6th Revision). 1948. Geneva, Switzerland: World Health Organization. Vol. 1, 376 pp.; Vol. 2 (Alphabetical Index), 524 pp.

Manual of the International Statistical Classification of Diseases, Injuries, and Causes of Death (Based on the Recommendations of the Seventh Revision Conference, 1955, and Adopted by the Ninth World Health Assembly under the WHO Nomenclature Regulations). 1957. Geneva, Switzerland: World Health Organization. Vol. 1, 393 pp.; Vol. 2 (Alphabetical Index), 540 pp.

March, H. C. 1944. Leukemia in Radiologists. *Radiology*, 43:275–278.

Pifer, J. W., E. T. Toyocka, R. W. Murray, W. R. Ames, and L. H. Hempelmann. 1963. Neoplasms in Children Treated with X-Rays for Thymic Enlargement. I. Neoplasms and Mortality. *Journal of the National Cancer Institute*, 31:1333–1356.

Pochin, E. E. 1960. Leukemia Following Radioiodine Treatment of Thyrotoxicosis. *British Medical Journal*, 2:1545–1550.

Pohl, W. 1960. Plasmocytoma due to Roentgen Injury. *Medizinische Klinik*, 55: 1839–1842.

Saenger, E. L., G. E. Thoma, and E. A. Tompkins. 1968. Incidence of Leukemia Following Treatment of Hyperthyroidism. *Journal of the American Medical Association*, 205:855–862.

Schull, W. J., and J. V. Neel. 1962. Maternal Radiation and Mongolism. *Lancet*, 1:537–538.

Seltser, R., and P. E. Sartwell. 1965. The Influence of Occupational Exposure to Radiation on the Mortality of American Radiologists and Other Medical Specialists. *American Journal of Epidemiology*, 81:2–22.

Sigler, A. T., A. M. Lilienfeld, B. H. Cohen, and J. E. Westlake. 1965. Radiation Exposure in Parents of Children with Mongolism (Down's syndrome). *Bulletin of the Johns Hopkins Hospital*, 117:374–399.

Simpson, C. L., L. H. Hempelmann, and L. M. Fuller. 1955. Neoplasia in Children Treated with X-Rays in Infancy for Thymic Enlargement. *Radiology*, 64:840–845.

Stewart, A. 1961. Aetiology of Childhood Malignancies. *British Medical Journal*, 1:452–460.

Stewart, A., W. Pennybacker, and R. Barber. 1962. Adult Leukaemias and Diagnostic X-Rays. *British Medical Journal*, 2:882–890.

Stewart, A., J. Webb, and D. Hewitt. 1958. A Survey of Childhood Malignancies. *British Medical Journal*, 1:1495–1508.

Uchida, I. A., R. Holunga, and C. Lawler. 1968. Maternal Radiation and Chromosomal Aberrations. *Lancet*, 2:1045–1049.

Wald, N., G. E. Thoma, Jr., and G. Broun, Jr. 1962. "Hematologic Manifestations of Radiation Exposure in Man," *Progress in Hematology*, L. M. Tocantins, Ed. New York, New York, and London, England: Grune & Stratton. Vol. III. Pp. 1–52.

Wanebo, C. K., K. G. Johnson, K. Sato, and T. W. Thorslund. 1968a. Breast Cancer After Exposure to the Atomic Bombings of Hiroshima and Nagasaki. *New England Journal of Medicine*, 279:667–671.

———. 1968b. Lung Cancer Following Atomic Radiation. *American Review of Respiratory Diseases*, 98:778–787.

Werner, S. C., A. M. Gittelsohn, and A. B. Brill. 1961. Leukemia Following Radioiodine Therapy of Hyperthyroidism. *Journal of the American Medical Association*, 177:646–648.

Wood, J. W., H. Tamagaki, S. Neriishi, T. Sato, W. F. Sheldon, P. G. Archer, H. B. Hamilton, and K. G. Johnson. 1969. Thyroid Carcinoma in Atomic Bomb Survivors Hiroshima and Nagasaki. *American Journal of Epidemiology*, 89:4–14.

Discussion

Dr. Charles Miles, University of Utah, Salt Lake City, Utah: I would like to comment on Dr. Atkin's interesting presentation. There are no convincing reports in the literature for specific markers, other than for chronic myeloid leukemia. I wonder whether there is not perhaps another explanation for the apparent quasi-specificity. What is really specific may be a tendency for certain types of tumors toward karyotype instability. Or perhaps these conspicuous markers are more commonly found in tumors that are hard to diagnose early and that have progressed for a long period of time, such as ovarian cancer, gastric cancer, and lung cancer.

I suspect that a search for specific markers may be less fruitful than a search for mechanisms. For example, the loss of acrocentrics suggests that centric fusion is an important mechanism. Multiple minute chromosomes may represent a common mechanism which might be called a concatanation change in that once you get an abnormal chromosome it tends to be reduplicated; this may be the result of abnormal chromosomes toward nondisjunction. Another mechanism which has been illustrated is the polyploid cell with polarization which, I think, almost certainly occurs secondary to cell fusion, as originally argued by Nichols. This seems to be a very common mechanism in many cancers.

Dr. Mary Ester Gaulden, The University of Texas Southwestern Medical School at Dallas, Dallas, Texas: Dr. Lewis, do you know the different types of leukemias that occurred among the radiologists you surveyed? For example, is there a high incidence of chronic myelogenous leukemia in this group?

Dr. E. B. Lewis, California Institute of Technology, Pasadena, California: In the population of radiologists studied, 13 deaths were identified for which the underlying cause was given on the death certificate as leukemia. The breakdown of these deaths by type was as follows: two leukemias, type unspecified; three acute, cell type not specified; three granulocytic, chronicity not specified; one monocytic; one acute lymphatic; one acute granulocytic; one subacute granulocytic; and one acute monocytic leukemia. There were five additional deaths for which the contributory, but not the underlying, cause was given as leukemia. The breakdown for these was as follows: one lymphocytic, two granulocytic, one acute monocytic, and one chronic lymphocytic leukemia.

Dr. Alfred Zweidler, The University of Texas, Austin, Texas: I have done some studies similar to Dr. Atkin's but on a smaller scale using brain tumors, epidermal tumors, *etc.* I found about the same thing—a smaller variation than was expected from earlier studies—but I also found that probably the proposed deficiencies in some chromosome groups and the surplus in others might be due to a statistical phenomenon.

If you do a statistical analysis on a cultured cell line, as I did on H.Ep.-

2 cells, you find that many marker chromosomes are only recognized as such because their morphologies are far different from normal. For instance, all the acrocentrics are easily recognizable. If there is a slight change, it is labeled as a marker, and so a high proportion of the marker chromosomes are acrocentric. The same is the case for the larger chromosomes. The surplus in some marker chromosome types then accounts mainly for the deficiencies in the related normal groups, whereas the contrary is true, for instance, for the C group chromosomes. Since the C group contains a large area in the statistical morphological plotting, it is obvious that they have to have a surplus as compared with the groups with smaller areas, for instance D and G. Therefore, I don't believe that the data published so far about losses in specific groups or gains in other groups are significant.

Dr. N. B. Atkin, Mount Vernon Hospital, Northwood, Middlesex, England: I quite agree. I tried to make that point, but perhaps I didn't make it clear enough.

Dr. I. B. Weinstein, Columbia University College of Physicians and Surgeons, New York, New York: Dr. Atkin, in view of the widespread chromosomal changes which you see, what do we know about the effects of nonmalignant diseases of specific tissues and the effects of tissue regeneration or repair on chromosomal abnormalities? For example, are there karyotypic changes in inflammatory disease of the cervix or during wound healing, *etc.?*

Dr. Atkin: We know relatively little. However, we have a few observations and these are gradually increasing. For instance, the cervix uteri with chronic cervicitis, chronically inflamed tonsils removed at tonsillectomy, and endometrium in various hyperplastic conditions, which we have studied in direct preparation, have shown no chromosome abnormalities. We have in fact found no chromosome abnormalities in pathological tissues except where these are premalignant or possibly premalignant. The latter include Hashimoto's disease of the thyroid gland, in which we have found local chromosome abnormalities.

Session Chairman D. G. Harnden, Western General Hospital, Edinburgh, Scotland: I would like to add a comment to that. Miss Buckton in our laboratory has been looking for clones of cells in samples from people who have been treated with radiation. She has described four such clones, two in patients treated with X rays for ankylosing spondylitis and two in patients who were given Thorotrast. There is good evidence of distinct cytogenetic clone formation and no evidence of hematological disorders or of any malignant conditions in these patients.

Dr. L. D. Samuels, Children's Hospital, Columbus, Ohio: A few years ago, I directed a study of individuals in the Midwest whose drinking water was supplied by a well contaminated by radium and became interested in the problem of cancer induction by radium. Retrospectively, we were not able to do cytogenetic analyses, but even in our ongoing experimentation, we could not obtain good data on the cytogenetic effects. Do you have any comments on this problem, Dr. Lewis, or any observations about radiation effects in inducing osteosarcoma?

Dr. Lewis: Are you familiar with Court Brown's paper on luminous dial painters in England and the chromosome abnormalities in that group, or do you mean groups exposed to still lower doses?

Dr. Samuels: We were working with people exposed to a very low chronic dose of radiation.

Dr. Lewis: I do not know of chromosome studies in such groups.

Dr. Samuels: We found in our total population (about a million people) that there was a significant increase ($P < .07$) in the incidence of disease in the population ingesting radium in their drinking water. The dose levels concerned were in the range of two to four logs less than those to which the dial painters were exposed. These results were published in *Public Health Reports* in 1966.

Dr. A. L. Saadi, University of Michigan School of Medicine, Ann Arbor, Michigan: We have done some studies on preneoplastic stages in the thyroid gland in man and animals. We have induced thyroid carcinoma by placing animals on iodine-deficient diets. Some chromosomal abnormalities were found in the hyperplastic and preneoplastic stages in the rat's thyroid cells. We also found some chromosomal abnormalities in the thyroid cells of human beings with nodular goiters and Hashimoto's thyroiditis. Do you have any comments on this?

Dr. Atkin: Were these in cultures of the tissues?

Dr. Saadi: Some of them were in cultures and some of them were direct preparations.

Dr. Atkin: Did the chromosome abnormalities involve additional chromosomes—cells with 47 or more chromosomes?

Dr. Saadi: If I recall correctly, in three of the eight patients with nodular goiter, we found two additional chromosomes in the C group. In patients with Hashimoto's thyroiditis, we found fairly similar findings. I believe the additional chromosomes were in either the C or D groups. We definitely found some chromosomal abnormalities.

Dr. Atkin: This is in agreement with our findings on Hashimoto's disease. We have no observations on nodular goiter, but here again this might be classified as a premalignant condition.

Dr. William Benedict, Children's Hospital, Los Angeles, California: I should like to make a comment relative to chromosomal studies of solid tumors believed to be premalignant or benign. Working with Dr. Ian Porter at the Albany Medical Center, I have studied over 20 solid tumors, four of which were considered benign. Two colloid goiters contained cells with a normal diploid mode; however, a meningioma and a pseudomucinous cystadenoma contained aneuploid metaphases. In the meningioma, a mode of 38 chromosomes was present. Two long acrocentric markers and a large submetacentric marker were also present in each metaphase. In the cystadenoma, there were only three metaphases, one with 60 chromosomes, one with 150 chromosomes, and another with approximately 300 chromosomes. A long acrocentric marker was also present. Histologically, these two tumors were believed to represent benign neoplasms, but they may represent tumors containing areas undergoing early malignant transformation.

The Association Between Congenital Malformations and Cancer

ROBERT W. MILLER

Epidemiology Branch, National Cancer Institute, Bethesda, Maryland

In this age of electron microscopes, ultracentrifuges, and high-speed computers, it is still possible to make observations at the bedside that are important in etiologic research. Particularly useful in this regard is an approach we have designated as "laterospective," because, in a sense, one looks sideways for the coexistence of diseases previously thought to be unrelated. When concurrences are found, new avenues of research may be opened, for each disorder may then be examined in terms of what is known of the diseases with which it is associated. This approach has brought the recognition that certain congenital defects carry high risks of specific neoplasms. Such clinical-epidemiological findings provide a strategy for laboratory studies into subclinical abnormalities of possible etiologic or predictive value. This presentation concerns the approach with respect to one recently developed laboratory test of particular promise.

Clinical-Epidemiological Observations

At highest risk of leukemia thus far known is the child whose identical twin has developed the neoplasm. In a review of death certificates for all persons under 15 years of age in the United States, 1960 to 1964, we found that, among 10,390 deaths from leukemia, there were five pairs of like-sex twins under six years of age (Miller, 1968a). We estimated that among these deaths only 156 (1.5 per cent) were individual twins, a small number unlikely to generate any pairs in which both members would have leukemia by chance. Also against the play of chance are the observations that (1) the dates of death were very close for each twin pair—within 24 days to 7 months and (2) the frequency of twin-pairs, 5/156, was much greater than that of sib-pairs (not twins), 5/10,234. MacMahon and Levy (1964), who first recognized the increased concordance for leukemia in identical twins, estimated that when one member of the pair developed the neoplasm, the probability was 1:5 that the other twin would also be striken with the disease.

The risk of developing leukemia is apparently of similar magnitude in two genetically transmitted diseases, Bloom's syndrome and Fanconi's aplastic anemia (Sawitsky, Bloom, and German, 1966; Bloom, Warner, Gerald, and Diamond, 1966; Miller, 1967). The number of persons with these syndromes and leukemia, though small, indicates that the neoplasm occurs in adolescence or early adulthood, and in Fanconi's anemia may be limited to the monocytic type. Both syndromes are characterized by chromosomal fragility and rearrangements (quadriradials) in tissue culture. The suspicion that lysergic acid diethylamine tartrate (LSD 25) may be leukemogenic is based on similar breakage and rearrangements observed after use of the drug (Cohen, Marinello, and Black, 1967).

The frequency of leukemia among survivors of the Hiroshima atomic bomb who had been within 1,000 meters of the hypocenter is substantially less—1:60 over a 12-year period (Brill, Tomonaga, and Heyssel, 1962). Still lower is the risk of leukemia in Down's syndrome, about 1:95 (Miller, 1967).

Characteristic of the several groups predisposed to leukemia is a distinctive genetic feature. Identical twins have identical genes, Bloom's and Fanconi's syndromes display chromosomal fragility, ionizing radiation induces long-lasting chromosomal breaks, and in Down's syndrome there is congenital aneuploidy (Miller, 1967). Although each high-risk group has a distinctive genetic feature, there is no uniformity as to its nature.

Persons with high probability of developing leukemia do not carry a similar risk of lymphoma (Fraumeni and Miller, 1967), a neoplasm which is associated instead with inborn immunologic deficiencies (agammaglobulinemia, Wiskott-Aldrich syndrome, and ataxia telangiectasia). Thus, the constellation of diseases associated with leukemia is different from those associated with lymphoma.

In an entirely different orbit are Wilms' tumor, adrenocortical neoplasia, and primary liver cancer, which are associated with several congenital growth excesses (Miller, 1968b). Their relationships are shown schematically in Figure 1. Each of the three neoplasms occurs excessively with congenital hemihypertrophy, and these two categories of disease are independently associated with large pigmented or vascular nevi, among other hamartomas, and with the visceral cytomegaly syndrome to which Beckwith has recently called attention (1963). The syndrome consists of omphalocele, macroglossia, and cytomegaly of visceral organs including the three in which neoplasia has been observed

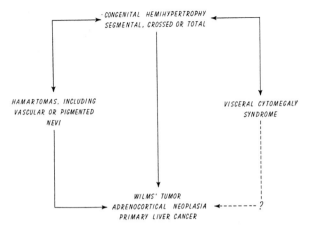

FIGURE 1. Relationships among four types of growth excess (after Miller, 1968b).

in association with hemihypertrophy. Still other congenital defects have been linked with neoplasia (Miller, 1968b), but are omitted here because they are peripheral to the main theme of this presentation.

A Laboratory Approach

Recently, a technique has been developed by Todaro, Green, and Swift (1966) to measure susceptibility of tissues in culture to transformation by viruses which are oncogenic in experimental animals. When one of these viruses, simian virus 40 (SV40), is added in vitro to skin fibroblasts from normal persons, some of the cells are transformed and grow in colonies instead of in a monolayer. The tissue culture properties of the transformed cells are the same as those which, in animal systems, are associated with tumor production upon inoculation into a susceptible host. A ten- to fiftyfold increase in the number of transformed colonies has been found when the test was applied to fibroblasts from persons with Fanconi's aplastic anemia (Todaro, 1968). As already noted, there is chromosomal fragility and apparently a high risk of leukemia in persons with this syndrome.

Patients with Down's syndrome have a different chromosomal abnormality (usually aneuploidy) and a risk of leukemia perhaps one fifteenth as great as in those with Fanconi's anemia. Their skin fibroblasts show only a three- to fivefold increase in susceptibility to transformation by SV40. The test has not been applied in D-trisomy, which has been described twice with leukemia despite the short life-span (Miller, 1967), but in the only instance in which cells from E-trisomy have been tested, increased susceptibility to transformation was observed (Todaro and Martin, 1967). Though the data are as yet fragmentary, it appears that cells from the autosomal trisomy syndromes may have in common greater transformability than usual and a predisposition to leukemia.

To determine if such an effect is limited to autosomal imbalance, evaluation should be made of the transformability of cells from persons with sex chromosome anomalies. Individual case reports describe the concurrence of Klinefelter's syndrome and leukemia (Fraumeni and Miller, 1967), an association which is difficult to evaluate epidemiologically because of problems in ascertainment, but which could be assessed through the transformation procedure.

By cloning fibroblasts from chromosomal mosaics, one may determine if susceptibility to transformation is limited to the aneuploid cells. Use of the test in balanced versus unbalanced translocations will indicate if transformability is influenced by variations in the chromosomal structural load.

Study of cells from the heterozygous parents of children with Fanconi's anemia revealed a five- to fortyfold increase in transformation— a susceptibility almost as great as in the homozygote (Todaro, 1968). The parents usually have no phenotypic or cytogenetic abnormality (Bloom, Warner, Gerald, and Diamond, 1966). An increased risk of leukemia among the relatives of persons with Fanconi's anemia has been suggested by Garriga and Crosby (1959), but their data, which are derived from a review of the scant literature on the subject, are open to question (Miller and Todaro, 1969).

Test results in the heterozygote indicate that the transformation procedure may be added to other recently described tissue culture techniques for detecting the carrier state (Danes and Bearn, 1968). Heightened susceptibility to transformation of cells from heterozygotes without demonstrable chromosomal abnormalities suggests that the test may indicate the presence of submicroscopic chromosomal aberrations.

Cell susceptibility may prove to be similarly increased in the heterozygote or homozygote for Bloom's syndrome, since it resembles Fanconi's anemia with respect to chromosomal findings and a predisposition to leukemia (Sawitsky, Bloom, and German, 1966).

In persons with inborn immunological deficiencies, cell sensitivity to transformation may help to determine the basis for the high risk of lymphoma-like disorders. A negative test would strengthen the concept that an intrinsic cellular susceptibility was not involved. The implications of a positive test might be clarified by comparable studies of persons on immunosuppressive drugs which, in renal transplantation at least, appear also to predispose to lymphoma (Medical News, 1968).

Applications of the test would be of interest in congenital hemihypertrophy and visceral cytomegaly, two growth disorders with usually no known immunological or cytogenetic abnormalities, but which are associated with one another and with neoplasms of several abdominal organs. The results would indicate the generality of the test procedure and could clarify the underlying biologic mechanisms.

The influence of environmental agents on transformation may be assessed. Pollack and Todaro (1968) have found a radiation dose-related effect when mouse or human fibroblasts in culture were infected with SV40 before or after irradiation. Persistence of the enhanced effect may be sought among heavily exposed Japanese survivors of the atomic bomb explosion or persons who have received radiotherapy. Enhancement might also be found after exposure to other agents which produce longlasting chromosomal breaks and are suspected to be leukemogenic; e.g., benzene, chloramphenicol, or LSD 25.

The test may have other research or diagnostic advantages. It might detect subclinical abnormality in the child whose identical twin has leukemia and whose risk of developing the neoplasm is the highest yet known (MacMahon and Levy, 1964). Study of parents whose children have monocytic leukemia may indicate whether the neoplasm is the only clinical evidence of Fanconi's anemia. When more than one child in a sibship develops leukemia of any type, studies of the sensitivity of the parents' fibroblasts in culture may indicate a covert heritable trait. (The same would be true in studies of familial cancer of any type.) It is, of course, most important to apply the test to cells from untreated children with leukemia or other neoplasms, and when positive, to evaluate the parents and sibs in a like manner.

The test may provide an explanation for the tremendous peak in mortality from leukemia at four years of age among white children in the United States, which is absent among nonwhite children (Fraumeni and Miller, 1967). Transformation studies may reveal that the peak is the result of an inherent pronounced susceptibility to leukemia, perhaps triggered by the child's first encounters with certain viruses, chemicals, and/or ionizing radiation.

Cells that are very sensitive to transformation, as in Fanconi's anemia, may be used to screen agents alone or in combination as to their oncogenic potential in man. Adenovirus type 12, which induces neoplasms in lower species and for which man is a natural host, does not transform normal human fibroblasts but does transform cells from persons with Fanconi's anemia (Todaro and Aaronson, 1968). This experience illustrates the value of the laboratory procedure in studies of agents with low transforming efficiency. As yet, irradiation or chemical carcinogens alone have not been reported to increase cell transformability, but such effects may be demonstrable if the sensitivity of fibroblasts now in use can be enhanced or if new cell lines of even greater susceptibility can be developed.

Summary

Clinical-epidemiological studies have identified persons at exceptionally high risk of developing certain neoplasms. Preexistent abnormalities associated with leukemia have a common distinctive genetic feature, either inherited or acquired—aneuploidy in Down's syndrome; chromosomal breakage after exposure to ionizing radiation or benzene; chromosomal fragility in Bloom's syndrome or Fanconi's aplastic anemia; and genetic identity in the child whose identical twin develops leukemia. These persons are not also at high risk of lymphoma, a neoplasm associated instead with inborn immunological deficiency (agammaglobulinemia, ataxia telangiectasia, or Wiskott-Aldrich syndrome). Still another constellation of diseases links congenital hemihypertrophy and other benign growth excesses with Wilms' tumor, adrenocortical neoplasia, or primary liver cancer.

Recognition of these relationships offers the laboratory investigator the opportunity to study high-risk groups in a search for subclinical abnormalities of value in predicting and preventing certain neoplasia or in determining its origins. Of particular promise in this regard is a recently developed quantitative measure of susceptibility to transformation of human skin fibroblasts in culture. This procedure has shown that susceptibility is substantially increased in the homozygote or the heterozygote for Fanconi's aplastic anemia—and to a lesser extent in those with Down's syndrome. The sensitive cells from Fanconi's syndrome are being used to screen agents as to their oncogenic potential in man.

REFERENCES

Beckwith, J. B. 1968. "Macroglossia, Omphalocele, Adrenal Cytomegaly, Gigantism, and Hyperplastic Visceromegaly," *Clinical Delineation of Birth Defects. II. Malformation Syndromes* (Birth Defects Original Article Series), D. Bergsma, and V. A. McKusick, Eds. New York, New York: National Foundation. Vol. 5. Pp. 188–196.

Bloom, G. E., S. Warner, P. S. Gerald, and L. K. Diamond. 1966. Chromosome Abnormalities in Constitutional Aplastic Anemia. *New England Journal of Medicine*, 274:8–14.

Brill, A. B., M. Tomonaga, and R. M. Heyssel. 1962. Leukemia in Man Following Exposure to Ionizing Radiation: A Summary of the Findings in Hiroshima and Nagasaki, and a Comparison with Other Human Experience. *Annals of Internal Medicine*, 56:590–609.

Cohen, M. M., M. J. Marinello, and N. Black. 1967. Chromosomal Damage in Human Leukocytes Induced by Lysergic Acid Diethylamide. *Science*, 155:1417–1419.

Danes, B. S., and A. G. Bearn. 1968. Metachromasia and Skin-Fibroblast Cultures in Juvenile Familial Amaurotic Idiocy. *Lancet*, 2:855–856.

Fraumeni, J. F., Jr., and R. W. Miller. 1967. Epidemiology of Human Leukemia: Recent Observations. *Journal of the National Cancer Institute*, 38:593–605.

Garriga, S., and W. H. Crosby. 1959. The Incidence of Leukemia in Families of Patients with Hypoplasia of the Marrow. *Blood, The Journal of Hematology*, 14:1008–1014.

MacMahon, B., and M. A. Levy. 1964. Prenatal Origin of Childhood Leukemia: Evidence from Twins. *New England Journal of Medicine*, 270:1082–1085.

Medical News. 1968. Neoplasms: A Complication of Organ Transplants? *Journal of the American Medical Association*, 206:246–247.

Miller, R. W. 1967. Persons with Exceptionally High Risk of Leukemia. *Cancer Research*, 27:2420–2423.

———. 1968a. Deaths from Childhood Cancer in Sibs. *New England Journal of Medicine*, 279:122–126.

———. 1968b. Relation Between Cancer and Congenital Defects: An Epidemiologic Evaluation. *Journal of the National Cancer Institute*, 40:1079–1085.

Miller, R. W., and G. J. Todaro. 1969. Viral Transformation of Cells from Persons at High Risk of Cancer. *Lancet*, 1:81–82.

Pollock, E. J., and G. J. Todaro. 1968. Radiation Enhancement of SV40 Transformation in 3T3 and Human Cells. *Nature*, 219:520–521.

Sawitsky, A., D. Bloom, and J. German. 1966. Chromosomal Breakage and Acute Leukemia in Congenital Telangiectatic Erythema and Stunted Growth. *Annals of Internal Medicine*, 65:487–495.

Todaro, G. J. 1968. "Variable Susceptibility of Human Cell Strains to SV40 Transformation," *Cell Cultures for Virus Vaccine Production* (National Cancer Institute Monograph 29), D. J. Merchant, Ed. Bethesda, Maryland: U. S. Department of Health, Education, and Welfare, Public Health Service, National Cancer Institute. Pp. 271–275.

Todaro, G. J., and S. A. Aaronson. 1968. Human Cell Strains Susceptible to Focus Formation by Human Adenovirus Type 12. *Proceedings of the National Academy of Sciences of the U.S.A.*, 61:1272–1278.

Todaro, G. J., H. Green, and M. R. Swift. 1966. Susceptibility of Human Diploid Fibroblast Strains to Transformation by SV40 Virus. *Science*, 153:1252–1254.

Todaro, G. J., and G. M. Martin. 1967. Increased Susceptibility of Down's Syndrome Fibroblasts to Transformation by SV40. *Proceedings of the Society for Experimental Biology and Medicine*, 124:1232–1236.

Genetic Varieties of Neoplasia

DAVID E. ANDERSON

Department of Biology, The University of Texas M. D. Anderson Hospital and Tumor Institute at Houston, Houston, Texas

Several hypotheses have been advanced to explain the nature of the change by which a cell is transformed into a cancer cell. The change in some cancers has been attributed to an alteration in the genetic apparatus of a somatic cell, resulting either from gene mutation(s) or from an abnormal chromosome complex. These alterations may be initiated by a variety of physical and chemical agents, including viruses. The transformation may be also caused by an alteration in the genetic apparatus of a germ cell (as opposed to a somatic cell), giving rise to transmissible hereditary material either at the gene or chromosome level and enhancing cancer susceptibility in recipient zygotes.

Evidence establishing the existence and importance of susceptibility genes for various neoplasms in experimental animals, particularly mice, long has been available. But in human beings, the possibility of such genes apparently is questioned or discounted. The few examples generally cited include von Recklinghausen's neurofibromatosis, retinoblastoma, several types of intestinal polyposis, and xeroderma pigmentosum. Many other examples are on record (Lynch, 1967) and probably are more numerous than is generally suspected. The purpose of the present report, therefore, is to summarize the genetic evidence supporting the concept of susceptibility genes in man. Hopefully, the summary also will direct attention to this class of neoplasms which, aside from their genetic and clinical interest, could serve as a source of experimental material for investigating the relationship between gene effects and neoplasms in man.

Materials and Methods

Only the most frequently observed genetically determined neoplasms are considered. The examples originated primarily from previously reported pedigrees, which included information on the disease status of the parents, sibs and/or children of a patient, as well as age and sex information. Compared to other possible approaches, *i.e.*, twin studies or retrospective surveys (Schull, 1959), pedigrees offer a profitable approach for evaluating genetic effects. By using pedigrees, one avoids many of the errors inherent in the other two approaches and acquires data amenable to tests of hypotheses concerning segregation ratios, linkage relations, and other questions of genetic interest. As a source of information, pedigrees might be criticized on the grounds that familial occurrences may result from chance or common exposure to environmental factors or that these constitute a biased sample containing an excess of multiple cases. These criticisms generally can be discounted if the familial occurrences pertain to specific histological types of neoplasms with characteristic ages at onset. These unique occurrences are indicative of a genetic basis, more so than those involving different types of neoplasms with variable or late ages at follows: (1) Those entities in which a neoplasm is the only known pheno-

The neoplasms were classified into four main categories according to their apparent relationship to the primary genetic defect, as reflected by the frequency of neoplasms in a genetic entity. The categories are as follows: (1) Those entities in which a neoplasm is the only known pheno-typic manifestation of a genetic defect, i.e., all individuals with a genetic entity have neoplasms. (2) Syndromes in which neoplasms may be one of several phenotypic manifestations of a genetic defect, and neoplasms occur in virtually all individuals with a syndrome. (3) Those entities in which a precursor lesion or disease state is the phenotypic manifestation of a genetic defect, and neoplasms (exclusive of leukemia and lymphoma) develop in a significant proportion of patients. (4) Entities in which a disease is the phenotypic manifestation of a genetic defect, and leukemia or lymphoma develops in a significant proportion of patients.

This method of classification is obviously arbitrary, particularly the classification of some of the entities in categories 2 and 3. Other methods have been proposed also and, in fact, have been used (Lynch, 1967). The most meaningful method would have been based on knowledge of the gene action underlying each entity, as has been possible for the numerous inherited metabolic diseases. In the absence of such knowledge, however, the present method was selected.

Results

GENETIC NEOPLASMS

The entities in which a neoplasm is the only known phenotypic manifestation of a genetic defect are shown in Table 1. The evidence supporting these entities as examples of genetic neoplasms will be summarized, except for retinoblastoma, which is well recognized and well documented. Since each of the entities manifested familial distribution patterns suggesting dominant inheritance, this was the null hypothesis tested in each case. The summaries pertain only to individuals in the age range in which the preponderance of a given neoplasm(s) occurred. In the absence of sex differences in affection rates, the sexes were combined. Propositi routinely were excluded from the analyses to avoid ascertainment bias.

TABLE 1. *Genetic Neoplasms*

Entity	Primary neoplasm(s)	Mode of inheritance
Chemodectoma	Nonchromaffin paraganglioma of carotid body and glomus jugulare	Autosomal dominant
Hereditary adeno-carcinomatosis	Adenocarcinoma of colon, uterus, stomach, and ovary	Autosomal dominant
Hereditary polyendocrine adenomatosis, including Zollinger-Ellison syndrome	Adenomas primarily of pituitary, parathyroid, and pancreas	Autosomal dominant
Pheochromocytoma	Pheochromocytoma, medullary thyroid carcinoma, cerebello-retinal hemangioblastoma, and neurofibromas	Autosomal dominant
Retinoblastoma	Retinoblastoma	Autosomal dominant

Pheochromocytoma

This is a catecholamine-secreting neoplasm of the adrenal medulla which occurs singly or in association with neurofibromatosis (Carmen and Brashear, 1960), von Hippel-Lindau's disease (Illingworth, 1967), or medullary thyroid carcinoma (Steiner, Goodman, and Powers, 1968). The thyroid carcinoma is a calcitonin-secreting medullary type with amyloid deposition; it is frequently bilateral and multifocal, features which also apply to pheochromocytoma. Both neoplasms tend to occur first between 20 and 30 years of age. Numerous pedigrees demonstrating pheochromocytoma and/or medullary thyroid carcinoma have been reported, the most recent by Schimke and Hartmann (1965), Ljungberg, Cederquist, and von Studnitz (1967), Huang and McLeish (1968), and Steiner, Goodman, and Powers (1968). The latter workers cited a comprehensive review of the literature on pheochromocytoma and summarized the results from 28 previously reported families. They also provided a detailed presentation of one large kindred containing 10 proved and 15 probable cases of pheochromocytoma, five of whom had medullary thyroid carcinoma. Three families with multiple occurrences of these two neoplasms are now under investigation at this institution, but the results are still incomplete.

The numerous pedigrees involving pheochromocytoma in association with medullary thyroid carcinoma (Table 2) reveal no significant difference in the affection rates of males and females. The results convincingly demonstrate a genetic basis for the disorder and an inheritance pattern for the occurrence of the neoplasm(s) in keeping with a classic dominant hypothesis, *i.e.*, the familial distribution of the neoplastic diathesis is compatible with the hypothesis of a single autosomal gene with a penetrance of 85 per cent and variable expressivity in the heterozygote who is at least 20 years of age. This reduced level of penetrance may result because these neoplasms do not always produce symptoms and may be detected only by special clinical investigations. It is still not known for certain whether pheochromocytoma alone or in association with neurofibromatosis, von Hippel-Lindau's disease, and/or medullary thyroid carcinoma represents different genetic entities stemming from different alleles or nonalleles, or whether they represent different manifestations of one allele. These associations presently are accounted for on the basis of similar embryologic origin of the affected organs (Williams, 1966).

TABLE 2. *Classification of Offspring (20 Years of Age and Above) of Parents With Pheochromocytoma and/or Medullary Thyroid Carcinoma*

Citation	Male		Female	
	Affected	Unaffected	Affected	Unaffected
Smits and Huizinga (1961)	9	10	5	10
Cushman (1962)				
Manning *et al.* (1963)	5	4	1	1
Finegold and Haddad (1963)				
Nourok (1964)				
Schimke and Hartmann (1965)	0	14	7	4
Ljungberg *et al.* (1967)	2	5	8	2
Huang and McLeish (1968)	7	4	1	7
Steiner, Goodman, and Powers (1968)	11	13	7	13
Total	34	50	29	37

	Chi-square	Degrees of freedom	Probability
Total	9.1	6	.10–.20
Deviation 1:1 ratio	3.8	1	.05–.10
Heterogeneity	5.3	5	.30–.50

Ljungberg, Cederquist, and von Studnitz (1967) consider pheochromocytomas to originate from chromaffin tissue and observed chromaffin-type granules in the cytoplasm of medullary thyroid carcinoma cells. They also demonstrated the presence of specific monamines and the presence of 5-hydroxytryptamine in both medullary thyroid carcinomas and pheochromocytomas. Consequently, they regard these associated tumors as representing a genetic defect of the chromaffin system.

The pheochromocytoma-medullary thyroid carcinoma complex is sometimes considered to represent partial expression or a variant of another genetic entity, namely, multiple endocrine adenomatosis. This possibility originates from clinical overlap between the two entities, but recent clinical and genetic evidence provides no convincing support for this notion (Schimke and Hartmann, 1965; Steiner, Goodman, and Powers, 1968).

Multiple Endocrine Adenomatosis

This entity is characterized by the multiple occurrence of adenomas of the anterior pituitary, parathyroids, and pancreas. Neoplasms of the thyroid and adrenal cortex also may develop as well as bronchial and intestinal carcinoids. The clinical picture is variable, depending upon which glands are affected and which tumors are functioning and interacting. The entity tends to develop between 30 and 40 years of age, with death occurring at about 43 years of age (Wermer, 1963). The association of peptic ulcer with nonfunctioning islet cell tumors of the pancreas and excessive gastric secretion is sometimes regarded as a separate entity and called the Zollinger-Ellison syndrome, but its frequent occurrence in the same pedigrees (and patients) manifesting multiple endocrine adenomatosis indicates that these symptoms are likely different manifestations of one genetic defect (Wermer, 1954; Schmid, Labhart, and Rossier, 1961; Moldawer, 1962). An animal counterpart of this disorder in which gastric carcinoids arise as focal or multicentric proliferations of argyrophil cells was recently described (Snell and Stewart, 1969).

Extensive pedigrees have been reported and discussed by Wermer (1954, 1963), Schmid, Labhart, and Rossier (1961), Ballard, Frame, and Hartsock (1964), and Johnson, Summerskill, Anderson, and Keating (1967) and are summarized in Table 3. The previous studies provide no evidence of a significant sex difference in the affection rate. The results fully document multiple endocrine adenomatosis as an example of a genetic neoplasm, the expression and familial distribution of which are controlled by an autosomal gene with high penetrance but variable expressivity in the heterozygote.

TABLE 3. *Classification of Offspring (20 Years of Age and Above) of Parents With Multiple Endocrine Adenomatosis*

	Male		Female	
Citation	Affected	Unaffected	Affected	Unaffected
Schmid *et al.* (1961)	7	2	4	3
Moldawer (1962)	0	0	1	1
Danowski *et al.* (1962)	6	2	7	5
Berdjis (1962)	0	1	1	2
Wermer (1963)	11	10	8	9
Ballard *et al.* (1964)	4	5	6	7
Stocks (1967)	4	2	2	5
Johnson *et al.* (1967)	6	7	9	8
Total	38	29	38	40

	Chi-square	Degrees of freedom	Probability
Total	5.3	8	.70–.80
Deviation 1:1 ratio	0.3	1	.50–.70
Heterogeneity	5.0	7	.50–.70

Wermer (1963) proposed the concept of mosaic pleiotropism to account for the occurrence of multiple tumors in this disease entity. He suggested that the cells of these diverse organs harbor some specific factor(s) rendering them responsive to the action of the mutant gene. However, another possibility is that the organs are comprised of specific cells (argyrophil?) in which the effect of the mutant gene, either through activation or inactivation, is to change the metabolic character of the cells, rendering them neoplastic.

Hereditary Adenocarcinomatosis

The above proposals (excluding the concept of the argyrophil cells) might well be applied to hereditary adenocarcinomatosis (also referred to as cancer families or multiple cancer syndrome) since it too is characterized by neoplasms in diverse organs. The primary lesions, adenocarcinomas, occur in one or several organs; they are seen most frequently in the colon, uterus, stomach, and occasionally the ovaries. These neoplasms occur at about 40 years of age, which is one to two decades earlier than the types which occur sporadically in the general population. One of the earliest and clearest illustrations of this disorder was provided by Warthin (1913). He described a family (Family G) in which there was a significant frequency of uterine and gastrointestinal cancer. This was a three-generation family originating with a man who died of cancer of the stomach or intestine. He had 10 children, in five of whom either uterine or gastrointestinal cancer developed. These five siblings had a total of 35 children, in 12 of whom similar neoplasms developed. A further report on this family was presented by Hauser and Weller (1936). Lynch (1967) provided the latest pedigree, but failed to specify the types and sites of neoplasms in the affected family members.

These associated neoplasms have now been observed and recorded in a sufficient number of cases to indicate that they constitute a distinct disease entity. The type of involvement in this entity is illustrated by the case of a patient at The University of Texas M. D. Anderson Hospital and Tumor Institute at Houston who first developed a neoplasm of the

TABLE 4. *Classification of Offspring (25 Years of Age and Above) of Parents with Adenocarcinomatosis*

Citation	Male		Unknown sex	Female		Unknown sex
	Affected	Un-affected	Affected	Affected	Un-affected	Unaffected
Hauser and Weller (1936)	13	18		20	14	
Savage (1956)	1	3		7	6	
Mathis (1962)	4	9		6	4	
Heinzelmann (1964)	5	3		3	4	
Kluge (1964)	3	1	1	1	0	3
Bieler and Heim (1965)	5	4		3	7	
Aure and Nilsson (1965)	4	5		3	4	
Kartagener and Wyler (1966)	2	4		1	3	
Lynch et al. (1966) Family N	3	13		15	20	8
Lynch et al. (1966) Family M	6	5		9	7	
Peltokallio and Peltokallio (1966)	3	5		3	1	
Lynch and Krush (1967) Family 3	3	1	1	4	2	
Lynch and Krush (1967) Family 4	1	3		2	4	
Lynch and Krush (1967) Family 5	6	0		2	4	
Total	59	74	2	79	80	11

	Chi-square	Degrees of freedom	Probability
Total	18.1	14	.20–.30
Deviation 1:1 ratio	1.9	1	.10–.20
Heterogeneity	16.2	13	.20–.30

transverse colon at age 42, followed in six months by an adenocarcinoma of the endometrium, and in another three months by an adenocarcinoma of the rectosigmoid. Eight of 15 of her adult relatives also manifested adenocarcinomas of the colon and/or uterus (Figure 1). This family was previously reported as Family 5 by Lynch and Krush (1967) and Family 6 by Lynch (1967). The various other pedigrees manifesting this entity are summarized in Table 4.

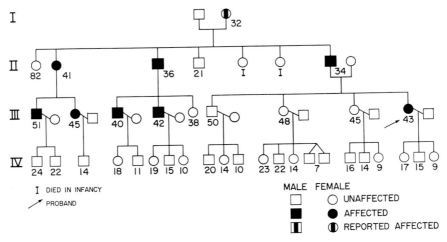

FIGURE 1. Pedigree of family with hereditary adenocarcinomatosis. All affected individuals have verified adenocarcinoma of colon and/or uterus.

The results for combined sexes clearly indicate that the different families are homogeneous in exhibiting the 1:1 ratio expected with dominant inheritance; only one family (Family N [Lynch *et al.*, 1966]) differs from expectation. The total sex ratio in this family also differs from expectation unless the eight unaffected individuals of unspecified sex were all males. The reasons for these discrepancies are not known. Reasons for the deficiency of affected individuals may be that these neoplasms of the colon are not always readily detected by proctosigmoidoscopy and that information on unexamined individuals was obtained by questionnaires. This type of information is not always complete, and if the questionnaires were not returned or if they pertained to individuals below the usual age at onset and in whom the disease would not yet have developed, such individuals would then be classified as unaffected.

Lynch *et al.* (1966) raised the intriguing possibility of cytoplasmic inheritance to account for a predominance of female transmission in their two families. This possibility was evaluated by comparing the frequency of the disease in children from affected fathers to the frequency from affected mothers. This reciprocal test provided no evidence of maternal transmission to the sexes, either separately or combined (P >.50). The familial distribution of this neoplastic entity, therefore, clearly is compatible with the hypothesis of a single autosomal gene, with a surprisingly high penetrance of 90 per cent in the heterozygote who is at least 25 years of age.

Warthin (1913) introduced the term "cancer families" in referring to a large number of families with various types of cancers. This term since has been used in referring specifically to his Family G, as well as to other families with this entity. However, this usage is not in keeping with its original connotation. The other terms "familial colonic cancer" or "multiple cancer syndrome" likewise have general connotations. A more specific term, "hereditary adenocarcinomatosis," would seem appropriate and therefore is proposed for this entity. The new term would direct attention to the genetic etiology, the primary type(s) of neoplasm(s), and moreover, would emphasize the multiple nature of the neoplasms.

Chemodectomas

A similar analytic procedure was employed in evaluating the genetic basis for neoplasms of the chemoreceptor system, notably the carotid body and glomus jugulare. The neoplasms usually occur sporadically, but in some patients, they have a definite genetic basis. A number of familial occurrences have been described, and pedigrees complete enough for analysis have been reported by Sprong and Kirby (1949), Rush (1963), Kroll, Alexander, Cochios, and Pechet (1964), and Katz (1964). The patients in these pedigrees had onset of disease at an average age of 34 years. Interestingly, among 47 familial patients documented as to side of involvement, 34 per cent had bilateral tumors. This frequency is grossly in excess of the 2 to 5 per cent frequency of bilaterality generally cited for sporadic cases. The four pedigrees showing segregation of the neoplasm were composed of 57 individuals at genetic risk who were over 20 years of age. Of these, 31 developed chemodectomas. The deviation chi-square of 0.4 had a probability range from .50 to .70 and the heterogeneity chi-square of 4.0 for three degrees of freedom had a range from .20 to .30, results which are fully compatible with the hypothesis of a single gene with expression in the heterozygote.

TABLE 5. *Genetic Neoplasms in Syndromes*

Disease entity	Neoplasm(s)	Mode of inheritance
Nevoid basal cell carcinoma syndrome (basal cell carcinomas, jaw cysts, and skeletal anomalies)	Basal cell carcinomas, and medulloblastoma	Autosomal dominant
Tylosis (keratosis palmaris et plantaris)	Squamous cell carcinoma of esophagus	Autosomal dominant
Von Hippel-Lindau's disease (cerebelloretinal hemangioblastomatosis)	Hemangioblastomas, and pheochromocytoma	Autosomal dominant
Von Recklinghausen's neurofibromatosis (neurofibromas, and cafe-au-lait spots)	Neurofibromas, neuromas, meningiomas, gliomas and sarcomas, and pheochromocytoma	Autosomal dominant

Miscellaneous

Other hereditary types of neoplasms, *i.e.* multiple glomus tumors, ovarian papillary adenocarcinoma, ovarian dysgerminoma, and ocular malignant melanoma, also could have been included in Table 1, but these are rare when compared to the other genetic neoplasms. Several neoplasms have been described in siblings, including medulloblastoma, Ewing's sarcoma, osteogenic sarcoma, and hepatocellular carcinoma, but the significance of these rare occurrences, whether the consequence of chance, a genetic defect, or common exposure to some exogenous agent, cannot be evaluated at present.

GENETIC NEOPLASMS IN SYNDROMES

The genetic entities in which neoplasms are an integral and consistent component of a syndrome complex are summarized in Table 5. Similar to the previous entities, these are all characterized by dominant inheritance patterns, *i.e.*, the familial distribution patterns accord with the hypothesis of a single gene with expression in the heterozygote. Each is an established clinicogenetic entity, particularly von Hippel-Lindau's disease (Illingworth, 1967) and von Recklinghausen's neurofibromatosis (Crowe, Schull, and Neel, 1956).

Tylosis

This entity, characterized by diffuse thickening of the palms and soles and by onset of disease between 5 and 15 years of age, is likewise well established, but its association with squamous cell carcinoma of the esophagus in some families is worthy of emphasis. Howel-Evans, Mc-Connell, Clarke, and Sheppard (1957) described two families with 48 tylotics, 18 of whom developed esophogeal carcinoma at an average age of 45 years and 95 per cent of whom were estimated to develop the neoplasm if they survived to age 65. There was no evidence that the tylosis gene segregating in these families caused a precancerous keratotic lesion in the esophagus, nor was there evidence of linkage between this gene locus and various blood group marker loci. Another family with this association was described by Shine and Allison (1966). In addition to esophageal carcinoma which appeared at age 61, they noted a congenitally abnormal esophagus in two and perhaps three generations in their family. They interpreted these findings as indicating a different allele from that involved in the families reported by Howel-Evans, McConnell, Clarke, and Sheppard (1957), which is considered to be different from that usually responsible for the diffuse form of tylosis.

Nevoid Basal Cell Carcinoma Syndrome

This syndrome is the most recent addition to the category of genetic neoplasms in syndromes. The primary features consist of multiple basal cell carcinomas, epithelial cell-lined jaw cysts, ectopic calcification of soft tissues, and a variety of congenital skeletal anomalies. Medulloblastoma also has been observed in a few patients, but at a higher frequency than that expected by chance. The syndrome apparently is not rare since almost 200 patients have been described since 1959. The basal cell carcinomas, which develop from multiple and multicentric foci, are first detected at about 20 years of age, and over 95 per cent of the patients with the syndrome who reach age 40 manifest lesions; this is well below the average age when onset of sporadic basal cell carcinoma occurs. The skeletal anomalies are congenital, and jaw cysts generally are detected around 15 years of age. Thus, these features can be used to identify individuals at risk to the subsequent development of basal cell carcinomas before actual onset of disease, information which is useful in the management of this disorder.

The segregation of the syndrome (including the basal cell carcinomas) in numerous families is fully consistent with the hypothesis of a single gene with high penetrance and multiple effects in the heterozygote (Anderson, Taylor, Falls, and Davidson, 1967). This gene locus recently was found to show a hint of linkage with the Rh blood group locus, ex-

TABLE 6. *Genetic Diseases with Associated Neoplasms*

Disease entity	Associated neoplastic disease	Mode of inheritance	Reference
Albinism	Squamous and basal cell carcinoma of skin, depending on sunlight exposure	AR	Fitzpatrick and Quevedo (1960)
Diaphysial aclasis (multiple exostoses)	Chondrosarcoma in 5 to 11% of patients	AD	Burkhart, Burke, and Kelly (1965)
Discrete polyps of colon and rectum	Adenocarcinoma of colon and rectum in high proportion of patients	AD?	McConnell (1966)
Gardner's syndrome (polyps, osteomas, fibrous and sebaceous cysts)	Adenocarcinoma of intestine in high proportion of patients	AD	McConnell (1966)
Hereditary polyposis coli	Adenocarcinoma of colon and rectum in 50% of patients by age 30 and about 100% by age 60	AD	Veale (1965)
Peutz-Jegher's syndrome (intestinal polyps and melanin spots on buccal mucosa, lips, and digits)	Adenocarcinoma of intestine rare but reported	AD	McConnell (1966)
Osteogenesis imperfecta	Osteosarcoma rare but reported	AD	Klenerman, Ockenden, and Townsend (1967)
Tuberous sclerosis (adenoma sebaceum, mental retardation, and epilepsy)	Astrocytoma, gliomas, and rhabdomyoma in 1 to 3% of patients	AD	Zaremba (1968)
Werner's syndrome (scleroderma-like skin, subcutaneous calcifications, cataracts, diabetes, and arteriosclerosis)	Sarcomatous neoplasms primarily and meningioma in 10% of patients	AR	Epstein *et al.* (1966)
Xeroderma pigmentosum	Squamous and basal cell carcinomas and malignant melanomas of skin and eyes in a high proportion of patients	AR	Cleaver (1968)

Abbreviations: AD, autosomal dominant; AR, autosomal recessive.

hibiting a 12 per cent probability of linkage at a recombination fraction between 0.20 and 0.25. The other blood group marker loci had probabilities of about 3 per cent (Anderson, 1968). No significant decrease in the relative fitness of affected individuals was observed for those who were married or for the total individuals in each sex (Anderson, unpublished data). The population frequency and mutation rate of the disorder have not yet been estimated.

GENETIC DISEASES WITH ASSOCIATED NEOPLASMS

The genetic diseases in which a precursor lesion (and not the neoplasm) is the major phenotypic manifestation of a genetic defect are summarized in Table 6. These are all well-known clinicogenetic entities and need not be discussed. The entities characterized by polyploid precursor lesions exhibit high liabilities to the development of neoplasms, but as a whole, they are not as high in incidence nor do they occur as early in age as the entities in Tables 1 and 5. Consequently, although the entities themselves may be in accord with genetic expectation, the associated neoplasms may not always be so, an occurrence which is particularly true of those with low liabilities.

Malignant melanoma might have been included in the table since the majority of these lesions are known to develop from preexisting junctional nevi and since a significant majority of the patients have light or sandy complexions. A genetic basis has been implicated for some patients with this neoplasm (Anderson, Smith, and McBride, 1967). However, the nature of the underlying genetic mechanism, which may involve at least two loci, is not yet understood.

GENETIC DISEASES WITH ASSOCIATED LEUKEMIA AND LYMPHOMA

The entities comprising this category are summarized in Table 7. The majority are immunodeficiency diseases generally occurring in children. All are recessively inherited, *i.e.*, they involve gene defects leading to disease expression only in the homozygote and possibly to some other type of manifestation in the heterozygous carrier. Their liabilities to leukemia and lymphoma are higher than can be accounted for by chance, but they are distinctly lower than those cited for previously described entities (Miller, 1966). For example, Miller reported that, among 20 patients with Bloom's syndrome, two died of leukemia; of 68 patients with Fanconi's anemia, three developed leukemia; and of 43 patients with Chediak-Higashi syndrome, two developed malignant lymphoma. Of further interest, ataxia telangiectasia, Bloom's syndrome, and

TABLE 7. *Genetic Diseases with Associated Leukemia and Lymphoma*

Disease entity	Types of leukemia or lymphoma	Mode of inheritance
Acquired agammaglobulinemia	Malignant lymphoma	AR
Ataxia telangiectasia or Louis-Barr syndrome (cerebral ataxia, oculocutaneous telangiectasia, and sinopulmonary infection)	Malignant lymphoma, lymphosarcoma, and acute lymphocytic leukemia	AR
Bloom's syndrome (congenital telangiectatic erythema and stunted growth)	Acute myeloid leukemia	AR
Bruton's sex-linked agammaglobulinemia (pneumonia, suppurative otitis media, and meningitis)	Acute lymphatic and lymphocytic leukemia and malignant lymphoma	SLR
Chediak-Higashi syndrome (partial albinism, horizontal nystagmus, and recurrent fevers and infections)	Malignant lymphoma	AR
Fanconi's aplastic anemia (constitutional aplastic anemia)	Acute monocytic or myeloblastic leukemia	AR
Wiskott-Aldrich syndrome (chronic eczema, thrombocytopenia, and recurrent infections)	Reticuloendothelioma, malignant lymphoma, and myeloid leukemia	SLR

Abbreviations: AR, autosomal recessive; SLR, sex-linked recessive.

Fanconi's aplastic anemia also are associated with high frequencies of chromosome breaks and rearrangements. These diseases, their associated malignant conditions, and the implications of the associations are the subject of a number of recent reports (Report of a WHO Scientific Group, 1968; Hirschhorn and Bloch-Shtacher, 1970, pages 191 to 202, this volume). The entities associated with chromosome anomalies, such as Down's syndrome, in which leukemia also may develop are discussed by Miller (1970, see pages 78 to 84, this volume).

Familial occurrences of various types of leukemia and lymphoma have been described, and examples and reviews of the literature are provided by Heath and Moloney (1965), Gunz (1966), and Rigby, Pratt, Rosenlof, and Lemon (1968). The significance of such occurrences in relation to a possible viral agent, genetically determined cell receptor sites, and a genetically susceptible cell population are discussed by Peterson, Cooper, and Good (1965).

Miller and Todaro (1969) recently have proposed that persons at high risk to leukemia, such as members of families with immunodeficiency diseases, Fanconi's aplastic anemia, Bloom's syndrome, or other abnormalities, might be detected by the degree of sensitivity of their fibroblasts to viral transformation. It is important to determine if this technique has applicability to detecting persons at high risk to other genetically determined types of neoplasms.

Discussion

A number of neoplasms in man exhibit familial distribution patterns which conform to classic gene segregation hypotheses, thereby lending credence to the concept of cancer susceptibility genes. Some have highly specific effects leading to the development of specific histologic types of neoplasms at fairly early ages (Tables 1 and 5), but have no apparent effect on enhancing susceptibility to neoplasms in general. These specific neoplasms develop from multiple or multicentric foci in one or more organs, presumably wherever a certain cell type is found. How the genes act in causing certain cells to become neoplastic is not known. However, those genes responsible for the entities in Tables 1 and 5 must have important effects on the transformation process in view of the close agreement between the actual distribution patterns of neoplasms and genetic expectation, the early onset of the neoplasms, and their high specificity (in numerous families from diverse geographic areas and ethnic origins). Therefore, environmental factors apparently have little influence.

The genes responsible for the development of polyploid precursor lesions characterizing the entities in Table 6 also must have important effects on the development of neoplasms, but to a lesser degree than the previous entities. Environmental factors, including age effects, also could be involved, explaining the fact that only a certain fraction of precursor lesions undergo neoplastic transformation in individuals at young ages, compared to a higher fraction at later ages.

The entities with low frequencies of associated neoplasms, including all but one of the recessively inherited entities, provide a different picture (Tables 6 and 7). The neoplasms are generally more varied in histologic type, but are confined to a tissue system such as the skin or lymphoreticular system. Moreover, the distribution of associated neoplasms does not correspond to genetic expectation, with the possible exception of those in xeroderma pigmentosum. These observations suggest that the mutant gene is responsible mainly for the development of the primary disease and not the neoplasms, which appear to develop secondarily and possibly as a result of exposure to some special environmental factor(s). Such factors have already been implicated in several of the disorders, for example, ultraviolet light in albinism (Fitzpatrick and Quevedo, 1960) and xeroderma pigmentosum (Cleaver, 1968). The immunodeficiency diseases are considered to result from mutant genes leading to defective or immature populations of cells in the thymus-dependent and/or immunoglobulin systems. Other factors responsible for the subsequent development of leukemia or lymphoma have not yet been fully delineated, although a virus has been proposed by Peterson, Cooper, and Good (1965). The development of leukemia in patients with Fanconi's aplastic anemia and Bloom's syndrome also may depend upon exposure of susceptible cells to environmental factors (see Hirschhorn and Bloch-Shtacher, 1970, pages 191 to 202, this volume). An infectious agent has been implicated in osteogenic sarcoma (Morton and Malmgren, 1968). It is interesting to note that osteogenesis imperfecta, in addition to the occasional occurrence of osteogenic sarcomas, may also be associated with leukemia, according to Miller (1966). Osteogenesis imperfecta in association with leukemia has been observed recently at this institution. It is apparent, therefore, that the genetic mechanism leading to the development of neoplasms is clearly different in each of the entities, as evidenced by lesion specificity, age at onset of disease, and the relative contribution of genetic and environmental factors.

Aside from these problems, genetically determined neoplasms also have important practical clinical relevance. They are characterized by occurrence or first recognition of disease at an early age. The neoplasms in recessively inherited diseases usually begin in childhood or early adulthood; the neoplasms in dominantly inherited diseases have a later onset, but still occur one to two decades earlier than the same neoplasms occurring sporadically in the general population. Moreover, the entities are characterized by multiple lesions originating from multiple or multicentric foci. These characteristics have definite relevance to recognition and diagnosis, as well as to management. Some of the entities are associated with developmental anomalies by which individuals at risk can be identified before the clinical onset of neoplasms. The detection of these entities immediately should raise the possibility of their occurrence in other relatives. Such awareness could and should lead to earlier detection than is now possible and could lead also to the recognition and removal of known precursor lesions from which neoplasms are known to originate.

These various genetic varieties have been utilized to only a limited extent in genetic, clinical, and other types of studies. They pose many interesting problems and might well be utilized as a source of experimental material, particularly for investigating the relationship between gene effects and neoplasms in man.

Summary

Evidence is presented demonstrating that a number of neoplasms in man exhibit familial distribution patterns which conform to classic gene segregation hypotheses. Their existence, therefore, supports the concept of cancer susceptibility genes. It was proposed that in the majority of dominantly inherited neoplastic diatheses, the defective gene is important in the development of specific types of neoplasms and environmental factors have little effect. In recessively inherited entities and in some dominantly inherited disorders with low liabilities to neoplasms, the defective gene is primarily responsible for the development of a disease and not the neoplasms, which appear to develop secondarily and possibly as a consequence of some exogenous agent(s). The genetic varieties of neoplasms, which are characterized by early ages at onset of disease and lesion multiplicity, have important practical applicability to early cancer detection. Genetic neoplasms, in addition to their clinical and genetic interest, could serve as a source of material for investigating the relationship between gene effects and neoplasms.

ACKNOWLEDGMENT

This study was supported in part by grant CA-08381 from the National Cancer Institute.

REFERENCES

Anderson, D. E. 1968. Linkage Analysis of the Nevoid Basal Cell Carcinoma Syndrome. *Annals of Human Genetics*, 32:113–123.

———. Unpublished data.

Anderson, D. E., J. L. Smith, Jr., and C. M. McBride. 1967. Hereditary Aspects of Malignant Melanoma. *Journal of the American Medical Association*, 200:741–746.

Anderson, D. E., W. B. Taylor, H. F. Falls, and R. T. Davidson. 1967. The Nevoid Basal Cell Carcinoma Syndrome. *The American Journal of Human Genetics*, 19:12–22.

Aure, J. C., and S. Nilsson. 1965. Familial Disposition of Cancer of the Gastrointestinal Tract. *Acta chirurgica scandanavica*, 129:644–648.

Ballard, H. S., B. Frame, and R. J. Hartsock. 1964. Familial Multiple Endocrine Adenoma-Peptic Ulcer Complex. *Medicine*, 43:481–516.

Berdjis, C. C. 1962. Pluriglandular Syndrome. II. Multiple Endocrine Adenomas in Man. A Report of Five Cases and a Review of Literature. *Oncologia*, 15:288–311.

Bieler, V., and U. Heim. 1965. Double Carcinoma in Sibs. Familial Occurrence of Genital and Intestinal Carcinomas. *Schweizerische medizinische Wochenschrift*, 95:496–497.

Burkhart, J. M., E. C. Burke, and P. J. Kelly. 1965. The Chondrodystrophies. *Mayo Clinic Proceedings*, 40:481–499.

Carmen, C. T., and R. E. Brashear. 1960. Pheochromocytoma as an Inherited Abnormality: Report of the Tenth Affected Kindred and Review of the Literature. *New England Journal of Medicine*, 263:419–423.

Cleaver, J. E. 1968. Defective Repair Replication of DNA in Xeroderma Pigmentosum. *Nature*, 218:652–656.

Crowe, F. W., W. J. Schull, and J. V. Neel. 1956. *Multiple Neurofibromatosis*. Springfield, Illinois: Charles C Thomas, 181 pp.

Cushman, P. 1962. Familial Endocrine Tumors. Report of Two Unrelated Kindred Affected with Pheochromocytomas, One Also with Multiple Thyroid Carcinomas. *The American Journal of Medicine*, 32:352–360.

Danowski, T. S., F. M. Mateer, and E. E. Longabaugh. 1962. Endocrine Adenomatosis (Polyendocrine Disease): Familial Occurrences. *Acta medica scandinavica*, 172:559–566.

Epstein, C. J., G. M. Martin, A. L. Schultz, and A. G. Motulsky. 1966. Werner's Syndrome. *Medicine*, 45:177–221.

Finegold, M. J., and J. R. Haddad. 1963. Multiple Endocrine Tumors. *Archives of Pathology*, 76:449–455.

Fitzpatrick, T. B., and W. C. Quevedo, Jr. 1960. "Albinism", *The Metabolic Basis of Inherited Disease*, J. B. Stanbury, J. B. Wyngaarden, and D. S. Fredrickson, Eds. New York, New York; Toronto, Canada; Sydney, Australia; and London, England: McGraw-Hill Book Company. 2nd Edition. Pp. 324–340.

Gunz, F. W. 1966. Studies on the Incidence and Aetiology of Leukemia in New Zealand. *New Zealand Medical Journal*, 65 (Supplement): 857–862.

Hauser, I. J., and C. V. Weller. 1936. A Further Report on the Cancer Family of Warthin. *American Journal of Cancer*, 27:434–449.

Heath, C. W., and W. C. Moloney. 1965. Familial Leukemia: Five Cases of Acute Leukemia in Three Generations. *New England Journal of Medicine*, 272:882–887.

Heinzelmann, F. 1964. Uber eine Krebsfamilie: Ein Beitrag zur Frage der Hereditat des Colonkarzinoms. *Helvetica chirurgica acta*, 3:316–324.

Hirschhorn, K., and N. Bloch-Shtacher. 1970. "Transformation of Genetically Abnormal Cells," *Genetic Concepts and Neoplasia* (The University of Texas M. D. Anderson Hospital and Tumor Institute at Houston, 23rd Annual Symposium on Fundamental Cancer Research, 1969). Baltimore, Maryland: The Williams & Wilkins Co. Pp. 191–202.

Howel-Evans, W., R. B. McConnell, C. A. Clarke, and P. M. Sheppard. 1957. Carcinoma of the Oesophagus with Keratosis Palmaris et Plantaris (Tylosis). *Quarterly Journal of Medicine*, 27:413–429.

Huang, S., and W. A. McLeish. 1968. Pheochromocytoma and Medullary Carcinoma of Thyroid. *Cancer*, 21:302–311.

Illingworth, R. D. 1967. Phaeochromocytoma and Cerebellar Haemangioblastoma. *Journal of Neurology, Neurosurgery, and Psychiatry*, 30:443–445.

Johnson, G. J., W. H. J. Summerskill, V. E. Anderson, and F. R. Keating, Jr. 1967. Clinical and Genetic Investigation of a Large Kindred with Multiple Endocrine Adenomatosis. *New England Journal of Medicine*, 277:1379–1385.

Kartagener, M., and J. Wyler. 1966. Familiare Haufung von Doppelmalignomen. *Schweizerische medizinische Wochenschrift*, 96:218–219.

Katz, A. D. 1964. Carotid Body Tumors in a Large Family Group. *American Journal of Surgery*, 108:570–573.

Klenerman, L., B. G. Ockenden, and A. C. Townsend. 1967. Osteosarcoma Occurring in Osteogenesis Imperfecta. Report of Two Cases. *The Journal of Bone and Joint Surgery*, 49B:314–323.

Kluge, T. 1964. Familial Cancer of the Colon. *Acta chirurgica scandinavica*, 127: 392–398.

Kroll, A. J., B. Alexander, F. Cochios, and L. Pechet. 1964. Hereditary Deficiencies of Clotting Factors VII and X Associated with Carotid-Body Tumors. *New England Journal of Medicine*, 270:6–13.

Ljungberg, O., E. Cederquist, and W. von Studnitz. 1967. Medullary Thyroid Carcinoma and Phaeochromocytoma: A Familial Chromaffinomatosis. *British Medical Journal*, 1:279–281.

Lynch, H. T. 1967. "Hereditary Factors in Carcinoma," Vol. 12 in *Recent Results in Cancer Research*. New York, New York: Springer-Verlag New York Inc., 186 pp.

Lynch, H. T., and A. J. Krush. 1967. Heredity and Adenocarcinoma of the Colon. *Gastroenterology*, 53:517–527.

Lynch, H. T., M. W. Shaw, C. W. Magnuson, A. L. Larsen, and A. J. Krush. 1966. Hereditary Factors in Cancer. Study of Two Large Midwestern Kindreds. *Archives of Internal Medicine*, 117:206–212.

Manning, P. C., G. D. Molnar, B. M. Black, J. T. Priestley. and L. B. Woolner. 1963. Pheochromocytoma, Hyperparathyroidism and Thyroid Carcinoma Occurring Coincidentally. Report of a Case. *New England Journal of Medicine*, 268:68–72.

Mathis, M. 1962. Familiares Colonkarzinom. *Schweizerische medizinische Wochenschrift*, 92:1673–1678.

McConnell, R. B. 1966. *The Genetics of Gastro-Intestinal Disorders*. London, England: Oxford University Press, 282 pp.

Miller, R. W. 1966. Relation Between Cancer and Congenital Defects in Man. *New England Journal of Medicine*, 275:87–93.

————. 1970. "The Association Between Congenital Malformations and Cancer," *Genetic Concepts and Neoplasia* (The University of Texas M. D. Anderson Hospital and Tumor Institute at Houston, 23rd Annual Symposium on Fundamental Cancer Research, 1969). Baltimore, Maryland: The Williams & Wilkins Co. Pp. 78–84.

Miller, R. W., and G. J. Todaro. 1969. Viral Transformation of Cells from Persons at High Risk of Cancer. *Lancet*, 1:81–82.

Moldawer, M. 1962. Multiple Endocrine Tumors and Zollinger-Ellison Syndrome in Families: One or Two Syndromes? A Report of Two New Families. *Metabolism*, 11:153–166.

Morton, D. L., and R. A. Malmgren. 1968. Human Osteosarcomas: Immunologic Evidence Suggesting an Associated Infectious Agent. *Science*, 162:1279–1281.

Nourok, D. S. 1964. Familial Pheochromocytoma and Thyroid Carcinoma. *Annals of Internal Medicine*, 60:1028–1040.

Peltokallio, P., and V. Peltokallio. 1966. Relationship of Familial Factors to Carcinoma of the Colon. *Diseases of the Colon and Rectum*, 9:367–370.

Peterson, R. D. A., M. D. Cooper, and R. A. Good. 1965. "Disorders of the Thymus and Other Lymphoid Tissues," *Progress in Medical Genetics*, A. G. Steinberg and A. G. Bearn, Eds. New York, New York, and London, England: Grune & Stratton, Inc. Vol. IV. Pp. 1–31.

Report of a WHO Scientific Group. 1968. *Genetics of the Immune Response* (Technical Report Series No. 402). Geneva, Switzerland: World Health Organization. Pp. 27–52.

Rigby, P. G., P. T. Pratt, R. C. Rosenlof, and H. M. Lemon. 1968. Genetic Relationships in Familial Leukemia and Lymphoma. *Archives of Internal Medicine*, 121: 67–70.

Rush, B. F. 1963. Familial Bilateral Carotid Body Tumors. *Annals of Surgery*, 157:633–636.

Savage, D. 1956. A Family History of Uterine and Gastro-Intestinal Cancer. *British Medical Journal*, 2:341–343.

Schimke, R. N., and W. H. Hartmann. 1965. Familial Amyloid Producing Medullary Thyroid Carcinoma and Pheochromocytoma: A Distinct Genetic Entity. *Annals of Internal Medicine*, 63:1027–1039.

Schmid, J. R., A. Labhart, and P. H. Rossier. 1961. Relationship of Multiple Endocrine Adenomas to the Syndrome of Ulcerogenic Islet Cell Adenomas (Zollinger-Ellison): Occurrence of Both Syndromes in One Family. *American Journal of Medicine*, 31:343–353.

Schull, W. J. 1959. "Genetics of Man: Some of the Developments of the Last Decade," *Genetics and Cancer* (The University of Texas M. D. Anderson Hospital and Tumor Institute, 13th Annual Symposium on Fundamental Cancer Research, 1959). Austin, Texas: The University of Texas Press. Pp. 377–390.

Shine, I., and P. R. Allison. 1966. Carcinoma of the Oesophagus with Tylosis (Keratosis Palmaris et Plantaris). *Lancet*, 1:951–953.

Smits, M., and J. Huizinga. 1961. Familial Occurrence of Phaeochromocytoma. *Acta genetica et statistica medica*, 11:137–153.

Snell, K. C., and H. L. Stewart. 1969. Malignant Argyrophilic Gastric Carcinoids of Praomys (Mastomys) Natalensis. *Science*, 163:470.

Sprong, D. H., and F. G. Kirby. 1949. Familial Carotid Body Tumors. *Annals of Western Medicine and Surgery*, 3:241–242.

Steiner, A. L., A. D. Goodman, and S. R. Powers. 1968. Study of a Kindred with Pheochromocytoma, Medullary Thyroid Carcinoma, Hyperparathyroidism and Cushing's Disease: Multiple Endocrine Neoplasia, Type 2. *Medicine*, 47:371–409.

Stocks, A. E. 1967. Problems of the Syndrome of Familial Multiple Endocrine Adenomas. *Australasian Annals of Medicine*, 16:278–288.

Veale, A. M. O. 1965. *Intestinal Polyposis*. Cambridge, England: Cambridge University Press, 104 pp.

Warthin, A. S. 1913. Heredity with Reference to Carcinoma. *Archives of Internal Medicine*, 12:546–555.

Wermer, P. 1954. Genetic Aspects of Adenomatosis of Endocrine Glands. *The American Journal of Medicine*, 16:363–371.

———. 1963. Endocrine Adenomatosis and Peptic Ulcer in a Large Kindred: Inherited Multiple Tumors and Mosaic Pleiotropism in Man. *The American Journal of Medicine*, 35:205–212.

Williams, E. D. 1966. Histogenesis of Medullary Carcinoma of the Thyroid. *Journal of Clinical Pathology*, 19:114–118.

Zaremba, J. 1968. Tuberous Sclerosis: A Clinical and Genetical Investigation. *Journal of Mental Deficiency*, 12:63–80.

Discussion

Dr. L. D. Samuels, Children's Hospital, Columbus, Ohio: I want to report a possible addition to the list of associated congenital diseases and neoplasms. We have seen a child with congenital ("hereditary") spherocytosis. After a therapeutic splenectomy, she developed adenocarcinoma of the bowel which was successfully managed. Three years later, she developed reticulum cell sarcoma of the mediastinum which was successfully irradiated; three years after this, she developed an adenocarcinoma of her scalp which was successfully excised. Now, at age 18, she is apparently free of tumors. Last year her brother developed an identical reticulum cell sarcoma of the mediastinum which has progressed despite treatment and to which he is succumbing.

This is our first experience in Columbus, in a rather large population of children with cancer, of such an association of multifocal, multiple, germ cell-type cancers in one patient, and the occurrence in her brother is the first of the familial lymphomas. Plans for detailed family cytogenetic studies are in progress. There is a further intriguing association in that this girl had autoimmune disease between her second and third neoplasms. I would be interested in seeing simian virus 40 (SV40) transformation studies done in this family.

Do you know of any associations of congenital spherocytosis with neoplasm?

Dr. Robert W. Miller, National Cancer Institute, Bethesda, Maryland: We know of no such concurrence, but I would like to make a point that your experience brings out; namely, familial cancer aggregations and double primaries may have something in common. One may see distributed over the families the various tumors that may occur in individual patients as double primaries. Perhaps some of you know of the study that was done at Roswell Park in which 150 consecutive autopsies of children with cancer revealed that seven had double primaries—a very high frequency.

I strongly urge that your case be reported for scientists who may be able to use it later in conjunction with other information concerning the etiology of childhood cancer.

Dr. Robert DeMars, University of Wisconsin, Madison, Wisconsin: I will address myself mainly to Dr. Anderson on the use of genetic terminology. I suggest that many of the pedigrees that are labeled as autosomal dominants in the neoplasms to which you have referred could actually be interpreted as autosomal recessives. We must relate the terms dominant and recessive not only to the level of the individual as a whole, as you have done, but also to the level of the individual cell, or cells, which are involved. This hasn't been done here.

I think many pedigrees are consistent with the notion that one of the parents in these families might be heterozygous for a recessive and that the neoplasms appear as a result of subsequent somatic mutations in which individual cells become homozygous for a recessive neoplasm-causing gene. Can you critically exclude that possibility in any of the cases that you called autosomal dominant? It's obviously important if we want to understand the relationship between the genotypes and the phenotype called cancer.

Dr. David E. Anderson, The University of Texas M. D. Anderson Hospital and Tumor Institute at Houston, Houston, Texas: Obviously I can not say whether a neoplastic cell is recessive or dominant, since all of our information was based on the phenotype as you say. A number of different genetic mechanisms must be involved in these different genetically determined neoplasms, as I tried to point out.

Dr. Richard Bottomley, Oklahoma Medical Research Foundation, Oklahoma City, Oklahoma: Another possible genetic neoplasm is suggested by a family we recently described with an increased incidence of leukemia, sarcomas, and breast cancer. In the most recent generation, cancer has occurred in the children; we have treated two siblings with acute leukemia. Another sibling had a renal cell carcinoma at birth. The mother of these children had bilateral breast carcinomas and later developed acute myeloblastic leukemia. The leukemic cells in both the bone marrow and peripheral blood had a modal chromosome number of 45. Fibrosarcomas are another neoplasm which occurs frequently in this family. Also, we have noticed what has been called anticipation in this family; that is, the neoplasms seem to appear at a younger age in the later generations. Anticipation has been discounted in some of the previous studies of diabetes and so forth; however, about 50 per cent of the siblings in the affected branches of this family have already died from neoplasms, so anticipation may be a real phenomenon in this family.

Dr. Miller: I think these occurrences are much more common than people now appreciate, and that current family histories are obtained too casually. Family histories of cancer patients, particularly children, would be much more valuable in research concerning the origin of cancer if the pedigree included the major diseases in all relatives up to, say, first cousins. We are hearing increasingly about these rare occurrences, and when one is able to synthesize multiple individual reports, some very important observations can result.

Dr. Ursula Reincke, Brookhaven National Laboratory, Upton, New York: I would like to ask Dr. Miller about virus transformation. Two questions: Does virus transformation, when enhanced, lead only to more colonies or also to different colonies in the fibroblast cultures? And, is there any suggestion about the common base which might exist between the enhanced viral transformation in culture and genetic susceptibility to tumor development in the patient?

Dr. Miller: Let me say first that I am a pediatrician by birth and an epidemiologist more recently. I am not a virologist, but as I understand it, the transformed colonies are different. Monolayers of cultured cells are fibroblasts; the transformed colonies look like epithelial cells. I am told that one may regard the transformed colonies as "microtumors."

If I understand your second question, it is "Do all specimens that show transformation have in common a genetic disorder or cytogenetic disorder?" That remains to be defined. I might say that the test described is not mine. I am interested in the clinical and the epidemiological aspects of the problem. The test was developed by Drs. Todaro, Green, and Swift at New York University. Its limits have yet to be defined.

Dr. Debdas Mukerjee, The University of Texas M. D. Anderson Hospital and Tumor Institute at Houston, Houston, Texas: I'd like to report observations similar to those of Dr. Todaro, which Dr. Robert Miller has quoted. A patient who was diagnosed as probably having Klinefelter's syndrome was referred to us by Dr. Anderson's group at Anderson Hospital. We found that this patient had two populations of cells and was thus a mosaic. This patient had a lung tumor. Following cloning techniques, we isolated two groups of cultures, one with XY and the other with XXY cell strains. We infected these cultures with SV40 following the standard infection techniques and used Dr. Todaro's technique of determining transformation frequency. We found that the XXY cell strain showed a higher transformation frequency than the XY strain. Transformation frequency of the patient's XY cell strain was higher than that of the cultures with cells with a normal human karyotype from so-called control individuals. These findings perhaps suggest a clue that the tumor in this patient originated from abnormal cells having XXY sex chromosomes.

Session Chairman D. G. Harnden, Western General Hospital, Edinburgh, Scotland: May I ask if you have done sex chromosome studies on the tumor?

Dr. Mukerjee: We intend to do this shortly, as soon as we have histological slides of the tumor. We plan to determine the frequency of sex chromatin-positive cells in the tumor. From that, we might be able to confirm our supposition.

Dr. William Sly, Washington University School of Medicine, St. Louis, Missouri: In studies of transformation frequency of a cell line from a single patient by SV40, such as Dr. Mukerjee reported, it is important to examine the parents before assuming an increased frequency of transformation is related to a karyotype abnormality. Since we know from Dr. Todaro's studies that at least one recessive gene can increase the cellular susceptibility to transformation, it would be important to show that no such recessive gene is present in the aneuploid cell line under study. This could be inferred if cells from neither parent of the person whose cells are studied demonstrate increased susceptibility to transformation.

Dr. Miller: Dr. Mukerjee, may I ask whether you plan to do studies on mosaics for Down's syndrome?

Dr. Mukerjee: We do plan to study transformation frequency in other mosaics as soon as we get them.

Dr. Miller: May I mention one other point that may or may not be useful. Cats with Klinefelter's syndrome can be recognized because they are males with three coat colors (tri-colored cats). They might serve both for in vivo and in vitro studies.

Dr. Harnden: Dr. Miller, how many of the cases of Klinefelter's syndrome associated with leukemia were first ascertained because they were cases of Klinefelter's syndrome, and how many because they were cases of leukemia? This makes a very big difference to any alleged association.

Dr. Miller: Those cases were from the literature and I don't remember. Klinefelter's syndrome is sufficiently frequent that it will be found with lymphomas by chance often enough to account for all of the cases in the series. I think that the viral transformation test may very well help to clarify the relationship between the cytogenetic abnormality and the cancer. The other approach, which has already been described by Dr. Harnden, is a prospective study of a large series of patients with sex chromosome anomalies, but this takes a long time.

Dr. Patrick Conen, Hospital for Sick Children, Toronto, Canada: I think the answer to Dr. Harnden's question is that most cases of Kinefelter's syndrome associated with tumors or leukemias were initially investigated because of the malignant disease.

Now, may I make two points: We have followed patients with various chromosome abnormalities and we found XO/XX mosaicism in a newborn child with ambiguous genitalia. At laparotomy, the gonads were removed; no abnormality was noted in the other organs. At three years of age, the patient was found to have a Wilms' tumor which was not resected. This is a reversal of your particular series. We have also seen a short girl at 12 years of age with clinical features of Turner's syndrome and a deletion of part of one X chromosome. Six months later, the child presented with a rapidly enlarging abdominal mass which proved to be an embryonal carcinoma involving one gonad; the other gonad was a streak. You suggested association between trisomy-D syndrome and leukemia, which should be considered with caution because one reported case was stillborn. Diagnosis of leukemia is difficult in newborns. Histopathologic distinction between infiltration by leukemic cells and marked extramedullary hematopoiesis in the newborn is difficult.

Dr. H. W. Kloepfer, Tulane University School of Medicine, New Orleans, Louisiana: I want to suggest another genetic entity associated with a tumor—testicular feminization (or simulant female). Such individuals are phenotypically females, but have normal-appearing X and Y chromosomes in all their nuclei, as typically found in males. Inheritance is compatible with a sex-linked or sex-limited gene. Our study included four kindreds. From our study and from a review of the literature, it was concluded that 20 to 50 per cent of these simulant females develop tumors around the XY gonads which are located in the position of ovaries. Often these simulant females are "superfemales" in all phenotypic characteristics. They have no uterus and are sterile. Testicular feminization is a congenital condition which definitely is associated with a neoplasm.

Dr. Anderson: What type of neoplasm was involved?

Dr. Kloepfer: This study was done by William H. Sternberg and David L. Barclay (*Journal of the American Medical Women's Association*, 22:885–893, November, 1967). The neoplasms most commonly seen were seminomas (germinomas).

Dr. Miller: I think there are a number of other associations between cancer and congenital defects that are too numerous and too involved to describe in the time available. In this regard, though, I would like to ask Dr. Anderson if he believes that medullary cancer of the thyroid overlaps with multiple neurofibromatosis since both carry a high frequency of pheochromocytomas and oral neurofibroma-like lesions.

Dr. Anderson: Neurofibromas and neuromas have been observed in association with the thyroid carcinoma-pheochromocytoma complex. Pheochromocytomas may also occur in association with neurofibromatosis and von Hippel-Lindau's disease. These associations suggest some overlap, perhaps stemming to their embryologic origin. In spite of these associations, I still believe that neurofibromatosis and the thyroid carcinoma-pheochromocytoma result from different gene defects.

Dr. J. Undevia, Cancer Research Institute, Bombay, India: I would like to report a few observations on a small "Parsi community" in Bombay who migrated to India some 1,300 years ago from Iran. They have a high incidence of consanguinity, ranging from 25 to 6 per cent during the last 50 years. Breast cancer is reported to be very high in this community. An increased incidence of malignant diseases has been observed in certain pedigrees with consanguinity. One such pedigree consisting of three generations revealed two cases of leukemia, two cases of breast cancer, and two cases of testicular tumors, one of which was revealed by histological evidence. Dr. Anderson, I would like to know whether you have observed any evidence of consanguinity in your pedigree studies.

Dr. Anderson: Consanguinity has been observed in some of the reported recessively inherited entities. In our own series, however, we have observed consanguinity in only one large family with malignant melanoma.

Neoplasia and Immunologic Factors: A Case Study

ALEXANDER BEARN

Cornell Medical Center, New York, New York

Case reports, however well-documented, must always be interpreted with caution. At times, however, they may provide important clues to our understanding of disease. Indeed, it was Dr. R. A. Good who first introduced the felicitous phrase "experiments of nature" to describe these uniquely informative cases.

The case I will report was described by Litwin, Allen, and Kunkel (1966). It concerns a 43-year-old woman with rheumatoid arthritis. When first examined, she showed evidence of a malignant epidermoid cancer of the lung. In addition to the neoplastic lesion, the patient demonstrated an extraordinarily high titer of rheumatoid factor in the serum. Indeed, the titer of one to 16,384, obtained using the Ripley coated red cell test, is one of the highest seen in Dr. Kunkel's laboratory. The patient also had a notable eosinophilia approximating 50 per cent. She exhibited many subcutaneous nodules which histologically were typical of rheumatoid arthritis.

A remarkable change occurred in this patient when the tumor was removed. The rheumatoid factors fell rapidly to zero, the eosinophil count returned to normal, and the patient had a complete clinical remission with a melting away of the rheumatoid nodules. It is worthwhile to note that the tumor was surrounded by a massive plasma cell infiltrate. The patient remained asymptomatic and well until the tumor recurred and the rheumatoid factor titers began to rise.

What can be learned from this case? Clearly, one can only speculate. It seems plausible, however, to imagine that the profound immunological response of this patient was incited by the tumor. Thus, when the tumor was removed and the inciting agent was no longer present, the immune reaction of the host declined.

I believe this case tells us something concerning the immunological reactions of the host to tumors and I hope it will serve to encourage others to look for similar cases. It would be beneficial to know whether host gamma globulin was deposited on the tumor in this case. Unfortunately, for a variety of reasons, this could not be determined.

REFERENCE

Litwin, S., J. Allen, and H. Kunkel. 1966. Disappearance of the Clinical and Serologic Manifestations of Rheumatoid Arthritis Following a Thoracotomy for a Lung Tumor. (Abstract.) *Arthritis and Rheumatism*, 9:865.

Genetic Marker Studies in Neoplasia

PHILIP J. FIALKOW

Departments of Genetics and Medicine, University of Washington, Seattle, Washington

This paper deals with two aspects of the study of genetic markers in neoplasms: the use of such markers to determine whether tumors have single or multiple cell origins, and the use of neoplasms with proved single cell origin to study gene localization and inactivation.

Cellular Origin and Development of Tumors

The cellular origin and development of tumors can be investigated by studying neoplasms which arise in individuals who have two or more genetically distinct types of cells, *i.e.*, in subjects who have cellular mosaicism. Such individuals include the mammalian female who has two different cell types by virtue of the fixed genetic inactivation of one of the two X chromosomes, which occurs early in embryogenesis in each somatic cell (Figure 1). The initial choice as to which X chromosome is to be inactive in a given cell is probably random; however, once made, it is fixed not only for that cell, but for all its descendants (Lyon, 1961; Russell, 1961; Beutler, Yeh, and Fairbanks, 1962; Davidson, Nitowsky, and Childs, 1963). This type of inactivation has been demonstrated for several X-linked loci in man, including the one for glucose-6-phosphate dehydrogenase (G-6-PD).

The common electrophoretic varieties of G-6-PD are shown in Figure 2. In subjects heterozygous at this locus for the B gene (Gd^B) and a variant gene such as A (Gd^A) (Figure 2), a given cell or clone of cells shows only one of the two enzyme types seen in a mixture of their cells (Beutler, Yeh, and Fairbanks, 1962; Davidson, Nitowsky, and Childs, 1963; DeMars and Nance, 1964). For example, electrophoretic analysis of G-6-PD in an extract of cultured skin fibroblasts from a subject heterozygous at this locus shows both types of enzyme; however, when single cells are removed from these cell mixtures and grown into clones, only a single enzyme type is found in each clone (Davidson, Nitowsky, and Childs, 1963; DeMars and Nance, 1964). Similarly, neoplasms arising

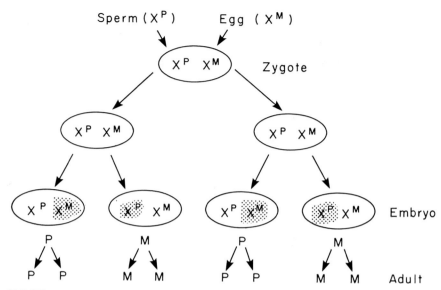

FIGURE 1. Diagrammatic representation of the inactive-X hypothesis. One of the two X chromosomes in the female zygote is inherited from the mother (X^M) and the other is of paternal origin (X^P). At some time early in embryogenesis, the two X chromosomes begin to behave differently in each somatic cell. Only one of these is genetically active, while the other is inactive (the shaded X chromosome). The initial choice as to which X chromosome is to be inactive in a given cell is probably random; however, once made, it is fixed not only for that cell, but for all its descendants. Thus, the adult female is a mosaic of two cell types—those with an active X^M and those with an active X^P.

from a single cell should exhibit only one enzyme type, while those with multicellular origin might contain both enzymes. Since approximately one third of Negro females are Gd^A/Gd^B heterozygotes, many tumors can be investigated in this manner.

In the first application of this system to the study of neoplasms, Linder and Gartler (1965) evaluated leiomyomas of the uterus in G-6-PD heterozygotes. Normal uterine muscle adjacent to the tumors had both A and B enzyme types, but only one type was present in each tumor. These observations strongly suggest a single cell origin of these tumors. Gartler *et al.* (1966) subsequently studied multiple trichoepithelioma, a hereditary skin tumor arising at many sites. In contrast to leiomyomas, this tumor had both enzyme types, suggesting a multicellular origin. As outlined below, a similar experimental approach has recently been applied

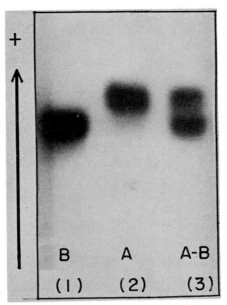

FIGURE 2. Starch gel electrophoretic phenotypes of G-6-PD. The enzyme was derived from a Gd^B/Gd^B homozygote (1), a Gd^A/Gd^A homozygote (2), and a Gd^A/Gd^B heterozygote (3).

to the study of chronic myelocytic leukemia (Fialkow, Gartler, and Yoshida, 1967).

CHRONIC MYELOCYTIC LEUKEMIA (CML)

Three questions were explored in the CML study; (1) Does CML have a clonal origin? (2) In which type of cell does leukemia arise? (3) What is the fate of the abnormal cells during remission?

Clonal Origin of CML

Three female subjects with CML and heterozygous for the Gd^A and Gd^B genes were identified by electrophoretic analyses of skin fibroblasts. Although both A and B enzyme types were present in the fibroblasts of all three patients, extracts of their peripheral blood granulocytes contained only a single enzyme type. The fact that this single gene expression occurred in preparations derived from millions of granulocytes strongly favors a clonal origin of the leukemia cells in CML and supports the likelihood that the clone arises as a result of a rare event occurring in a single cell. In all three patients, the single enzyme type of the leukemia cells was A. This finding may be the result of chance alone; a larger series might have included some Gd^A/Gd^B heterozygotes with CML whose leukemia cells showed only B type enzyme.

Earlier studies utilizing another kind of marker, the Philadelphia[1] (Ph[1]) chromosome (Nowell and Hungerford, 1960), also suggest a clonal origin of CML. This small marker G-group chromosome (Figure 3) is consistently seen in dividing bone marrow cells in almost all typical cases of CML (Sandberg, Ishihara, Crosswhite, and Hauschka, 1962; Tough et al., 1963; Whang et al., 1963), but it is not seen in cells such as lymphocytes and fibroblasts. Furthermore, it is the cytogenetic abnormality most specific for any type of human neoplasia since it is found almost exclusively in one disease. Its discoverers postulated that this chromosomal abnormality endows the leukocytes with their neoplastic character (Nowell and Hungerford, 1961). However, before the studies with G-6-PD, it was not possible to state with certainty whether the malignant leukocytes in CML were derived from one or from many parent cells. For example, multicellular origin could have been caused by the presence of some etiologic agent having affinity for a specific region of deoxyribonucleic acid (DNA) on the involved G-group chromosome. In this case, the Ph[1] chromosome could arise independently in many cells. The G-6-PD evidence strongly supports the argument that the abnormal cells in clinically apparent CML have a single cell origin. Al-

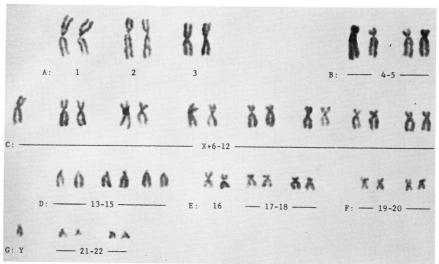

FIGURE 3. Karyotype of a cell with the Ph[1] chromosome.

ternatively, several abnormal cells could be present at an early stage, but one clone selectively overgrows the others.

Tough and associates (1961) reported one case of CML in which there may have been two abnormal clones. Their patient had features of Klinefelter's syndrome, which is usually associated with an extra X chromosome (47,XXY). Only cells of this type were found in the skin, but mosaicism of these cells and normal cells (46,XY) was observed in cells from the peripheral blood. Presence of the Ph[1] chromosome in some of both types of peripheral blood cells suggested its origin from at least two stem cells. However, as the authors noted, the Ph[1] chromosome could have arisen in a stem cell for only one cell line (*e.g.* 47,XXY) which subsequently underwent an error in mitosis to give rise to the other cell line.

The Cell Type in Which the Leukemia Arises

The observation that in many cases of CML almost 100 per cent of dividing marrow cells have the Ph[1] chromosome has been interpreted as evidence in support of the hypothesis that erythrocytes and granulocytes have a common stem cell (Sandberg, Ishihara, Crosswhite, and Hauschka, 1962; Trujillo and Ohno, 1962; Tough *et al.*, 1963; Whang *et al.*, 1963). More recently, the Ph[1] chromosome has been directly demonstrated in erythrocyte precursor cells (Clein and Flemans, 1966; Rastrick, Fitzgerald, and Gunz, 1968) and it is probably also present in platelet precursor cells (Sandberg, Ishihara, Crosswhite, and Hauschka, 1962; Trujillo and Ohno, 1962; Whang *et al.*, 1963). Moreover, as shown in Table 1, in our CML cases with two enzyme types in skin and a single type in granulocytes, only a single enzyme type was observed in the mature red cells. This was observed even though two enzyme types are found in red

TABLE 1. *G-6-PD Phenotypes in Three Patients with CML*

Case no.	Skin fibroblasts	G-6-PD phenotypes in various tissues	
		Peripheral blood	
		Granulocytes	Red cells
1	AB	A	A
2	AB	A	A
3	AB	A	A

Abbreviations: G-6-PD, glucose-6-phosphate dehydrogenase; CML, chronic myelocytic leukemia.

blood cells in at least 95 per cent of normal subjects who are known to be heterozygous for the Gd^A and Gd^B genes. These observations indicate that the initial transformation in CML occurs in a stem cell common to both the red cell and granulocyte but not the fibroblast.

The Fate of the Abnormal Cells During Remission

Still another question which may be answered using G-6-PD as a cell marker is whether during remission the abnormal clone persists, or normal cells repopulate the marrow. Two of the patients with CML who were heterozygous for the G-6-PD A and B genes had chemotherapeutically induced remissions during which the single enzyme type persisted in peripheral blood cells. This finding and the fact that the percentage of marrow cells with the Ph[1] chromosome does not decline during remission provide clear evidence that the abnormal clone persists during remission.

Since the genetic data indicate that not only the granulocytes, but also the red cells and probably the platelets are affected in CML, the initial transformation in CML must occur in a myelogenous stem cell. However, on the basis of morphologic criteria, CML is not considered to be a stem cell leukemia. The predominant picture in the bone marrow is an overgrowth of myelocytes and more mature granulocytic cells with little evidence of increased stem cell proliferation. To reconcile these morphological observations with the genetic data, it seems necessary to postulate that in CML the normal stem cell population is replaced by CML stem cells which in turn give rise to the hyperproliferative myelocytic cells.

CARCINOMA

Only a small number of G-6-PD studies in patients with carcinoma have been reported. We have studied a squamous cell carcinoma of the maxillary antrum in a Gd^A/Gd^B heterozygote (Fialkow, Klein, Gartler, and Clifford, unpublished data). The finding of two enzyme types in blood cells and only one enzyme type in the tumor suggested a clonal origin for this neoplasm (see Addendum). Beutler, Collins, and Irwin (1967) and McCurdy (1968) have investigated some other types of carcinomas including two originating in the colon, one in the liver, and one in the breast. In all four cases, both A and B enzyme types were demonstrated in tumor material. Thus, it seems possible that these carcinomas had a multicellular origin.

In the case of multicellular origin, it is appropriate to ask whether distant metastases originate from one or from several primary tumor cells.

In a patient with carcinoma of the colon, 28 metastatic nodules were studied, and it was found that the majority contained predominantly only one or the other type of G-6-PD, suggesting that they originated from single malignant cells (Beutler, Collins, and Irwin, 1967). In contrast, metastatic tumor nodules from a primary hepatic carcinoma contained both enzyme types (McCurdy, 1968). It would be of considerable interest to study similar lesions in other patients.

BURKITT'S LYMPHOMA

The decision to study this tumor was prompted by three reasons: (1) Considerable evidence suggests that it has a viral etiology. (2) Its high frequency of therapeutically induced remissions might enable one to determine if exacerbations result from reemergence of the original malignant cell line or from a second malignant transformation, perhaps resulting from recurrent or persistent viral infection. (3) Knowledge of whether this disease is uni- or multicentric in origin may be important in determining therapeutic approaches. The study is still in progress (Fialkow, Klein, Gartler, and Clifford, 1970); therefore, the following results are preliminary (see Addendum).

Peripheral blood and biopsy specimens of tumors were obtained in Nairobi and shipped to Seattle for G-6-PD studies. Lysates of red and white cells were subjected to starch gel electrophoresis (Fildes and Parr, 1963) within four days of removal from the patients. Satisfactory electrophoretic analyses of homogenates prepared from tumor specimens were obtained after centrifugation (8,000 × g), but in a few instances the enzyme was partially purified using a diethylaminoethyl (DEAE)-cellulose column.

Thus far, seven females with Burkitt's lymphoma who are heterozygous for the A and B genes at the G-6-PD locus have been identified by hemolysate electrophoresis. Specimens from one or two tumors have been studied in three patients. In all instances, only a single enzyme type was found in the tumor material (Table 2). Although these findings are consistent with a clonal origin of Burkitt's lymphoma, there are at least three alternative possibilities. First, the one or two tumors we studied from each patient could have been multicellular in origin, but during the course of the disease, one cell line (either A or B) outgrew the others. Second, since Burkitt's lymphoma is characterized by multiple tumors, the tumors we studied in each case may not have been the site of the primary transformation. In other words, several cells might have been transformed at some hypothetical primary site and thereafter single cells

TABLE 2. *G-6-PD Phenotypes in Patients with Burkitt's Lymphoma*

Case no.	Red blood cell G-6-PD	Tumor		
		No.	G-6-PD	
			Direct	Culture
36	AB	1	B	B
		2	B	—
72	AB	1	A	A
79	AB	1	B	—

Abbreviation: G-6-PD, glucose-6-phosphate dehydrogenase.

traveling to distant sites gave rise to other tumor masses. In such an instance, any tumor but the hypothetical primary tumor might have a unicellular origin. Third, the disease could begin at several foci, each of which gives rise to a tumor mass with its own unicellular origin. Study of many tumors obtained from the same patient should be informative, because, if Burkitt's lymphoma has a unifocal clonal origin, all such tumors should exhibit one enzyme type and all should be either type A or type B (see Addendum).

Unexpected and as yet incompletely explained findings relate to the leukocyte G-6-PD phenotype of one patient. In 30 normal Gd^A/Gd^B heterozygotes studied, when both A and B enzyme types were found in red cells, they were both also present in peripheral blood granulocytes and lymphocytes. This was also found in six of the seven patients with Burkitt's lymphoma whose red cells had both type A and B enzyme. However, in one of these seven patients, only a single enzyme type was found in lysates of peripheral blood leukocytes, suggesting that these particular cells had a clonal origin. This patient has clinically advanced disease but does not have "leukemia." We do not know with certainty from which type of peripheral blood leukocyte the clone arose. However, since blood lymphocytes known to be essentially free of granulocytes exhibited a single enzyme type, and since involvement of granulocytes has not been suggested in this disease, we suspect that the clone arose from a lymphocyte.

In many respects, the findings in Burkitt's lymphoma are the counterparts to those seen in chronic myelocytic leukemia. In each case, the basic abnormality is present in a stem cell. In CML, the red cells and granulocytes are affected, but not the lymphocytes; the abnormality is localized to a myelogenous stem cell which is distinct from a lymphoid stem cell. In Burkitt's lymphoma, lymphoid cells are affected but not red cells (and probably not granulocytes). The two diseases involve two different stem cells. Consequently, these data strengthen the arguments for the existence of a myelogenous stem cell distinct from a lymphoid stem cell, but the G-6-PD tumor data do not allow conclusions to be made about the existence in adult life of a more totipotential stem cell which can give rise to both myelogenous and lymphoid stem cells.

OTHER MALIGNANT CONDITIONS

One Gd^A/Gd^B heterozygote with lymphosarcoma (Beutler, Collins, and Irwin, 1967), another with multiple myeloma, and a third with chronic lymphocytic leukemia (McCurdy, 1968) have been reported. Single cell origin was suggested for the lymphosarcoma and the multiple myeloma. In the latter case, this conclusion is in accord with data previously obtained using immunoglobulins as cell markers. (Mårtensson, 1963). Multiple cell origin was suggested for the chronic lymphocytic leukemia, but the lymphocyte preparation from this patient was moderately contaminated with platelets (McCurdy, 1968).

Genetic Studies of Tumors With Clonal Origin

In the preceding portion of this communication, the application of X-linked markers to the study of the cellular origin and development of neoplasms has been discussed. In this section, the application of this knowledge to the study of gene inactivation and localization is discussed.

XG LOCUS

As discussed above, only one of the two genes for X-linked traits is assumed to be active in somatic cells of adult mammalian females. However, it is not known whether every genetic locus on the X chromosome undergoes inactivation. The evidence has been particularly conflicting for the X-linked locus which controls the red blood cell antigen Xg^a.

Red cells from males whose single X chromosomes have the Xg^a allele are agglutinated in the antiglobulin (Coombs') test after treatment with anti-Xg^a and have the phenotype Xg(a+). Red cells from males with the thus far silent Xg allele are Xg(a−). About 67 per cent of North American Caucasian males are Xg(a+) and 33 per cent are Xg(a−). The corresponding frequencies for Xg(a+) and Xg(a−) females are 89 per cent and 11 per cent, respectively (Race and Sanger, 1968). The Xg^a/Xg^a homozygote cannot be distinguished phenotypically from the Xg^a/Xg heterozygote, but, on genetic evidence, approximately one half of Xg(a+) females are homozygous for the Xg^a gene and one half are Xg^a/Xg heterozygotes. If one of the two Xg loci is inactivated, single red cells from heterozygous females should be either Xg(a+) or Xg(a−).

Since it has been shown that at least 90 per cent of the red cells in patients with CML are derived from a single precursor cell, such a clonally derived cell population is equivalent to a single red cell and can be used to test for inactivation at this locus.* Thus, if the Xg locus undergoes inactivation, half of the Xg^a/Xg heterozygous females with CML should have an Xg(a−) phenotype.

Family studies demonstrated that at least 11 women with CML were Xg^a/Xg heterozygotes, but all were typed as Xg(a+) (Fialkow, Lisker, Giblett, and Zavala, 1970). If one of these genes were randomly inactivated in the CML clone, the probability that all 11 heterozygotes would be Xg(a+) is one in 2,048. Therefore, these findings suggest that the Xg locus may not be inactivated and is an exception to the inactive-X hypothesis. However, although there is no supportive evidence, it is possible that the Xg^a antigen is synthesized elsewhere and is subsequently attached to the red cell. In this case, our method would be unable to detect inactivation, since it would be necessary to study the cells in which the antigen is made.

Other methods have been applied to this problem; our data are in agreement with the conclusions reached by Gorman, Di Re, Treacy, and Cahan (1963). These investigators showed that they could detect artificial 50:50 mixtures of red cells from an Xg(a+) and an Xg(a−) male. However, even after extensive efforts, they could not detect a mixture of Xg(a+) and Xg(a−) cells in a known Xg^a/Xg heterozygote, suggesting that the Xg locus is not inactivated. Lee, MacDiarmid, Cartwright, and Wintrobe (1968), however, reached a different conclusion. They studied two females who were probably heterozygous for both Xg and an X-linked form of microcytic anemia, and reported data suggesting that the Xg locus does undergo inactivation. The microcytic cells were separated from the normal cells and were Xg(a+), whereas the normal cells were Xg(a−). These observations suggest that only the Xg^a allele was active in the microcytic cells, whereas only the Xg allele was active in the normal cells. The reason leading to the discrepancy between this con-

---

* This utilization of red cells from patients with CML assumes that the phenotype of such blood specimens reflects the phenotype of the CML clone and not the possible small number of "contaminating" normal cells (less than 10 per cent) which may be present. That the former is the case is suggested by the observation that no visible agglutination occurred with anti-Xg^a in artificial mixtures of cells from Xg(a−) and Xg(a+) males in the proportion of 90 per cent to 10 per cent.

clusion and the one reached by Gorman and colleagues (Gorman, Di Re, Treacy, and Cahan, 1963) and by our laboratory is not clear.

AUTOSOMAL LOCI

Up to this point, only inactivation of genes on the X chromosome has been discussed, but the CML system can also be used to study the question of whether genes on the autosomes undergo similar inactivation. Using other techniques in normal subjects, autosomal inactivation has been demonstrated only for gamma globulin genes (Pernis and Chiappino, 1964). Results of cloning experiments have excluded inactivation of the loci controlling 6-phosphogluconate dehydrogenase (6-PGD), lactate dehydrogenase, phosphoglucomutase and the branched chain amino acid decarboxylase (Davidson, Glen-Bott, and Harris, 1965; Sigman and Gartler, 1966). If autosomal inactivation occurs for other loci, only one of the two genes for the trait under study should be active in the clonally derived granulocyte and red cell populations in CML, *i.e.* they should have a hemizygous phenotype. However, a hemizygous phenotype would also be observed if one of the two genes were missing or deleted, since the consequences would be the same as if that gene were present but inactive. Since the blood cells in CML have a deletion of part of a chromosome (the Ph^1 chromosome), a hemizygous phenotype for a trait could be interpreted to mean that one of the genes for the trait was on the missing segment of the Ph^1 chromosome or that one of the genes was inactive. To investigate these possibilities, we have studied markers for autosomal loci in 49 patients with CML and in 38 of their families (Fialkow *et al.*, 1969). An anomaly was found for only one autosomal locus—6-PGD (Fialkow *et al.*, 1969).

6-Phosphogluconate Dehydrogenase

The common allele at this locus is designated Pd^A and the less common allele Pd^B. The starch gel electrophoretic phenotype of 6-PGD in granulocytes of normal subjects homozygous for either of these alleles is a single band with characteristic mobility (Figure 4). The phenotype in a Pd^A/Pd^B heterozygote has both A and B bands as well as a band with intermediate mobility which probably represents a hybrid of A and B subunits (Parr and Fitch, 1967; Carter, Fildes, Fitch, and Parr, 1968) (Figure 4). Of the 48 patients with CML studied, 44 had A, two had A-B, and two had B phenotypes indistinguishable from those of normal subjects. The patients with the B and A-B phenotypes and 28 of the remaining patients, including the only two children with CML, were shown to have the Ph¹ chromosome. In the remaining 21 cases, it was either not possible to do cytogenetic studies or they are still in progress; however, these patients had the typical symptoms and course of CML, and it is known that almost all such cases have the Philadelphia chromosome. The anomaly of 6-PGD inheritance was found in the family of one of the patients with a B phenotype.

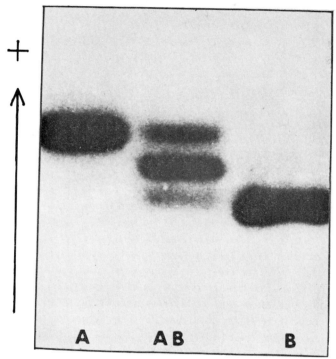

FIGURE 4. Starch gel electrophoretic phenotypes of 6-PGD in granulocytes derived from normal subjects: Pd^A/Pd^A homozygote; Pd^A/Pd^B heterozygote; Pd^B/Pd^B homozygote.

Both the red cells and granulocytes of the index case, Mrs. I, consistently had the B phenotype typical of homozygosity for the Pd^B gene. However, both her children had A phenotypes typical of Pd^A homozygosity, indicating that Mrs. I had to be a carrier of a Pd^A gene even though it was not expressed in her blood cells. Her carrier status was confirmed by analysis of her skin fibroblasts which revealed an A-B phenotype characteristic of a Pd^A/Pd^B heterozygote (Figure 5). No other examples of anomalous inheritance of 6-PGD were found in this study.

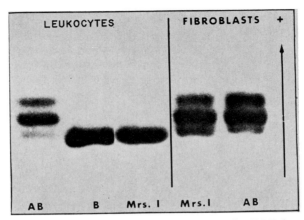

FIGURE 5. Starch gel electrophoretic phenotypes of 6-PGD in granulocytes and skin fibroblasts from normal subjects and from Mrs. I. From left to right, the granulocytes are from a Pd^A/Pd^B heterozygote, a Pd^B/Pd^B homozygote, and Mrs. I. The fibroblasts are from Mrs. I (left) and a Pd^A/Pd^B heterozygote (right).

Autosomal inactivation does not occur at the 6-PGD locus in normal individuals (Davidson, Glen-Bott, and Harris, 1965), nor does it generally occur in CML, since two other patients with this disease had blood cell phenotypes typical of Pd^A/Pd^B heterozygosity. Tentatively, we favor the possibility that one of the two 6-PGD genes was deleted in the CML progenitor cell. If this assumption is correct, since two other Ph^1-positive 6-PGD heterozygotes exhibited a heterozygous phenotype in their blood cells, it must be concluded either that the site of breakage in the Ph^1 chromosome varies, or that an additional microscopically undetected deletion occurred in another chromosome. Further studies of Ph^1-positive patients with CML and perhaps of patients with Down's syndrome may resolve this problem (the extra G-group chromosome in subjects with Down's syndrome may be the same chromosome affected in CML; therefore, these patients may have three 6-PGD genes).

Regardless of what genetic change explains the 6-PGD anomaly in Mrs. I, it probably occurred in only one cell. To reconcile this assumption with the observation that all or most of Mrs. I's blood cells had this change, it seems reasonable to assume that these cells are descended from the one cell in which the genetic change originally occurred. Consequently, this observation provides additional support for the earlier conclusion that leukemic cells in CML have a single cell origin. Moreover, the fact that both the red cells and granulocytes exhibited evidence of the genetic change supports the conclusion that these cells have a common precursor stem cell which is the site of the transformation in CML.

Other Autosomal Loci

The 49 patients with CML and 117 of their first-degree relatives in 48 families were studied with starch gel electrophoresis for seven other autosomal blood-cell enzyme loci. They were also tested with antibodies defining the antigens of eight autosomal blood-group systems (Fialkow *et al.*, in preparation). No anomalies of inheritance were found and at least one heterozygote was observed for each autosomal blood group system tested: Rh, MNS, ABO, Duffy, Kidd, Kell, Lutheran, and Diego. These data confirm earlier suggestions that inactivation does not generally occur at any of these autosomal blood group loci.

The number of Rh, MNS, Duffy, and Kidd heterozygotes observed is sufficiently large so that, together with the family data, they indicate that these loci are not on the deleted segment of the Ph^1 chromosome. The same is probably true for the other loci although the identification of a large number of heterozygotes for these blood-group systems was precluded by the low frequencies of the appropriate alleles.

Of the seven autosomal blood-cell enzyme loci studied, heterozygotes were identified for the red cell acid phosphatase, phosphoglucomutase, adenylate kinase, adenosine deaminase, and glutathione reductase loci. Autosomal inactivation has previously been excluded for some of these loci by other investigators (Davidson, Glen-Bott, and Harris, 1965; Sigman and Gartler, 1966); our data confirm and extend those studies. No lactate dehydrogenase or phosphohexose isomerase heterozygotes were observed, nor would any be expected in this small sample.

Thus, it may be concluded that although autosomal inactivation occurs in specialized systems such as immunoglobulins, it is not a generalized phenomenon. The reasons for this may lie in the possible selective advantages or disadvantages associated with autosomal inactivation. For example, inactivation at gamma globulin loci is efficient to the organism, since when a clone of immunocytes is required to produce a specific antibody, only the genes controlling that antibody would be active whereas immunoglobulin genes specifying unrequired antibodies would be inactive. Inactivation at the immunoglobulin loci could also be beneficial because it prevents the formation of hybrid molecules which may not function well as specific antibodies. In the blood-cell enzyme systems such as lactate dehydrogenase, hybrid formation may actually be advantageous and it would not be beneficial to have one gene inactive.

Summary and Concluding Remarks

We have used the X-linked G-6-PD markers to study the cellular origin and development of CML and Burkitt's lymphoma. The data strongly support the suggestion raised by cytogenetic studies that CML has a clonal origin, and that the initial transformation occurs in a stem cell common to both granulocytes and red cells. Preliminary observations in Burkitt's lymphoma suggest unicellular origin for individual tumors.

The demonstration that peripheral blood cells in patients with CML have a unicellular origin allows these cells to be used for studying gene localization and inactivation. Our data suggest that the X-linked Xg locus may be an exception to the inactive-X hypothesis. Extensive study of markers for 16 autosomal loci provides no evidence for inactivation similar to that which occurs at the X-linked G-6-PD locus. One anomaly discovered in the 6-PGD system may have been caused by gene deletion.

The tumors that have been studied with G-6-PD markers by ourselves and by others are listed in Table 3. Some neoplasms such as uterine leiomyomas and CML appear consistently to have unicellular origin, whereas others, e.g. hereditary trichoepitheliomas, have multicellular origin. It seems likely that these differences in cellular origin are related to differences in the inducing factors for various tumors. Since approximately one third of Negro females are heterozygous for the A and B genes at the G-6-PD locus, the system can be applied to many other neoplasms.

If similar studies could be performed on tumors with known etiology, the results might have implications for neoplasms with unknown causes.

TABLE 3. *Uni- or Multicellular Origin of Tumors Determined by G-6-PD Markers**

TUMOR

A. Unicellular origin
  1. Leiomyoma of the uterus
  2. Chronic myelocytic leukemia
  3. Burkitt's lymphoma
  4. Carcinoma of maxillary antrum (1 case)
  5. Multiple myeloma (1 case)
  6. Lymphosarcoma (1 case)

B. Multicellular origin
  1. Hereditary trichoepithelioma
  2. Carcinomas of the colon (2 cases), liver (1 case), and breast (1 case)

* See text for references.
Abbreviation: G-6-PD, glucose-6-phosphate dehydrogenase.

Unfortunately, the etiologic factors in most human neoplasms are not known, but further efforts along these lines might most profitably be directed at tumors which originate in defined circumstances. For example, do the genetic neoplasms (Anderson, 1970, see pages 85 to 104, this volume); or those which arise in subjects with immunologic abnormalities (Good, 1969; Sinkovics, Trujillo, Pienta, and Ahearn, 1970, see pages 138 to 190, this volume) or those caused by radiation exposure (Lewis, 1970, see pages 57 to 73, this volume) have uni- or multicellular origin? Still another approach would be to study induced tumors in lower organisms such as mice. This depends upon the discovery of suitable X-linked markers which are demonstrable at the cellular level in these animals. It could then be directly determined whether tumors associated with immunologic, genetic, and chromosomal abnormalities and those induced by viruses, radiation, and chemical carcinogens have uni- or multicellular origin. Such information might have important implications for the etiology and ultimately for the prevention and therapy of neoplasms in man.

ADDENDUM

Twenty biopsy specimens from seven females with Burkitt's lymphoma who are heterozygous for the B and A^+ or A^- genes at the glucose-6-phosphate dehydrogenase (G-6-PD) locus have now been studied (Fialkow, Klein, Gartler, and Clifford, 1970). In most instances, multiple sections from each biopsy specimen were studied histologically without knowledge of the G-6-PD phenotype, and a rough assessment was made of the relative proportion of tumor cells present. Three specimens were excluded because they were judged to contain 0, 0, and 40 per cent tumor cells. Each of the other 17 biopsy specimens contained more than 75 per cent tumor cells. Single tumors were examined from four patients; each had only one type of enzyme (one had type A, three had type B). The two tumors studied from each of two other patients had B phenotypes, as did the four tumors studied in the seventh patient. These observations are consistent with the notion that individual Burkitt's tumors, and perhaps the entire disease process, has a clonal origin.

Specimens of solid tumors have now been studied in 11 females heterozygous at the G-6-PD locus (Fialkow, Klein, Gartler, and Clifford, unpublished data). Single enzyme types were found in single specimens from one carcinoma of the thyroid (enzyme type B), one carcinoma of the salivary gland (type A), one malignant melanoma (type A), one neuroblastoma (type A), one carcinoma of the maxillary antrum (type A), and two carcinomas of the soft palate (both type B). However, two enzyme types were found in each of four carcinomas of the postnasal space. Since this tumor is characterized by considerable lymphoid infiltration, the finding of two enzyme types in and of itself cannot as yet be taken as firm evidence of multiple cell origin.

ACKNOWLEDGMENT

The research reported in this article was supported in part by Public Health Service grant GM 15253.

REFERENCES

Anderson, D. E. 1970. "Genetic Varieties of Neoplasia," *Genetic Concepts and Neoplasia* (The University of Texas M. D. Anderson Hospital and Tumor Institute at Houston, 23rd Annual Symposium on Fundamental Cancer Research, 1969). Baltimore, Maryland: The Williams & Wilkins Co. Pp. 85–104.

Beutler, E., Z. Collins, and L. E. Irwin. 1967. Value of Genetic Variants of Glucose-6-Phosphate Dehydrogenase in Tracing the Origin of Malignant Tumors. *New England Journal of Medicine*, 276:389–391.

Beutler, E., M. Yeh, and V. F. Fairbanks. 1962. The Normal Human Female as a Mosaic of X-Chromosome Activity: Studies Using Gene for G-6-PD Deficiency as a Marker. *Proceedings of the National Academy of Sciences of the U.S.A.*, 48:9–16.

Carter, N. D., R. A. Fildes, L. I. Fitch, and C. W. Parr. 1968. Genetically Determined Electrophoretic Variations of Human Phosphogluconate Dehydrogenase. *Acta genetica et statistica medica*, 18:109–122.

Clein, G. P., and R. J. Flemans. 1966. Involvement of the Erythroid Series in Blastic Crisis of Chronic Myeloid Leukaemia: Further Evidence for the Presence of Philadelphia Chromosome in Erythroblasts. *British Journal of Haematology*, 12:754–758.

Davidson, R. G., A. M. Glen-Bott, and H. Harris. 1965. Clonal Study of Three Autosomal Loci in Heterozygotes. Read at the Annual Meeting of the American Society of Human Genetics, Seattle, Washington, August 25–27, 1965.

Davidson, R. G., H. M. Nitowsky, and B. Childs. 1963. Demonstration of Two Populations of Cells in the Human Female Heterozygous for Glucose-6-Phosphate Dehydrogenase Variants. *Proceedings of the National Academy of Sciences of the U.S.A.*, 50:481–485.

DeMars, R., and W. E. Nance. 1964. "Electrophoretic Variants of Glucose-6-Phosphate Dehydrogenase and the Single-Active-X in Cultivated Human Cells," *Retention of Functional Differentiation in Cultured Cells* (The Wistar Institute Monograph No. 1), V. Defendi, Ed. Philadelphia, Pennsylvania: The Wistar Institute Press. Pp. 35–48.

Fialkow, P. J., G. Klein, S. M. Gartler, and P. Clifford. 1970. Clonal Origin for Individual Burkitt Tumors. *Lancet*. (In press.)

———. Unpublished data.

Fialkow, P. J., S. M. Gartler, and A. Yoshida. 1967. Clonal Origin of Chronic Myelocytic Leukemia in Man. *Proceedings of the National Academy of Sciences of the U.S.A.*, 58:1468–1471.

Fialkow, P. J., R. Lisker, J. Detter, E. R. Giblett, and C. Zavala. 1969. 6-Phosphogluconate Dehydrogenase: Hemizygous Manifestation in a Patient with Leukemia. *Science*, 163:194–195.

———. (In preparation.)

Fialkow, P. J., R. Lisker, E. R. Giblett, and C. Zavala. 1970. Xg Locus: Failure to Detect Inactivation in Females with Chronic Myelocytic Leukemia. *Nature*. (In press.)

Fildes, R. A., and C. W. Parr. 1963. Human Red-Cell Phosphogluconate Dehydrogenase. *Nature*, 200:890–891.

Gartler, S. M., L. Ziprkowski, A. Krakowski, R. Ezra, A. Szeinberg, and A. Adam. 1966. Glucose-6-Phosphate Dehydrogenase Mosaicism as a Tracer in the Study of Hereditary Multiple Trichoepithelioma. *The American Journal of Human Genetics*, 18:282–287.

Good, R. A. 1969. "Inherited Immunologic Deficiency States and Lymphoreticular Neoplasia," *Program and Abstracts of Papers of the Twenty-Third Annual Symposium on Fundamental Cancer Research, "Genetic Concepts and Neoplasia,"* (March 5, 6, and 7, 1969, The University of Texas M. D. Anderson Hospital and Tumor Institute at Houston, Houston, Texas). Pp. 11–14.

Gorman, J. G., J. Di Re, A. M. Treacy, and A. Cahan. 1963. The Application of -Xg^a Antiserum to the Question of Red Cell Mosaicism in Female Heterozygotes. *Journal of Laboratory and Clinical Medicine*, 61:642–649.

Lee, G. R., W. D. MacDiarmid, G. E. Cartwright, and M. M. Wintrobe. 1968. Hereditary, X-Linked, Sideroachrestic Anemia. The Isolation of Two Erythrocyte Populations Differing in Xg^a Blood Type and Porphyrin Content. *Blood, The Journal of Hematology*, 32:59–70.

Lewis, E. B. 1970. "Ionizing Radiation and Tumor Production," *Genetic Concepts and Neoplasia* (The University of Texas M. D. Anderson Hospital and Tumor Institute at Houston, 23rd Annual Symposium on Fundamental Cancer Research, 1969). Baltimore, Maryland: The Williams & Wilkins Co. Pp. 57–73.

Linder, D., and S. M. Gartler. 1965. Glucose-6-Phosphate Dehydrogenase Mosaicism: Utilization as a Cell Marker in the Study of Leiomyomas. *Science*, 150:67–69.

Lyon, M. F. 1961. Gene Action in the X-Chromosome of the Mouse (*Mus musculus* L.). *Nature*, 190:372–373.

Mårtensson, L. 1963. On "A Key Point of Modern Biochemical Genetics." *Lancet*, 1:946–947.

McCurdy, P. R. 1968. Discussion of: Jones, P. D.: "Genetics of G-6-PD Deficiency," *Hereditary Disorders of Erythrocyte Metabolism* (City of Hope Symposium Series), E. Beutler, Ed. New York, New York: Grune & Stratton, Inc. Vol. I. Pp. 121–125.

Nowell, P. C., and D. A. Hungerford. 1960. A Minute Chromosome in Human Chronic Granulocytic Leukemia. *Science*, 132:1497.

———. 1961. Chromosome Studies in Human Leukemia. II. Chronic Granulocytic Leukemia. *Journal of the National Cancer Institute*, 27:1013–1035.

Parr, C. W., and L. I. Fitch. 1967. Inherited Quantitative Variations of Human Phosphogluconate Dehydrogenase. *Annals of Human Genetics*, 30:339–353.

Pernis, B., and G. Chiappino. 1964. Identification in Human Lymphoid Tissues of Cells that Produce Group 1 or Group 2 Gamma-Globulins. *Immunology*, 7:500–506.

Race, R. R., and R. Sanger. 1968. "The X-linked Blood Groups, Xg," *Blood Groups in Man*. Philadelphia, Pennsylvania: F. A. Davis Co. 5th edition. Pp. 522–536.

Rastrick, J. M., P. H. Fitzgerald, and F. W. Gunz. 1968. Direct Evidence for Presence of Ph^1 Chromosome in Erythroid Cells. *British Medical Journal*, 1:96–98.

Russell, L. B. 1961. Genetics of Mammalian Sex Chromosomes. *Science*, 133:1795–1803.

Sandberg, A. A., T. Ishihara, L. H. Crosswhite, and T. S. Hauschka. 1962. Comparison of Chromosome Constitution in Chronic Myelocytic Leukemia and Other Myeloproliferative Disorders. *Blood, The Journal of Hematology*, 20:393–423.

Sigman, B., and S. M. Gartler. 1966. The Absence of Inactivation at Two Autosomal Loci. *Humangenetik*, 2:372–377.

Sinkovics, J. G., J. M. Trujillo, R. J. Pienta, and M. G. Ahearn. 1970. "Leukemo-genesis Stemming from Autoimmune Disease," *Genetic Concepts and Neoplasia* (The University of Texas M. D. Anderson Hospital and Tumor Institute at Houston, 23rd Annual Symposium on Fundamental Cancer Research, 1969). Baltimore, Maryland: The Williams & Wilkins Co. Pp. 138–190.

Tough, I. M., W. M. Court Brown, A. G. Baikie, K. E. Buckton, D. G. Harnden, P. A. Jacobs, M. J. King, and J. A. McBride. 1961. Cytogenetic Studies in Chronic Myeloid Leukaemia and Acute Leukaemia Associated with Mongolism. *Lancet*, 1:411–417.

Tough, I. M., P. A. Jacobs, W. M. Court Brown, A. G. Baikie, and E. R. D. Williamson. 1963. Cytogenetic Studies on Bone-Marrow in Chronic Myeloid Leukaemia. *Lancet*, 1:844–846.

Trujillo, J. M. 1964. "Chromosomal Alteration of Erythropoietic Cells in Chronic Myeloid Leukemia," *Proceedings of the IX Congress of the International Society of Hematology*. Mexico City, Mexico: Universidad Nacional Autonoma de Mexico. Vol. I. P. 305.

Whang, J., E. Frei, III, J. H. Tjio, P. P. Carbone, and G. Brecher. 1963. The Distribution of the Philadelphia Chromosome in Patients with Chronic Myelogenous Leukemia. *Blood, The Journal of Hematology*, 22:664–673.

Discussion

Dr. R. DeMars, University of Wisconsin, Madison, Wisconsin: You have left out the assumption of your tests, Dr. Fialkow. You infer from single allele expression in a malignant tumor that the tumor is of a single cell origin. When you find double allele expression in a tumor, you conclude that it is of multiple cellular origin. There are at least two other possibilities. One is that in some tumors, which are, after all, abnormal cells with certain control mechanisms removed, perhaps the inactive X has been derepressed, so that a tumor might have arisen in a single cell but now both X's are expressed. The second possibility was raised along with the original statement of the idea as a possible pitfall in this test (R. DeMars, in *Metabolic Control Mechanisms in Animal Cells*, H. B. Andervont, Ed. [National Cancer Institute Monograph 13] pp. 181–195, April 1964). This possibility is that cells fuse and that a tumor that originated as a single malignant cell may actually be the progeny of a malignant cell with single allele expression having fused with an adjacent cell, so that the primordial event was indeed a single cell event. Have you tackled that assumption and those possibilities?

Dr. Philip J. Fialkow, University of Washington, Seattle, Washington: Considering your last point first, none of our data tell us anything about the original primordial event. We can say only that the malignant cells we see in the patients with chronic myelogenous leukemia (CML) have a clonal origin. There could have been many so-called malignant cells, but one clone outgrew the others; similarly, the clone could have arisen from a cell which was the result of the fusion of two cells.

With regard to your first point, we have considered this and we think it unlikely. Many attempts have been made to activiate the repressed

X chromosome, but these have been unsuccessful. Of course, one could argue that this may occur in the malignant process. However, take as an example, the carcinoma of the colon (E. Beutler, Z. Collins, and L. E. Irwin: *New England Journal of Medicine*, 276:389–391, 1967), in which two enzyme types were found in the primary tumor; the metastases of this cancer contained predominantly only one or the other type of G-6-PD, making it unlikely that the inactive-X has been derepressed.

Dr. S. D. Handmaker, National Institutes of Health, Bethesda, Maryland: Dr. Fialkow, in your patient with CML expressing one allele at the 6-phosphogluconate dehydrogenase (6-PGD) locus, the simplest hypothesis is that this locus is on the distal portion of the long arm of the G-group chromosome which gives rise to the Philadelphia (Ph[1]) chromosome. In light of this relationship, are you able to confirm this hypothesis by detecting dosage effects in patients with G-trisomy?

Dr. Fialkow: We thought after our initial observations with this patient that the 6-PGD locus was on the deleted segment of the Ph[1] chromosome. However, we then found two patients who had CML and the Ph[1] chromosome who were heterozygous in the blood cells. Therefore, if you postulate that the locus is on the deleted segment, then you must also postulate that this deletion varies in size and/or location from one patient to another. This may very well be the case.

We have been reluctant to do studies of dosage effects in patients with Down's syndrome because of the generalized quantitative abnormalities which are seen in blood cell enzymes in these patients. We prefer to use qualitative markers. We would like to start with subjects with Down's syndrome who have A-B 6-PGD phenotypes and study their parents. One might observe an excess of heterozygotes in their mothers.

Dr. R. Bottomley, Oklahoma Medical Research Foundation, Oklahoma City, Oklahoma: This remark is in regard to the family I mentioned earlier that had an increased incidence of acute leukemia and sarcomas. The mother of two siblings with sarcomas has not developed a malignancy, even though you would expect her to carry the abnormal gene. She does, however, have rather severe rheumatoid arthritis. We thought this might represent another manifestation of this genetic abnormality.

Dr. R. A. Good, Pediatrics Research Laboratories, Variety Club Heart Hospital, Minneapolis, Minnesota: Have you had a chance to study immunological parameters in that family?

Dr. Bottomley: No, but we would very much like to do this.

Dr. Good: I think this is a possibly fruitful avenue of investigation. We have seen in patients with immunological deficiency diseases, particularly those with broadly based immunologic deficiencies involving both the lymphoid and plasma cell systems, a high frequency of rheumatoid diseases, and other forms of mesenchymal disease. Sometimes these patients may also have malignant disease. I think the patient seen in Dr. Kunkel's laboratory is a fascinating case in point. It looks as though whatever the stimulus is, it is deriving from the tumor. It is inducing the host to form autoantibodies against the components of his own immunoglobulins. It is somewhat like subacute bacterial endocarditis. Certain kinds of rheumatoid factors are formed until you get rid of the infection; then they go away.

Dr. C. P. Miles, University of Utah, Salt Lake City, Utah: Dr. Fialkow, when you look at primary tumors and find two bands, how do you rule out the influence of the nonneoplastic stroma?

Dr. Fialkow: May I refer for a moment to those cases which have been studied by P. R. McCurdy (*Hereditary Disorders of Erythrocyte Metabolism* [City of Hope Symposium Series], E. Beutler, Ed. New York, New York: Grune & Stratton, Inc. Vol. I. Pp. 121–125, 1968) and E. Beutler, Z. Collins, and L. E. Irwin (*New England Journal of Medicine,* 276:389–391, 1967). Their technique is to look at histological sections of tumor specimens to try to estimate how much of the specimen consists of stromal tissue. In the tumors that we studied, CML and Burkitt's lymphoma, this is less of a problem since there is generally very little stromal tissue present.

Dr. D. L. Ruchnagel, University of Michigan Medical School, Ann Arbor, Michigan: Dr. Fialkow, it seems to me that another hypothesis to explain some of your observations is that in CML, the Ph^1 chromosome is merely a manifestation of specific or nonspecific secondary chromosomal damage. The erythroblasts containing the Ph^1 chromosome, then, need not be derived from the same stem cell as the granulocytes. Deletion of segments containing a 6-PGD allele might be a manifestation of the same type of damage, not necessarily of the same chromosome. This might also explain your 6-PGD and the Xg^a findings.

Dr. Fialkow: If the Ph^1 chromosome does occur secondarily to the malignancy, it certainly is a highly specific change, as you point out. Although I believe this is somewhat unlikely, it cannot be excluded.

Dr. A. G. Bearn, Cornell University Medical College, New York, New York: I think it is interesting to note that one other locus on the X chromosome which exhibits the Lyonization effect is the X-linked form of Hurler's syndrome, sometimes known as Hunter's syndrome. This locus is quite closely linked to the glucose-6-phosphate dehydrogenase (G-6-PD) locus, whereas the Xg blood group locus is further away. I think one might be a little disturbed by the failure of Lyonization of the Xg locus if the Xg locus were also closely linked to the G-6-PD.

Dr. DeMars: Another possibility is that the type of phenotype that you are studying is Xg. This is a surface cellular antigen and in red cells these last a long time after the cells are enucleated. If there is even limited expression of both X's before the enucleation process has occurred, you might have persistence of even a small amount of antigen for a long time and never be able to find a purely negative population, which would be the only kind of result that would have meaning in your system.

Dr. Fialkow: It would imply then that both genes would be active before enucleation.

Dr. DeMars: Even a partial expression of the so-called inactive X could result in a weak Xg+ reaction. Perhaps we should not think of the X chromosome as "off" or "on." This has been defined in an in vitro system with cells removed from the regulatory processes of the body; in the body, the X chromosome may actually behave more like rheostats.

Dr. Fialkow: If the G-6-PD gene on the "inactive" X chromosome was partially active, we saw no evidence of it.

Dr. DeMars: The G-6-PD decays rapidly in red cells.

Dr. Fialkow: We studied leukocytes as well, but we did not see this.

Dr. H. T. Pruessner, Corpus Christi, Texas: Twenty or 30 years ago, the condition of thymicolymphaticus was managed with radiation. Do you know of any study on what has happened to these people immunologically and cancer-wise.

Dr. Good: As you may be aware, there have been some studies done on the immunological capacity of patients who have been irradiated in this way but nothing really has been found in these patients. From the standpoint of malignancy, I think the only thing that holds up is evidence that in some of these patients there has been sufficient irradiation to increase the incidence of cellular malignant changes. But from the standpoint of the development of the lymphoid system in man, and as we interpret it in light of data from experimental animals, you wouldn't expect that the destruction of lymphocytes within the thymus would have any lasting influence on immunological capacity. Cells of thymic origin are basically of bone marrow origin. They thrive in the thymus and undergo an extensive proliferation; some are actually destroyed in the thymus and some leave the thymus as immunologically competent cells. When you irradiate and destroy all the cells in the thymus, it is only a matter of a few days before you have another group of cells filling up that gap. You cannot measure this, even in mice given much larger doses of radiation than were used in the children. Very little can be demonstrated for radiation given in the neonatal period before there has been significant development of the peripheral lymphoid tissue.

Dr. Pruessner: But it doesn't destroy the thymus mechanisms.

Dr. Good: No. The thymus is derived from the epithelium in the third and fourth branchial pouch. Although this hasn't actually been proved yet, it appears that the inducing microchemical environment exists within the thymus and is somehow or other a consequence of the characteristic of those epithelially derived cells and their products.

Dr. Pruessner: You have reported on many things that will suppress the immune system. Have you found anything that might indicate how you could awaken it?

Dr. Good: That is a complicated question. There are many ways of enhancing immunological response; turning it on once the basic cells of a system have been depleted is not so easy. For example, some patients are born without a thymus; they have no thymus-dependent system, but their plasma cell system immunoglobulins are sound. Two such patients have been corrected simply by putting in an embryonic thymus. We have been able to correct completely the immunological function in these patients by putting in the stem cell source from a matched sibling. We can do it with stem cells from members of the general population, but we would kill the children with the graft. We can match the siblings with respect to the HLA locus and match by the Bock techniques. Once in our laboratory, once in Holland, and once in a patient with Aldrich syndrome (this latter was done by Dr. Bock in Wisconsin) reconstitution was accomplished with stem cell source. We have markers here and know that female cells are the responding lymphoid cells in the peripheral blood that are producing antibodies and so on.

Dr. J. L. Biedler, Sloan-Kettering Institute, New York, New York: I would like to ask, in regard to the G-6-PD story, how many relatively histologically pure, normal tissues from heterozygotes have been studied? Might this not bear upon the possible studies of different tumor types at different sites that you mention? Also, if granulocytes could be separated in pure form from lymphocytes, might these not turn out to be pure A or pure B in normal individuals?

Dr. Fialkow: S. M. Gartler and colleagues and we have studied at least 50 nonleukemic heterozygotes at the G-6-PD locus. Some of these were genetically proven and others phenotypically shown to be heterozygotes for the A and B genes. If the red cells have two bands, so do the peripheral blood leukocytes in at least over 95 per cent of the cases. Furthermore, in an effort to see whether there is a totipotential stem cell—or was one —Gartler and co-workers have separated granulocytes from lymphocytes and compared the relative amounts of A band to B band in each of these cell types. Almost total concordance was found, suggesting very strongly that there at least was such a stem cell.

Dr. J. Allred, The University of Texas M. D. Anderson Hospital and Tumor Institute at Houston, Houston, Texas: Dr. Fialkow, you base your presentation on the assumption that an A type cell becoming malignant is identifiable as the A phenotype. Yet every case that you presented was from heterozygous tissue. Therefore, I don't see how you established the case of homozygotes of A type tissue or homozygotes of B type tissue having only the A or only the B type and malignant tissue. Statistically establishing this case would seem to be necessary.

Dr. Fialkow: We studied subjects with CML who were homozygous for the B gene, and the phenotypes in their leukocytes and red cells were always B. We also studied homozygotes for the A genes with similar results. Is that what you mean?

Dr. Allred: Did you study enough cases?

Dr. Fialkow: We studied about five in each category. Would you expect an A homozygote to suddenly develop a B gene or something of that sort?

Dr. Allred: It is called an A homozygote because if the B was present it was not seen. Perhaps its expression was masked. Anyway, it is not necessary for an A to develop a B gene. It is only necessary for you to fail to find the A phenotype expression in the malignant homozygote. After all, when a cell becomes malignant it undergoes considerable change. This trivial case must be established. There is no reason to assume that it is axiomatic.

Dr. Fialkow: The way we knew the patient was heterozygous was to study normal tissues first. Then we studied malignant tissue. When we studied subjects whose normal tissues had only a single enzyme type, suggesting that they were homozygotes, we found only that same type in the granulocytes.

Dr. Allred: But the presence of one differing case would be very difficult to picture, wouldn't it?

Dr. Fialkow: If we found one it would add difficulty to a lot of pictures, yes.

Dr. Good: Do the tumors of those patients who are A or B have the potentiality for another differentiation?

Dr. Fialkow: We didn't find this to be the case. We started by studying the normal tissue, such as skin, and we did not find that the tumor differed in the homozygotes.

Dr. E. J. Lappat, The University of Texas M. D. Anderson Hospital and Tumor Institute at Houston, Houston, Texas: I would like to compliment you on your excellent work, Dr. Fialkow. In addition, I would like to ask your consideration of embryological development during the time of the inactivation of the X chromosome. The stage in which this occurs, as determined by Park, is at the morula stage, or around 16 days gestation. Although this is a timed event, from the studies made to date, the number of "pro-genitor" cells for developmental tissue clones present at this time seems to be a chance event. In other words, if only one cell that is going to differentiate toward hematopoietic system development is present, then inactivation at this time would result in all cells being of the same derivation. However, if at least two or more cells are present, then random inactivation of the X chromosome would result in mosaicism of this tissue, which might be the same as or different from that of the skin. You base your findings of only A or B type cells in patients with CML as proof of a clonal derivation of malignant cells. Might this not instead be the result of there being only one normal cell type derived at the morula stage and that this cell type at that stage is different from skin or another organ tissue also? Have you tested other tissues?

Dr. Fialkow: We know that over 95 per cent of subjects who have A-B phenotypes in red cells will have similar phenotypes in granulocytes. If you find A and B cells in peripheral skin, you find A and B enzyme in granulocytes although fewer cases have been studied. In the lymphocytes, agreement with granulocytes is 100 per cent in the 50 cases studied. In other words, if granulocytes have an A-B type, lymphocytes do as well.

Dr. Lappat: Again, I am sure you have worked this out long enough for sufficient data, but this is one of the things that first interested us and many others in this area, that you would have a different marrow type from the skin type. This is what prompted my question. I wonder if you have, in any instance, found this similarity in the normal?

Dr. Fialkow: The red cells and granulocytes reflect the amount, except in a small percentage of cases.

Dr. Lappat: No, I meant this dissimilarity of content between the marrow and peripheral blood of the skin or another organ.

Dr. Fialkow: In so far as red cells and granulocytes reflect the marrow, only a small percentage of cases are dissimilar from skin.

Dr. J. Undevia, Cancer Research Institute, Bombay, India: Beaconsfield has indicated some relationship between the incidence of G-6-PD deficiency and malignancy in the Caucasians and the Orientals. In Caucasians, the incidence of malignant growth is higher with very low frequency of G-6-PD deficiency, whereas in Orientals, the opposite is true. I wonder if you can shed any light on this, because in Bombay, from observations on a small sample, breast cancer in Parsi females showed two types of clinical manifestations. Progress of the disease showed a bimodal pattern. The possibility of a carrier state for G-6-PD deficiency of protection may be responsible for two patterns in the clinical course of the disease.

Dr. Fialkow: Our own data would shed no light on this. However, as you know, there are numerous examples in which one or another of a type of genetic marker appears to be correlated with the presence of the disease, such as group A in gastric carcinoma. So this is conceivable for G-6-PD, but I have no data.

Dr. DeMars: I think you have done very nice work here. I think your foundation statements ought to be just right, and so I want to address myself to the last comment that was made about your work. You say that you have concordance between two cell types just about every time. This is a qualitative statment—if you find A and B in one you find them both in the other—but this is not quite enough to lay the ghost.

Dr. Fialkow: This is quantitative as well.

Dr. DeMars: Well, then it differs from observations that others have made. Walter Nance and I, in our clonal study, compared samples of red cells and fibroblasts from heterozygotes. In fibroblasts of different heterozygotes for the same pair of alleles, A and B, you find some heterozygotes that have 5 per cent A and others with 95 per cent A. Other heterozygotes showed the reverse relation. If you study the red cells of these same individuals, you can find the mirror image in terms of relative amounts of these two types (R. DeMars and W. Nance, in *Retention of Functional Differentiation in Cultured Cells* [The Wistar Institute Monograph No. 1], V. Defendi, Ed., pp. 35–48, 1964).

Dr. Fialkow: I agree with you in respect to fibroblast and peripheral blood cells. However, in comparing granulocytes to lymphocytes, Gartler and colleagues have found almost complete quantitative concordance.

Leukemogenesis Stemming from Autoimmune Disease

JOSEPH G. SINKOVICS, JOSE M. TRUJILLO,
ROMAN J. PIENTA, AND MICHAEL J. AHEARN

Section of Clinical Tumor Virology and Immunology, Department of Medicine, and Research Clinical Pathology, Hematology and Microbiology Units, Department of Pathology, The University of Texas M. D. Anderson Hospital and Tumor Institute at Houston, Houston, Texas

The establishment of new lymphoid cell clones appears to be the essential pathological process in both autoimmune and malignant lymphoproliferative diseases. The purpose of this presentation is to explore the possibility that a common etiologic agent may be responsible for certain types of autoimmune and malignant pathological entities of the lymphoreticular system.

Antigens and Immune Responses

The genetic control of immunological processes expresses itself in three ways: (1) in coding for cellular antigens, (2) in the maintenance of the immunological integrity of the individual, and (3) in the capacity of ribonucleic acid (RNA) extracts to determine various immunological reaction patterns. Exogenous agents, however, often alter cellular antigenic patterns and may disconcert the afferent and efferent flow of immune reactions.

NEOANTIGENS

New cell antigens most often arise during virus infections and represent various parts of the virion. Disintegrating virus-cell complexes, in cases of cytopathogenic viruses and virus carrier cells without cell death, exert an antigenic impulse on the host. Especially strong antigenic stimulation derives from cells that carry cytoplasmic viruses of mild cytopathogenic effects. Most of these viruses leave the host cells through a budding process during which the cell membrane acquires a large number of new (viral) antigenic sites. While cell-free virus particles are dealt with by virus-neutralizing antibodies, cell-virus complexes characteristically evoke a cell-mediated immune reaction, the chief executors of which are small lymphocytes—hence the perivascular cuffing and diffuse lymphocytic infiltration of virus-infected parenchymatous organs. The primary function of this type of immune reaction is the elimination of cells recognized as nonself. Thus, the execution of antiviral immunity necessarily involves the destruction of large numbers of virus-carrier host cells. For instance, infection with measles virus results in no immediate cell death; rather, infected cells fuse to form virus antigen-carrying giant cells. These cells now will be recognized by lymphoid cells as antigenically foreign. The foreignness of the cells will evoke an immune reaction of the homograft rejection type. Reactions of virus-infected cells and immune lymphocytes will result in cell death and virus will be liberated from the disintegrating cells. The measles rash is the visible manifestation of the delayed hypersensitivity or graft-rejection type of reaction. Another immunological faculty, *i.e.*, virus-neutralizing antibody, will then eliminate the cell-free virus particles. In children with agammaglobulinemia, measles runs an uncomplicated course (Good and Zak, 1956); in children with defective thymus-dependent lymphocytes, measles appears in the form of fatal giant cell pneumonia. Thus, cell-mediated immune reactions, rather than antibody-synthesizing faculties carry the burden of immune defense in this virus infection (Burnet, 1968). The severe bronchiolitis of infants infected with respiratory syncytial virus may be the consequence of the destructive action of passively transferred maternal virus-neutralizing antibody reacting with virus antigen-carrier host cells (Chanock *et al.*, 1967). Thus, both major faculties of immunity, the cell-mediated reactions and antibody production, are operational in antiviral immunity and both faculties may cause cell damage to the host during the process of eliminating a virus infection. However, the normal host regenerates most lost tissues and recovers. Failure of one of these immune faculties, especially the cell-mediated reactions, results in severe, long-lasting virus infections such as giant cell pneumonia of measles (Burnet, 1968) and the congenital rubella syndrome (Dent *et al.*, 1968). Certain viruses are able to incapacitate lymphocytes; for instance, upon stimulation with an antigen, lymphocytes exposed to rubella virus fail to undergo blastic transformation (Simons and Fitzgerald, 1968), a reaction necessary for the development of specifically sensitized lymphoid cell clones.

The continuous appearance of new cellular antigens throughout cell generations is often associated with malignant transformation of the neoantigen-synthesizing cells. Both the antigens located intranuclearly and at the cell membrane are thought to be coded for by the viral genome or fragments thereof, as its functions are integrated with those of the cellular genome. Thus, in virus-induced tumors of various species, the neoantigens are identical and specific for the causative virus; for instance, human cells transformed by the simian vacuolating virus (SV40) will protect hamsters against the oncogenic effect of this virus by virtue of the identity of new antigens on the transformed human and hamster cells (Girardi, 1965). Antigenic cross-reactivity between tumors induced in mice, hamsters, and fowl by the Schmidt-Ruppin strain of the Rous sarcoma virus (RSV) was also shown (Sjögren and Hellström, 1967). In these systems, no infectious virus particles were formed, regardless of whether the oncogenic virus was of the RNA or deoxyribonucleic acid (DNA)-containing type. The newly acquired cell antigens are not incorporated into the mature virions during infectious or cytocidal cycles of DNA viruses.

The new antigens of tumor cells induced by RNA viruses are virion-associated. For instance, murine leukemic cells liberate mature leukemia virus particles through a cytoplasmic budding process. The new membrane-associated antigens of these cells may not be more than those of the protruding virus ribonucleoprotein and envelope protein antigens (Figure 1). It appears as if the envelope antigens of murine leukemia viruses (MLV) possess a finer type of specificity, as measured by virus-neutralization tests, than do the group-specific soluble antigens (Aoki, Boyse, and Old, 1968; Sinkovics, 1967a). Unfortunately, the term "soluble antigens" has been used to denote two entirely different components of the mouse leukemia virus particle. Subunits of the viral coat occur in blood and tissues of leukemic or nonleukemic strains of mice with high incidence of leukemia (Aoki, Boyse, and Old, 1968). These subunits readily adsorb to cell membranes and may be identified by tests utilizing cytotoxic antibody and complement; the coat subunits of Gross (G) virus can be distinguished serologically from those of Friend, Moloney, and Rauscher (FMR) murine leukemia viruses (Aoki, Boyse, and Old, 1968). Another soluble antigen of mouse leukemia viruses derives from the ribonucleoprotein core of the virus. Soluble antigens of this type deriving from G or FMR viruses do not exhibit serologically distinct antigenic features (Geering, Old, and Boyse, 1966). Thus, the viral coat and its subunits are type specific. Entirely analogous situations have been demonstrated for the chicken leukosis and sarcoma viruses (Huebner, 1967) and, much earlier, for the influenza viruses (Francis and Maassab, 1965). Thus, the true soluble antigens of oncogenic RNA viruses are those liberated from the ribonucleoprotein core of the virus.

The most commonly used serologic methods for typing oncogenic RNA viruses are the virus-neutralizing, cytotoxic (or complement-dependent cytolytic), and complement-fixation tests. It is not known with certainty what virus antigen these tests measure. The cytotoxic and virus-neutralizing antibodies were shown not to be identical (Sinkovics, Shullenberger, Howe, and Bertin, 1966; Steeves, 1968), but different classes of antibodies may be directed to the same antigen.

A murine leukemia virus is capable of activating latent genes of host cells. This is evident in the thymus-leukemia (TL) complex. When mouse thymus cells not carrying the TL antigen, synthesized by normal thymus cells of other mouse strains, undergo virus-induced leukemic transformation, the TL antigen will appear on the leukemic cells. When these cells are exposed to anti-TL immune serum without complement, the synthesis of TL antigen will cease and addition of complement will not evoke cell lysis. Maintenance of these cells in TL antibody-free environment will result in the resumption of TL antigen synthesis (Boyse, Old, Stockert, and Shigeno, 1968). Thus, phenotypic alteration of the cell membrane occurred under the effect of antibody.

The mammary carcinoma virus of mice maintains a cell-virus relationship similar to that of leukemia viruses and cells. Genetic interaction between Gross leukemia virus and Bittner's mammary tumor virus probably occurred in DBA/2 mice; leukemic cells of these mice possessed mammary tumor virus antigens, as demonstrated in cytotoxic tests (Nowinski *et al.*, 1968).

Cells transformed to the malignant state by chemical carcinogens express highly individual neoantigenic characteristics; even different tumors induced by the same carcinogen in one host display individual

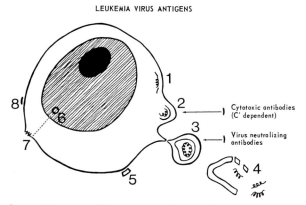

FIGURE 1. Leukemic cell showing release of leukemia virus: 1, Ribonucleoprotein strands of the virus, 2, budding virus particle, 3, mature virus particle released from cell, 4, virus particle releasing subunits of its envelope and ribonucleoprotein strands, 5, envelope subunits of the virus readsorbed on cell surface, 6, locus coding for synthesis of TL-antigen, 7, TL-antigen at cell membrane, 8, under the effect of antibody (without complement), the synthesis of TL-antigen ceases.

neoantigenicity (Klein, 1968). The pathomechanism of chemical carcinogenesis is not known; cell genome mutation, activation of depressed genes, suppression of interferon, and induction of a latent oncogenic virus are to be considered to explain neoantigen formation.

Finally, embryonal antigens may be resynthesized if derepression of cellular genes in malignant cells occurs; however, such derepression may be one of the functions of the viral genome during malignant transformation. Fetal antigens were demonstrated in tumors of the large intestine of man (Gold, Gold, and Freedman, 1968). In normal bone marrow of man, antigens were found that reacted with antibodies directed to human leukemic cell antigens and/or viruslike particles of leukemic plasma of man; the amount of this antigen in leukemic cells was four to eight times that in normal cells (Yohn et al., 1968). The group-specific chicken leukosis virus antigen, as detected by complement-fixation test, was found to occur in normal chicken embryo cells; apparently, a very similar antigen is resynthesized by cultured chicken fibroblasts upon infection with viruses of fowl leukemia and sarcoma (Dougherty and Di Stefano, 1966). The transplantation antigen of hamster cells, appearing after transformation by polyoma virus, was dependent on the polyoma virus genome, and also was detected in hamster embryo cells (Pearson and Freeman, 1968). It has been suggested that normal embryonic antigens become inactive when the neonatal stage of development is reached; the genome of the polyoma virus acts to sustain genetic functions necessary for unrestricted growth and some of the derepressed cellular genes code for the synthesis of surface antigens recognized as transplantation antigen in tumor cells (Pearson and Freeman, 1968).

Certain genes active during fetal life normally are repressed later. Derepression by chemical or viral agents may simply result in the restoration of the fetal status of a cell. If the derepressing agent is unnecessary for maintaining the fetal status of the cell, derepressed cells may assume growth characteristics that are neoplastic even after the disappearance of the derepressing factor. Thus, certain tumor cells may display fetal antigens as neoantigens without an associated viral antigen.

IMMUNOLOGICAL INTEGRITY

The immunological homeostasis of multicellular organisms is maintained by faculties that (1) tolerate the host's own healthy components as self, (2) recognize, and (3) eliminate antigenically foreign substances, and (4) register within the immunological memory all encounters with foreign agents. Transplantation immunologists are in search of measures that would selectively compromise the host's immunological integrity to the extent that a foreign graft, strongly antigenic as it may be, would be accepted or tolerated. Tumor immunologists are in search of measures that would increase the host's immunological integrity to the extent that an autochthonous tumor, acting as a foreign graft, weakly antigenic as it may be, would be rejected.

Lymphocytes have been recognized as the major effectors of immunological integrity. The pool of lymphocytes consists of a heterogeneous population of lymphoid cells. Uncommitted lymphocytes recognize foreign substances by bodily contact. It has not been proved completely whether lymphocytes are able to recognize antigens and respond to them; in certain in vivo systems, such as rats bearing renal homografts, contact between lymphocyte and allogeneic cells results in sensitization of lymphocytes (Strober and Gowans, 1965). In other systems, mainly in vitro, an interaction between macrophages and uncommitted lymphocytes has occurred (Cline and Swett, 1968). During this interaction, bodily contact between the macrophage and the surrounding lymphocytes is established; prior to this, the macrophage had engulfed and processed the antigenic material. From macrophage to lymphocytes passes a specific RNA attached to the antigen (Fishman and Adler, 1963; Bishop, Pisciotta, and Abramoff, 1967). The transfer of this complex occurs through cytoplasmic bridges or through the foot appendages of lymphocytes (Schoenberg, Mumaw, Moore, and Weisberger, 1964; McFarland and Heilman, 1965). Under the effect of the immunogenic RNA-antigen complex, the recipient lymphocytes undergo blastic transformation and differentiate (Bach and Hirschhorn, 1965; Cline and Swett, 1968). Thymus-dependent lymphocytes will be executors of delayed hypersensitivity reactions and homograft and tumor rejections. These reactions require direct contact between sensitized lymphocytes and antigenic target. Upon such contact, the lymphocytes release a protein which has the function of arresting passerby monocytes. Such monocytes convert into histiocytes and release lysosomal hydrolases; thus, cell damage in the immediate vicinity ensues. The protein released by the sensitized lymphocytes was also shown to be directly cytotoxic to target cells (Ruddle and Waksman, 1968). Lymphocytes dependent on gut-associated lymphatic tissue will become antibody producers. After subsidence of the antigenic impulse, the proliferation of the lymphoid cell clones involved in the reaction ceases, and the remaining committed lymphoid cells survive to function as memory cells (Celada, 1967).

While antibody promotes granulocytic and macrophage action, and with complement and properdin causes cell lysis, certain types of antibody may hinder rejection reactions carried out by sensitized lymphocytes. Antibody covering antigenic sites of foreign cells may prevent recognition; and if recognition is achieved, block of surface antigens by antibody may prevent the execution of rejection (Snell, Winn, Stimpfling, and Parker, 1960; Amos, Prioleau, and Hutchin, 1968; Kaliss, 1962). In murine homologous disease, severe hepatitis and liver necrosis of the recipients were found; in a complement-free in vitro system, immune serum directed against the recipient's liver cells prevented the cytopathic damage which occurred when recipient's liver cells were exposed to immune donor lymphocytes in the presence of normal heat-inactivated serum (Sinkovics and Howe, 1964). Enhancement of cells with normal histocompatibility isoantigens occurs frequently; in addition, enhancement of malignant cells carrying protruding viral surface antigens also has been documented recently. An ascitic murine lymphoma (Boyse, Old, and Stockert, 1962), Friend virus-carrier lymphoma cells in actively or passively preimmunized syngeneic mice (McCoy, Fefer, and Glynn, 1968), and murine sarcomas caused by the Harvey virus (Bubenik and Turano, 1968) were shown to be immunologically enhanced by immune sera. When a mouse sarcoma carrying attenuated mouse leukemia virus was superinfected with Newcastle disease virus (NDV), accelerated growth of this tumor occurred in mice treated with anti-NDV-immune serum (Sinkovics and Howe, 1969).

Malignant cells, even if not of lymphoid type, manufactured globulins (Abelev, 1968; Charney, 1968). The question arises whether tumors exhibiting rapid growth rate in immunocompetent hosts could have acquired the ability to synthesize a globulin which would cover neoantigenic sites. Such an autoantibody would permit the tumor cells to masquerade as entirely self, thus escaping recognition and immune rejection.

Perhaps the most archaic reaction known to exist in order to maintain immunological homeostasis is allogeneic inhibition (Klein, 1966). This contact-dependent surveillance function of neighboring cells has been demonstrated both in vivo and in vitro between cells and cell-free extracts, and shows the capacity of allogeneic extracts to inhibit target cells more effectively than syngeneic extracts (Hellström and Hellström, 1967).

RNA TRANSFER IN IMMUNE REACTIONS

Both delayed hypersensitivity-type reactions and antibody production could be transferred from presensitized cells to normal cells by RNA extracts. RNA extract of rabbit lymphoid cells presensitized to skin allograft enabled normal recipient rabbits to mount accelerated graft rejection against this allograft; and normal rabbit lymphocytes, after exposure in vitro to RNA deriving from sensitized rabbit lymphocytes, acquired the capacity to transfer hypersensitivity reaction (Mannick and Egdahl, 1964). RNA extracted from mouse spleen cells, after immunization with sheep red blood cells, was incubated with spleen cells of nonimmunized mice. The hemolytic plaque assay of Jerne revealed that significant numbers of the normal spleen cells achieved the capacity to form antibody to sheep erythrocytes (Cohen and Parks, 1964). The RNA nature of Lawrence's classical transfer factor is very probable but it has not as yet been proved.

Another immunological interaction requiring transfer of RNA occurs between antigen-processing macrophages and uncommitted lymphocytes (Fishman and Adler, 1963).

A third type of RNA transfer occurs between lymphocytes taken from animals immunized against a heterologous tumor and lymphoreticular cells of the tumor-bearing host; not the small lymphocytes, but large antigen-stimulated pyroninophilic lymphoid cells of the donor were essential in initiating this reaction. These donor cells seed the spleen of the tumor-bearing heterologous host but fail to persist there over 48 hours. However, after the elimination of the donor cells, the recipient's splenic lymphoid cells begin to show gamma globulin of the donor type. Coincidentally, temporary regressions of the tumor occur. Presumably, the tumor-bearing host receives RNA-mediated instructions for both antibody production and for the development of antitumor cytotoxic lymphocytes from the heterologous donor cells termed "messenger cells" (Alexander, 1968). Most remarkably, the tumor-bearing immunologically competent recipients did not accept instruction from the heterologous antirecipient messenger cells to form autoantibody and autoaggressive lymphocytes; thus, no homologous disease occurred. Therefore, the recipient's lymphoreticular cells must have exercised keen discernment between coded messages deriving from the heterologous donor cells and appear to have been able to reject all instructions concerning antiself immunization. Although not yet demonstrated experimentally, this extraordinary faculty of the recipient's immune system must have also counteracted interferon action. Interferon was found to be induced most readily by the introduction of heterologous nucleic acids into cell systems (Jensen, Neal, Owens, and Warren, 1963). In patients with malignant diseases, the administration of homologous immune thoracic duct lymphocytes resulted in both temporary regression of the tumor and in fatal graft-*versus*-host reaction without regression of the tumor (Andrews *et al.*, 1967); the administration to two patients of heterologous lymphocytes from sheep immunized against malignant melanoma resulted in no tumor regression but in severe toxic reaction (Mathé *et al.*, 1967).

Autoimmune Oncogenesis in Man

AUTOIMMUNE DISEASES

A large number of pathological entities characterized by autoantibody formation, vasculitis, and lymphocytic infiltration or granuloma formation in parenchymatous organs lack well-defined causative agents; most of these pathological processes formerly were called collagen diseases but, recently, the term "autoimmune diseases" has gained acceptance. Autoimmune diseases frequently occur simultaneously with both immune deficiency diseases (Seligmann, Fudenberg, and Good, 1968) and with various types of malignant diseases, but occur most often with malignant lymphoma and its variants.

The pathogenesis of autoimmune diseases is diverse. In autoimmune hemolytic anemia, there is an anti-erythrocyte globulin, but the parenchymal organs are not infiltrated by lymphoid cells; phagocytosis in the spleen removes the antibody-coated erythrocytes from the circulation. In rheumatoid arthritis, a macroglobulin is manufactured. This 19S globulin forms complexes with 7S globulins, thus behaving as an antiglobulin autoantibody. The globulin complexes are taken up by cells of the synovial membranes and by polymorphonuclear leukocytes within the synovial membrane. These cells release lysosomal enzymes, inflicting cell damage to both membrane and cartilage (Hollander, McCarty, Astorga, and Castro-Murillo, 1965). In Sjögren's syndrome, new germinal follicles of lymphoid tissue appear in the parotid gland. Both the salivary and lacrimal glands are heavily infiltrated by lymphocytes, and the parenchyma undergoes atrophy clinically manifested as keratoconjunctivitis sicca and xerostomia. The appearance of new lymphoid germinal follicles in the parotid gland may represent reversion to an embryonic status, since normal fetal parotid tissue at the time of birth contains lymphoid germinal follicles which normally involute later (Fichtelius, 1968). A similar pathogenesis probably dominates the course of Hashimoto's thyroiditis and of myasthenia gravis. In the former disease, the thyroid gland undergoes atrophy, as it is heavily infiltrated by lymphocytes and plasma cells. Hashimoto's thyroiditis with the formation of new lymphoid germinal centers occurs in Sjögren's syndrome (Shulman and Harvey, 1964). In myasthenia gravis, thymic tumors consisting of lymphoid follicles, lymphorrhages (large pools of lymphocytes among muscle fibers), antimuscle globulins, and sarcolemma degenerations occur; probably, antibody action at the myoneural junction causes the major biochemical defects (Simpson, 1966). In systemic lupus erythematosus, the kidney and liver parenchyma may be infiltrated by lymphocytes and plasma cells, but the major pathological process is vasculitis involving both arteries and veins. The diverse clinical picture of systemic lupus erythematosus is the result of the varied sites where arteritis is the most severe. As a rule, glomerulitis commonly occurs. It has been postulated that complexes of antigens, whether cellular or viral in origin, and globulins directed against these antigens, precipitate in the basement membrane of the glomerulus, as well as in the vascular endothelium. The complexes consume complement and inflict severe cell damage (Dixon, 1968; Koffler, Schur, and Kunkel, 1967). The lupus cell consists of a semiautolysed cell nucleus, opsonized by antinuclear globulin and phagocytized by one or more polymorphonuclear leukocytes. Several autoimmune processes, such as relapsing panniculitis (Macoul, 1967), thrombotic thrombocytopenic purpura (Levine and Shearn, 1964), Sjögren's syndrome, diffuse pulmonary fibrosis known as Hamman-Rich syndrome (which is associated with hyperglobulinemia, splenomegaly, and eosinophilia), and drug reactions (most notoriously to treatment with hydralazine) may exhibit the in vitro lupus cell phenomenon (Dubois, 1966; Gahagan, 1965). Another group of autoimmune diseases is characterized mainly by vasculitis. In polyarteritis nodosa, a delayed hypersensitivity-type reaction destroys the vascular endothelium, evoking large inflammatory cellular infiltrations (Fordham, Epstein, Huffines, and Harrington, 1964). Malignant disease may be associated with extensive polyarteritis (Case Records of the Massachusetts General Hospital, 1957). These inflammatory reactions assume a chronic granulomatous and necrotizing appearance in Wegener's granulomatosis with major involvement in the upper and lower respiratory tract and in the glomeruli; hyperglobulinemia also occurs (Berman, Rydell, and Eichenholz, 1963). Progressive systemic sclerosis, or scleroderma, is characterized by little inflammatory reaction and by hypertrophy, swelling, and condensation of collagen; the formation of dense fibroblastic connective tissue, which is a late reparative event in chronic inflammation, leads to atrophy of epidermis, skeletal and smooth muscle, and myocardium. Fibrinoid necrosis of the small arteries produces ischemic parenchymal changes (Tuffanelli and Winkelman, 1962).

Rheumatic fever, poststreptococcal glomerulonephritis, allergic demyelinating encephalopathies, and those allergic angiopathies and purpuras that have an identifiable chemical or biological etiological agent resemble in many respects the various pathological and clinical manifestations of autoimmune diseases.

The pathogenesis of autoimmune diseases encompasses the whole spectrum of immunological faculties, alone or in combination (Table 1). The same immunological faculties may be recognized in cases of hyperacute, chronic, cell-mediated, or antibody-facilitated homograft rejections. A further important feature of autoimmune diseases is immunological deficiency, as tested with exogenous antigens. Anergy and defective thymus-dependent immune reactions in Hodgkin's disease (Aisenberg, 1966), impaired reactivity to blastogenic stimuli of lymphocytes deriving from patients with Hodgkin's disease and Sjögren's syndrome (Hersh and Oppenheim, 1965; Leventhal, Waldorf, and Talal, 1967), and other related diseases have been demonstrated. Still another feature of these pathological entities, as it occurs in immune deficiency syndromes, too, is an increased incidence of malignant diseases. Most malignant diseases occur, however, without signs of overt immune deficiency or autoimmune diseases; thus, the combination of autoimmune and malignant diseases is rare and unusual.

AUTOIMMUNE AND MALIGNANT DISEASES

Malignant diseases following or coinciding with autoimmune diseases may be divided into four categories: (1) carcinoma of the parenchyma that appears to be the target of an autoimmune attack, (2) lymphoreticular malignant diseases probably represented by the progeny of the autoimmune lymphoid cell clones, (3) malignant diseases of the lymphoreticular system without a well-defined malignant cell type and with an increased incidence of carcinoma of various organs other than those involved in autoimmune reactions, and (4) malignant diseases followed by "autoimmune" reactions. Examples of the first group are carcinoma of the stomach following autoimmune gastric atrophy and pernicious anemia (Hitchcock, Maclean, and Sullivan, 1957; Irvine, Davies, Delamore, and William, 1962), and carcinoma of the colon following ulcerative colitis (Weckesser and Chinn, 1953; Wright and Truelove, 1966). The pathological mechanism of carcinogenesis in the organs exposed to immunological attack is not known, but the demonstration of chromosomal damage in connective tissue cells in vitro by immunologically aggressive lymphocytes may provide an explanation (Fialkow, 1967). However, chronic inflammatory processes of different types, such as genitourinary schistosomiasis, are known to promote carcinogenesis; thus, the pathomechanism may not necessarily require "autoimmunity."

The second group is most remarkable because it is not the target

TABLE 1. *Autoimmune Diseases of Man*

Autoantibody
    Hemolytic anemia
    Idiopathic thrombocytopenic purpura
Autoantibody with leukocytic reaction
    Rheumatoid arthritis
Autoantibody with immune complex vasculitis
    Systemic lupus erythematosus
Autoantibody with delayed hypersensitivity
    Rheumatoid nodule
    Hashimoto's thyroiditis
    Sjögren's syndrome
    Lupoid hepatitis
    Myasthenia gravis
Delayed hypersensitivity
    Sarcoidosis
    Hodgkin's disease
Delayed hypersensitivity with vasculitis
    Polyarteritis nodosa
    Wegener's granulomatosis
Postinflammatory reparative sclerosis
    Progressive systemic sclerosis
    Hodgkin's disease

organs of the autoimmune attack, but the attacking immunological faculties that undergo malignant transformation. Sjögren's syndrome is not known to be associated with parotid or lacrimal gland carcinoma, but with lymphoreticular neoplasia. Reticulum cell sarcoma, malignant lymphoma, and pseudolymphoma arise in the parotid gland or elsewhere in patients with this autoimmune disease (Abramson, Goodman, and Kolodny, 1968; Bunim *et al.*, 1964; Hornbaker, Foster, Williams, and Davis, 1966; Talal and Bunim, 1964; Talal, Sokoloff, and Barth, 1967). In a patient with long-lasting myasthenia gravis, chronic lymphocytic leukemia with autoimmune hemolytic anemia developed (Cohen and Waxman, 1967). Hashimoto's thyroiditis is seldom considered the initiating factor of thyroid carcinoma (Lindsay, 1960), and most inflammatory reactions seen in carcinomatous thyroid glands are secondary in nature. However, lymphosarcoma of the thyroid gland is known to follow Hashimoto's thyroiditis (Fujimoto, Suzuki, Abe, and Brooks, 1967; Talal and Bunim, 1964; Woolner, McConahey, and Beahrs, 1959). In patients with rheumatoid arthritis or systemic lupus erythematosus, the synovial membrane, vascular endothelium, liver, or kidney parenchyma do not undergo malignant transformation (Duthie *et al.*, 1964); however, lymphosarcoma, reticulum cell sarcoma, and Hodgkin's disease may develop (Cammarata, Rodnan, and Jensen, 1963).

In the third category, the pathogenesis of Hodgkin's disease remains an unsolved puzzle. Patients tested with exogenous antigens are deficient in delayed hypersensitivity reactions and sometimes in primary antibody response (Aisenberg, 1966; Miller, 1965), but the clinical and pathological picture of the disease resembles that of chronic inflammatory diseases and delayed hypersensitivity reactions. It has been likened to runt or homologous disease (Smithers, 1967). It is difficult to define the malignant cells in Hodgkin's disease, for the cells that make up the tumors appear inflammatory and reparatory rather than malignant. Hodgkin's disease may represent a lack of self-tolerance by the thymus-dependent lymphoid system, a feature normally acquired during fetal life: delayed sensitivity-type reactions are carried out against the host but not against exogenous pathogens. It may also be surmised that normal components of the thymic- and gut-associated lymphoid systems attempt to reject the autoaggressive immune faculties. The significant increase in the incidence of second primary malignant tumors in patients with malignant lymphoma, chronic lymphocytic leukemia, and Hodgkin's disease has recently been reviewed (Miller, 1968). Termination of Hodgkin's disease in monocytic, lymphocytic, and myelogenous leukemia (Lacher and Sussman, 1963; Oberfield, 1966; Tornyos, Macossay, and Györkey, 1967), and the association of systemic lupus erythematosus with leukemia (Deaton and Levin, 1967) are of great interest; in these cases, malignant transformation of the entire hematopoietic and lymphoreticular system takes place in succession. A patient with Hodgkin's disease developed 21 tumors of four histologic types; this patient showed normal lymphocytic reaction to phytohemagglutinin (PHA) but had a defective immunoglobulin A (IgA) system (Whitelaw, 1968).

Thus, the immunosuppressed status, whether the result of an inherent disorder of the immune system or of treatment with immunosuppressive drugs, permits or evokes the arising of malignant tumors. Immunosuppressive treatment may cause immunocompetent recipients of tissue transplants to become susceptible to tumors; when this occurs, the type of tumor most commonly found (malignant lymphoma) originates in the suppressed lymphoreticular system (Doak, Montgomerie, North, and Smith, 1968). It has been suggested that most malignant diseases of the lymphoreticular system are "immunoproliferative" and result from accumulation of lymphoid cells reacting to undefined stimulation (Dameshek, 1967a and 1967b).

The fourth category of malignant and autoimmune diseases is represented by a large number of disorders, such as arthritis, thrombophlebitis migrans, acanthosis nigricans, *etc.*; of these, hemolytic anemia, positive according to the Coombs' test, as most commonly seen with chronic lymphocytic leukemia (Geller, 1964), leukoencephalopathy, dermatomyositis, and nephrosis, may be of "autoimmune" origin. Dermatomyositis antedated and demyelinating encephalopathy followed the onset of Hodgkin's disease in one case (Deep, Fraumeni, Tashima, and McDivitt, 1964). Arthritis clinically resembling rheumatoid joint disease preceding or following malignant disease was described (Strandberg and Jarlov, 1961). The nephrotic syndrome associated with tumors (Lee, Yamauchi, and Hopper, 1966), especially that occurring in patients with lymphoreticular malignant diseases (Brodovski, Samuels, Migliore, and Howe, 1968), may be caused by immune complex glomerulitis, since complexes of tumor antigens with antibodies are deposited in the glomeruli (Lee, Yamauchi, and Hopper, 1966). An in vitro phenomenon, probably of autoimmune type, is the destruction of fibroblast-like cells upon contact with autochthonous lymphocytes deriving from patients with leukemia and lymphoma (Sinkovics, 1962b; Sinkovics, Howe, and Shullenberger, 1964).

CASE HISTORIES

The following brief case histories illustrate the lack of overt immune defect or autoimmune disease in a patient with three primary carcinomas, some characteristics of autoimmune diseases, and the overlap of autoimmune and malignant diseases.

Case 1. A 61-year-old woman was admitted in 1967 because of rectal adenocarcinoma. She had had radical mastectomy followed by radiotherapy in 1953 for carcinoma of the right breast. The uterus was removed in 1959 because of fibroid adenoma. The bone survey revealed widespread osteoblastic metastases. The patient died with massive pulmonary embolization 12 days after a partial sigmoid resection. Preterminally, anemia, leukopenia, and thrombocytopenia developed, probably because of massive replacement of bone marrow by tumor. Upper gastrointestinal tract candidiasis set in before death. Autopsy revealed, in addition, mixed papillary and follicular thyroid carcinoma and adenomatous colonic polyps. The breast carcinoma had metastasized widely to bones, spleen, and adrenals.

Comment: Multiple primary malignant tumors may occur without clinically evident immune defects or autoimmune diseases; however, this patient was not studied specifically for possible immune deficiencies before the terminal phase of her disease.

Case 2. A 35-year-old woman was admitted in 1965 for arthritis and recurrent swelling of the parotid glands. The result of the latex rheumatoid

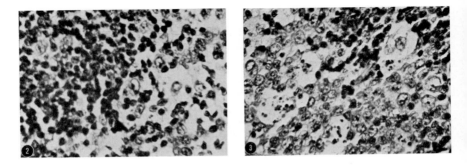

FIGURE 2. Section of new lymphoid follicle in parotid gland showing germinal center and cuff of small lymphocytes from a patient with Sjögren's syndrome. Reduced from × 54 oil immersion objective and × 10 ocular.

FIGURE 3. Increased activity of phagocytic histiocytes within new lymphoid germinal center in parotid gland from a patient with Sjögren's syndrome. Reduced from × 54 oil immersion objective and × 10 ocular.

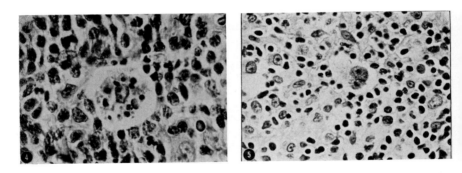

FIGURE 4. Phagocytic histiocyte in newly formed lymphoepithelial structures in parotid gland from a case of Sjögren's syndrome. Reduced from × 70 oil immersion objective and × 10 ocular.

FIGURE 5. Section of lymph node from a case of Hodgkin's disease complicated by autoimmune hemolytic anemia; Reed-Sternberg cell is present. Reduced from × 54 oil immersion objective and × 10 ocular.

arthritis test was 4+ and the result of the latex antithyroid globulin test was negative. Surgical biopsy of the parotid gland revealed extensive lymphocytic infiltration consistent with Sjögren's syndrome (Figures 2 and 3).

Case 3. A 66-year-old man was referred to our hospital in 1960 with epigastric discomfort. Gastric atrophy was found. In 1967, xerostomia developed. The salivary glands were enlarged; the small joints of the hands were painful, and several episodes of Raynaud's phenomenon occurred. Biopsy revealed a benign lymphoepithelial proliferation of the salivary glands (Figure 4). The amount of globulins was elevated in polyclonal fashion and the rheumatoid factor was positive.

Case 4. A 33-year-old man was admitted in 1968 for an emergency decompressive laminectomy because of paraplegia. Six years earlier he had idiopathic thrombocytopenic purpura. He was hypertensive and azotemic. Kidney biopsy showed fulminant glomerulitis. Hyperglobulinemia and positive lupus cell phenomenon were present. Immunosuppressive treatment with corticosteroids, nitrogen mustard, and cyclophosphamide was not effective. At autopsy, the severe, widespread vasculitis characteristic of systemic lupus erythematosus was found (Sinkovics, Györkey, and Thoma, 1969).

Case 5. A 24-year-old woman developed systemic Hodgkin's disease in 1959 (Figure 5). Treatment with corticosteroids and X-irradiation resulted in considerable improvement. In 1962, hypersplenism with hemolytic anemia, leukopenia, and thrombocytopenia occurred. Clinical improvement occurred after splenectomy. In 1965, mediastinal lymphadenopathy, pleural effusion, jaundice, and severe pancytopenia with hypoglobulinemia developed. Septicemia with *Alkalescens dispar* set in. Prednisone, gamma globulin, kanamycin, and chloramphenicol were given, as was a short course of cyclophosphamide. The patient died; the husband refused to permit an autopsy.

Comment: It appeared that fever and pancytopenia occurred during active phases of Hodgkin's disease; as X-ray therapy eliminated the involved cervical lymph nodes, fever and pancytopenia subsided. As Hodgkin's disease recurred in other areas (*i.e.* spleen), "autoimmune" features reappeared. After splenectomy, the patient again improved; massive involvement of the mediastinal lymph nodes by Hodgkin's disease elicited the final and terminal phase of pancytopenia and lymphoreticular tissue depletion.

Case 6. A 46-year-old woman developed skin rash and arthritis in 1960. Muscle biopsy established the diagnosis of polyarteritis. Corticosteroids were given. In 1962, pruritic skin lesions developed. The biopsy revealed lesions resembling those of mycosis fungoides. Early in 1963, left axillary lymphadenopathy was found; the histology was compatible with mixed granuloma-type Hodgkin's disease. Cyclophosphamide was added to the corticosteroid regimen. Later in 1963, anemia ensued and bone marrow biopsy revealed myelosclerosis and atypical reticulum cells. In December 1963, gum hypertrophy and pharyngeal ulceration were noted. The blood count showed 166,-000 white cells per mm^3 with 6 per cent monocytes, 53 per cent blast cells, 40 per cent promonocytes, 1 per cent lymphocytes. The hemaglobin varied from 3 to 6.8 g per 100 ml. The platelet count was 3,000 per mm^3. Purinethol and transfusions were given. The white blood cell count dropped to 4,000 per

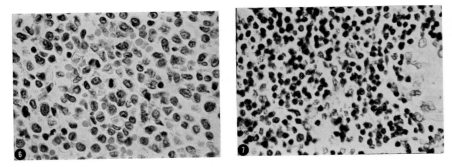

FIGURE 6. Section of the spleen of a patient who died after Hodgkin's disease was replaced by acute myelomonocytic leukemia. Reduced from × 54 oil immersion objective and × 10 ocular.

FIGURE 7. New lymphoid follicle with germinal center and cuff of small lymphocytes in the thyroid gland of a patient with Hashimoto's thyroiditis and histiocytic reticulum cell sarcoma of the thyroid. Reduced from × 54 oil immersion objective and × 10 ocular.

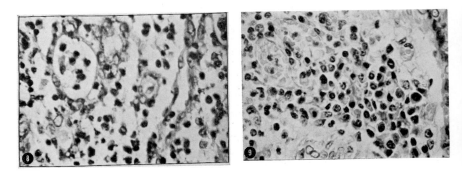

FIGURE 8. Lymphoreticular cells showing numerous mitotic forms in a case of Hashimoto's thyroiditis and histiocytic reticulum cell sarcoma of the thyroid. Reduced from × 54 oil immersion objective and × 10 ocular.

FIGURE 9. Lymphoid cells infiltrating the wall of colon in a case of ulcerative colitis. Reduced from × 54 oil immersion objective and × 10 ocular.

mm³ with 84 per cent promonocytes. The patient died because of cerebellar hemorrhage. Autopsy findings were compatible with those of monocytic or myelomonocytic leukemia (Figure 6).

Case 7. A 42-year-old woman who had been taking corticosteroids for severe crippling rheumatoid arthritis for 10 years developed ductal cell carcinoma and rhabdomyosarcoma of the left breast. After mastectomy, the rhabdomyosarcoma metastasized to both lungs. Treatment with vincristine and cyclophosphamide failed and the patient died.

Case 8. A 58-year-old man had thyroidectomy in 1967 because of a nodule in the right lobe of the gland. The histology revealed histiocytic reticulum cell sarcoma and marked thyroiditis in both lobes (Figures 7 and 8). Eight months after surgical therapy, the patient showed no recurrence or generalization of the tumor.

Case 9. A 74-year-old woman was admitted in July 1967 because of an obstructive lesion of the large intestine. The left para-aortic nodes showed typical Hodgkin's disease with Reed-Sternberg cells. The colonic lesion was a mucin-producing adenocarcinoma infiltrating the bladder dome and small intestines. The patient was seen with colostomy functioning well in August 1968.

Case 10. A 48-year-old woman was admitted for total colectomy with permanent ileostomy because of ulcerative colitis of 4 years duration. Chronic ulcerative colitis with pseudopolyps and no neoplastic lesions were found (Figure 9).

Case 11. A 51-year-old woman had had ulcerative colitis for 20 years and had been treated periodically with corticosteroids. In 1965, she was admitted for colonic resection because of adenocarcinoma. In 1968, the tumor recurred and total colectomy was performed (Figure 10).

Case 12. A 46-year-old man was admitted in 1957 because of episodes of nasal bleeding and discharge. His general condition was good; there was no hypertension, the serology was negative, and the urinary sediment was normal. The blood count and serum proteins were also normal. Biopsies revealed a chronic granulomatous inflammatory lesion in the nasopharynx negative for fungi and acid-fast bacilli in specifically stained sections and in culture. Repeated nasopharyngeal biopsies showed an unclassified malignant tumor with histologic pattern compatible with malignant lymphoma or pleomorphic reticulum cell sarcoma (Figure 11). Retroperitoneal lymph node metastases, hepatomegaly, jaundice, and ascites developed followed by anemia, leukopenia, and thrombocytopenia. Corticosteroids were given in large doses. The patient died in a hemorrhagic shock; permission for autopsy was denied.

Murine Autoimmune Disease and Malignant Lymphoreticular Tumors

Murine lymphoma and related neoplasms provide a good insight

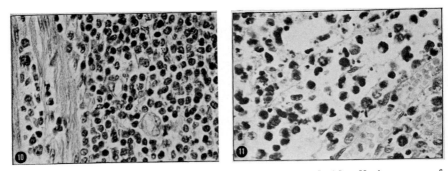

FIGURE 10. Heavy infiltration of the colon by lymphoid cells in a case of ulcerative colitis associated with adenocarcinoma of the colon (not shown). Reduced from × 54 oil immersion objective and × 10 ocular.

FIGURE 11. Malignant lymphoreticular cell proliferation in nasopharyngeal lesion first appearing as granulomatous disease. Reduced from × 54 oil immersion objective and × 10 ocular.

into the immunosuppressive, autoimmune, and malignant features of lymphoreticular tumors.

PLASMACYTIC TUMORS

BALB/c mice were shown to develop plasma cell neoplasms after intraperitoneal injection of paraffin oil adjuvant with or without heat-killed bacteria (Potter and MacCardle, 1964). A methylcholanthrene-induced plasmacytoma of C3H mice yielded, after passages in BALB/c mice, a virus which caused lymphocytic leukemia in newborn BALB/c mice (Breyere, Moloney, and Jordan, 1966). Hemolytic anemia positive according to the Coombs' test, paraproteinemia, and generalized amyloidosis were induced in mice inoculated with cell-free material deriving from plasma cell neoplasms (Rask-Nielsen, 1963; Rask-Nielsen, McIntire, and Ebbesen, 1968).

LUPUS-LIKE AUTOIMMUNE DISEASE AND MALIGNANT LYMPHOMA

The New Zealand black (NZB) mice develop new lymphoid germinal follicles in the thymus (Burnet and Holmes, 1964). Burnet postulated that autoimmune "forbidden clones" of lymphoid cells are formed here (Burnet, 1958). Coombs' positive hemolytic anemia, the lupus erythematosus cell phenomenon, lymphoreticular hyperplasia, and immune-complex glomerulonephritis follow (East, de Sousa, and Parrott, 1965). The autoimmune disease terminates as malignant lymphoma (East and de Sousa, 1966). Immunosuppressive treatment with azathioprine of the autoimmune phase results in accelerated onset of malignant lymphoma (Casey, 1968). NZB mice carry type C virus particles morphologically identical with other known murine leukemia viruses (East, Prosser, Holborow, and Jaquet, 1967; Mellors and Huang, 1966; Yumoto and Dmochowski, 1968). The disease complex of NZB mice was transferred entirely or in part with virus into recipient Swiss mice (Mellors and Huang, 1967).

RUNT (HOMOLOGOUS) DISEASE—ITS ASSOCIATION WITH MALIGNANT LYMPHOMA

The graft-*versus*-host reaction, initiated in an immunologically compromised recipient by immunocompetent donor cells, consists of proliferation and atrophy of lymphoreticular tissue; in addition, Coombs' positive hemolytic anemia, and dermatitis, enteritis, hepatitis, and runting occur (McBride, 1966). The pathogenesis of runt (homologous) disease is not clear. The initiation of the syndrome is clearly immunological, but, as lymphoid depletion proceeds, nonspecific symptoms and signs arise; passenger viruses of mice may initiate runting syndromes (Sinkovics and Howe, 1964).

When newborn mice were injected with immunocompetent cells of mice differing in a weak histocompatibility H-1 locus, no overt runt disease was seen; however, an increased incidence of malignant lymphomas was later observed in the recipients (Walford, 1966; Walford and Hildemann, 1965). F_1 hybrid mice injected with parental spleen cells develop both acute fatal and chronic runt (homologous) disease. In chronically runted mice, autoimmune hemolytic anemia, disorganization of the lymphoreticular structures, and malignant lymphoma developed. The malignant cells were of host, rather than donor, origin; upon serial passage, some tumors elicited runt (allogeneic) disease in the host (Schwartz, André-Schwartz, Armstrong and Beldotti, 1966; Schwartz and André-Schwartz, 1968).

CHRONIC VIRUS INFECTION WITH RUNT DISEASE AND MALIGNANT LYMPHOMA

Lymphocytic choriomeningitis virus was shown to elicit a chronic disease in mice characterized by wasting and immune complex-type glomerulonephritis (Hotchin and Collins, 1964). It was postulated and experimentally proved that the parenchyma acquires virus antigens to which the lymphoreticular system immunologically responds, causing delayed sensitivity-type tissue destruction; thymectomy and antilymphocyte serum abolish this immune reaction (Levey *et al.*, 1963; Földes *et al.*, 1965; Rowe, Black, and Levey, 1963; Volkert and Lundstedt, 1968). In this case, the lymphoreticular system may be considered normal and the parenchyma antigenically abnormal. It would be interesting to know the exact incidence of lymphoreticular and other malignant diseases in mice with chronic lymphocytic choriomeningitis infection and autoimmune late disease.

Mice with chronic reovirus 3 infection become runted and display a multiplicity of chronic inflammatory reactions; no infectious reovirus can be isolated from such mice. Spleen cells of chronically runted mice caused malignant lymphoma in one isologous mouse, and a cell passage line of this lymphoma was established. This murine lymphoma clinically and pathologically resembles Burkitt's tumor in man (Stanley and Keast, 1967). The lymphoma cells do not manufacture mature virus particles of either the mouse leukemia virus or the reovirus type; a reovirus type 3-specific antigen is detectable on the lymphoma cells. It has been suggested that reovirus can transform normal lymphoid cells into both autoimmune and malignant clones (Keast and Papadimitriou, 1966; Stanley and Keast, 1967).

Experimental Leads to Murine Autoimmune and Malignant Lymphoreticular Diseases

An important area of leukemia research, the association of murine lymphoma with autoimmune processes, has not as yet been systematically studied in our laboratory. Several observations relevant to this association have been made during the past eight years; however, these observations cannot be regarded as more than leads in need of further experimental pursuit.

LYMPHOID CELLS OF HOMOLOGOUS IMMUNE ACTIVITY IN A MURINE LYMPHOMA—TRANSFER OF AUTOIMMUNE HEMOLYTIC ANEMIA WITH CELL-FREE MATERIAL

In 1960, murine leukemic lymphoblasts deriving from short-term tissue cultures were inoculated into newborn noninbred Swiss mice of the strain in which the lymphoma originated. Both runt (homologous) disease and malignant lymphoma occurred in the recipients. The runt disease was accompanied by hemolytic anemia positive to the Coombs' test, and spleen cells of some mice with runt disease caused malignant lymphoma at the site of inoculation upon transfer into newborn mice. Cell-free extracts of the lymphoma occasionally caused autoimmune hemolytic anemia followed by lymphocytic leukemia (Sinkovics, 1962a, 1962c, 1963). Glomerulitis occurred in these mice but was not recognized at the time these experiments were performed.

SPLENIC AND THYMIC ATROPHY IN MICE CARRYING A LYMPHOSARCOMA

In 1964, in vivo and in vitro cell passage lines of a murine lymphosarcoma were established. The in vivo line grows in the form of large noninvasive lymphoblastic tumors. Mice bearing early passages of this tumor often showed depletion in the thymus, lymph nodes, and spleen (Sinkovics *et al.*, 1968). In classical murine runt (homologous) disease caused by a foreign immunocompetent graft, there is lymphatic depletion comparable to that which occurred in the murine lymphoma in question. This murine lymphoma shows the "starry sky" histological pattern comparable to that exhibited by Burkitt's tumor (Butler, Szakacs, and Sinkovics, 1967) and may characterize any lymphoma in which histoincompatibility between host macrophages and neoplastic lymphoblasts exists. Type C murine leukemia virus particles budding from leukemic lymphocytes may provide the foreign antigenic stimulus (Szakacs *et al.*, 1968).

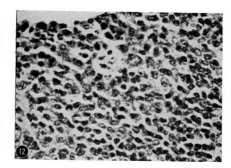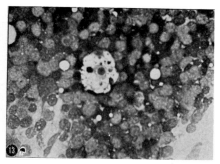

FIGURE 12. The hypercellular spleen of mice immunized with complete Freund's adjuvant; increased activity of phagocytic histiocytes. Reduced from × 54 oil immersion objective and × 10 ocular.

FIGURE 13. Print preparation of a malignant lymphoma occurring four months after inoculation of live spleen cells from donors immunized with Freund's adjuvant. Sheets of lymphoblasts are interspersed by phagocytic histiocytes. Reduced from × 70 oil immersion objective and × 10 ocular.

RUNT DISEASE AND LYMPHOMA OCCURRING AFTER TRANSFER OF SPLEEN
CELLS OF MICE IMMUNIZED WITH FREUND'S ADJUVANT

In 1964, noninbred low-leukemia Swiss mice were actively immunized with murine leukemia viruses. One control group received three intraperitoneal injections of complete Freund's adjuvant only. Sterile fibrinous peritonitis with emigration of macrophages, splenomegaly, and wasting developed in two mice. Five million viable spleen cells from these mice were inoculated intravenously into each of eight newborn Swiss mice of the same line. A severe but nonfatal runt disease occurred in half of the recipients (Sinkovics and Howe, 1965). The same number of live spleen cells derived from normal Swiss donors of this line failed to cause runt disease and lymphoma. Runted mice showed anemia and leukopenia. Of the eight littermates, three developed malignant lymphoma after four to six months of incubation in the group given spleen cells from donors immunized with Freund's adjuvant (Figures 12 and 13).

This experiment suggests autoimmunization of mice injected with Freund's adjuvant and the capacity of the autoimmune cell clones to initiate both autoimmune and malignant lymphoreticular diseases in newborn recipients. However, mice with virus-induced leukemias were kept in the same room during this experiment.

RUNT DISEASE AND LYMPHOMA IN MICE AFTER INFECTION WITH AN
ATTENUATED MOUSE LEUKEMIA VIRUS

A long-term tissue culture line harboring leukemia virus of decreased leukemogenic but good immunizing potency was established (Sinkovics, Groves, Bertin, and Shullenberger, 1969). Fluid harvested from this culture and inoculated into newborn mice of the same line caused a wasting syndrome. Passage of spleen cells of runted suckling mice resulted in the development of runting, hemolytic anemia, and malignant lymphoma in recipient mice of the same line inoculated at birth (Sinkovics et al., 1968). Since runting is a nonspecific response of conventional newborn mice to various deleterious agents, both infectious and hormonal, and it may be stress related (Heim, Martinez, and Good, 1967; Keast and Walters, 1968; Reed and Jutila, 1965), the observation of runting alone does not allow formation of the conclusion that autoimmunity was followed by lymphoma formation. The likelihood that a not fully virulent mouse leukemia virus could first initiate autoimmune and, later, malignant lymphoid cell clones, however, deserves further experimental pursuit (Sinkovics, 1967b).

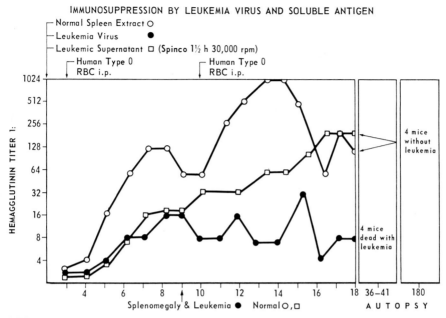

FIGURE 14. Good primary and secondary hemagglutinin response in mice pretreated with normal mouse spleen extract. Depressed primary and secondary hemagglutinin response in mice pretreated with leukemic mouse spleen extract. Depressed primary and delayed secondary hemagglutinin response in mice pretreated with "soluble antigens" of leukemia virus.

IMMUNOSUPPRESSION BY LEUKEMIA VIRUS—THE EFFECT OF SOLUBLE ANTIGENS

Before Jerne's classical hemolytic plaque assay was available, production of antibody to human O-type red blood cells by preleukemic and leukemic mice was studied by testing the blood serum of individual mice for agglutinins (Figure 14). Mice inoculated with Rauscher's leukemia virus showed decreased hemagglutinin production, both in the primary and secondary responses. However, it was shown in 1965 that soluble viral antigens also exerted immunosuppressive action, in that the primary response was depressed and the secondary response was comparable to a primary response (Sinkovics, unpublished data). Immunodepression of mice inoculated with leukemia viruses has been amply documented utilizing hemolytic plaque assay and 2-mercaptoethanol treatment of sera for demonstration of decreased 7S and 19S antibody production, and skin grafting for demonstration of impaired delayed sensitivity reactions

(Ceglowski and Friedman, 1968; Cremer, Taylor, and Hagens, 1966; Dent, Peterson, and Good, 1965; Friedman and Ceglowski, 1968; Metcalf and Moulds, 1967; Peterson, Hendrickson, and Good, 1963; Salaman, 1968). Leukemia virus carrier preleukemic mice were also found in the state of immunosuppression, but spleen cells of young NZB mice were able to induce graft-*versus*-host reaction in NZB×A F_1 hybrids (Stutman, Yunis, and Good, 1968).

AN EARLY ASSAULT ON THE LYMPHORETICULAR SYSTEM—ITS EFFECT ON LEUKEMOGENESIS

A number of interventions are known to alter the hematopoietic and immunological homeostasis. Erythroagglutinin-free phytohemagglutinin (PHA) exerts a mitogenic effect on splenic cells of intravenously injected adult mice. Initially, lymphocytopoiesis, erythropoiesis, and granulocytopoiesis are stimulated; five days later, numerous lymphoid cells die. Finally, antibody production to PHA occurs (Gamble, 1966). The effects of PHA on the immunologic homeostasis are controversial. Both suppression of graft-*versus*-host reaction by treatment of donors with PHA (Marcus, Rigas, and Siegel, 1968) and decreased resistance to a mouse lymphoma (Hirano, Sinkovics, Shullenberger, and Howe, 1967) were observed. It has been suggested that PHA is immunosuppressive when given intraperitoneally, but is immunostimulating when given intravenously (Elves, 1968). However, pokeweed mitogen injected intraperitoneally into newborn hamsters prevented oncogenesis by adenovirus type 12. An accelerated maturation of immunological competence was postulated (Haase, Kasel, and Chessin, 1968).

Intravenous inoculation of *Bordetella pertussis* vaccine into adult mice evokes a hyperleukocytosis consisting mainly of lymphocytes; the germinal centers are depleted. A second injection meets with immunity and no leukocytosis follows (Morse, 1965). During the period of extreme lymphocytosis, mice exhibited decreased resistance to cell-transplanted lymphomas (Floersheim, 1967; Hirano, Sinkovics, Shullenberger, and Howe, 1967). Mice pretreated with pertussis vaccine failed to exhibit lymphoid cell proliferation upon challenge with PHA (Hirano, Sinkovics, Shullenberger, and Howe, 1967).

Incorporation of antigens into Freund's adjuvant elicits an increased immune response (Freund, 1951; Hilleman, 1966). The oily component of the adjuvant may cause plasmacytic neoplasms in susceptible mice (Potter and MacCardle, 1964). Mycobacteria, conversely, may convey increased resistance: *Bacillus Calmette-Guerin* delayed the onset of leukemia and mammary tumors in mice tolerant to the causative viruses of these neoplasms (Old *et al.*, 1961). Repeated injections of complete Freund's adjuvant prolonged the life of leukemic mice (Siegel and Morton, 1967). Administration of Freund's adjuvant before RSV (Rauscher, Fink and Kvedar, 1963) or murine lymphoma cells (Hirano, Sinkovics, Shullenberger, and Howe, 1967) increased susceptibility, whereas increased resistance to tumor growth occurred when the adjuvant was given after the oncogenic agents. A tumor growth-stimulating effect of Freund's adjuvant in mice injected with polyoma virus and in rats injected with RSV recently has been reported (Ter-Grigorov and Irlin, 1968). Complete Freund's adjuvant elicits profound histological changes in the thymus; plasma cells, new lymphoid follicles, and giant Hassal bodies infiltrated by granulocytes appear (Svet-Moldavsky and Raffkina, 1963). Other lymphoreticular structures evidently also undergo both morphological and functional alterations.

Patients receiving anticonvulsant preparations, especially diphenylhydantoin, occasionally develop lymphoreticular proliferative disorders closely resembling malignant lymphoma and Hodgkin's disease. The fatal outcome of some of these lymphoproliferative disorders indicates that they are malignant diseases rather than pseudolymphomas (Hyman and Sommers, 1966; Gams, Neal, and Conrad, 1968).

Methylether of cellulose in colloid suspension causes hypersplenism in rats with hemolytic anemia, nephrosis resulting from glomerular damage, hyperglobulinemia, and storage of the compound in the reticuloendothelial system (Benkö, 1958). Rats pretreated with methylcellulose show increased tumor rejections (Benkö and Tiboldi, 1959; Lazar, Hruban, Slesers, and Lazar, 1963). Splenectomy abolished the increased rate of tumor rejection in methylcellulose-pretreated rats (Lazar, Hruban, Slesers, and Lazar, 1963).

In a study recently initiated in our laboratory, the above agents were inoculated into newborn low-leukemia Timco Swiss and high-leukemia AKR mice with the expectation that an early assault on the ontogenesis of the hematopoietic and immune systems would alter late leukemogenesis.

Table 2 summarizes the pathological effects of PHA and pertussis vaccine after intravenous inoculation into newborn mice. It appears that PHA accelerates morphological immune maturation, because small lymphocytes in the thymic cortex and the splenic follicles appeared earlier than in untreated mice. However, the thymic and splenic architecture in mice given pertussis vaccine at birth remained immature; these organs were hypercellular and dominated by granulocytopoiesis. Exceptionally,

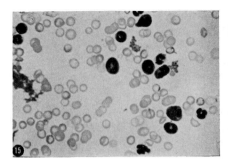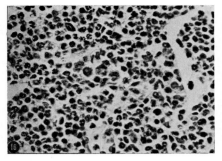

FIGURE 15. Blood film of 3-week-old mouse after receiving intravenous inoculation of pertussis vaccine at birth. Note clumps of platelets and large number of immature, mainly granulocytic, cells. Reduced from × 54 oil immersion objective and × 10 ocular.

FIGURE 16. Lymph node of 3-week-old mouse after receiving intravenous inoculation of pertussis vaccine at birth. Extensive granulocytopoiesis. Reduced from × 54 oil immersion objective and × 10 ocular.

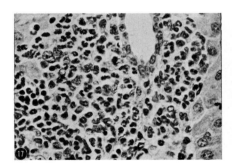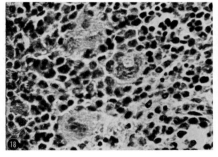

FIGURE 17. Liver of 3-week-old mouse after receiving intravenous inoculation of pertussis vaccine at birth. Large perivascular colony of granulocytes. Reduced from × 54 oil immersion objective and × 10 ocular.

FIGURE 18. Spleen of 3-week-old mouse after receiving intravenous inoculation of pertussis vaccine at birth. Note extensive granulocytopoiesis in red pulp and increased numbers of megakaryocytes. Reduced from × 70 oil immersion objective and × 10 ocular.

TABLE 2. *Early Assault on the Hematopoietic and Immune Faculties*

Agent	Effect
Phytohemagglutinin	Lymphocytopoiesis, lymphatic depletion, RD
Freund's complete adjuvant	Activation of RES
Pertussis vaccine	Granulocytopoiesis, thrombocythemia
Methylcellulose	Hypersplenism
Homologous disease*	Lymphatic atrophy, hepatitis, RD
Chimerism†	No adverse effect

* Spleen cells of adult C57BL mice injected intravenously into newborn AKR mice.
† Spleen and thymus cells of newborn C57BL mice injected intravenously into newborn AKR mice.
Abbreviations: RD, runt disease; RES, reticuloendothelial system.

a sustained leukemoid reaction and runting were observed (Figures 15 to 18). Runting occurred in 20 per cent of PHA-inoculated newborn AKR mice and was fatal in 25 per cent of the cases (Figure 19). Survivors of the runting syndrome showed splenic and thymic atrophy and anemia (Figure 20). Low-leukemia Timco Swiss newborn mice did not develop runting after inoculation with PHA. These runting syndromes were compared with homologous disease (Figures 21 to 23) caused by normal adult and PHA-pretreated adult C57BL spleen cells in newborn AKR mice (Table 3). A runting syndrome alone is not satisfactory proof of

TABLE 3. *Comparison of Runting Syndromes*

Organs altered	Agents used		
	PHA	Pertussis vaccine	Adult C57BL spleen cells
Thymus	Atrophy	Hypercellular, immature	Atrophy
Spleen	Atrophy	Extensive granulocyto-poiesis	Atrophy, phagocytic histiocytes
Lymph nodes	Atrophy	Extensive granulocyto-poiesis	Atrophy
Blood	Anemia; leukopenia	Granulocytosis; thrombo-cytosis	Anemia; leukopenia
Liver	Normal	Granulocytopoiesis	Necrosis; infiltrated by cells
Incidence*	20%	< 5%	>50%
Outcome	25% Fatal	<10% Fatal	>75% Fatal

* Dose dependent.
Abbreviation: PHA, phytohemagglutinin.

autoimmune reactions; agents causing lymphoid depletion in newborn mice are known to elicit runting. The Mikulska-Gorer and the Coombs' tests are being used in our laboratory in order to recognize autoantibody adsorbed to erythrocytes.

FIGURE 19. Four-week-old normal and runted A K R mice; runting occurred after intravenous inoculation of PHA at birth.

FIGURE 20. Splenic atrophy of AKR mouse with runt disease after intravenous inoculation of PHA at birth. Small lymphoid follicle without germinal center and hypocellular red pulp. Reduced from × 54 oil immersion objective and × 10 ocular.

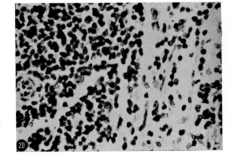

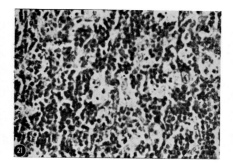 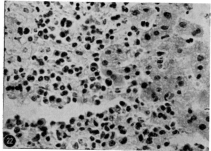

FIGURE 21. Increased number of phagocytic histiocytes in the spleen of runted AKR mouse inoculated at birth with viable spleen cells of adult C57BL mice. Reduced from $\times$ 54 oil immersion objective and $\times$ 10 ocular.

FIGURE 22. Infiltration of the liver by lymphoid cells and necrosis of the parenchyma in a runted AKR mouse inoculated at birth with viable spleen cells of adult C57BL mice. Reduced from $\times$ 54 oil immersion objective and $\times$ 10 ocular.

Survivors of mice pretreated at birth with the formerly described agents and with homologous cells deriving from the spleens of adult and newborn C57BL mice are under observation for leukemia incidence. It will be of great importance to learn the effects of the early and profound alterations in hematopoiesis and lymphopoiesis on leukemogenesis later. For instance newborn AKR mice inoculated with spleen and thymus cells of newborn C57BL mice might be chimeras, hosting both self-lymphoid cells prone to develop leukemia and donated lymphoid cells resistant to leukemogenesis. Since these experiments are three to four months old at this writing, no conclusions are yet possible. Mice pretreated with PHA, pertussis vaccine, and complete Freund's adjuvant at birth were challenged with murine lymphoma and sarcoma cells carrying leukemia virus and were compared with similarly challenged controls. The preliminary results are included in the Addendum.

IMMUNOCOMPETENCE OF MALIGNANT MURINE LYMPHOBLASTS

A suspension culture of lymphoblasts was established from the in vivo passages of a lymphosarcoma carried in Timco Swiss mice (Sinkovics *et al.*, 1968). The in vivo passage line consists of cells of diploid chromosomal sets, whereas cells of the established suspension culture display chromosomal sets in the tetraploid range. Lymphoblasts of the suspension culture (Figure 24) retain full pathogenicity causing lymphosarcoma

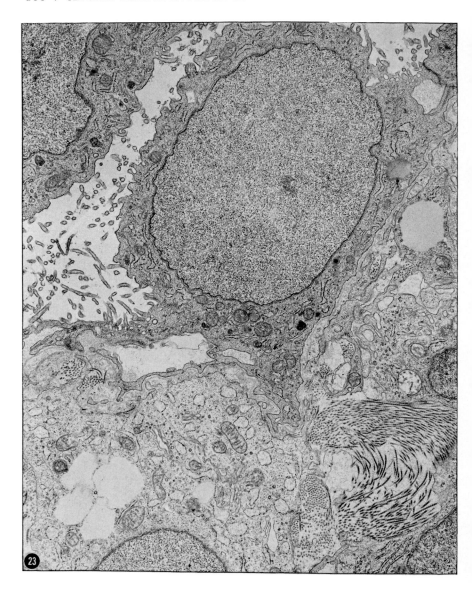

FIGURE 23. Dark lymphoid cell extends two cytoplasmic protrusions touching vacuolized liver cell in the liver of a runted AKR mouse inoculated at birth with viable spleen cells of adult C57BL mice. Reduced from electron optics × 5,500, final magnification × 27,500.

TABLE 4. *Neutralization of Rauscher Mouse Leukemia Virus by Globulins Isolated from Tissue Culture Medium*

Test material* (in dilutions)	Virus dilution†	No. mice	Average foci/spleen	Foci/ml	Per cent inhibition when compared with F-10 Medium
818–2 GG 1/2	$10^{-2.5}$	10	0.2	1.0	99.3
818–2 GG 1/4	$10^{-2.5}$	10	5.6	28.0	80.1
F-10 GG 1/2	$10^{-2.5}$	10	26.5	132.5	5.7
Mouse Anti-RMLV 1/5	$10^{-2.5}$	9	17.2	86.0	38.8
Rabbit Anti-RMLV 1/5	$10^{-2.5}$	10	0.7	3.5	97.5
Diluent	$10^{-2.5}$	10	17.0	85.0	39.5
F-10 Medium (undiluted)	$10^{-2.5}$	10	28.1	140.5	. . .

* Diluted and mixed with an equal volume of virus.

818–2 GG = Globulin fraction from culture 818 (culture 818 consists of lymphoblasts elaborating both mouse leukemia virus and globulin).

F-10 GG = Globulin fraction from F-10 medium (without 818 lymphoblasts).

† RMLV: Rauscher mouse leukemia virus.

in mice, release type C murine leukemia virus particles (Figure 25), and manufacture globulin molecules of the gamma 2a and gamma 1 classes (Trujillo *et al.*, 1970). It was of interest to study whether the globulins produced by these cells had any specific neutralizing effect on the leukemia virus particles. Globulin precipitated from spent medium of the suspension culture neutralized the Rauscher virus in a spleen focus assay (Table 4) (Pienta and Sinkovics, 1969).

The production of virus-neutralizing antibody in suspension cultures of these lymphoma cells may offer an explanation for the accumulation of immature virus particles within cytoplasmic vacuoles (Figure 26) (Ahearn and Sinkovics, 1969). This finding is similar to that observed

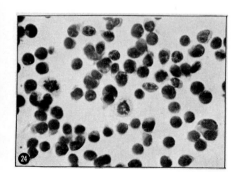

FIGURE 24. Suspension culture of malignant murine lymphoblasts. Reduced from × 54 oil immersion objective and × 10 ocular.

when Friend leukemia virus-producing tumor cells were grown in mice immune to Friend leukemia (Kobayashi, Kodama, and Takeda, 1966).

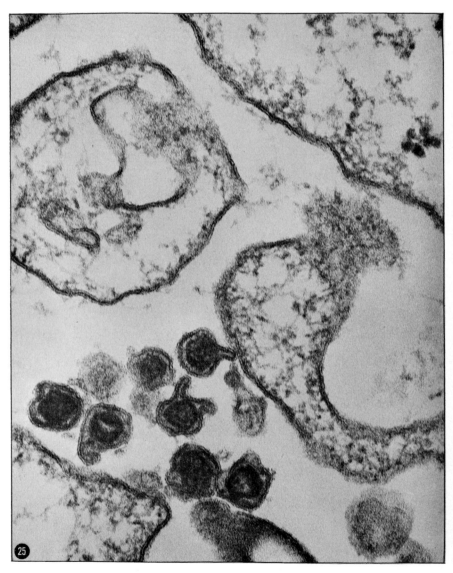

FIGURE 25. Group of extracellular murine leukemia virus particles in suspension culture of malignant murine lymphoblasts. Reduced from electron optics, × 250,000 final magnification.

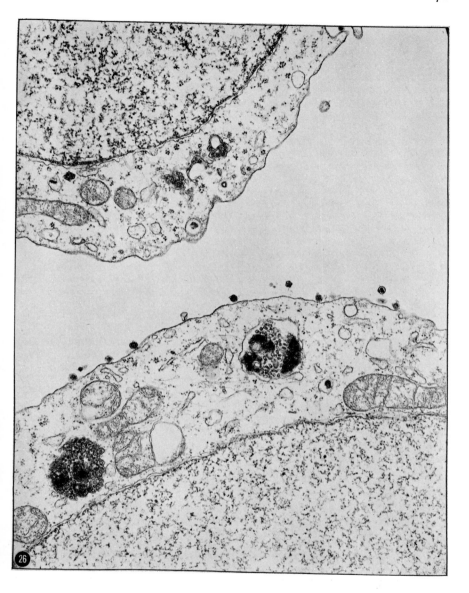

FIGURE 26. Mature extracellular and immature intracellular leukemia virus particles in suspension culture of malignant murine lymphoblasts. Intracellular particles appear degenerated and occur in cytoplasmic vesicles. Reduced from electron optics × 8,000, final magnification × 36,000.

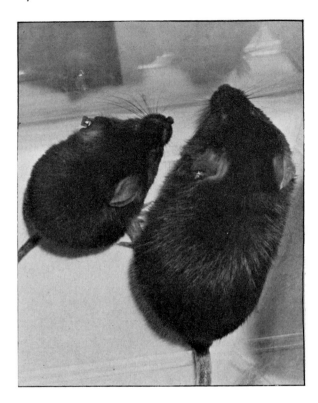

FIGURE 27. Four-week-old C57BL mice, one healthy and one runted. Runted mouse received cultured malignant Swiss mouse lymphoblasts at birth.

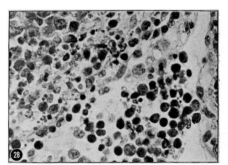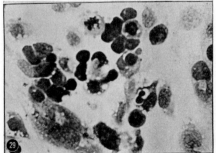

FIGURE 28. Growth of malignant Swiss mouse lymphoblasts in the liver of C57BL recipient; there is coagulation necrosis of the parenchyma. Reduced from × 54 oil immersion objective and × 10 ocular.

FIGURE 29. Vacuolization of monolayer cells grown from liver of C57BL mice upon contact with malignant Swiss mouse lymphoblasts harvested from the liver of other C57BL mice. Reduced from × 54 oil immersion objective and × 10 ocular.

Cultured lymphoblasts were inoculated into homologous newborn C57BL mice; extensive growth in the liver and in the mesenteric node occurred. Since runting and liver necrosis also occurred occasionally (Figures 27 and 28), and these are features of runt (homologous) disease (Arakawa *et al.*, 1966) but not of leukemia, an investigation of whether the lymphoma cells react immunologically to homologous liver cells was undertaken. Lymphoma cells recovered from C57BL mice were tested in Jerne's hemolytic plaque assay for hemolytic antibodies produced against C57BL erythrocytes. No antibodies could be shown. Lymphoma cells harvested from C57BL mice were placed on cultured liver cells of newborn C57BL mice. Extensive emperipolesis, interactions of lymphoblasts with macrophages, and vacuolization of C57BL cells occurred (Figure 29), but no cytopathic damage could be demonstrated clearly (Sinkovics and Shirato, 1969). Thus, exposure of malignant Timco Swiss lymphoblasts to homologous C57BL tissue antigens failed to elicit in the lymphoblasts an immune response that could be measured by the tests applied.

However, the elaboration of both leukemia virus and virus-neutralizing globulin molecules by these cells may endow these cells with a film of globulin molecules of self-antigenicity; the globulin presumably coats the viral surface antigens. Thus, on account of this "self-enhancing" antibody, rapid and extensive growth of these cells in the mouse line of origin may occur because recognition of nonself (viral) antigenicity by the tumor-bearing host is hindered. This finding explains why macrophages exercised defensive function against this lymphoma, whereas immune lymphocytes failed to do so (Sinkovics *et al.*, 1968; Szakacs *et al.*, 1968). Macrophages engulf opsonized foreign antigens, but lymphocytes may fail to recognize foreign antigens coated by self-globulin.

A Working Hypothesis Concerning Autoimmune and Malignant Lymphoreticular Cell Proliferations

It was shown that autoimmune diseases are accompanied by an immunosuppressed state and by increased incidence of malignant disease. It was also indicated that some immune reactions are directed by specific RNA transferred from cell to cell. The metagon concept may be inserted here. The M_1 and M_2 genes of stock 540 (Mexico) *Paramecium aurelia* exercise their function by RNA-containing cytoplasmic mediators called metagons. The cell characteristic controlled by these genes through the action of metagons is permissiveness toward bacterium-like symbiotic mu particles to reside in the cytoplasm. The possession of mu particles makes a paramecium "mate killer," *i.e.* conjugation with paramecia lacking mu particles results in death of the descendants of the sensitive paramecium. Metagons can be transferred from cell to cell and remain functional. Thus, a very important cell characteristic, tolerance toward a microorganism, can be regulated by a messenger RNA (mRNA)-like structure (Beale, 1964). Metagons from paramecia can be transmitted to *Didinium nasutum*, where metagons replicate like an RNA virus or like Wright's plasmagens (Gibson and Sonneborn, 1964).

The question now naturally arises whether the agent which selectively alters the immunological homeostasis of a host might be an RNA-containing biological entity causing suppression of certain immunological faculties, followed by the emergence of new, phenotypically or genotypically changed lymphoid cell clones. The nature of this biological agent would be such that most of the individual particles would be defective or incomplete; the genome carried by these particles would suffice to code for the further replication of particles. Actively proliferating lymphoid cells would be required to increase the proliferation rate of these particles. When increased lymphoreticular cell proliferation occurred in an immunosuppressed host, particles of this hypothetical agent would replicate to an extent that would allow constellations favorable for genetic recombination between the individual incomplete particles to take place. Through genetic recombination or multiplicity reactivation, some of the progeny of these particles would acquire a full genome. In possession of a full genome, the particles in question would act as leukemogenic viruses. Stem cells of the lymphopoietic and hematopoietic series would then be converted into malignant cells and the initial immune deficiency, through a stage of autoimmune disease, would culminate in the establishment of malignant lymphoma or related diseases.

Murine leukemia viruses possess the prerequisites of both immunosuppressive and oncogenic agents. Virus particles of low virulence, as measured by the leukemogenic potency, readily occur in "wild" populations of mouse leukemia viruses (Pope, 1963), and repeated passages were required to increase virulence, *i.e.* the leukemogenic potency of the virus (Gross, 1958). Mouse leukemia viruses grown in tissue cultures for prolonged periods of time undergo attenuation (Barski and Youn, 1965; Sinkovics, Groves, Bertin, and Shullenberger, 1969; Wright and Lasfargues, 1966). Attenuation was thought to result from losses of fragments of the viral genome (Sinkovics, 1967a), because the leukemogenic potency appeared to be restored by multiplicity reactivation in the presence of small numbers of virulent particles. Mouse leukemia viruses are able to replicate not only in hematopoietic or lymphoid cells, but also in various parenchymal cells in vivo and in vitro (Feldman and Gross, 1967;

Peries, Levy, Boiron and Bernard, 1964; Seman and Dmochowski, 1965).
These viruses may resist neutralizing effect of antibody (Sinkovics,
Pienta, Fiorentino, and Bertin, 1967) and glomerulonephritis occurs in
leukemic mice (Recher *et al.*, 1966; Sinkovics *et al.*, 1968), probably
because of the deposition of virus (or viral soluble antigen) and antibody
complexes in the glomeruli. Lymphocytic choriomeningitis virus was
shown to cause this type of glomerulitis in mice which are virus carriers
(Dixon, 1968). Mouse leukemia viruses exercise a potent immunosuppressive effect (Ceglowski and Friedman, 1968) and this effect takes
place before the development of leukemia. Probably, the soluble antigen
of the leukemia virus suffices to block macrophages and lymphocytes and
the soluble antigen is probably produced in great excess during virus
replication. Presumably, the soluble antigen is immunosuppressive even
when it derives from virus particles of low virulence. Therefore, a preleukemic host with small numbers of virus particles may exhibit signs
of immunosuppression. If this immunosuppression is selective, an over-
compensatory attempt of less-suppressed lymphoreticular cells may be
expected. Since leukemia viruses also replicate in parenchymal cells, the
parenchymal neoantigens may evoke "autoimmune" reactions in hosts
not tolerant to the virus. Thus, immunosuppression and autoimmunity
could now coexist. Time and replication would provide the optimal environment for leukemia virus particles of low leukemogenic potency to
acquire a full leukemogenic genome by recombination with other partially defective particles. Thus, mouse leukemia viruses clearly exhibit
the potential to both initiate and sustain immune deficiency, autoimmune, and leukemic processes (Table 5).

Could man then possibly harbor an agent similar to mouse leukemia
viruses? With favorable genetic or hormonal status of the host, this agent
might commence replication and release soluble antigens to create the
state of a selective immunosuppression. A complicated structure of

TABLE 5. *Biological Characterization of Mouse Leukemia Viruses*

Affinity to both lymphoreticular-hematopoietic and parenchymal cells
Immunosuppressive (to lymphoreticular cells)
Neoantigenic (within parenchymal cells)
Resist neutralization by antibody
Antibody-virus complexes (immune complex glomerulitis)
Leukemogenic part of genome is labile ("wild" viruses of low leukemogenic
  potency; attenuation in culture)
Recombination ("multiplicity reactivation") with fully leukemogenic genome
Associated with immune deficiency, autoimmune, and malignant diseases

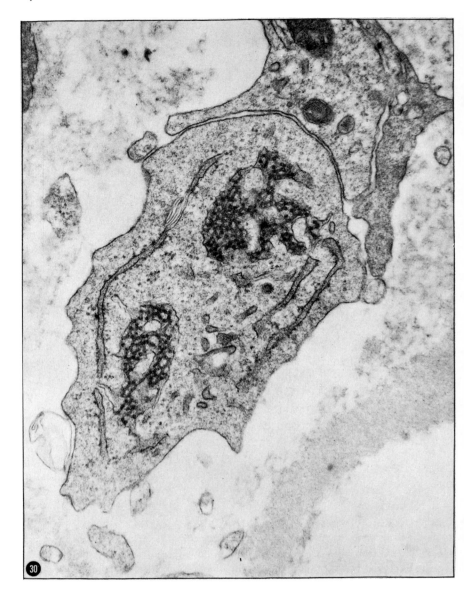

FIGURE 30. Tubular structures resembling ribonucleoprotein strands of a myxovirus in the cytoplasm of a vascular endothelial cell in kidney biopsy specimen deriving from a case of systemic lupus erythematosus. Electron microscopy, reduced from × 60,000. (Courtesy of Dr. F. Györkey.)

immune defects and overcompensating immune faculties would build up. Lymphoid cells carrying the agent or its soluble antigens might be genetically altered, *i.e.*, instructed by the genome of the agent, to disregard homeostasis; these cells would commit acts of autoaggression. Remaining immunocompetent cells would recognize as foreign and attempt to reject both the autoaggressive clones and the parenchymal cell in which this agent might reside. Recombinations and emergence of fully leukemogenic particles of this hypothetical agent would arise in due course (Table 6).

TABLE 6. *Working Hypothesis: Viral Etiology of Acquired Immune Deficiency, Autoimmune and Malignant Diseases of the Lymphoreticular System*

Action	Reaction
Phase I.	
RNA-containing defective viral agent	
1. Renders lymphoreticular cells nonreactive (by soluble antigens?)	1. Immunosuppression
2. Renders parenchymal cells neoantigenic (by occupying cytoplasm)	2. Autoimmunity
Phase II.	
Replication of agent leads to	
1. Genetic recombinations ("multiplicity reactivation")	
2. Virus particles with full genome emerge	3. Leukemogenesis

Particles resembling those of the type C mouse leukemia viruses have been sighted in leukemia and malignant lymphoma of man but never isolated and identified (Dmochowski *et al.*, 1967). Recently, one of us (J.G.S.) suggested that subviral structures should be searched for in autoimmune diseases; soon after the initiation of such studies, tubular structures and occasional budding cytoplasmic particles were found in kidney biopsy specimens from patients with systemic lupus erythematosus (Györkey, Sinkovics, Min, and Györkey, 1969; Sinkovics, Györkey, and Thoma, 1969) (Figure 30). These structures resemble the ribonucleoprotein strands of myxoviruses. Similar structures have also been described recently in cultured human sarcoma cells and lymphoblasts (Chessin *et al.*, 1968; Sinkovics, Györkey, and Shullenberger, 1969; Stewart, 1968) and, earlier, in tumors that were induced by RSV in primates but failed to replicate fully mature virus particles (Munroe, Shipkey, Erlandson, and Windle, 1964). Entirely comparable structures have been described in brain cells of patients with Dawson's encephalopathy (Shaw, Buchan, and Clarkson, 1967) and in muscle cells of patients with polymyositis (Chou, 1968). The identification of these filaments as subviral structures requires further work. Even if it is shown that these structures are viral ribonucleoprotein strands entirely similar to those released by various myxoviruses, further work still will be needed to show that these structures are etiologically related to autoimmune or malignant lymphoreticular diseases in man. The possession of such RNA strands, however, may alter the surface antigenicity of parenchymal cells or the immunological potentialities of lymphoreticular cells. The existence of ribonucleoprotein strands of viral origin in the cytoplasm of certain cells would represent a newly recognized form of cell-virus relationship. It was known that viruses either undergo complete infectious replication often but not necessarily resulting in cell death, or viral DNA integrates itself with the cellular genome resulting in malignant transformation. Thus, the virus etiology of autoimmune and malignant lymphoreticular diseases in both mouse and man appears to be the most promising lead to follow.

ADDENDUM

In the tenth month of life, AKR mice treated at birth with *Bordetella pertussis* vaccine show a tenfold decrease, and AKR mice recovering from runt (homologous) disease caused by lymphoid cells of C57BL mice show a fivefold decrease of leukemia incidence. Other agents used in this study did not significantly alter leukemogenesis.

It has recently been proposed that the tetraploid malignant murine lymphoblasts which produce both leukemia virus and a "self-enhancing antibody" arise by fusion of a diploid lymphoma cell with a plasma cell-producing leukemia virus-neutralizing antibody (Sinkovics, Drewinko, and Thornell, 1970).

After the first description of subviral structures resembling ribonucleoprotein strands of a myxovirus in systemic lupus erythematosus (Sinkovics, Györkey, and Thoma, 1969), subsequent reports confirmed this finding fully. These structures represent a new type of virus-cell interaction. It was known that viruses either undergo full infectious cycles of replication in host cells or integrate viral genetic material with that of the host cell nucleus, thereby causing malignant transformation morphologically, biologically, and antigenically. The existence of viral ribonucleoprotein strands without envelope proteins within the cytoplasm of host cells may represent a relationship in which no infectious virus can be identified by conventional techniques, but no morphological or biological malignant transformation of the host cell has as yet taken place; however, virus-carrier parenchymal cells become antigenic targets of the intact lymphoreticular faculties of the host and lymphoid cells harboring viral ribonucleoprotein strands become either immunologically incompetent or autoaggressive (Sinkovics, 1969, 1970).

ACKNOWLEDGMENTS

The authors thank Miss Francine M. Mikulik, Mrs. Elaine Thornell, Mrs. Carol Hunter, and Mr. Jerry Cabiness for technical assistance in experimental work. Dr. W. O. Russell, Head, Department of Pathology, generously released funds to initiate some recent studies. It is a pleasure to acknowledge many stimulating consultations with Dr. C. C. Shullenberger who permitted the authors to refer to patients attended by the staff of the Hematology Service, Department of Medicine. Mrs. Anita Miller was kind enough to transcribe a handwritten draft into a typed manuscript. This work was supported by United States Public Health Service research grants CA-7923, CA-6939, and CA-5831.

ABBREVIATIONS

FMR—Friend, Moloney, Rauscher murine leukemia viruses
G—Gross murine leukemia virus
MLV—Murine leukemia virus
NDV—Newcastle's disease virus
PHA—Phytohemagglutinin
RSV—Rous sarcoma virus

REFERENCES

Abelev, G. I. 1968. Production of Embryonal Serum α-Globulin by Hepatomas: Review of Experimental and Clinical Data. *Cancer Research*, 28:1344–1350.

Abramson, A. L., M. Goodman, and H. Kolodny. 1968. Sjögren's Syndrome: Additional Diagnostic Tools. *Archives of Otolaryngology*, 88:91–94.

Ahearn, M. G., and J. G. Sinkovics. 1969. Immunocompetence of Leukemic Murine Lymphoblasts. III. Morphology of Virus Replication in Presence of Immune Globulin. (In preparation.)

Aisenberg, A. C. 1966. Immunologic Status of Hodgkin's Disease. *Cancer*, 19:385–394.

Alexander, P. 1968. Immunotherapy of Cancer: Experiments with Primary Tumours and Syngeneic Tumour Grafts. *Progress in Experimental Tumor Research*, 10: 22–71.

Amos, D. B., W. H. Prioleau, Jr., and P. Hutchin. 1968. Histochemical Changes during Growth of C3H Ascites Tumor BP8 in C57BL Mice; Effects of Enhancing Antiserum. *Journal of Surgical Research*, 8:122–127.

Andrews, G. A., C. C. Congdon, C. L. Edwards, N. Gengozian, B. Nelson, and H. Vodopick. 1967. Preliminary Trials of Clinical Immunotherapy. *Cancer Research*, 27:2535–2541.

Aoki, T., E. A. Boyse, and L. J. Old. 1968. Wild-Type Gross Leukemia Virus. 1. Soluble Antigen (GSA) in the Plasma and Tissues of Infected Mice. *Journal of the National Cancer Institute*, 41:89–96.

Arakawa, K., A. M. Jézéquel, S. I. Macvie, R. Johnston, Z. M. Perz, and J. W. Steiner. 1966. The Liver in Murine Transplantation (Runt) Disease. Observations of the

Acute Lesions by Light and Electron Microscopy. *American Journal of Pathology*, 49:257–299.

Bach, F. H., and K. Hirschhorn. 1965. The In Vitro Immune Response of Peripheral Blood Lymphocytes. *Seminars in Hematology*, 2:68–89.

Barski, G., and J. K. Youn. 1965. Immunization against Rauscher Mouse Leukemia with Tissue Culture Material. *Science*, 149:751–752.

Beale, G. H. 1964. "Genes and Cytoplasmic Particles in Paramecium," *Cellular Control Mechanisms and Cancer*, P. Emmelot and O. Mühlbock, Eds. Amsterdam, The Netherlands, and New York, New York: Elsevier Publishing Co. Pp. 8–18.

Benkö, S. 1958. Reticuloses and Experimentally Induced Reticuloses Due to Storage of Methylcellulose. *Acta medica Academiae scientiarum hungaricae*, 12:115–135.

Benkö, S., and T. Tiboldi. 1959. Behandlung der Benevolenskajaschen Rattensarkoma mit Milzzellsuspension und Methylcellulose. *Acta medica Academiae scientiarum hungaricae*, 13:37–47.

Berman, D. A., R. E. Rydell, and A. Eichenholz. 1963. Wegener's Granulomatosis: A Clinicopathologic Study of Four Cases. *Annals of Internal Medicine*, 59:521–530.

Bishop, D. C., A. V. Pisciotta, and P. Abramoff. 1967. Synthesis of Normal and "Immunogenic RNA" in Peritoneal Macrophage Cells. *Journal of Immunology*, 99:751–759.

Boyse, E. A., L. J. Old, and E. Stockert. 1962. Immunological Enhancement of a Leukaemia. *Nature*, 194:1142–1144.

Boyse, E. A., L. J. Old, E. Stockert, and N. Shigeno. 1968. Genetic Origin of Tumor Antigens. *Cancer Research*, 28:1280–1287.

Breyere, E. J., J. B. Moloney, and W. P. Jordan. 1966. Biological Studies on a Leukemia Virus Extracted from C3H Plasma Cell Tumor. *Journal of the National Cancer Institute*, 37:699–705.

Brodovsky, H. S., M. L. Samuels, P. J. Migliore, and C. D. Howe. 1968. Chronic Lymphocytic Leukemia, Hodgkin's Disease, and the Nephrotic Syndrome. *Archives of Internal Medicine*, 121:71–75.

Bubenik, J., and A. Turano. 1968. Enhancing Effect on Tumour Growth of Humoral Antibodies against Tumour Specific Transplantation Antigens in Tumours Induced by Murine Sarcoma Virus (Harvey). *Nature*, 220:928–930.

Bunim, J. J., W. W. Buchanan, P. T. Wertlake, L. Sokoloff, K. J. Bloch, J. S. Beck, and F. P. Alepa. 1964. Clinical, Pathologic, and Serologic Studies in Sjögren's Syndrome. Combined Clinical Staff Conference at the National Institutes of Health. *Annals of Internal Medicine*, 61:509–530.

Burnet, F. M. 1958. *The Clonal Selection Theory of Acquired Immunity*. Nashville, Tennessee: Vanderbilt University Press. 209 pp.

———. 1968. Measles as an Index of Immunological Function. *Lancet*, 2:610–613.

Burnet, F. M., and M. C. Holmes. 1964. Thymic Changes in the Mouse Strain NZB in Relation to the Auto-immune State. *Journal of Pathology and Bacteriology*, 88: 229–241.

Butler, J. J., A. Szakacs, and J. G. Sinkovics. 1967. Virus-induced Murine Lymphoma Resembling Burkitt's Tumor. *American Journal of Pathology*, 51:629–637.

Cammarata, R. J., G. P. Rodnan, and W. N. Jensen. 1963. Systemic Rheumatic Disease and Malignant Lymphoma. *Archives of Internal Medicine*, 111:330–337.

Case Records of the Massachusetts General Hospital: Case 43451. 1957. *New England Journal of Medicine*, 257:935–940.

Casey, T. P. 1968. The Development of Lymphomas in Mice with Autoimmune Disorders Treated with Azathioprine. *Blood, The Journal of Hematology*, 31: 396–399.

Ceglowski, W. S., and H. Friedman. 1968. Immunosuppressive Effects of Friend and Rauscher Leukemia Disease Viruses on Cellular and Humoral Antibody Formation. *Journal of the National Cancer Institute*, 40:983–995.

Celada, F. 1967. Quantitative Studies of the Adoptive Immunological Memory in Mice. II. Linear Transmission of Cellular Memory. *Journal of Experimental Medicine*, 125:199–211.

Chanock, R. M., C. B. Smith, W. T. Friedewald, R. H. Parrott, B. R. Forsyth, H. V. Coates, A. Z. Kapikian, and M. A. Gharpure. 1967. "Resistance to Parainfluenza and Respiratory Syncytial Virus Infection—Implications for Effective Immunization and Preliminary Study of an Attenuated Strain of Respiratory Syncytial Virus," *First International Conference on Vaccines against Viral and Rickettsial Diseases of Man*. Washington, D.C.: Pan American Health Organization. Pp. 53–61.

Charney, J. 1968. Production of Self-Directed Antibody by Tumour Cells. *Nature*, 220:504–506.

Chessin, L. N., P. R. Glade, J. A. Kasel, H. L. Moses, R. B. Herberman, and Y. Hirshaut. 1968. The Circulating Lymphocyte—Its Role in Infectious Mononucleosis. *Annals of Internal Medicine*, 69:333–359.

Chou, S.-M. 1968. Myxovirus-Like Structures and Accompanying Nuclear Changes in Chronic Polymyositis. *Archives of Pathology*, 86:649–658.

Cline, J. M., and V. C. Swett. 1968. The Interaction of Human Monocytes and Lymphocytes. *Journal of Experimental Medicine*, 128:1309–1324.

Cohen, E. P., and J. J. Parks. 1964. Antibody Production by Nonimmune Spleen Cells Incubated with RNA from Immunized Mice. *Science*, 144:1012–1013.

Cohen, S. M., and S. Waxman. 1967. Myasthenia Gravis, Chronic Lymphocytic Leukemia, and Autoimmune Hemolytic Anemia. "A Spectrum of Thymic Abnormalities?" *Archives of Internal Medicine*, 120:717–720.

Cremer, N. E., D. O. N. Taylor, and S. J. Hagens. 1966. Antibody Formation, Latency and Leukemia: Infection with Moloney Virus. *The Journal of Immunology*, 96:495–508.

Dameshek, W. 1967a. "Certain Forms of Leukemia as Immunoproliferative Disorders," *Carcinogenesis: A Broad Critique* (The University of Texas M. D. Anderson Hospital and Tumor Institute, 20th Annual Symposium on Fundamental Cancer Research, 1966). Baltimore, Maryland: The Williams & Wilkins Company. Pp. 141–155.

———. 1967b. Chronic Lymphocytic Leukemia: An Accumulative Disease of Immunologically Incompetent Lymphocytes. *Blood, The Journal of Hematology*, 29:566–584.

Deaton, J. G., and W. C. Levin. 1967. Systemic Lupus Erythematosus and Acute Myeloblastic Leukemia. Report of Their Coexistence and a Survey of Possible Associating Features. *Archives of Internal Medicine*, 120:345–348.

Deep, W. D., J. F. Fraumeni, C. K. Tashima, and R. McDivitt. 1964. Leukoencephalopathy and Dermatomyositis in Hodgkin's Disease. A Case Report. *Archives of Internal Medicine*, 113:635–640.

Dent, P. B., G. B. Olson, R. A. Good, W. E. Rawls, M. A. South, and J. L. Melnick. 1968. Rubella-Virus/Leucocyte Interaction and Its Role in the Pathogenesis of the Congenital Rubella Syndrome. *Lancet*, 1:291–293.

Dent, P. B., R. D. A. Peterson, and R. A. Good. 1965. A Defect in Cellular Immunity during the Incubation Period of Passage A Leukemia in C3H Mice. *Proceedings of the Society for Experimental Biology and Medicine*, 119:869–871.

Dixon, F. J. 1968. The Pathogenesis of Glomerulonephritis. *The American Journal of Medicine*, 44:493–498.

Dmochowski, L., T. Yumoto, C. E. Grey, R. L. Hales, P. L. Langford, H. G. Taylor, E. J Freireich, C. C. Shullenberger, J. A. Shively, and C. D. Howe. 1967. Electron Microscopic Studies of Human Leukemia and Lymphoma. *Cancer*, 20:760–777.

Doak, P. B., J. Z. Montgomerie, J. D. K. North, and F. Smith. 1968. Reticulum Cell Sarcoma after Renal Homotransplantation and Azathioprine and Prednisone Therapy. *British Medical Journal*, 4:746–748.

Dougherty, R. M., and H. S. Di Stefano. 1966. Lack of Relationship between Infection with Avian Leukosis Virus and Presence of COFAL Antigen in Chicken Embryos. *Virology*, 29:586–595.

Dubois, E. L. 1966. "The Lupus Erythematosus Cell Test," *Lupus Erythematosus*, E. L. Dubois, Ed. New York, New York: McGraw-Hill Book Company. Pp. 302–331.

Duthie, J. J., P. E. Brown, L. H. Truelove, F. D. Baragar, and A. J. Lawrie. 1964. Course and Prognosis in Rheumatoid Arthritis. A Further Report. *Annals of Rheumatic Diseases*, 23:193–204.

East, J., and M. A. B. de Sousa. 1966. "The Thymus Autoimmunity and Malignancy in New Zealand Black Mice," *Conference on Murine Leukemia* (National Cancer Institute Monograph 22), M. A. Rich and J. B. Moloney, Eds. Bethesda, Maryland: U.S. Department of Health, Education, and Welfare, Public Health Service, National Cancer Institute. Pp. 605–614.

East, J., M. A. B. de Sousa, and D. M. V. Parrott. 1965. Immunopathology of New Zealand Black (NZB) Mice. *Transplantation*, 3:711–729.

East, J., P. R. Prosser, E. J. Holborow, and H. Jaquet. 1967. Autoimmune Reactions and Virus-Like Particles in Germ-Free NZB Mice. *Lancet*, 1:755–757.

Elves, M. W. 1968. On the Mechanism of Action of Phytohemagglutinin on Immunological Reactions. *International Archives of Allergy*, 37:353–367.

Feldman, D. G., and L. Gross. 1967. Electron Microscopic Study of the Distribution of the Mouse Leukemia Virus (Gross) in Genital Organs of Virus-Injected C3Hf Mice and AK Mice. *Cancer Research*, 27:1513–1527.

Fialkow, P. J. 1967. "Immunologic" Oncogenesis. *Blood, The Journal of Hematology*, 30:388–394.

Fichtelius, K. E. 1968. Theliolymphoid Organs—A New Look at Lymphoreticular Structures. *Experimental Hematology*, 17:3–5.

Fishman, M., and F. L. Adler. 1963. Antibody Formation Initiated In Vitro. II. Antibody Synthesis in X-Irradiated Recipients of Diffusion Chambers Containing

Nucleic Acid Derived from Macrophages Incubated with Antigen. *Journal of Experimental Medicine*, 117:595–602.

Floersheim, G. L. 1967. Facilitation of Tumour Growth by *Bacillus pertussis. Nature*, 216:1235–1236.

Földes, P., I. Szeri, Z. Bános, P. Anderlik, and M. Balázs. 1965. LCM Infection of Mice Thymectomized in Newborn Age. *Acta microbiologica Academiae scientiarum hungaricae*, 11:277–282.

Fordham, C. C., III, F. H. Epstein, W. D. Huffines, and J .T. Harrington. 1964. Polyarteritis and Acute Post-Streptococcal Glomerulonephritis. *Annals of Internal Medicine*, 61:89–97.

Francis, T., Jr., and H. F. Maassab. 1965. "Influenza Viruses," *Viral and Rickettsial Infections of Man*, F. L. Horsfall and I. Tamm, Eds. Philadelphia, Pennsylvania, and Montreal, Canada: J. B. Lippincott Co. 4th edition. Pp. 689–740.

Freund, J. 1951. The Effect of Paraffin Oil and Mycobacteria on Antibody Formation and Sensitization. A Review. *American Journal of Clinical Pathology*, 21: 645–656.

Friedman, H., and W. S. Ceglowski. 1968. Cellular Basis for the Immunosuppressive Properties of a Leukaemogenic Virus. *Nature*, 218:1232–1234.

Fujimoto, Y., H. Suzuki, K. Abe, and J. R. Brooks. 1967. Autoantibodies in Malignant Lymphoma of the Thyroid Gland. *New England Journal of Medicine*, 276: 380–383.

Gahagan, R. B. 1965. Sjögren's Syndrome and Lupus Erythematosus: A Case Report. *Archives of Internal Medicine*, 115:235–238.

Gamble, C. N. 1966. The Effects of Phytohemagglutinin on Mouse Spleen Cells In Vivo. *Blood, The Journal of Hematology*, 28:175–185.

Gams, R. A., J. A. Neal, and F. G. Conrad. 1968. Hydantoin-Induced Pseudo-lymphoma. *Annals of Internal Medicine*, 69:557–568.

Geering, G., L. J. Old, and E. A. Boyse. 1966. Antigens of Leukemias Induced by Naturally Occurring Murine Leukemia Virus: Their Relation to the Antigens of Gross Virus and Other Murine Leukemia Viruses. *Journal of Experimental Medicine*, 124:753–772.

Geller, W. 1964. Chronic Lymphocytic Leukemia with Hemolytic Anemia. A Long Survival. *Archives of Internal Medicine*, 114:444–448.

Gibson, I., and T. M. Sonneborn. 1964. Is the Metagon an m-RNA in Paramecium and a Virus in Didinium? *Proceedings of the National Academy of Sciences of the U.S.A.*, 52:869–876.

Girardi, A. J. 1965. Prevention of SV40 Virus Oncogenesis in Hamsters. I. Tumor Resistance Induced by Human Cells Transformed by SV40. *Proceedings of the National Academy of Sciences of the U.S.A.*, 54:445–451.

Gold, P., M. Gold, and S. O. Freedman. 1968. Cellular Localization of Carcinoembryonic Antigens of the Human Digestive System. *Cancer Research*, 28:1331–1334.

Good, R. A., and S. J. Zak. 1956. Disturbances in Gamma Globulin Synthesis as "Experiments of Nature"; E. Mead Johnson Award. *Pediatrics*, 18:109–149.

Gross, L. 1958. High Susceptibility of 1 to 14 Days Old C3H Mice to "Passage A" Leukemia Filtrates. *Proceedings of the Society for Experimental Biology and Medicine*, 97:300–304.

Györkey, F., J. G. Sinkovics, K. W. Min, and P. Györkey. 1969. Systemic Lupus

Erythematosus and Myxovirus. (Letter to the Editor) *New England Journal of Medicine*, 280:333.

Haase, A. T., J. A. Kasel, and L. N. Chessin. 1968. Adenovirus Type 12 Oncogenicity in Newborn Hamsters: The Effect of Pokeweed Mitogen. *The Journal of Immunology*, 101:806–807.

Heim, L. R., C. Martinez, and R. A. Good. 1967. Cause of Homologous Disease. *Nature*, 214:26–29.

Hellström, K. E., and I. Hellström. 1967. Allogeneic Inhibition of Transplanted Tumor Cells. *Progress In Experimental Tumor Research*, 9:40–76.

Hersh, E. M., and J. J. Oppenheim. 1965. Impaired In Vitro Lymphocyte Transformation in Hodgkin's Disease. *New England Journal of Medicine*, 273:1006–1012.

Hilleman, M. R. 1966. Critical Appraisal of Emulsified Oil Adjuvants Applied to Viral Vaccines. *Progress in Medical Virology*, 8:131–182.

Hirano, M., J. G. Sinkovics, C. C. Shullenberger, and C. D. Howe. 1967. Murine Lymphoma: Augmented Growth in Mice with Pertussin Vaccine-Induced Lymphocytosis. *Science*, 158:1061–1064.

Hitchcock, C. R., L. D. Maclean, and W. A. Sullivan. 1957. The Secretory and Clinical Aspects of Achlorhydria and Gastric Atrophy as Precursors of Gastric Cancer. *Journal of the National Cancer Institute*, 18:795–811.

Hollander, J. L., D. J. McCarty, Jr., G. Astorga, and E. Castro-Murillo. 1965. Studies on the Pathogenesis of Rheumatoid Joint Inflammation. I. The "R.A. Cell" and a Working Hypothesis. *Annals of Internal Medicine*, 62:271–280.

Hornbaker, J. H., Jr., E. A. Foster, G. S. Williams, and J. S. Davis. 1966. Sjögren's Syndrome and Nodular Reticulum Cell Sarcoma. *Archives of Internal Medicine*, 118:449–452.

Hotchin, J., and D. N. Collins. 1964. Glomerulonephritis and Late Disease of Mice Following Neonatal Virus Infection. *Nature*, 203:1357–1359.

Huebner, R. J. 1967. "In Vitro Methods for Detection and Assay of Leukemia Viruses," *Carcinogenesis: A Broad Critique* (The University of Texas M. D. Anderson Hospital and Tumor Institute, 20th Annual Symposium on Fundamental Cancer Research, 1966. Baltimore, Maryland: The Williams & Wilkins Company. Pp. 23–46.

Hyman, G. A., and S. G. Sommers. 1966. The Development of Hodgkin's Disease and Lymphoma During Anticonvulsant Therapy. *Blood, The Journal of Hematology*, 28:416–427.

Irvine, W. J., S. H. Davies, I. W. Delamore, and A. W. William. 1962. Immunological Relationship Between Pernicious Anaemia and Thyroid Disease. *British Medical Journal*, 2:454–456.

Jensen, K. E., A. L. Neal, R. E. Owens, and J. Warren. 1963. Interferon Responses of Chick Embryo Fibroblasts to Nucleic Acids and Related Compounds. *Nature*, 200:433–434.

Kaliss, N. 1962. The Elements of Immunological Enhancement: A Consideration of Mechanisms. *Annals of the New York Academy of Sciences*, 101:64–79.

Keast, D., and J. M. Papadimitriou. 1966. Virus Induction of Autoimmune Disease and Neoplasia. *Lancet*, 2:589–590.

Keast, D., and M. N. I. Walters. 1968. The Pathology of Murine Runting and its Modification by Neomycin Sulphate Gavages. *Immunology*, 15:247–262.

Klein, G. 1966. Tumor Antigens. *Annual Review of Microbiology*, 20:223–252.

————. 1968. Tumor-Specific Transplantation Antigens: G. H. A. Clowes Memorial Lecture. *Cancer Research*, 28:625–635.

Kobayashi, H., T. Kodama, and K. Takeda. 1966. Electronmicroscopy of Friend Tumour Cell with Special Reference to Influence of Friend Virus Immunity on Friend Tumour Cell. *Nature*, 212:1260.

Koffler, D., P. H. Schur, and H. G. Kunkel. 1967. Immunological Studies Concerning the Nephritis of Systemic Lupus Erythematosus. *Journal of Experimental Medicine*, 126:607–624.

Lacher, M. J., and L. N. Sussman. 1963. Leukemia and Hodgkin's Disease. *Annals of Internal Medicine*, 59:369–378.

Lazar, A., Z. Hruban, A. Slesers, and D. Lazar. 1963. Methylcellulose-Induced Regression of Murphy-Sturm Lymphosarcoma in the Rat. *Journal of the American Medical Association*, 183:119–121.

Lee, J. C., H. Yamauchi, and J. Hopper. 1966. The Association of Cancer and the Nephrotic Syndrome. *Annals of Internal Medicine*, 64:41–51.

Leventhal, B. F., D. S. Waldorf, and N. Talal. 1967. Impaired Lymphocyte Transformation and Delayed Hypersensitivity in Sjögren's Syndrome. *Journal of Clinical Investigation*, 46:1338–1345.

Levey, R. H., N. Trainin, L. W. Law, P. H. Black, and W. P. Rowe. 1963. Lymphocytic Choriomeningitis Infection in Neonatally Thymectomized Mice Bearing Diffusion Chambers Containing Thymus. *Science*, 142:483–485.

Levine, S., and M. A. Shearn. 1964. Thrombotic Thrombocytopenic Purpura and Systemic Lupus Erythematosus. *Archives of Internal Medicine*, 113:826–836.

Lindsay, S. 1960. *Carcinoma of the Thyroid Gland (A Clinical and Pathologic Study of 293 Patients at the University of California Hospital)*. Springfield, Illinois: Charles C Thomas, 168 pp.

Macoul, K. L. 1967. Panniculitis, Vasculitis, and a Positive Lupus Erythematosus Cell Test. *Journal of the American Medical Association*, 199:428–430.

Mannick, J. A., and R. H. Egdahl. 1964. Transfer of Heightened Immunity to Skin Homografts by Lymphoid RNA. *Journal of Clinical Investigation*, 43:2166–2177.

Marcus, Z., D. A. Rigas, and B. V. Siegel. 1968. Suppression of Graft-versus-Host Reaction by Phytohemagglutinin. *Experientia*, 24:836–837.

Mathé, G., L. Schwarzenberg, J. L. Amiel, M. Schneider, A. Cattan, and J. R. Schlumberger. 1967. The Role of Immunology in the Treatment of Leukemias and Hematosarcomas. *Cancer Research*, 27:2542–2553.

McBride, R. A. 1966. Graft-*versus*-Host Reaction in Lymphoid Proliferation. *Cancer Research*, 26:1135–1151.

McCoy, J. L., A. Fefer, and J. P. Glynn. 1968. Inhibition and Enhancement of Syngeneic Friend Virus-Induced Lymphoma Cells by Passively Transferred Anti-Friend Serum. *Experimental Hematology*, 16:24–26.

McFarland, W., and D. H. Heilman. 1965. Lymphocyte Foot Appendage: Its Role in Lymphocyte Function and in Immunological Reactions. *Nature*, 205:887–888.

Mellors, R. C., and C. Y. Huang. 1966. Immunopathology of NZB/Bl Mice. V. Virus Like (Filterable) Agent Separable from Lymphoma Cells and Identifiable by Electron Microscopy. *Journal of Experimental Medicine*, 124:1031–1038.

————. 1967. Immunopathology of NZB/Bl Mice. VI. Virus Separable from Spleen and Pathogenic for Swiss Mice. *Journal of Experimental Medicine*, 126:53–62.

Metcalf, D., and R. Moulds. 1967. Immune Responses in Preleukaemic and Leukaemic AKR Mice. *International Journal of Cancer*, 2:53–58.

Miller, D. G. 1965. "Hodgkin's Disease, Lymphosarcoma, and Chronic Lymphocytic Leukemia," *Immunological Diseases*, M. Samter, Ed. Boston, Massachusetts: Little, Brown & Co. Pp. 372–393.

————. 1968. The Immunologic Capability of Patients with Lymphoma. *Cancer Research*, 28:1441–1448.

Morse, S. I. 1965. Studies on the Lymphocytosis Induced in Mice by *Bordetella pertussis*. *Journal of Experimental Medicine*, 121:49–68.

Munroe, J. S., F. Shipkey, R. A. Erlandson, and W. F. Windle. 1964. "Tumors Induced in Juvenile and Adult Primates by Chicken Sarcoma Virus," *International Conference on Avian Tumor Viruses* (National Cancer Institute Monograph 17), J. W. Beard, Ed. Bethesda, Maryland: U.S. Department of Health, Education, and Welfare, Public Health Service, National Cancer Institute. Pp. 365–388.

Nowinski, R. C., L. J. Old, E. A. Boyse, E. deHarven, and G. Geering. 1968. Group-Specific Viral Antigens in the Milk and Tissues of Mice Naturally Infected with Mammary Tumor Virus or Gross Leukemia Virus. *Virology*, 34:617–629.

Oberfield, R. A. 1966. Coexistence of Chronic Lymphocytic Leukemia and Hodgkin's Disease. A Case Report. *Journal of the American Medical Association*, 195:865–867.

Old, L. J., B. Benacerraf, D. A. Clarke, E. A. Carswell, and E. Stockert. 1961. The Role of Reticuloendothelial System in the Host Reaction to Neoplasia. *Cancer Research*, 21:1281–1301.

Pearson, G., and G. Freeman. 1968. Evidence Suggesting a Relationship between Polyoma Virus-Induced Transplantation Antigen and Normal Embryonic Antigen. *Cancer Research*, 28:1665–1673.

Peries, J., J. P. Levy, M. Boiron, and J. Bernard. 1964. Multiplication of Rauscher Virus in Cultures of Mouse Kidney Cells. *Nature*, 203:672–673.

Peterson, R. D. A., R. Hendrickson, and R. A. Good. 1963. Reduced Antibody Forming Capacity During the Incubation Period of Passage A Leukemia in C_3H Mice. *Proceedings of the Society for Experimental Biology and Medicine*, 114:517–520.

Pienta, R. J., and J. G. Sinkovics. 1969. Immunocompetence of Leukemic Murine Lymphoblasts. II. Neutralization of Leukemia Virus with Globulin. (in preparation.)

Pope, J. H. 1963. Detection of an Avirulent Virus Apparently Related to Friend Virus. *Australian Journal of Experimental Biology and Medical Science*, 41:349–362.

Potter, M., and R. C. MacCardle. 1964. Histology of Developing Plasma Cell Neoplasia Induced by Mineral Oil in BALB/c Mice. *Journal of the National Cancer Institute*, 33:497–515.

Rask-Nielsen, R. 1963. Evidence of Murine, Virus-Induced, Paraprotein-Producing Leukaemia and its Relation to Other Virus-Induced Leukaemias. *Nature*, 200:440–453.

————. 1964. Coombs-Positive Hemolytic Anemia and Generalized Amyloidosis in Mice Following Transmission of Subcellular Leukemic Material. *Proceedings of the Society for Experimental Biology and Medicine*, 116:1154–1159.

Rask-Nielsen, R., K. R. McIntire, and P. Ebbesen. 1968. Plasma Cell Leukemia in BALB/c Mice Inoculated with Subcellular Material. II. Serological Changes. *Journal of the National Cancer Institute*, 41:495–504.

Rauscher, F. J., M. A. Fink, and J. P. Kvedar. 1963. Enhancement of Host Response to Subliminal Doses of Rous Sarcoma Virus by Freund's Adjuvant. *Journal of the National Cancer Institute*, 30:645–659.

Recher, L., T. Tanaka, J. A. Sykes, T. Yumoto, G. Seman, L. Young, and L. Dmochowski. 1966. "Further Studies on the Biological Relationship of Murine Leukemia Viruses and on Kidney Lesions of Mice with Leukemia Induced by These Viruses," *Conference on Murine Leukemia* (National Cancer Institute Monograph 22), M. A. Rich and J. B. Moloney, Eds. Bethesda, Maryland: U.S. Department of Health, Education, and Welfare, Public Health Service, National Cancer Institute. Pp. 459–478.

Reed, N. D., and J. W. Jutila. 1965. Wasting Disease Induced with Cortisol Acetate: Studies in Germ-Free Mice. *Science*, 150:356–357.

Rowe, W. P., P. H. Black, and R. H. Levey. 1963. Protective Effect of Neonatal Thymectomy on Mouse LCM Infection. *Proceedings of the Society for Experimental Biology and Medicine*, 114:248–251.

Ruddle, N. H., and B. H. Waksman. 1968. Cytotoxicity Mediated by Soluble Antigen and Lymphocytes in Delayed Hypersensitivity. III. Analysis of Mechanism. *Journal of Experimental Medicine*, 128:1267–1279.

Salaman, M. H. 1968. The Effect of Some Leukemogenic Viruses on Immune Reactions. *Bibliotheca Haematologica*, 30:92–96.

Schoenberg, M. D., V. R. Mumaw, R. D. Moore, and A. S. Weisberger. 1964. Cytoplasmic Interaction between Macrophages and Lymphocytic Cells in Antibody Synthesis. *Science*, 143:964–965.

Schwartz, R. S., and J. André-Schwartz. 1968. Malignant Lymphoproliferative Diseases: Interactions Between Immunological Abnormalities and Oncogenic Viruses. *Annual Review of Medicine*, 19:269–282.

Schwartz, R. S., J. André-Schwartz, M. Y. K. Armstrong, and L. Beldotti. 1966. Neoplastic Sequelae of Allogenic Disease. I. Theoretical Considerations and Experimental Design. *Annals of the New York Academy of Sciences*, 129:804–821.

Seligmann, M., H. H. Fudenberg, and R. A. Good. 1968. Editorial: A Proposed Classification of Primary Immunologic Deficiencies. *The American Journal of Medicine*, 45:817–825.

Seman, G., and L. Dmochowski. 1965. Studies on the Possible Transmission of Virus and Mycoplasma in Leukemia. *Medical Record and Annals*, 58:400–405, 424.

Shaw, C.-M., G. C. Buchan, and C. B. Clarkson. 1967. Myxovirus as a Possible Etiologic Agent in Subacute Inclusion-body Encephalitis. *New England Journal of Medicine*, 277:511–515.

Shulman, L. E., and A. McGehee Harvey. 1964. Hashimoto's Thyroiditis in False-Positive Reactors to the Tests for Syphilis. *The American Journal of Medicine*, 36:174–187.

Siegel, B. V., and J. I. Morton. 1967. Influence of Immunologic Hyperstimulation on Murine Viral Leukemogenesis. *Blood, The Journal of Hematology*, 29:585–593.

Simons, M. J., and M. G. Fitzgerald. 1968. Rubella Virus and Human Lymphocytes in Culture. *Lancet*, 2:937–940.

Simpson, J. 1966. Myasthenia Gravis and Autoimmune Disease: Clinical Aspects. *Annals of the New York Academy of Sciences*, 135:506–516.

Sinkovics, J. G. 1962a. Abnormal Immune and Other Complicating Phenomena Associated with a Viral Mouse Leukemia. *Journal of Infectious Diseases*, 110: 282–296.

————. 1962b. Intracellular Lymphocytes in Leukaemia. *Nature*, 196:80–81.

————. 1962c. Observations on Various Runting Syndromes in Mice. *Archiv für die Gesamte Virusforschung*, 12:143–147.

————. 1963. "Lymphoid Cells of Homologous Immune Activity in Mouse Leukemia," *Conceptual Advances in Immunology and Oncology* (The University of Texas M. D. Anderson Hospital and Tumor Institute, 16th Annual Symposium on Fundamental Cancer Research, 1962). New York, New York: Hoeber Medical Division, Harper & Row, Publishers, Inc. Pp. 165–182.

————. 1967a. "The Causative Viruses of Murine Leukemia and Their Identification Through Immune Responses of the Host," *Carcinogenesis: A Broad Critique* (The University of Texas M. D. Anderson Hospital and Tumor Institute, 20th Annual Symposium on Fundamental Cancer Research, 1966). Baltimore, Maryland: The Williams & Wilkins Co. Pp. 157–175.

————. 1967b. "The Complex Pathogenicity of Tumors. Project M 18/gm 1: Comparison of Runt (Homologous) Disease and Leukemia," *Research Report* 1967. Houston, Texas: The University of Texas M. D. Anderson Hospital and Tumor Institute. Pp. 280–282.

————. 1969. Working Hypothesis: Viral Etiology of Autoimmune Diseases. *New England Journal of Medicine*, 280:903–904.

————. 1970. Structures Resembling Viral Ribonucleoprotein Strands in Systemic Lupus Erythematosus. *Arthritis and Rheumatism.* (in press.)

————. Unpublished data.

Sinkovics, J. G., B. Drewinko, and E. W. Thornell. 1970. Immunoresistant Tetraploid Lymphoma Cells. *Lancet*, 1:139–140.

Sinkovics, J. G., G. F. Groves, B. A. Bertin, and C. C. Shullenberger. 1969. A System of Tissue Cultures for the Study of a Mouse Leukemia Virus. *Journal of Infectious Diseases*, 119:19–38.

Sinkovics, J. G., F. Györkey, and C. C. Shullenberger. 1969. "A Comparison of Murine and Human Leukemia," *Myeloproliferative Disorders of Animals and Man*, W. J. Clarke and E. B. Howard, Eds. Washington, D.C.: U.S. Atomic Energy Commission. (in press.)

Sinkovics, J. G., F. Györkey, and G. W. Thoma. 1969. A Rapidly Fatal Case of Systemic Lupus Erythematosus. Subviral Structures in the Kidney and Activities of Lymphocytes in Culture. *Texas Reports on Biology and Medicine*, 27:887–908.

Sinkovics, J. G., M. Hirano, A. Szakacs, C. C. Shullenberger, and C. D. Howe. 1968. "Growth of Lymphoreticular Malignant Cells in the Preconditioned Murine Host," *The Proliferation and Spread of Neoplastic Cells* (The University of Texas M. D. Anderson Hospital and Tumor Institute at Houston, 21st Annual Symposium on Fundamental Cancer Research, 1967). Baltimore, Maryland: The Williams & Wilkins Co. Pp. 615–639.

Sinkovics, J. G., and C. D. Howe. 1964. Approaches to the Pathogenesis of Runt (Homologous) Disease. *Texas Reports on Biology and Medicine*, 22:591–608.

————. 1965. Project M 18/gm 1: Comparison of Runt (Homologous) Disease and Leukemia. *Research Report* 1965. Houston, Texas: The University of Texas M. D. Anderson Hospital and Tumor Institute. Pp. 256–258.

————. 1969. Superinfection of Tumors with Viruses. *Experientia*, 25:733–734.

Sinkovics, J. G., C. D. Howe, and C. C. Shullenberger. 1964. Cellular Activities in Tissue Cultures of Leukemic Human Bone Marrow. *Blood, The Journal of Hematology*, 24:389–401.

Sinkovics, J. G., R. J. Pienta, M. Fiorentino, and B. A. Bertin. 1967. Neutralization of Sublines of a Mouse Leukemia Virus with Murine Antibody, as Measured by the Spleen Focus Assay. *Cancer Research*, 27:88–94.

Sinkovics, J. G., and E. Shirato. 1969. Immunocompetence of Leukemic Murine Lymphoblasts. IV. Attempts at Demonstration of a Homologous Graft *versus* Host Reaction. (in preparation.)

Sinkovics, J. G., C. C. Shullenberger, C. D. Howe, and B. A. Bertin. 1966. Mouse Leukaemia, A Dichotomy of Virus Neutralizing and Cytotoxic Antibodies. *Archiv für die Gesamte Virusforschung*, 19:75–80.

Sjögren, H. O., and I. Hellström. 1967. I. "In Vivo and In Vitro Demonstration of Specific Transplantation Antigens in Polyoma, Rous and Adeno 12 Mouse Sarcomas," *Subviral Carcinogenesis* (First International Symposium on Tumor Viruses), Y. Ito, Ed. Nagoya, Japan: Research Institute, Aichi Cancer Center, and The Japanese Cancer Association. Pp. 207–217.

Smithers, D. W. 1967. Hodgkin's Disease. II. *British Medical Journal*, 2:337–341.

Snell, G. D., H. J. Winn, J. H. Stimpfling, and S. J. Parker. 1960. Depression by Antibody of the Immune Response to Homografts and its Role in Immunological Enhancement. *Journal of Experimental Medicine*, 112:293–314.

Stanley, N. F., and D. Keast. 1967. "Murine Infection with Reovirus 3 as a Model for the Virus Induction of Autoimmune Disease and Neoplasia," *Perspectives in Virology V—Virus-Directed Host Response*, M. Pollard, Ed. New York, New York: Academic Press, Inc. Pp. 281–289.

Steeves, R. A. 1968. Cellular Antigen of Friend Virus-Induced Leukemias. *Cancer Research*, 28:338–342.

Stewart, S. E. 1968. The Isolation of a Myxo Type Virus from Two Human Sarcomas. *Bibliotheca Haematologica*, 30:333–334.

Strandberg, B., and N. V. Jarlov. 1961. Cancer, Arthritis and Rheumatoid Arthritis. *Rheumatism*, 17:45–52.

Strober, S., and J. L. Gowans. 1965. The Role of Lymphocytes in the Sensitization of Rats to Renal Homografts. *Journal of Experimental Medicine*, 122:347–360.

Stutman, O., E. J. Yunis, and R. A. Good. 1968. Deficient Immunologic Functions of NZB Mice. *Proceedings of the Society for Experimental Biology and Medicine*, 127:1204–1207.

Svet-Moldavsky, G. J., and L. I. Raffkina. 1963. Thymus Lymphatic Nodes Interrelations Following Injection of Freund's Adjuvant. *Nature*, 197:52–53.

Szakacs, A., J. G. Sinkovics, J. J. Butler, B. M. Levy, and C. F. Tessmer. 1968. Electron Microscopic Observations of the Interaction of Macrophages and Lymphocytes in a Virus-Induced Murine Lymphoma. *Journal of Infectious Diseases*, 118:240–252.

Talal, N., and J. J. Bunim. 1964. The Development of Malignant Lymphoma in the Course of Sjögren's Syndrome. *The American Journal of Medicine*, 36:529–540.

Talal, N., L. Sokoloff, and W. F. Barth. 1967. Extrasalivary Lymphoid Abnormalities in Sjögren's Syndrome (Reticulum Cell Sarcoma, "Pseudolymphoma," Macroglobulinemia). *The American Journal of Medicine*, 43:50–65.

Ter-Grigorov, J. S., and I. S. Irlin. 1968. The Stimulating Effect of Complete Freund's Adjuvant on Tumor Induction by Polyoma Virus in Mice and by Rous Sarcoma Virus in Rats. *International Journal of Cancer*, 3:760–764.

Tornyos, K., C. R. Macossay, and F. Györkey. 1967. Chronic Lymphocytic Leukemia and Hodgkin's Disease in the Same Patient. Report of a Case, Giving Immunological and Diagnostic Considerations. *Cancer*, 20:552–557.

Trujillo, J. M., M. J. Ahearn, R. J. Pienta, C. Gott, and J. G. Sinkovics. 1970. Immunocompetence of Leukemic Murine Lymphoblasts. I. Ultrastructure, Virus and Globulin Production. *Cancer Research.* (in press.)

Tuffanelli, D. L., and R. K. Winkelman. 1962. Scleroderma and Its Relationship to the "Collagenoses": Dermatomyositis, Lupus Erythematosus, Rheumatoid Arthritis, and Sjögren's Syndrome. *The American Journal of Medicine,* 243:133–146.

Volkert, M., and C. Lundsted. 1968. The Provocation of Latent Lymphocytic Choriomeningitis Virus Infections in Mice by Treatment with Antilymphocytic Serum. *Journal of Experimental Medicine,* 127:327–339.

Walford, R. L. 1966. Increased Incidence of Lymphoma after Injections of Mice with Cells Differing at Weak Histocompatibility Loci. *Science,* 152:78–80.

Walford, R. L., and W. H. Hildeman. 1965. Life Span and Lymphoma Incidence of Mice Injected at Birth with Spleen Cells across a Weak Histocompatibility Locus. *American Journal of Pathology,* 47:713–721.

Weckesser, E. C., and A. B. Chinn. 1953. Carcinoma of the Colon Complicating Chronic Ulcerative Colitis. *Journal of the American Medical Association,* 152:905–908.

Whitelaw, D. M. 1968. Multiple Primary Carcinomas Associated with Hodgkin's Disease. *Canadian Medical Association Journal,* 99:291–294.

Woolner, L. B., W. M. McConahey, and O. H. Beahrs. 1959. Struma Lymphomatosa (Hashimoto's Thyroiditis) and Related Thyroidal Disorders. *The Journal of Clinical Endocrinology and Metabolism,* 19:53–83.

Wright, B. S., and J. C. Lasfargues. 1966. "Attenuation of the Rauscher Murine Leukemia Virus through Serial Passages in Tissue Culture." *Conference on Murine Leukemia* (National Cancer Institute Monograph 22), M. A. Rich and J. B. Moloney, Eds. Bethesda, Maryland: U.S. Department of Health, Education, and Welfare, Public Health Service, National Cancer Institute. Pp. 685–700.

Wright, R., and S. C. Truelove. 1966. Autoimmune Reactions in Ulcerative Colitis. *Gut,* 7:32–40.

Yohn, D. S., J. S. Horoszewicz, R. R. Ellison, A. Mittelman, L. S. Chai, and J. T. Grace, Jr. 1968. Immunofluorescent Studies in Human Leukemia. *Cancer Research,* 28:1692–1702.

Yumoto, T., and L. Dmochowski. 1968. Further Studies on Renal Lesions of New Zealand (NZB/BL) Strain Mice. *Texas Reports on Biology and Medicine,* 26:381–400.

represents the ideal example of the studies to be described. Homozygotes frequently have congenital anomalies; the most common is absence of both radii, but a number of other defects have been described. These children are short in stature, are unusually susceptible to viral diseases (many die during an attack of a childhood exanthem), and gradually develop an aplastic anemia which may, however, not manifest itself until adult life. These individuals have general bone marrow failure resulting in anemia, granulocytopenia resulting in susceptibility to infection, and thrombocytopenia often leading to death because of bleeding episodes. Among those that survive all of these conditions, a large proportion succumb to leukemia or other neoplasms (Garriga and Crosby, 1959). Heterozygotes for Fanconi's anemia also appear to have an increased susceptibility to leukemia.

It has now been demonstrated that many patients with Fanconi's anemia, have a remarkably increased susceptibility to chromosomal breakage and abnormal reunion (Swift and Hirschhorn, 1966). These abnormalities can be demonstrated most easily in cultured lymphocytes, cultured skin fibroblasts, or other cultured tissues; to a lesser extent, they can be shown in direct preparations of bone marrow cells, especially during viral infection. The types of chromosomal abnormalities seen are manifold, including chromatid and chromosome breaks, dicentrics, rings, and, perhaps more important, exchange figures signifying reciprocal translocation on the chromatid level.

Studies of heterozygotes in our laboratory have recently produced results indicating chromosomal instability. For example, in addition to a slight increase in break frequency, we have found a significant increase in trisomic cells in some carriers of this gene. During our early work on the chromosomal aspect of this disease, those in our laboratory collaborated in a study with Todaro to compare the ability to transform normal fibroblasts and those derived from heterozygotes and homozygotes for Fanconi's anemia by exposure to the oncogenic simian virus 40 (SV40) (Todaro, Green, and Swift, 1966). That this virus could alter the growth pattern of human cells had been demonstrated (Shein and Enders, 1962) and we and others had observed that chromosomal changes, including rearrangements, could be found very early after exposure of cultured human cells to SV40 (Wolman, Hirschhorn, and Todaro, 1964). Thus, it occurred to us that cells already showing chromosomal instability and derived from patients susceptible to neoplasia may show a different response to exposure to SV40. This was unquestionably demonstrated in Todaro's study (Todaro, Green, and Swift, 1966). Exposure of normal human fibroblasts to SV40 followed by culture in the absence of the virus

Transformation of Genetically Abnormal Cells

KURT HIRSCHHORN AND NAVAH BLOCH-SHTACHER

Division of Medical Genetics, Department of Pediatrics, Mount Sinai School of Medicine, New York, New York

Theories to explain the mechanisms of carcinogenesis have filled the scientific and lay literature for many years. These theories have covered widely diverse factors ranging from the supernatural, through environmental, nutritional, infectious, chemical, and ionizing agents, to genetic or chromosomal disturbances. More recently, there has been a tendency to relate the various environmental agents to possible genetic effects acting on a somatic cellular level. In some ways, this recent trend is reminiscent of Boveri's original chromosomal theory of cancer, first stated in 1902 and fully published in 1914 shortly after the restatement of Mendel's laws and long before the modern era of human cytogenetics.

In most theory papers, however, little attention is given to the concept of individual genetic susceptibility to cancer or to the clues derived from the studies of cells from such susceptible individuals. A notable exception is the recent hypothesis of Miller and Todaro (1969); Todaro was responsible for much of the work dealing with in vitro studies of cellular transformation, particularly of cells derived from patients susceptible to cancer. Their hypothesis, based on the finding of increased neoplastic transformation by certain oncogenic viruses of cultured fibroblasts derived from such patients, suggests this method for the prediction of increased susceptibility to neoplasia. However, Miller and Todaro failed to propose a unifying mechanism relating the genetic defect found in the patients to their high susceptibility to neoplasia. In this paper, we will review some of the relevant information, as well as some of our own preliminary data, in an attempt to translate the clue of increased transformability of genetically abnormal cells into a more generally applicable basis for the interrelationship between environment, genetic change, and neoplasia.

Fanconi's Anemia

Fanconi's anemia, a rare disorder caused by an autosomal gene, for about two weeks resulted in the appearance of two to four transformed colonies in dishes seeded with about 10,000 cells. Identical experiments on cells derived from patients with Fanconi's anemia resulted in a ten- to fiftyfold increase in colony formation. Cells derived from heterozygotes for this gene demonstrated a five- to tenfold increase in colony formation.

Similar results have recently been reported by Todaro and Aaronson (1968) with the use of adenovirus type 12, another virus known to be oncogenic in experimental animals. The colonies so derived demonstrated an altered growth pattern in that the cells grew on top of each other in several layers rather than remaining in a monolayer. This phenomenon, referred to as loss of contact inhibition, has been associated with growth patterns shown by neoplastic cells or by cells derived from experimental animals and made neoplastic in vitro (Aaronson and Todaro, 1968). Essentially identical findings have been reported by Todaro and Martin (1967) for cultured fibroblasts derived from patients with trisomy 21 (Down's syndrome or mongolism). These patients, on the basis of epidemiological studies (Miller, 1967), have long been known to have a remarkably increased susceptibility to leukemia. This increased susceptibility may result, as it probably does in the case of Fanconi's anemia, from an enhanced response to environmental agents capable of causing neoplastic transformation in vivo. It, therefore, may be that what is measured by increased transformability in vitro represents the same enhanced response.

Measurement of Transformation

It would appear to be of some importance to consider the method of measurement of transformation. It has now become traditional to use loss of contact inhibition as a measurement. It must be remembered that the original definition was restricted to contact inhibition of movement (Abercrombie and Heaysman, 1954). More recently, however, many, if not most, workers in the field have interpreted it to mean contact inhibition of growth. Some authors, such as Carter (1968) in his recent theoretical paper, have attempted to show a common control mechanism for cell movement and cell division. Carter hypothesized that cell variation accounts for a loss of tissue homeostasis and thereby leads to a failure of contact inhibition. Other workers, such as Holley and Kiernan (1968), have questioned the specificity of loss of contact inhibition and claim to be able to produce such loss by replenishment of serum factors, which supposedly can also be found in human urine. While this may be perfectly correct, one must remember that all good studies dealing with transformation use internal controls against which the experimental cultures are measured. The important question, then, is whether the transforming agent produces a measurable difference.

It is, of course, legitimate to ask whether loss of contact inhibition is necessarily synonymous with neoplastic transformation. This question has not been resolved for human cells, but, in general, a good correlation exists in a variety of other mammalian cell systems. Aaronson and Todaro (1968), for example, have recently shown the acquisition of malignant potential of mouse embryo cells cultured under conditions which result in the loss of contact inhibition. Unfortunately, their measurements are related to cell division rather than cell movement. However, from their morphological description, it is apparent that the increased cell division is caused by the loss of contact inhibition of cell movement which results in multilayered colonies.

Another method for screening cell cultures for transformation is by observing chromosomal changes. It is virtually impossible to be certain whether the chromosomal changes in SV40-treated cells from human beings precede abnormal growth or occur simultaneously with it. However, our studies (Wolman, Hirschhorn, and Todaro, 1964) indicate that perhaps chromosomal endoreduplication or tetraploidy may be the first event observed during transformation. It appears to be advisable that transformation studies should be monitored by both methods, i.e., growth pattern and chromosomal status.

Chemical Carcinogens

Although numerous studies have demonstrated the transformability of various mammalian cells (usually of embryonic origin) by chemical carcinogens, there have been no reports of such transformation in cultures of normal fibroblasts from human beings. We have recently begun a study using 3-4 benzo(a)pyrene (BP) in an attempt to transform cells from both normal and abnormal individuals, measuring such transformation by abnormal growth and/or chromosomal instability (Bloch-Shtacher and Hirschhorn, in preparation). As has been the experience of others, we have been unable to observe any changes in cultures derived from normal individuals following exposure to from 1 through 30 μg BP

FIGURE 1. a—Fibroblasts from patient with Fanconi's anemia, treated with 20 μg BP, showing formation of a colony with loss of contact inhibition. b— Same fibroblasts as in Figure 1a but not treated with BP.

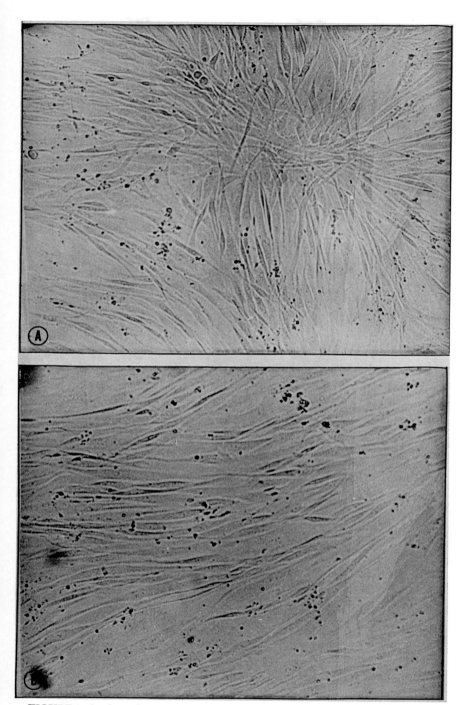

FIGURE 1: See legend on page 194.

per ml of medium. In all types of cells, 50 μg/ml proved to be toxic. However, preliminary results using cells from a patient with Fanconi's anemia and another with trisomy 21 seem to be promising. The optimal dosage for transformation of these types of cells from man appears to be 20 μg BP/ml of medium. In these studies, the cells from the patient with Fanconi's anemia were exposed to BP for a period of five to six weeks. During this period, it became apparent that the treated cells were beginning to demonstrate loss of contact inhibition of movement as evidenced by areas of cells becoming multilayered (Figure 1a). The untreated cells behaved like normal fibroblasts and remained in monolayers (Figure 1b). The treated cells were then transferred to medium without BP and were maintained by feeding twice a week and by trypsinization for subculture when necessary. Untreated cells were maintained in the same way. The treated cells continued to show abnormal morphological and growth patterns and could not be distinguished from known transformed cell lines.

To quantitate the increased growth caused by this loss of contact inhibition, replicate cultures were plated and periodically killed. Growth curves were based on a measurement of total purines and pyrimidines by the method of McIntyre and Smith (1958). The results (Figure 2) indicate an increasing growth rate of the treated cells at a time when the untreated cells remained relatively stable. Similar studies on fibroblasts from a child with trisomy 21 have also revealed differences following treatment with BP (Table 1). After exposure of these cells to 20 and 30 μg BP/ml of medium for 12 days, they were returned into medium without BP; 12 days later they were harvested for chromosome studies. The results indicated significant increases in the percentage of endoreduplications in the treated cells. The treated cultures also had some increase in tetraploid cells and an occasional cell with chromosome breaks. It appears, therefore, that with BP, just as with oncogenic viruses, genetically abnormal cells derived from individuals with a high susceptibility to leukemia demonstrate an increased susceptibility to those alter-

TABLE 1. *Endoreduplications in Cells with Trisomy 21 with and Without Treatment with Benzpyrene (BP)*

Exposure	Number of cells counted	Number of endoreduplications	Per cent
Untreated	70	10	14
BP, 20 μg/ml	100	35	35
BP, 30 μg/ml	70	40	57

ations in tissue culture which have been previously correlated with neo-plastic transformation.

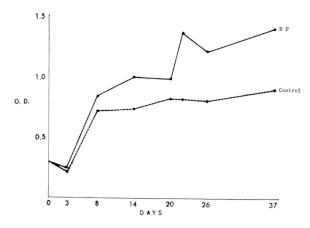

FIGURE 2. Growth curves of fibroblasts from a patient with Fanconi's anemia, untreated (control) and treated with 20 μg BP. Optical density units (OD) represent total purines and pyrimidines.

Genetically Abnormal Cells

The term "genetically abnormal cell" should not be confined to the examples cited. Cleaver's (1968) recent demonstration that cells from patients suffering from the genetic disorder xeroderma pigmentosum, which predisposes to skin cancer, lack the ability to repair damaged deoxyribonucleic acid (DNA), exemplifies the interrelationship of gene mutation, genetic imbalance, and susceptibility to cancer. Chronic myelogenous leukemia (CML), associated with genetically abnormal cells containing the Philadelphia chromosome, often turns into acute leukemia. This could well be the result of increased transformability by environmental agents, including, perhaps, some of the therapeutic modalities employed in the management of CML. A similar situation may exist for polycythemia vera; in cells from patients with this disease, Kay, Lawler, and Millard (1966) and workers in our laboratory have observed a deletion of part of an F chromosome following treatment with [32]P. Polycythemia vera, as well, may turn into acute leukemia. X rays are a known chromosome damaging agent and mutagen, and exposure to X rays results in an increased risk of leukemia or other neoplasia (Buckton, Jacobs, Court Brown, and Doll, 1962). Cells exposed to ionizing radiation certainly become genetically abnormal; it is, therefore, of interest that Pollock and Todaro (1968) have shown that irradiation of mouse cells or normal human cells in vitro enhances transformability by SV40. An important study pertinent to this point is that of Sanders and

Burford (1968), who demonstrated that mammalian cells made neo-plastic in vitro by SV40 and other agents (including BP) showed an unusual response when exposed to N-nitrosomethylurea. This water-soluble potent carcinogen was capable of transforming these cells, already genetically abnormal, to an even more malignant state, a phenomenon which Sanders and Burford term "hyperconversion."

These diverse observations seem to indicate that the existence of chromosomal abnormality or instability makes a cell more susceptible to induced, and perhaps to spontaneous change in the direction of uncon-trolled growth or neoplasia. In at least some of these instances, such behavior of cells in vitro mimics the high incidence of neoplasia in patients harboring such chromosomally abnormal cells.

Genetic Imbalance and Neoplasia

It is apparent that what such genetically abnormal cells show is what has been called "genetic imbalance," which means the existence of duplications, deficiencies, foreign genetic material, or, in special cases, even point mutations. With the exception of the point mutations, all of these conditions imply a gross loss of genetic homeostasis brought about by shifts in relative dosages of structural, and, if they exist in diploid organisms, regulatory genes. Such imbalance presumably makes the genetically abnormal cell, and therefore the individual harboring it, more susceptible to oncogenesis, whether caused by failure of normal cell interaction and recognition or by environmental agents. Simple mutations, such as those in families with intestinal polyposis, or perhaps even in some families demonstrating an unusually high incidence of cancer, could also act by either of these mechanisms. Infection with certain viruses may bring new genetic information into the cell and disturb the existing control of growth potential.

Most of the situations discussed in this paper, however, are associated with chromosomal aberrations. The argument as to which comes first, chromosomal aberration or neoplastic growth, can best be answered in the cases of Fanconi's anemia and trisomy 21. The multiple chromosome rearrangements in individuals with Fanconi's anemia can be seen in early infancy long before any sign of leukemia, which may not occur until adulthood. The chromosomal aberrations are not likely to be the result of the neoplasm. To suggest that neoplasia precedes genetic im-balance would imply that the fertilized ovum with trisomy 21 is a malig-nant cell. Most chromosomally induced susceptibility to neoplasia may be caused by chromatid breakage in two chromosomes with reciprocal translocation. At the next cell division, this breakage results in a variety of possible products. These may be normal and contain a balanced reciprocal translocation without loss or gain of genetic material; however, in most cases, they will be genetically abnormal because of duplication and deficiency (Hirschhorn, 1968b). While abnormality will often be apparent by the presence of a chromosome that is too long or too short, exchange of equally sized or imperceptibly small pieces may not be detectable, even in the imbalanced cell. The most famous example of a neoplastic disease with a short chromosome is, of course, CML associated with the short G chromosome called the Philadelphia chromosome (Nowell and Hungerford, 1960). I have previously suggested (Hirschhorn, 1968b) that this apparent deletion may be the product of a translocation and therefore represent a duplication-deficiency state. The findings that the Philadelphia chromosome-containing cells associated with CML are derived from a single event in one precursor cell (Fialkow, Gartler, and Yoshida, 1967), and that this aberration can be found in asymptomatic individuals (Hirschhorn, 1968a), indicate that this genetic change also precedes the malignant state, rather than resulting from it.

The fundamental question is how genetic change can produce the altered growth pattern called neoplasia. Two major possibilities have been considered. One deals with genetically induced changes in the cell membrane resulting in either lack of cell-cell recognition (Carter, 1968) or lack of recognizability by the body's normal defense mechanisms responsible for the elimination of altered cells (Thomas, 1959).

The other possibility can be classed as genetically induced change in nutritional requirements. Lederberg, in 1946, suggested that a cell which loses its need for a nutrient essential for normal cells may be at an advantage in an internal environment in which that nutrient is scarce. Alternatively, the opposite situation could just as well be true: if a cell, because of a genetic alteration, loses the ability to manufacture a substance essential for its metabolism but freely available in its environment, that cell may be at an advantage over its normal neighbors which continue to manufacture the particular substance. This advantage would result from the availability of energy for growth-promoting activities rather than for the production of a freely available nutrient. The end result of all these mechanisms, as well as numerous others, would be the cellular selective advantage in vivo which we call cancer. Although this appears to be an oversimplification, at least it represents a testable hypothesis to which the methods described in this paper can be applied.

Future Studies

Cells transformed in vitro under controlled conditions can be readily studied for surface antigens and nutritional requirements which may give clues to the mechanisms of transformation. Such clues could then be applied in a direct study of neoplastic cells derived from patients, both for comparison to the in vitro situation and for possible therapeutic trials.

Another potential use of this system is for the screening of potentially carcinogenic agents. Because of our demonstration of the transformability of genetically abnormal cells by BP, it becomes worthwhile to examine the behavior of these cells in the presence of known carcinogens, as well as the ever-growing list of chromosome-breaking or mutagenic chemicals assumed to be potentially oncogenic (Hirschhorn and Cohen, 1968).

Finally, and perhaps most important, the method of in vitro transformation could lead to the detection of individuals with an increased susceptibility to cancer, e.g., members of families with a high incidence of neoplasia. Those individuals whose cells show enhanced transformability by oncogenic agents by either increased loss of contact inhibition or abnormal chromosomal alteration could then be followed by periodic scrutiny for the purpose of early diagnosis of neoplasia. We believe that it will be primarily by the use of these and other cell culture techniques that the currently unresolved problems discussed in this paper will become amenable to solution.

ACKNOWLEDGMENTS

This work was supported in part by a grant from the United States Public Health Service (HD-02552). One author (K. H.) is a Career Scientist of the New York City Health Research Council (I-513).

REFERENCES

Aaronson, S. A., and G. J. Todaro. 1968. Basis for the Acquisition of Malignant Potential by Mouse Cells Cultivated In Vitro. Science, 162:1024–1026.

Abercrombie, M., and J. E. M. Heaysman. 1954. Observations on the Social Behaviour of Cells in Tissue Culture. Experimental Cell Research, 6:293–306.

Bloch-Shtacher, N., and K. Hirschhorn. 1969. Transformation of Genetically Abnormal Cells by Chemical Carcinogens. (in preparation.)

Boveri, T. H. 1914. Zur Frage der Entstehung maligner Tumoren. Jena, Germany: Gustav Fischer, 64 pp.

Buckton, K. E., P. A. Jacobs, W. M. Court Brown, and R. Doll. 1962. A Study of the Chromosome Damage Persisting after X-Ray Therapy for Ankylosing Spondylitis. Lancet, 2:676–682.

Carter, S. B. 1968. Tissue Homeostasis and the Biological Basis of Cancer. Nature, 220:970–974.

Cleaver, J. E. 1968. Defective Repair Replication of DNA in Xeroderma Pigmentosum. Nature, 218:652–656.

Fialkow, P. J., S. M. Gartler, and A. Yoshida. 1967. Clonal Origin of Chronic Myelogenous Leukemia in Man. *Proceedings of the National Academy of Sciences of the U.S.A.*, 58:1468–1471.

Garriga, S., and W. H. Crosby. 1959. The Incidence of Leukemia in Families of Patients with Hypoplasia of the Marrow. *Blood, The Journal of Hematology*, 14: 1008–1014.

Hirschhorn, K. 1968a. "Cytogenetic Alterations in Leukemia," *Perspectives in Leukemia*, W. Dameshek and R. M. Dutcher, Eds. New York, New York, and London, England: Grune and Stratton, Inc. Pp. 113–122.

————. 1968b. Cytogenetic and Immunologic Abnormalities Related to Leukemia. *Proceedings of the Sixth National Cancer Conference.* (in press.)

Hirschhorn, K., and M. M. Cohen. 1968. Drug-Induced Chromosomal Aberrations. *Annals of the New York Academy of Sciences*, 151:977–987.

Holley, R. W., and J. A. Kiernan. 1968. Contact Inhibition of Cell Division in 3T3 Cells. *Proceedings of the National Academy of Sciences of the U.S.A.*, 60:300–304.

Kay, H. E. M., S. D. Lawler, and R. E. Millard. 1966. The Chromosomes in Polycythaemia Vera. *British Journal of Haematology*, 12:507–527.

Lederberg, J. 1946. A Nutritional Concept of Cancer. *Science*, 104:428.

McIntyre, F. C., and M. F. Smith. 1958. A New Chemical Method for Measuring Cell Populations in Tissue Cultures. *Proceedings of the Society for Experimental Biology and Medicine*, 98:76–79.

Miller, R. W. 1967. Persons with Exceptionally High Risk of Leukemia. *Cancer Research*, 27:2420–2423.

Miller, R. W., and G. J. Todaro. 1969. Viral Transformation of Cells from Persons at High Risk of Cancer. *Lancet*, 1:81–82.

Nowell, P. C., and D. A. Hungerford. 1960. A Minute Chromosome in Human Chronic Granulocytic Leukemia. *Science*, 132:1497.

Pollock, E. J., and G. J. Todaro. 1968. Radiation Enhancement of SV40 Transformation in 3T3 and Human Cells. *Nature*, 219:520–521.

Sanders, F. K., and B. O. Burford. 1968. Morphological Conversion, Hyperconversion and Reversion of Mammalian Cells Treated In Vitro with N-Nitrosomethylurea. *Nature*, 220:448–453.

Shein, H. M., and J. F. Enders. 1962. Transformation Induced by Simian Virus$_{40}$ in Human Renal Cell Cultures. 1. Morphology and Growth Characteristics. *Proceedings of the National Academy of Sciences of the U.S.A.*, 48:1164–1172.

Swift, M. R., and K. Hirschhorn. 1966. Fanconi's Anemia. Inherited Susceptibility to Chromosomal Breakage in Various Tissues. *Annals of Internal Medicine*, 65: 496–503.

Thomas, L. 1959. Discussion of: Medawar, P. B.: "Reactions to Homologous Tissue Antigens in Relation to Hypersensitivity," *Cellular and Humoral Aspects of the Hypersensitive States* (A Symposium held at the New York Academy of Medicine), H. Sherwood Lawrence, Ed. New York, New York: Hoeber-Harper. Pp. 529–532.

Todaro, G. J., and S. A. Aaronson. 1968. Human Cell Strains Susceptible to Focus Formation by Human Adenovirus Type 12. *Proceedings of the National Academy of Sciences of the U.S.A.*, 61:1272–1278.

Todaro, G. J., H. Green, and M. R. Swift. 1966. Susceptibility of Human Diploid Fibroblast Strains to Transformation by SV40 Virus. *Science*, 153:1252–1254.

Todaro, G. J., and G. M. Martin. 1967. Increased Susceptibility of Down's Syndrome

Fibroblasts to Transformation by SV40. *Proceedings of the Society for Experimental Biology and Medicine,* 124:1232–1236.

Wolman, S. R., K. Hirschhorn, and G. J. Todaro. 1964. Early Chromosomal Changes in SV40-Infected Human Fibroblast Cultures. *Cytogenetics,* 3:45–61.

Discussion

Dr. Fred Rapp, Baylor College of Medicine, Houston, Texas: Dr. Hirschhorn, the increased frequency of transformation following the infection of cells from patients with Fanconi's anemia by either viruses or chemical carcinogens is a very fascinating observation. I wonder whether we can relate this observation to the abnormal karyotype seen in those cells. For example, is it possible that such cells take up more of the carcinogen or does the virus absorb or penetrate more efficiently into those cells? Have any studies been carried out to measure the induction of virus-specific tumor antigens within 24 to 48 hours after exposure of the cells to the virus? With the low frequency of transformation, it is premature to attribute anything to the cell until we determine whether the same rate of absorption and penetration occurs in normal and abnormal cell types.

Dr. Kurt Hirschhorn, Mount Sinai School of Medicine, New York, New York: I couldn't agree with you more in terms of the virus situation if that were the only finding. In fact, in an older paper of ours we postulated this mechanism as perhaps being partly responsible for the transformation in terms of easier release or activation of some lysosomal enzymes. This may also be responsible for the breakage of the chromosomes. This is an old hypothesis, but I think that the benzpyrene studies would not fit into it because we find equal intracellular inclusion of benzpyrene in cells from both normal individuals and patients with Fanconi's anemia. In fact, as hard as we try, even in embryonic cells, we cannot get transformation with benzypyrene in normal cells.

Dr. S. D. Handmaker, National Institutes of Health, Bethesda, Maryland: Dr. Hirschhorn, have you or has anyone else examined the susceptibility to transformation of cells from patients with ataxia telangiectasia, Chediak-Higashi syndrome, or Bruton's agammaglobulinemia, all of which predispose to malignancy but none of which has a gross chromosomal abnormality?

Dr. Hirschhorn: We have not and I don't know whether Dr. Todaro has. In any case of the diseases that you have mentioned, at least 50 per cent of the patients with ataxia telangiectasia do have chromosomal abnormalities identical to those found in patients with Fanconi's anemia and Bloom's syndrome. In regard to the other conditions, and perhaps even ataxia, it may be more likely that the mechanism is a lack of surveillance, as suggested by Dr. Good. I'm not saying that this is the mechanism for neoplasia; I'm saying that in these particular cells, "neo-plastic transformation" is perhaps related to these mechanisms.

Dr. L. D. Samuels, Children's Hospital, Columbus, Ohio: Do you believe the SV40 transformation test might be of clinical value in predicting indi-vidual susceptibility in a family with a high incidence of cancer by history?

Dr. Hirschhorn: We are not going to know until we try it.

Dr. K. O. Williams, University of Southern California Children's Hospital, Los Angeles, California: Dr. Hirschhorn, is there a difference in the chemical transformation of the cells in children with Down's syndrome at different ages, such as the newborn and the older child with Down's syndrome? Might such a difference explain the reported phenomenom of "pseudoleukemia" seen in the newborn period, as opposed to true leukemia seen in older children with Down's syndrome?

Dr. Hirschhorn: We have no data on this. The only observation I can relate to you is that a couple of months ago we obtained a foreskin sample from a child with Down's syndrome, obtained within a couple of days after birth. This child developed this so-called leukemoid reaction of mongo-lism. We are still not sure whether this is going to turn into leukemia or not. In any case, the fibroblasts from this sample are showing what looks like spontaneous loss of contact inhibition. This is something which must be followed up.

Dr. Williams: In this child, was there any evidence of a viral infection to account for the leukemoid reaction or "pseudoleukemia"?

Dr. Hirschhorn: None that we could detect.

Dr. I. B. Weinstein, Columbia University College of Physicians and Surgeons, New York, New York: I believe that emphasis of the fact that genetic factors influence susceptibility to cancer in the human being is extremely important. I believe also, however, that there is a very strong message to be learned from the abundant work in this area done in rodents and chickens; namely, the genetic influences to susceptibility may be very highly specific, both for certain viruses or for certain chemical carcino-gens. For example, the H2 locus in mice appears to influence suscepti-bility to the Gross leukemia virus but not necessarily to a DNA virus or a chemical carcinogen. Therefore, I think it is unlikely that there will be a single test for susceptibility to cancer of cells from human beings. One should probably test the carcinogens suspected in each case. For example, in leukemia patients, it is more likely that RNA viruses rather than SV40-type viruses might be of interest. Would you comment on this?

Dr. Hirschhorn: I agree with you completely. However, I am not sure as to which types of viruses or carcinogens should be tested. I think once this technique is available, it can be automated. One can probably grow large quantities or multiple dishes of fibroblasts and screen these with a variety of agents.

Dr. A. A. Saadi, University of Michigan Medical School, Ann Arbor, Michigan: Dr. Hirschhorn, have you looked at the ultrastructure of the membrane utilizing freeze-cleaving or freeze-etching techniques to see the changes in the membrane particles?

Dr. Hirschhorn: These studies are now in progress, but I have no results.

Interactions Between the Genetic Apparatus and Exogenous Agents

The Induction of Genetically Heterogeneous Cell Populations by Adenoviruses

H. F. STICH

Cancer Research Center, University of British Columbia, Vancouver, British Columbia, Canada

Chemical and physical mutagens, including several carcinogens, are able to convert a genetically homogeneous cell population into a heterogeneous one which comprises the source for mutant cell clones. A similar but more complex pattern appears to occur in cell cultures exposed to viruses (Moorhead and Saksela 1965; Stich and Yohn, 1967). In the latter system, new cell variants may result from virus-elicited mutations of the host genome, the addition of a viral genome (or part of it) to that of the host cell (Doerfler, 1968), the occurrence of mutants in the infecting virus population (Takemori, Riggs, and Aldrich, 1968), the possible appearance of mutants in the integrated viral genome, or from any combination of these and probably many other events. It is obvious that the multitude of possible alterations involving the interaction of host and viral genome makes understanding virus-induced oncogenesis and mutagenesis of higher organisms a formidable task. A review of cell variants encountered in primary or secondary cultures of Syrian hamster cells exposed to adenovirus 12 (Ad 12) may provide an example of the complex changes in cell population resulting from a nonlytic virus infection.

Cellular Tumor (T)-Antigen Content

The relative amount of Ad 12 T-antigen per cell was estimated by microphotometric evaluation of cell-bound, fluorescein-labeled T-antibodies (Stich and Yohn, unpublished data). Although this method is tedious and time-consuming, it yields information on the degree of variation of T-antigen per nucleus, cytoplasm, or entire cell. The results, part of which are summarized in the histogram shown in Figure 1, showed that the amount of T-antigen of individual cells spreads over a considerable range. In any sample taken from 24 to 62 hours postinfection, the

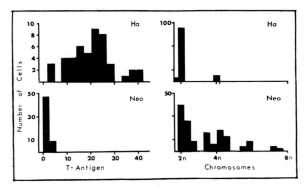

FIGURE 1. Microphotometric measurements of the T-antigen content in individual cells and the variation of chromosome numbers in Ad 12-infected secondary cultures (Ha) and in Ad 12-induced neoplastic cells (Neo) of Syrian hamsters. About 96 per cent of the neoplastic cells with a diploid chromosome number are pseudodiploid.

largest amount of T-antigen per cell can be as much as 40 times larger than the smallest detectable amount. Compared to the considerable variation of the T-antigen content in abortively infected hamster cells, the amount of T-antigen per Ad 12-transformed cells is relatively uniform (Stich and Yohn, unpublished data). Surprisingly small differences were also encountered between the average T-antigen content of three primary and two cultured Ad 12 neoplasms of Syrian hamsters. The amount of T-antigen per neoplastic cell is in the range of the average T-antigen content found in hamster cells infected with an input multiplicity of one and sampled 28 hours postinfection.

A comparison between variations in the amount of T-antigen and of chromosome complements is of particular interest (Figure 1). The values for T-antigen content per infected primary or secondary hamster cells, which have normal diploid karyotypes, vary widely. Conversely, neoplastic cells show considerable numerical and structural chromosome variations, but contain a relatively uniform amount of T-antigen. The formation of T-antigen and its control does not appear to depend on a particular karyotype, but rather seems to reflect the number of virus genomes per cell. The varying amounts of T-antigen synthesized could be caused by a normal distribution of viral genomes per cell.

Intracellular Distribution of T-Antigen

The localization of T-antigen, which appears in thread- and fleck-like structures in nucleus or cytoplasm, is affected by cell strain, type of infection (lytic or abortive), cell division, and period of T-antigen formation. Some examples are given in Figure 2. A considerable variation has been also encountered among cells of Ad 12-infected diploid hamster cell cultures: T-antigen-containing flecks can accumulate in nucleus (Figure 2c), cytoplasm (Figure 2d), or both. In cells at division or shortly after division, all the T-antigen-containing flecks are in the cytoplasm. These cytoplasmic flecks seem to be released from the dividing nucleus

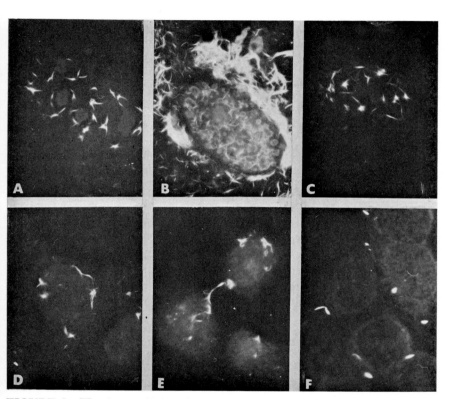

FIGURE 2. The intracellular distribution of T-antigen as revealed by the fluorescein-labeled antibody technique. a—Ad 12-infected H.Ep.-2 cell showing intranuclear T-antigen containing flecks; b—green monkey cell from a primary culture infected with Ad 12 and sampled 24 hours postinfection. An excessive number of T-antigen-containing flecks accumulate in the cytoplasm; c, d, and e—Ad 12-infected Syrian hamster cells of a secondary culture showing the T-antigen-containing flecks restricted to the nucleus (c), distributed in the cytoplasm (d), and in the cytoplasm of two daughter cells at advanced telophase (e); f—T-antigen containing flecks in several Ad 12-induced neoplastic cells of Syrian hamsters.

and are not included into the newly formed telophase nuclei (Figure 2e). In this connection, it is interesting to note the virtual restriction of T-antigen-containing flecks to the cytoplasm of neoplastic cells of three primary Ad 12 neoplasms and two cultured Ad 12 neoplasms.

Anomalies of the Mitotic Apparatus and Numerical Chromosome Aberrations

Abnormal chromosome numbers seem to stem mainly from anomalies of the mitotic apparatus, including multipolar mitosis, nondisjunction, incomplete separation of anaphase/telophase nuclei, lagging chromosomes, etc. All these mitotic irregularities were found to occur in hamster cells infected with human adenoviruses Ad 2, 4, 7, 12, or 18 and simian adenovirus SA7 and SV15 (Stich, Van Hoosier, and Trentin, 1964; Cooper, Yohn, and Stich, 1968). The capacity to interfere with the mitotic apparatus seems to differ among the tested adenoviruses: e.g., Ad 2 and 4 arrest dividing cells at metaphase, producing a colchicine-like effect. Ad 12 and 18 lack this capacity, but elicit multipolar mitosis, endoreduplication, and incomplete separation of anaphase/telophase nuclei (Figure 3). An accurate enumeration of cells with abnormal chromosome numbers is difficult because many lose their proliferative capacity. However, a rough estimate can be obtained by using microphotometric measurements of the deoxyribonucleic acid (DNA) content of nuclei in nondividing cells. It is assumed that a DNA content lower or higher than that of diploid cells indicates a loss or gain of chromosomes, respectively. Although this technique is relatively insensitive, as compared to actual chromosome analyses, its application revealed a considerable number of

TABLE 1. *Incidence (per cent) of Diploid (2n), Tetraploid (4n), Subdiploid (2n–) and Hyperdiploid to Subtetraploid (2n to 4n) Cells in a Secondary Culture of Syrian Hamster Cells Before and After Exposure to Ad 12 at 100 X Input Multiplicity and in Clones Derived from an Ad 12-Infected Cell Population.**

Cell population	2n Diploid	4n Tetraploid	2n– Subdiploid	2n to 4n	Total no. of cells analyzed
Control	92	7	0.9	0.1	180
Ad 12	56	33	7	4	220
Clones	100	—	—	—	420

* Estimates are based on microphotometric evaluation of Feulgen-stained preparations.
Abbreviation: Ad 12, adenovirus 12-infected Syrian hamster cells.

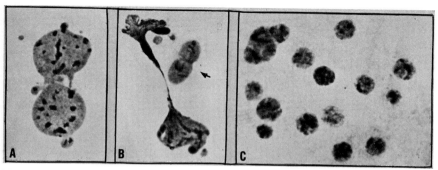

FIGURE 3. Various mitotic irregularities of secondary Syrian hamster cells exposed to Ad 12 and sampled 24 hours postinfection. a—partially fused nuclei, possibly the result of an incomplete anaphase/telophase; b—highly irregular telophase with several micronuclei (arrow); c—micronucleated cell. Orcein-stained preparation.

cells with a DNA content deviating from the diploid value (Table 1). Attempts to establish clones of cells with either aneuploid chromosome numbers or abnormal chromosomes have failed so far. This seems to be mainly the result of the relatively small number (107) of analyzed clones, since such karyotypically abnormal cells both occur and divide in Ad 12-infected cell populations.

Structural Chromosome Aberrations

Single or multiple chromatid and chromosome breaks comprise the main type of chromosome aberrations in Ad 12-infected hamster cells. It is tempting to assume that the abnormal karyotypes of Ad 12-transformed cells emerge from this wave of chromosome aberrations which follows viral infection; however, at the present time, such an assumption can be neither substantiated nor discarded. Chromosomes with a new morphology were observed in less than 1 per cent of cells harvested two to four days postinfection with Ad 12 at 100 × input multiplicity and were virtually absent from samples taken at later intervals. By about seven days postinfection, cells with normal diploid or tetraploid karyotypes had overgrown the population. This loss of proliferative capacity, or inability of most karyotypically abnormal cells to compete with normal ones, is also expressed in decreased cloning efficiency (zur Hausen, 1968). Cloning ability is affected significantly only by viral doses which elicit a high incidence of chromosome fragmentation and mitotic irregularities, including incomplete separation of anaphase plates (Figure 4).

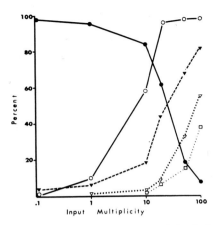

FIGURE 4. The clone-forming capacity (●——●) and the frequency of cells with T-antigen (○——○), chromosome aberrations (▼----▼), chromosome fragmentation (▽.....▽), and mitotic irregularities resulting from anomalies of the mitotic apparatus (□......□). Secondary cultures of Syrian hamster cells exposed to various input multiplicities of Ad 12 and sampled 24 hours post-infection.

Thus, cells with severe damage to mitotic apparatus or chromosome complement can hardly be considered to represent the raw material from which transformed cells emerge. The marked reduction in SA7-induced transformation frequency at a high input multiplicity could result from such an irreversible damage to chromosomes and/or mitotic apparatus (Casto, 1968). Mutagenesis and oncogenesis appear to result only from viral doses which cause few chromatid lesions and produce no damage, or only a reversible one, to the mitotic apparatus. It is even possible that most mutations occur at the subchromosomal level and do not involve major chromosome alterations (Nichols, 1968). Another point worth considering is the difference between the incidence of T-antigen-forming cells and that of chromosome aberrations; this is particularly evident at lower viral doses (Figure 4). However, it is difficult to decide whether the induction of chromosome or mitotic anomalies requires a minimal number of viral genomes or their products.

There seems to be little doubt that an abortive, noncytocidal adenovirus infection results in the formation of many cell variants, including karyotypically normal cells with viral genomes, karyotypically abnormal cells with or without viral genomes (judged by the presence or absence of T-antigen), and cells with a normal chromosome complement and without T-antigen. The latter ones may be the offspring of infected cells which have lost the viral genomes and repaired any induced chromatid lesions. Considering the small number of criteria used to distinguish different cell types, it can be concluded that the observed variety represents only a small fraction of a much wider spectrum. It is from this genetically heterogeneous cell population that the morphologically transformed cells stem. However, normal cells and karyotypically abnormal ones without detectable viral genomes also emerge from this same population. The latter type may be of particular interest because it represents a viral effect which could manifest itself in the absence of a viral genome in the cell. At present, it is difficult to decide which of the multitude of virus-elicited events are essential for transformation. The overwhelming majority of cell responses to infection may be completely irrelevant to transformation, which involves only a small proportion of all infected cells. This short survey should act as a reminder that the great variety of responses to viruses can be missed by exclusive reliance on methods which give only average values for relatively large cell populations.

REFERENCES

Casto, B. C. 1968. Adenovirus Transformation of Hamster Embryo Cells. *Journal of Virology*, 2:376–383.

Cooper, J. E. K., D. S. Yohn, and H. F. Stich. 1968. Viruses and Mammalian Chromosomes. X. Comparative Studies of the Chromosome Damage Induced by Human and Simian Adenoviruses. *Experimental Cell Research*, 53:225–240.

Doerfler, W. 1968. The Fate of the DNA of Adenovirus Type 12 in Baby Hamster Kidney Cells. *Proceedings of the National Academy of Sciences of the U.S.A.*, 60:636–643.

Hausen, H. zur. 1968. Chromosomal Aberrations and Cloning Efficiency in Adenovirus Type-12 Infected Hamster Cells. *Journal of Virology*, 2:915–917.

Moorhead, P. S., and E. Saksela. 1965. The Sequence of Chromosome Aberrations During SV40 Transformation of a Human Diploid Cell Strain. *Hereditas*, 52:271–284.

Nichols, W. W. 1968. "Somatic Mutation in Mammalian Cells," *Proceedings of XIIth International Congress on Genetics*. Vol. 2. Pp. 108–109.

Stich, H. F., G. L. Van Hoosier, and J. J. Trentin. 1964. Viruses and Mammalian Chromosomes. II. Chromosome Aberrations by Human Adenovirus Type 12. *Experimental Cell Research*, 34:400–403.

Stich, H. F., and D. S. Yohn. 1967. The Mutagenic Capacity of Adenoviruses for Mammalian Cells. *Nature*, 216:1292–1294.

———. Unpublished data.

Takemori, M., J. L. Riggs, and C. Aldrich. 1968. Genetic Studies with Tumorigenic Adenoviruses. I. Isolation of Cytocidal (cyt) Mutants of Adenovirus Type 12. *Virology*, 36:575–586.

Interactions of Chemical Carcinogens and Cellular Macromolecules: 4-Hydroxyaminoquinoline-1-Oxide and Polynucleotides

MARIKO TADA, MITSUHIKO TADA, AND TAIJO TAKAHASHI

Laboratory of Biochemistry, Aichi Cancer Center Research Institute, Nagoya, Japan

Interactions of chemical carcinogens and cellular macromolecules are essentially important to the understanding of the initiation process of carcinogenesis. Recent investigations using labeled carcinogens have provided new insight into the interactions of chemical carcinogens, or their active metabolites, with the cellular nucleic acids (Brookes, 1966; Warwick and Roberts, 1967; Warwick, 1967; Dingman and Sporn, 1967; Irving, Veazey, and Williard, 1967). We report here the interaction of a carcinogen, 4-hydroxyaminoquinoline-1-oxide (4HAQO), with the cellular nucleic acids.

4HAQO is assumed to be the active form of a carcinogen, 4-nitroquinoline-1-oxide (4NQO), whose carcinogenicity was first demonstrated by Nakahara, Fukuoka, and Sugimura (1957). Since their finding, many investigations on 4NQO carcinogenesis have been reported (see Nakahara, 1961; Endo, Ono, and Sugimura, in press); in vitro malignant transformation of cultured cells by 4NQO or 4HAQO also has been demonstrated using hamster embryonic cells (Sato and Kuroki, 1966; Kamahora and Kakunaga, 1966).

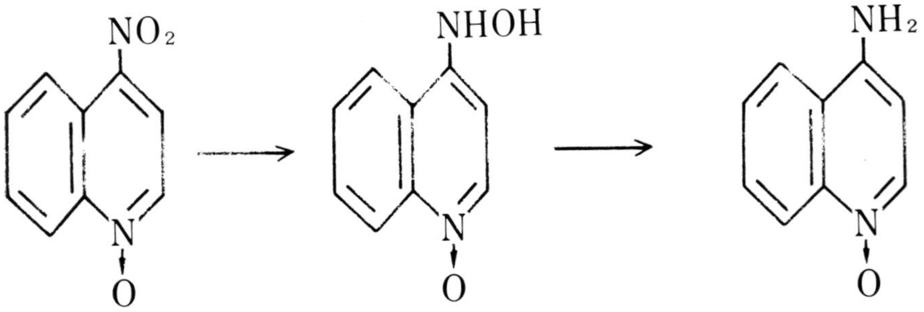

FIGURE 1. Metabolic conversions of 4NQO. From left to right, compounds are 4NQO, 4HAQO, and 4AQO.

TABLE 1. *Reducibilities by Hepatic Enzymes and Carcinogenic Activities of 4NQO Derivatives*

4NQO derivatives	Relative rate of reduction*	Carcinogenic activity†
4NQO	1.00	+
4NQO6C	2.95	+
6-Chloro-4NQO	4.05	+
2-Methyl-4NQO	0.22	+
4-Nitroquinoline	0.00	—
3-Methyl-4NQO	0.02	—
3-Chloro-4NQO	0.04	—
3-Methoxy-4NQO	0.01	—

* The reactions were carried out in the presence of 105,000 $\times$ *g* supernatant fraction of rat liver as an enzyme source; reduced nicotinamide adenine dinucleotide ($NADH_2$) was used as a hydrogen donor. Rate of reduction of 4NQO was normalized to 1.00. (From Sugimura, Otake, and Nagao [1966] and Sugimura [unpublished data].)

† Carcinogenic activity was tested by tumor formation at the site of subcutaneous injections in mice (Kawazoe, Tachibana, Aoki, and Nakahara, 1967).

Abbreviations: 4NQO, 4-nitroquinoline-1-oxide; 4NQO6C, 4-nitro-6-quinolinecarboxylic acid-1-oxide.

When 4NQO is administered, it is converted through 4HAQO to 4-aminoquinoline-1-oxide (4AQO) by reducing enzymes, one of which was identified in rat liver as a dehydrogenase using reduced nicotinamide adenine dinucleotide ($NADH_2$) or reduced nicotinamide adenine dinucleotide phosphate ($NADPH_2$) (Sugimura, Okabe, and Nagao, 1966) (Figure 1). Of the metabolites, 4HAQO is carcinogenic and 4AQO lacks carcinogenic activity. Furthermore, the reduction of 4NQO to 4HAQO is an essential process for 4NQO carcinogenesis. Therefore, 4HAQO is a key substance. Table 1 shows that the carcinogenic activities of 4NQO derivatives depend upon their reducibility (Sugimura, unpublished data).

Recent study by Andoh and Katsuta (1968) using ^{3}H-labeled 4NQO has shown that the major incorporation of radioactivity into the cellular components is into the protein fraction, with less incorporation into nucleic acid fractions, the same as reported for other carcinogens. Our interest has been focused on the interaction of 4HAQO with nucleic acids, mainly with deoxyribonucleic acid (DNA) as a genetic material. This report consists of two parts: (1) the binding of 4HAQO with DNA and ribonucleic acid (RNA) in the cell, and, especially, the nature of specific complexes between 4HAQO and DNA and (2) the structural and functional changes of DNA molecules by interaction with the carcinogen. Part of this work has been already published (Tada, Tada, and Takahashi, 1967).

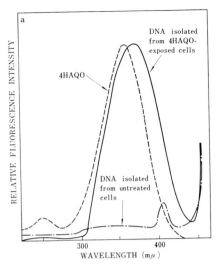
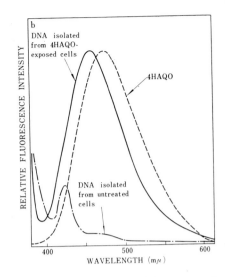

FIGURE 2. Excitation (a) and fluorescence (b) spectra of 4HAQO compared with those of DNA isolated from 4HAQO-exposed cells and from untreated cells. Fluorescence was measured in 1.5 mM sodium citrate (pH 7.3) containing 15 mM NaCl by a Hitachi Spectrofluorometer MPF-2. The figure shows uncorrected instrument readings. Concentrations of samples were 3 μM for 4HAQO and 1 mg/ml for DNA. (Redrawn from Tada, Tada, and Takahashi, 1967.)

The Binding of 4HAQO with DNA and RNA in the Cell

Rat ascites hepatoma cells, strain AH130, which were originally derived from a dimethylaminoazobenzene-induced hepatoma, were used throughout these experiments. 4HAQO was administered intraperitoneally by injection of 0.2 to 2.0 mg of 4HAQO in 0.5 ml of 50 per cent propyleneglycol. Ascites cells were collected 60 min after administration and washed with Hanks' solution. DNA was extracted from the cells by the method of Kay, Simmons, and Dounce (1952), followed by treatment with ribonuclease I$_2$ and phenol extraction. DNA was washed repeatedly with ethanol and acetone to remove free 4HAQO and its derivatives. The preparations contained less than 1 per cent protein. RNA was extracted from the cytoplasmic fraction at room temperature by the modification of the method of Scherrer and Darnell (1962). Total nucleic acids were obtained from whole cells in the same manner.

As shown in Figure 2, DNA isolated from 4HAQO-exposed cells was fluorescent; DNA isolated from untreated cells showed no characteristic fluorescence. While the fluorescence resembled that of 4HAQO, shifts were observed in both excitation and fluorescence maxima. Similar observations also were reported by Matsushima, Kobuna, and Sugimura (1967). RNA isolated from 4HAQO-exposed cells was also fluorescent and showed the same excitation and fluorescence spectra (Table 2). In another experiment, RNA and DNA were extracted together by phenol in the presence of sodium lauryl sulfate and chromatographed on a methylated albumin-kieselguhr (MAK) column. Figure 3 shows that fluorescence was associated with DNA and all species of RNA.

When the DNA preparation was heated to 100 C, much of the fluorescent compound was released and recovered from the supernatant solutions after ethanol precipitation of DNA. The fluorescence properties of the released compound were similar to those of the bound form. The fluorescent compound, both in the bound and released forms, was not identical with 4HAQO, 4AQO, 4NQO, or 4-hydroxyquinoline-1-oxide (4HQO), nor with the oxidative condensation product of 4HAQO which

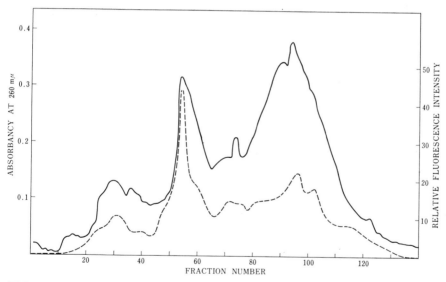

FIGURE 3. MAK chromatography of nucleic acids isolated from 4HAQO-exposed cells. Nucleic acids were loaded on a column which was prepared according to the method of Sueoka and Cheng (1962). Elution was carried out at 35 C with a linear gradient from 0.4 M to 1.6 M NaCl in 0.05 M phosphate buffer (pH 6.9). ——, Ultraviolet absorption at 260 mμ; ----, fluorescence intensity at 460 mμ excited at 375 mμ. From left to right, main peaks of ultraviolet absorption represent soluble RNA, DNA, and ribosomal RNA (Tada, Tada, and Takahashi, unpublished data).

TABLE 2. *Fluorescence Characteristics of Nucleic Acids Isolated from 4HAQO-Exposed Cells, 4HAQO, and its Derivatives**

	Excitation maxima (mμ)	Fluorescence maxima (mμ)
DNA isolated from 4HAQO-exposed cells	375	460
RNA isolated from 4HAQO-exposed cells	375	460
Released compound†	375	460
4HAQO	360	478
4AQO	365	478
4HQO	360	480
4NQO‡	360	480
Condensation product of 4HAQO§	420, 440, 470	550

* Fluorometry was carried out as described in the legend to Figure 2. (Reprinted from Tada, Tada, and Takahashi, 1967.)
† Compound released from the DNA-carcinogen complexes by heating.
‡ 4NQO becomes fluorescent by radiation of 360 mμ light.
§ Most probably 4,4'-azoxyquinoline-1,1'-dioxide.
Abbreviations: 4AQO, 4-aminoquinoline-1-oxide; 4HAQO, 4-hydroxyaminoquinoline-1-oxide; 4HQO, 4-hydroxyquinoline-1-oxide; 4NQO, 4-nitroquinoline-1-oxide.

is formed at pH 7.3 and is most probably 4,4'-azoxyquinoline-1,1'-dioxide (Ishizawa and Endo, 1967). Fluorescence characteristics of nucleic acids isolated from 4HAQO-exposed cells, 4HAQO, and its derivatives are summarized in Table 2.

Further studies on the nature of the fluorescent compounds bound to DNA and RNA also suggested that both interactions of the carcinogen with DNA and RNA were similar and that the compound was not identical to 4HAQO and its derivatives tested. Absorption spectra of the complexes with DNA and RNA had maxima at 360 mμ at pH 6, and both at 345 and 445 mμ at pH 12. The change of absorption maxima by pH was reversible.

Figure 4a shows the effect of pH on the fluorescence intensity of the complexes and the released compound. Both bound and released compounds showed similar pH-fluorescence curves, with a sharp peak at pH 9. In both compounds, these characteristics are quite different from those of 4HAQO, 4AQO, and 4HQO, as shown in Figure 4b.

DNA isolated from 4HAQO-exposed cells was hydrolyzed to 3'-mononucleotides by micrococcal nuclease and spleen phosphodiesterase, and the hydrolysate was chromatographed on a Dowex-1 column. The fluorescent material was eluted together with the nucleotides. The ribonuclease T$_2$-hydrolysate of RNA isolated from the exposed cells showed similar results. The finding that the fluorescent material still binds to nucleotides after enzymic digestion suggests that the fluorescent compound is associated with nucleic acids by covalent bonding rather than by intercalation.

Quite recently, Enomoto, Sato, Miller, and Miller (1968) have reported that diacetyl-4HAQO is much more reactive than 4HAQO and reacts with DNA in vitro in an atmosphere of nitrogen. It will be interesting to see whether the in vitro product reported by them has the same nature as that of our in vivo 4HAQO and DNA product.

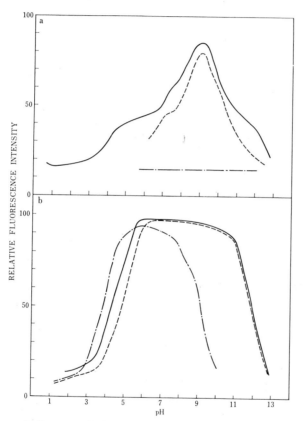

FIGURE 4. a—Influence of pH on the fluorescence of the DNA-carcinogen complexes isolated from 4HAQO-exposed cells (– – – –), the released compound from the complexes by heat (———), and DNA from untreated cells (—·——·——·). Excitation, 375 mμ; emission, 460 mμ (Tada, Tada, and Takahashi, unpublished data). b—Influence of pH on the fluorescence of 4HAQO (—·——·——·), 4AQO (———), and 4HQO (– – – –). The wavelengths of exciting light for 4HAQO, 4AQO, and 4HQO were 360, 365, and 360 mμ, respectively. Emission of 4HAQO, 4AQO, and 4HQO were measured at 478, 478, and 480 mμ, respectively (Tada, Tada, and Takahashi, unpublished data).

TABLE 3. *Binding of the Carcinogen to DNA and Its Effect on the Template Ability of DNA in the DNA-Dependent RNA Polymerase System**

Source of DNA	Relative fluorescence intensity at 460 mμ	^{14}C-GMP incorporation (counts/min/ mg DNA/hr)	Relative rate of incorporation (per cent)
DNA isolated from untreated cells	7	21,630	100
DNA isolated from 4HAQO-exposed cells	100	3,330	15
	70	8,680	40
	38	10,690	49
	30	13,710	63

* Various amounts of 4HAQO were administered intraperitoneally to give a final concentration of 0.05 to 0.5 mM in the ascites fluid.

The reaction mixture (0.25 ml) contained, in μmoles: Tris-HCl (pH 7.6), 30; magnesium acetate, 1.5; MnCl$_2$, 0.5; β-mercaptoethylamine, 1.5; 8-^{14}C-GTP, 0.1 (20 mμc); ATP, CTP, and UTP, 0.1 each; 10 μg of DNA; and 100 units of polymerase. After incubation for 60 min at 37 C, radioactivity incorporated in the fraction insoluble in cold 5 per cent trichloroacetic acid was measured in a windowless gas flow counter. Condition of fluorometry was as described in the legend to Figure 2. (From Tada, Tada, and Takahashi, 1967.)

Abbreviations: ATP, adenosine 5'-triphosphate; CTP, cytidine 5'-triphosphate; GMP, guanosine 5'-monophosphate; GTP, guanosine 5'-triphosphate; and UTP, uridine 5'-triphosphate.

Molecular Changes in DNA Isolated from 4HAQO-Exposed Cells

If 4HAQO really interacts with DNA, it would be expected that 4HAQO causes structural and functional changes in DNA molecules.

The average molecular weight for DNA was determined following the method of Studier (1965) using a Spinco model E ultracentrifuge. By this analysis, DNA's isolated from 4HAQO-exposed cells and from untreated cells have approximately the same molecular weight, *i.e.*, 8×10^6 and 11×10^6, respectively. When denaturation was performed, either by alkali or by heat, the single-stranded form of control DNA showed a molecular weight of 5.1×10^6, one half that of the native form. On the other hand, the single-stranded form of DNA isolated from 4HAQO-exposed cells showed a molecular weight of 1.4×10^6, one sixth of that of native DNA. This indicates that DNA isolated from 4HAQO-exposed cells must have an average of two breaks per single strand. It is not clear whether the breaks are present before denaturation or whether they occur at the interaction sites because of exposure to alkali or high temperature. Recently, single strand breaks of DNA by 4HAQO in vitro also were reported by Sugimura, Otake, and Matsushima (1968).

Another attempt to detect dysfunction of DNA was made by examining template ability of the carcinogen-DNA complexes for DNA-dependent RNA polymerase which was highly purified from *Escherichia coli* (Tada and Tada, 1970). The amount of fluorescent compound bound depended on the dose of the administered carcinogen and there was a reciprocal relationship between the extent of binding and total RNA synthesis (Table 3). However, 4HAQO and 4AQO did not affect the enzyme activity in the assay system at 2×10^{-6} M concentration. At this concentration, 4HAQO shows a fluorescence 10 times higher than that of the complexes. Therefore, the loss of template activity is caused by a modification of DNA, rather than by contamination of the DNA preparation by free 4HAQO or 4AQO.

To elucidate the mechanism of 4HAQO binding, we analyzed the template ability of DNA for the polymerase reaction. It is known that the polymerase reaction consists of at least four steps: (1) binding of enzyme at the definite sites on template DNA, (2) initiation of RNA synthesis, (3) chain elongation and synthesis of complementary RNA by enzyme sliding on the template DNA strand, and (4) termination. The RNA chains formed by RNA polymerase contain ribonucleoside triphosphates at their initiation points (Maitra and Hurwitz, 1965; Bremer, Konrad, Gaines, and Stent, 1965); thus, the label from γ-^{32}P-nucleoside triphosphates is incorporated only at the 5'-terminus (Figure 5).

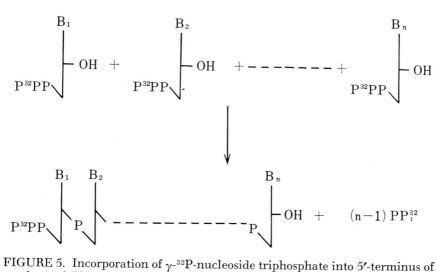

FIGURE 5. Incorporation of γ-^{32}P-nucleoside triphosphate into 5'-terminus of synthesized RNA.

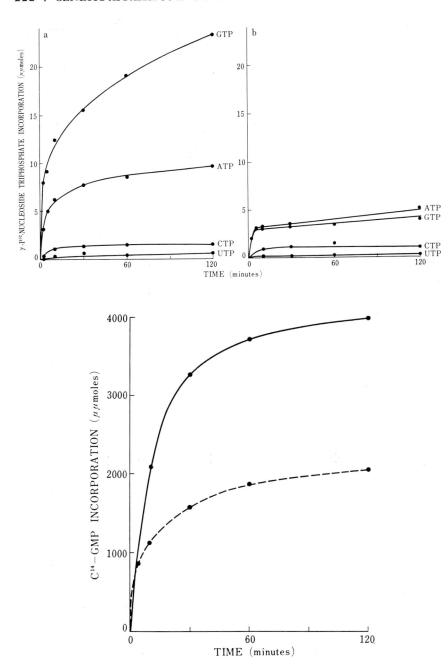

FIGURES 6 and 7: See legends on page 223.

FIGURE 6. Influence of the 4HAQO-interaction with DNA on initiation of RNA synthesis: a—DNA isolated from 4HAQO-exposed cells as template; b—DNA isolated from untreated cells as template. The reaction mixtures (1.5 ml) contained in each case Tris-HCl buffer, pH 7.6, 180 μmoles; magnesium acetate, 9 μmoles; $MnCl_2$, 3 μmoles; β-mercaptoethylamine, 9 μmoles; adenosine 5'-triphosphate (ATP), uridine 5'-triphosphate (UTP), cytidine 5'-triphosphate (CTP), and GTP, 0.6 μmole each, one labeled with ^{32}P in the γ-phosphorus (4 to 5 $\times$ 10^8 counts/min/μmole); DNA, 75 μg; and 75 units of RNA polymerase. Incubation was at 37 C. At the indicated time, 0.2-ml aliquots were removed for assay. The reactions were terminated by the addition of 1 mg of yeast RNA followed by 0.2 ml of 7 per cent $HClO_4$. The acid-insoluble pellet was washed essentially according to the procedure of Maitra and Hurwitz (1965). Radioactivity was counted in a gasflow counter (Tada, Tada, and Takahashi, unpublished data).

FIGURE 7. Influence of the 4HAQO-interaction with DNA on total RNA synthesis. – – – – –, DNA isolated from 4HAQO-exposed cells as template; ———, DNA isolated from untreated cells as template. The reactions were carried out as described in Figure 6, except that $8\text{-}^{14}C\text{-}GTP$ (0.2 mc/mmole) was used in place of ^{32}P label. Radioactivity incorporated in the fraction insoluble in cold trichloroacetic acid was measured in a windowless gas flow counter (Tada, Tada, and Takahashi, unpublished data).

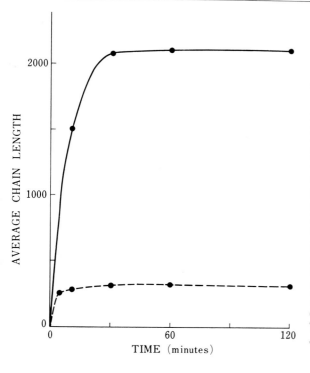

FIGURE 8. Influence of the 4HAQO interaction with DNA on the average c h a i n length of synthesized RNA. – – – –, DNA isolated from 4HAQO-exposed cells as template; —, DNA isolated from untreated cells as template. The average chain length was calculated as follows: 5$\times$ $^{14}C\text{-}GMP$ incorporation (as shown in Figure 7) divided by the total γ-^{32}P-nucleoside triphosphate incorporation (as shown in Figure 6) (Tada, Tada, and Takahashi, unpublished data).

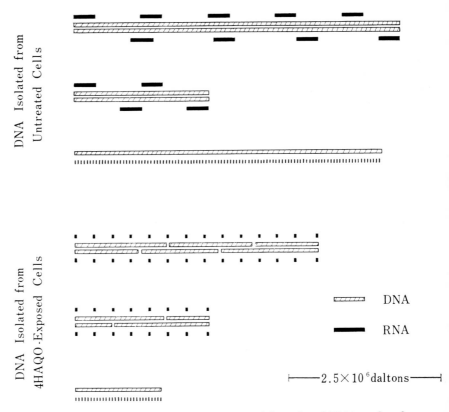

DNA Isolated from Untreated Cells

DNA Isolated from 4HAQO-Exposed Cells

▭▭▭ DNA

━━ RNA

⊢————2.5×10⁶daltons————⊣

FIGURE 9. Diagram of relative numbers and lengths of RNA molecules produced by transcription of DNA templates. The templates used were native DNA, sheared (half-length) DNA, and denatured (single-stranded) DNA from untreated and 4HAQO-exposed cells.

In the following studies, numbers of chain initiation were estimated by incorporation of γ-^{32}P-nucleoside triphosphates into the 5'-end of the synthesized RNA; the amount of total RNA synthesis was estimated by ^{14}C-labeled guanosine 5'-triphosphate (GTP) incorporation. The ratio of total RNA formed to total chain initiation represents the average chain length of the synthesized RNA.

By these criteria, we compared template abilities of DNA's isolated from both 4HAQO-exposed cells and from some untreated cells. The amounts of chain initiation occurring on DNA isolated from 4HAQO-exposed cells are shown in Figure 6a, and those occurring on normal DNA are shown in Figure 6b. RNA chains were initiated almost exclusively by purine nucleoside triphosphates, as reported by other workers (Maitra and Hurwitz, 1965; Bremer, Konrad, Gaines, and Stent, 1965). It is evident that the attack of 4HAQO on DNA results in a large increase in chain initiation. Nevertheless, Figure 7 shows that DNA isolated from 4HAQO-exposed cells supports less total RNA synthesis than did normal DNA. From these results, the average chain length of the RNA synthesized was calculated (Figure 8). The average chain length of RNA synthesized on normal DNA reached approximately 2,200 nucleotides, however, a large number of short RNA chains (approximately 320 nucleotides long) were synthesized on DNA isolated from 4HAQO-exposed cells. It is not yet known whether increase in initiation of RNA synthesis is caused by an increase in the number of initiation sites or by an increase in initiation frequency. When heat-denatured DNA was tested as template, a high rate of initiations occurred and very short RNA molecules (approximately 130 nucleotides long) were synthesized (data not shown; see Maitra and Hurwitz, 1965, and Tada and Tada, 1969). Half-length molecule of DNA, obtained by shearing, showed almost normal template ability (data not shown).

The relative numbers and average lengths of RNA molecules synthesized on various DNA templates are diagrammed in Figure 9. Changes in template ability similar to those caused by 4HAQO exposure are produced by denaturation of the DNA, although denaturation results in greater damage to the template ability. Thus, it seems likely that DNA isolated from 4HAQO-exposed cells may contain partly denatured or loose base-pairing segments in the molecule.

Summary

4HAQO, a reduced form of 4NQO, is highly carcinogenic. Our investigations by exposure of ascites hepatoma cells to 4HAQO have shown the formation of specific complexes between 4HAQO and cellular DNA or RNA. DNA and RNA isolated from 4HAQO-exposed cells had characteristic fluorescence similar to, but not identical with that of 4HAQO. The DNA-4HAQO complexes did not show normal template ability during transcription by purified DNA-dependent RNA polymerase from *E. coli*; a high rate of initiation and a low degree of total synthesis resulted in production of very short RNA molecules. Also, single strand breaks occurred in the DNA molecules of the complexes.

ACKNOWLEDGMENTS

The authors wish to express their sincere thanks to Miss K. Kunda for performing the analytical ultracentrifugation.

This study was supported in part by a Grant-in-Aid for Cancer Research from the Ministry of Education of Japan.

LIST OF ABBREVIATIONS

4AQO—4-aminoquinoline-1-oxide
ATP—adenosine 5'-triphosphate
CTP—cytidine 5'-triphosphate
DNA—deoxyribonucleic acid
GTP—guanosine 5'-triphosphate
4HAQO—4-hydroxyaminoquinoline-1-oxide
4HQO—4-hydroxyquinoline-1-oxide
NADH$_2$—reduced nicotinamide adenine dinucleotide
NADPH$_2$—reduced nicotinamide adenine dinucleotide phosphate
4NQO—4-nitroquinoline-1-oxide
4NQO6C—4-nitro-6-quinolinecarboxylic acid-1-oxide
RNA—ribonucleic acid
Tris—Tris(hydroxymethyl)-aminomethane
UTP—uridine 5'-triphosphate

REFERENCES

Andoh, T., and H. Katsuta. 1968. Carcinogenesis in Tissue Culture. XXIII. On the Binding of 4NQO in Culture to Macromolecules of Lp3 Cells Propagated in a Protein-free, Lipid-free Synthetic Medium. (Abstract) *Proceedings of the Twenty-Seventh Annual Meeting of the Japanese Cancer Association* (October, 1968, Tokyo, Japan). Pp. 94–95.

Bremer, H., M. W. Konrad, K. Gaines, and G. S. Stent. 1965. Direction of Chain Growth in Enzymic RNA Synthesis. *Journal of Molecular Biology*, 13:540–553.

Brookes, P. 1966. Quantitative Aspects of the Reaction of Some Carcinogens with Nucleic Acids and the Possible Significance of Such Reactions in the Process of Carcinogenesis. *Cancer Research*, 26:1994–2003.

Dingman, C. W., and M. B. Sporn. 1967. The Binding of Metabolites of Aminoazo Dyes to Rat Liver DNA In Vivo. *Cancer Research*, 27:938–944.

Endo, H., T. Ono, and T. Sugimura, Editors. *Chemistry and Biological Actions of 4-Nitroquinoline-1-oxide, a Carcinogen.* Heidelberg, Germany: Springer-Verlag. (in press.)

Enomoto, M., K. Sato, E. C. Miller, and J. A. Miller. 1968. Reactivity of the Diacetyl Derivative of the Carcinogen 4-Hydroxyaminoquinoline-1-oxide with DNA, RNA, and Other Nucleophiles. *Life Sciences*, 7 (Part II):1025–1032.

Irving, C. C., R. A. Veazey, and R. F. Williard. 1967. On the Significance and Mechanism of the Binding of 2-Acetylaminofluorene and N-Hydroxy-2-acetyl-aminofluorene to Rat-Liver Ribonucleic Acid In Vivo. *Cancer Research*, 27:720–725.

Ishizawa, M., and H. Endo. 1967. On the Mode of Action of a Potent Carcinogen, 4-Hydroxylaminoquinoline 1-Oxide on Bacteriophage T4. *Biochemical Pharmacology*, 16:637–646.

Kamahora, J., and T. Kakunaga. 1966. In Vitro Carcinogenesis of 4-Nitroquinoline-1-Oxide with Golden Hamster Embryonic Cells. *Proceedings of the Japan Academy*, 42:1079–1081.

Kawazoe, Y., M. Tachibana, K. Aoki, and W. Nakahara. 1967. The Structure-

Carcinogenicity Relationship Among Derivatives of 4-Nitro and 4-Hydroxylamino-quinoline 1-Oxides. *Biochemical Pharmacology*, 16:631–636.

Kay, E. R. M., N. S. Simmons, and A. L. Dounce. 1952. An Improved Preparation of Sodium Desoxyribonucleate. *The Journal of the American Chemical Society*, 74:1724–1726.

Maitra, U., and J. Hurwitz. 1965. The Role of DNA in RNA Synthesis. IX. Nucleoside Triphosphate Termini in RNA Polymerase Products. *Proceedings of the National Academy of Sciences of the U.S.A.*, 54:815–822.

Matsushima, T., I. Kobuna, and T. Sugimura. 1967. In Vivo Interaction of 4-Nitroquinoline-1-oxide and its Derivatives with DNA. *Nature*, 216:508.

Nakahara, W. 1961. Critique of Carcinogenic Mechanism. *Progress in Experimental Tumor Research*, 2:158–202.

Nakahara, W., F. Fukuoka, and T. Sugimura. 1957. Carcinogenic Action of 4-Nitroquinoline-N-Oxide. *Gann*, 48:129–137.

Sato, H., and T. Kuroki. 1966. Malignization In Vitro of Hamster Embryonic Cells by Chemical Carcinogens. *Proceedings of the Japan Academy*, 42:1211–1216.

Scherrer, K., and J. E. Darnell. 1962. Sedimentation Characteristics of Rapidly Labelled RNA from HeLa Cells. *Biochemical and Biophysical Research Communications*, 7:486–490.

Studier, F. W. 1965. Sedimentation Studies of the Size and Shape of DNA. *Journal of Molecular Biology*, 11:373–390.

Sueoka, N., and T. Cheng. 1962. Fractionation of Nucleic Acids with the Methylated Albumin Column. *Journal of Molecular Biology*, 4:161–172.

Sugimura, T. Unpublished data.

Sugimura, T., K. Okabe, and M. Nagao. 1966. The Metabolism of 4-Nitroquinoline-1-Oxide, a Carcinogen. III. An Enzyme Catalyzing the Conversion of 4-Nitroquinoline-1-Oxide to 4-Hydroxyaminoquinoline-1-Oxide in Rat Liver and Hepatomas. *Cancer Research*, 26:1717–1721.

Sugimura, T., H. Otake, and T. Matsushima. 1968. Single Strand Scissions of DNA Caused by a Carcinogen, 4-Hydroxyaminoquinoline 1-Oxide. *Nature*, 218:392.

Tada, M., and M. Tada. 1969. Nucleotide Sequences at the 5'-Termini of In Vitro Synthesized RNA. *Biochemical and Biophysical Research Communications*, 35:27–34.

———. 1970. Purification of DNA-dependent RNA Polymerase from *Escherichia coli*. *Journal of Biochemistry* (Tokyo), 67:139–141.

Tada, M., M. Tada, and T. Takahashi. 1967. Interaction of a Carcinogen, 4-Hydroxyaminoquinoline-1-oxide with Nucleic Acids. *Biochemical and Biophysical Research Communications*, 29:469–477.

———. Unpublished data.

Warwick, G. P. 1967. The Covalent Binding of Metabolites of 4-Dimethylamino-2-methylazobenzene to Rat-Liver Nucleic Acids, and the Carcinogenicity of the Compound in Partially Hepatectomized Rats. *The Biochemical Journal*, 104:6 p.

Warwick, G. P., and J. J. Roberts. 1967. Persistent Binding of Butter Yellow Metabolites to Rat Liver DNA. *Nature*, 213:1206–1207.

Mechanisms of Chemically Induced Chromosome Abnormalities

MAIMON M. COHEN, ROCHELLE HIRSCHHORN AND
ARNOLD I. FREEMAN

Division of Human Genetics, Department of Pediatrics,
School of Medicine, State University of New York at Buffalo, and
Buffalo Children's Hospital, Buffalo, New York;
Department of Medicine, New York University Medical Center, New York, New York,
and Department of Pediatrics, Roswell Park Memorial Institute, Buffalo, New York

The types of exogenous agents capable of causing chromosome aberrations include irradiation, viruses, physical stimuli, and chemicals. The chemicals can further be subdivided into those compounds affecting the biosynthesis of the informational macromolecules (deoxyribonucleic acid [DNA], ribonucleic acid [RNA], and protein); antitumor agents; antibiotics; mono- and bifunctional alkylating agents; nitroso compounds; and a miscellaneous group of heterogeneous agents (Lea, 1955; Revell, 1953; Kihlman, 1961, 1966; Ostertag, 1966; Cohen and Shaw, 1965). It should be emphasized that it is not necessarily the breaks per se, but the mechanisms by which they arise which are of the greatest interest and will ultimately yield information concerning chromosome structure and function. Although chromosome breaks might appear morphologically identical and their nonrandom distribution among and within chromosomes similar, regardless of the inducing agent (Cohen and Shaw, 1965), it is quite probable that various agents act through different mechanisms.

Most mechanisms of chromosome breakage are unknown; however, several suggestions based on the known biochemical action of some of these compounds have been made. One hypothesis concerns the interaction with nucleic acids and involves the inhibition of the ribonucleotide synthesis by such agents as adenine and azaserine. Since these compounds act at the level of purine synthesis, both DNA and RNA are affected (Kihlman, 1966). A second class of compounds acts after the separation of the common pathway of DNA and RNA synthesis, *e.g.* between purine and pyrimidine synthesis and the formation of the deoxyriboside triphosphates, as is the case for 5-fluorodeoxyuridine (FUdR) and 2'-adenine deoxyriboside (AdR) which affect DNA but not RNA synthesis (Kihlman, 1966). Yet a third mechanism is suggested by those agents which interact with primer DNA. Since primer DNA will serve in the biosynthesis of both DNA and RNA through polymerase reactions, such agents will inhibit the synthesis of both nucleic acids (Elliott, 1963; Reich, 1964; Warig, 1963).

A second group of mechanisms concerns the degradation and denaturation of DNA after its synthesis. This concept is supported by data from those agents which cause chromosomal damage subsequent to the synthesis (S) period, *i.e.* early prophase. It is obvious that the cytological damage, in such cases, cannot have a direct effect on DNA synthesis, which is completed before prophase begins. Therefore, such damage necessitates the interaction of the agent and the DNA-protein complex. The chemicals streptonigrin, caffeine, and actinomycin D have yielded evidence suggestive of such interaction. Streptonigrin initiates a rapid breakdown of *Escherichia coli* DNA (Radding, 1963), caffeine combines with DNA to alter its physical properties by denaturation (Ts'o, Helkamp, and Sander, 1962; Ts'o and Lu, 1964), and actinomycin D impairs DNA template capacity (Reich, 1964).

The action of many chromosome-breaking agents, however, is thought to be alkylation or the incorporation of anomalous base analogs leading to the production of abnormal DNA. It is generally considered that, in this case, the DNA itself, rather than its precursors, is affected and the alkylation of the heterocyclic nitrogen in the bases is the target (Stacey, Cobb, Cousens, and Alexander, 1958). Cross-linking of DNA moieties by agents such as mitomycin C (Schwartz, Sodergren, and Phillips, 1963; Iyer and Szybalski, 1963) is considered to be important in this process.

Additionally, several mechanisms not integrally related to DNA or precursor synthesis have been proposed. It has long been contended that the cytological effects of X-irradiation are a result of the formation of free radicals (Lea, 1955). It has also been suggested that faulty adenosine triphosphate (ATP) and protein synthesis requisite for the repair of chromosome breaks might be implicated and that the mutagenicity of some agents is not caused by actual chromosome breakage but by the prevention of successful repair of breaks (Wolff, 1960; Wolff and Luippold, 1955). Therefore, there might be an actual potentiation of the chromosome-breaking ability of some agents when used in combination with each other (Somers and Humphrey, 1963; Humphrey and Dewey, 1965).

A curious paradox exists between stages of the cell cycle and chromosome breakage induced by some agents. Many agents when utilized during the DNA S period yield aberrations which appear to be induced during G2, *e.g.* chromatid breaks. While some agents are active in almost all phases of the cell cycle, others, although present during G1 and S periods, seem to cause most of the chromosome damage during G2. Several explanations can be suggested to account for this phenomenon; one of the more engaging hypotheses involves a "delayed reaction" related to enzymatic release. It may be that the primary action of the drug or agent in question is not on the chromosome itself, but on some other cellular component. The initial effect may be to induce a metabolic imbalance involving enzymatic pathways which will ultimately be expressed as chromosome damage only at a later stage in cell cycle. Therefore, the quantitative "end point" of chromosome breakage may indeed be a secondary response to a metabolic insult occurring prior to mitosis but capable of expression only during chromosome visualization.

Such an hypothesis concerning the enzymatic digestion of DNA has been suggested by investigators who have demonstrated that degraded DNA resulting from mitomycin C treatment is an indirect effect produced by deoxyribonuclease (Kersten, 1962; Kersten, Kersten, Leopold, and Schnieders, 1964). Fragmentation of isolated dipteran lampbrush chromosomes in vitro by deoxyribonuclease has also been described (MacGregor and Callan, 1962). It is reasonable, therefore, to consider that the release of deoxyribonuclease during a period of the cell cycle when the chromosomes are quite vulnerable may lead to the subsequent production of chromosomal abnormalities. Supporting evidence for this hypothesis has been suggested by recent studies on lysosomes. Changes in various lysosomal enzymes have been implicated in viral pathogenicity (Allison and Mallucci, 1965; Mallucci and Allison, 1965). It has also been suggested that the release of lysosomal deoxyribonuclease caused by the destabilization of lysosomal membranes in human diploid cells produces chromosomal aberrations (Allison and Paton, 1965). Additionally, the injection of isogenic lysosomes into mice leads to the production of chromosome anomalies (Venuat, Theron, Bresson, and Cattan, 1968).

Therefore, the possibility that lysosomal destabilization with subsequent enzyme release might be implicated in chemically induced chromosome damage was investigated. It has been demonstrated that a variety of agents, predominantly glucocorticoids, possess that capability of stabilizing lysosomal membranes (see review by Weissman, 1968). The rationale underlying the following experiments was derived from the fact that pretreatment of cells with such "stabilizers" might serve to protect against labilization of lysosomal membranes, thereby inhibiting enzyme release and subsequent chromosome damage.

Materials and Methods

CELL CULTURES

Heparinized blood was obtained from normal healthy donors and allowed to settle by gravity in the syringe at 37 C for approximately two hours. Leukocyte-rich plasma was decanted into Falcon plastic tissue culture flasks and further incubated for two successive 30-minute periods to eliminate polymorphonuclear neutrophils (PMN). Following transfer, the cells were incubated for an additional 24 hours in Eagle's minimal essential medium (MEM) at 37 C. Cell counts following incubation indicated that small lymphocytes comprised 90 to 95 per cent of the cell population with approximately 5 to 10 per cent contamination by PMN's.

Cultures of this semipurified lymphocyte suspension (1 × 10⁶ cells/ ml) were initiated in Eagle's MEM (Spinner) medium with 25 per cent fetal calf serum, penicillin (100 units/ml), streptomycin (100 mg/ml), and 0.1 mg/ml phytohemagglutinin (PHA) (Burroughs-Wellcome, Inc., Beckenham, England). Two replicate cultures were incubated for each treatment in all cases and the results are presented as their mean. The cultures were incubated at 37 C for 72 hours, the last two hours in the presence of 0.05 µg/ml Colcemid (CIBA Pharmaceutical Inc., Summit, New Jersey) to accumulate cells in metaphase. At various times during this incubation period, different agents were added to the cultures.

The cells were harvested according to a modification of the method of Moorhead *et al.* (1960). After incubation, the medium was decanted and replaced by a hypotonic (1.0 per cent) sodium citrate solution (37 C for 15 minutes). Fixation was achieved by three changes of a 3:1 absolute methanol:glacial acetic acid solution. Slides were prepared by placing several drops of cell suspension on a microscope slide preimmersed in 70 per cent methanol and passing the slide through a flame for ignition.

ADDED EXOGENOUS AGENTS

Those drugs added to the cultures included the solvent, dimethyl sulfoxide (DMSO), various lysosomal stabilizers, the antibiotics streptonigrin and mitomycin C, and vitamin A alcohol.

Dimethyl sulfoxide

Because of the insolubility of the various lysosomal stabilizers and the vitamin A alcohol, DMSO (J. T. Baker Chemical Company, Phillipsburg, New Jersey, Lot #32079) was used as a solvent. The various drugs were initially dissolved in DMSO with subsequent solutions made using distilled water. The final concentration of DMSO in the cultures never exceeded 1.0 per cent.

Lysosomal Stabilizers

Four lysosomal stabilizers were added to the lymphocyte cultures in concentrations of 10^{-3} M, 10^{-5} M, and 10^{-7} M. Each of these concentrations was tested for 72, 48, 24. and 4 hours prior to harvest of the cells to assess their chromosome-breaking potential. The drugs used were:

1. Prednisolone acetate (PR)—Intra products, Dayton, Ohio (Lot #279).
2. Hydrocortisone 21-(dihydrogen phosphate) (HY)—Merck Sharp and Dohme Research Laboratory, West Point, New York (Lot #0585).
3. Chloroquine dihydrochloride (CL)—Winthrop Laboratories, New York, New York (Lot #RO15UK).
4. Cortisone acetate (CA)—Intra products, Dayton, Ohio (Lot #V11 B01-7479).

Vitamin A

Vitamin A alcohol was used as a lysosomal membrane labilizer. The drug was obtained from Dr. W. E. Scott (Hoffman-LaRoche, Inc., Nutley, New Jersey—Lot #NK-16). Vitamin A alcohol was dissolved in pure DMSO; subsequent dilutions were made in 10 per cent DMSO. Final concentrations of vitamin A in the lymphocyte cultures were 10^{-4} M, 10^{-5} M, and 10^{-7} M; these were tested for 48, 24, and 4 hours prior to harvest of the cells.

Chromosome-Breaking Agents

The streptomyces-derived antibiotics streptonigrin and mitomycin C were employed as chromosome-breaking agents. It has previously been demonstrated that both of these drugs have profound effects on the morphology of leukocyte chromosomes (Cohen, Shaw, and Craig, 1963; Cohen, 1963; Cohen and Shaw, 1964; Shaw and Cohen, 1965).

Streptonigrin (SN)

Streptonigrin was obtained from Dr. T. McBride of C. Pfizer, Inc.,

Brooklyn, New York. The powder was dissolved in acetone (1 mg/ml) and further dilutions were made with distilled water. From previous experiments (Cohen, Shaw, and Craig, 1963), it was known that a concentration of 0.01 μg/ml for the final 24 hours of culture yielded significant chromosomal damage and allowed the recovery of sufficient analyzable metaphase cells.

Mitomycin C (MC)

Mitomycin C was obtained from Bristol Laboratories, Inc.. Syracuse, New York (Lot #58F 606). The drug was dissolved in distilled water and used in a final concentration of 1.0 μg/ml for the last 24 hours of culture. This treatment regimen was based on previous experimentation (Cohen and Shaw, 1964).

Technique

To assess the effect of various lysosomal stabilizers on cell division and chromosomal integrity, the four drugs were added to the leukocyte cultures at those concentrations and times described above (Table 1). Additional experimentation combining the chromosome-breaking agents MC and SN with the lysosomal stabilizers CA and CL were performed as follows (Table 2): (1) Twenty-four hours prior to harvest of the cells, the chromosome-breaking agent (either SN [0.01 μg/ml] or MC [1.0 μg/ml]) was added to the cultures followed 6 hours later by the lysosomal stabilizer (either CA [1 $\times$ 10^{-5} M] or CL [1 $\times$ 10^{-5} M]). (2) The reverse of the above sequence, *e.g.* at 24 hours prior to harvest, the stabilizer was added, followed by the chromosome "breaker" at 18 hours prior to harvest. (3) Both the stabilizer and the chromosome-breaking agent were added simultaneously at 24 hours prior to harvest.

Vitamin A alcohol was tested at the three concentrations and at the three exposure times described above. Control cultures (with nothing added) were included in each experiment performed.

MICROSCOPIC SCORING OF SLIDES

After harvest, several slides per replicate culture were prepared, stained with 2 per cent acetorcein, and coded by individuals who did not participate in the microscopic scoring of the cells. It was hoped that a total of at least 100 metaphase cells per treatment would be scored for chromosomal damage. However, because of the cytotoxicity of some of the agents employed, this number of cells was not always obtained. Well-spread metaphase cells were selected under low magnification ($\times 250$) and chromosomes were scored under oil immersion phase contrast microscopy (approximately $\times 1{,}560$). Once a cell was selected under low power, it was included in the study.

CHROMOSOMAL ABNORMALITIES

Abnormalities were scored as breaks only if an obvious discontinuity of the chromatin was visible. Breaks were classified as chromatid if only one chromatid was affected and as "isochromatid" if both chromatids were broken at the same location. Both of these abnormalities were scored as single breaks. Single fragments were included with chromatid breaks,

TABLE 1. *Chromosomal Damage Induced by the Solvent Dimethyl Sulfoxide (DMSO) and the Four Lysosomal Stabilizing Agents Prednisolone Acetate (PR), Hydrocortisone 21 (HY), Chloroquine Dihydrochloride (CL), and Cortisone Acetate(CA)*

Treatment and concentration	Hr. prior to harvest				Total no. cells	Mean breaks per cell
	4	24	48	72		
Control						
Breaks	0.017	0.026	0.020	0.042	755	0.026
Gaps	0.029	0.032	0.020	0.021		0.022
Dimethyl sulfoxide (1%)						
Breaks	0.020	0.034	0.040	0.010	413	0.027
Gaps	0.020	0.022	0.016	0.000		0.015
Prednisolone						
10^{-7} M						
Breaks	0.030	0.040	0.030	0.011	365	0.027
Gaps	0.060	0.027	0.030	0.022		0.036
10^{-5} M						
Breaks	0.030	0.030	0.035	0.048	348	0.034
Gaps	0.080	0.030	0.012	0.016		0.037
10^{-3} M						
Breaks	0.022	0.013	....	....	168	0.018
Gaps	0.043	0.027	....	....		0.036
Hydrocortisone						
10^{-7} M						
Breaks	0.010	0.022	0.040	0.013	365	0.022
Gaps	0.020	0.067	0.050	0.000		0.036
10^{-5} M						
Breaks	0.020	0.020	0.010	0.040	375	0.021
Gaps	0.020	0.030	0.060	0.067		0.043
10^{-3} M						
Breaks	0.038	0.040	....	....	130	0.054
Gaps	0.025	0.060	....	....		0.054

continued

Treatment and concentration	Hr. prior to harvest				Total no. cells	Mean breaks per cell
	4	24	48	72		
Chloroquine						
10⁻⁷ M						
Breaks	0.035	0.020	0.027	0.000	332	0.018
Gaps	0.035	0.040	0.027	0.020		0.030
10⁻⁵ M						
Breaks	0.020	0.011	0.000	0.021	362	0.014
Gaps	0.030	0.022	0.013	0.032		0.025
10⁻³ M						
Breaks	....	....	....	....	0	0.000
Gaps	....	....	....	....	0	0.000
Cortisone acetate						
10⁻⁷ M						
Breaks	0.000	0.011	0.000	0.020	373	0.008
Gaps	0.020	0.045	0.036	0.000		0.024
10⁻⁵ M						
Breaks	0.012	0.044	0.048	0.000	358	0.042
Gaps	0.000	0.044	0.024	0.020		0.022
10⁻³ M						
Breaks	0.020	0.000	....	....	70	0.014
Gaps	0.000	0.000	....	....		0.000

while "double" fragments were scored as isochromatid breaks. Dicentric chromosome and quadriradial (QR) configurations were considered as containing two breaks. Attenuated nonstaining chromosomal regions other than the normal and obvious secondary constriction regions were scored separately as "gaps" but were not included in the calculation of the breakage rates. The data are reported as the mean number of breaks per cell.

MITOTIC RATE

The rate of cell division was quantitated by counting the number of metaphase cells in 250 leukocytes observed on each of eight slides per treatment. The percentage of mitosis, therefore, was based on the total of 2,000 cells per treatment.

LYSOSOMAL ENZYME ASSAYS

Young hybrid male albino rabbits were obtained from commercial sources and sacrificed by means of air embolization. Approximately 5 g

TABLE 2. *Chromosomal Damage Induced by 0.01 µg/ml Streptonigrin (SN) in Combination with the 1 × 10⁻⁵ M of the Lysosomal Stabilizers Cortisone Acetate (CA) or Chloroquine Dihydrochloride (CL)*

Treatment*	Breaks	Gaps	No. of quadriradials	Total cells	Mean breaks/cell
Control	0.040	0.087	0	300	0.040
SN	0.592	0.320	1	125	0.608
CA + SN	0.320	0.160	1†	125	0.336
SN + CA	0.224	0.120	2	125	0.256
CA + SN	0.192	0.144	0	125	0.192
CL + SN	0.344	0.232	0	125	0.344
SN + CL	0.208	0.176	0	125	0.208
CL + SN	0.192	0.208	0	125	0.192

* First drug added 24 hours prior to harvest and second drug added 18 hours prior to harvest.

† Represents a dicentric chromosome rather than a quadriradial configuration.

of liver were minced in ice cold 0.25 M sucrose; the pieces were further washed three times in 0.25 M sucrose and homogenized in 50 ml of 0.25 M sucrose in a glass homogenizer with a motor-driven Teflon pestle (Tri-R Instruments, Jamaica, New York) at maximum speed, using six up-and-down strokes of the pestle. The homogenate was centrifuged at 2,500 rpm in a Sorvall Model SS3 centrifuge for 10 minutes. The resulting supernatant was centrifuged at 12,500 rpm for 20 minutes and the pellet washed by resuspending gently in 25 ml 0.25 M sucrose and recentrifuged at 12,500 rpm for an additional 20 minutes. The pellet was then gently resuspended in 50 ml of 0.25 M sucrose and consisted of a large granule fraction enriched in acid hydrolase content. Aliquots (2 ml) of this granular fraction were incubated for one hour at 37 C in the presence of varying concentrations of mitomycin C (5.0 to 0.1 µg/ml), streptonigrin (0.05 to 0.001 µg/ml), diluent (water), or 0.1 per cent Triton X-100 (Rohm and Haas, Philadelphia, Pennsylvania). These were then centrifuged at 20,000 × g for 20 minutes at 4 C and the enzyme activity released into the supernatant determined. β-Glucuronidase was assayed by the method of Talalay, Fishman, and Huggins (1946) and acid phosphatase was assayed as previously described (Hirschhorn, Hirschhorn, and Weissmann, 1967). The results are expressed as the percentage of that enzyme activity released by incubation with Triton X-100.

ELECTRON MICROSCOPIC STUDIES

Leukocyte cultures, prepared from semipurified lymphocyte suspensions, were initiated as described above. At 24 hours prior to harvest, SN (0.01 μg/ml), MC (1.0 μg/ml), and vitamin A alcohol (10^{-5} M) were added to replicate cultures. Cultures allowed to progress for the entire 72-hour incubation period with nothing added served as controls. Upon completion of the incubation period, the cells were centrifuged and medium decanted. The remaining pellet of cells was then fixed in 1 per cent glutaraldehyde in Hanks' balanced salt solution (pH 6.4 to 7.0) and post-fixed in 1 per cent osmic acid. The cells were then rapidly dehydrated in a graded series of alcohols and embedded in Epon by conventional methods (Luft, 1961). Sections were cut on an LKB-III Ultramicrotome, double stained with uranyl acetate (Gibbon and Bradfield, 1957) and lead citrate (Reynolds, 1963), and then investigated in a Siemens Elmskop I.

To evaluate the effects of the various added exogenous agents, the number of lysosomes in thin sections per cell of 50 cells per replicate culture were counted. In addition, an attempt to evaluate the integrity of the lysosomal membrane and the contents of the lysosomes (*i.e.*, granular, vesicular) or with a particular membrane pattern was undertaken.

Results

LYSOSOMAL STABILIZERS

Mitotic suppression

Figure 1 illustrates the effect of the four lysosomal stabilizers HY, PR, CA, and CL on the rate of cell division. These compounds cause a suppression of mitotic rate which correlates with both dose and length of exposure time. The longer the cells were in contact with the drug, the lower the mitotic index. At 10^{-3} M, mitosis was almost completely inhibited for longer exposure times, while shorter treatments yielded a few cells in metaphase. However, at the concentration of 1×10^{-5} M, which still protects lysosomal membranes (Weissman, 1968) in spite of the mitotic suppression, adequate numbers of metaphase cells were obtained for analysis. Therefore, this concentration was used in subsequent experiments involving lysosomal stabilizers. The solvent DMSO (1 per cent) did not cause marked mitotic suppression when compared to control cultures (Figure 1—upper left).

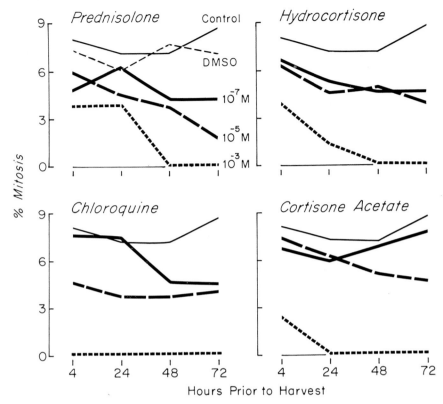

FIGURE 1. The effect of the four lysosomal stabilizers on the mitotic rate of human lymphocyte cultures: hydrocortisone (HY), prednisolone (PR), cortisone acetate (CA), and chloroquine (CL).

Chromosomal damage

There was no apparent increase in chromosomal damage induced by any of the lysosomal stabilizers nor the DMSO solvent (Table 1). The mean rate of chromosome breakage in control cultures was 0.026 breaks per cell. Similar frequencies were observed for DMSO (0.027) and the more dilute concentrations of the stabilizing drugs. Since at the 10^{-3} M concentration mitosis was almost completely inhibited, the number of metaphases scored was low. However, even in the few cells analyzed at this concentration, no obvious increase in chromosome damage was noted. Likewise, when considering only the "gaps," no obvious increase was observed in the treated cells. In most cases, the frequency of chromosome damage appeared to be correlated with concentration (Table 1), indicating a linear dose-response relationship.

CHROMOSOME-BREAKING AGENTS AND LYSOSOMAL STABILIZERS
Streptonigrin

By adding lysosomal stabilizing agents prior to or concomitant with a known chromosome-breaking agent, it was hoped that the chromosomes could be protected from damage. Table 2 notes results of investigations with SN combined with CA and CL. The control rate of chromosome damage was 0.040 breaks per cell in contrast to a fifteenfold increase (0.608 breaks per cell) with 0.01 μg SN/ml added to the cultures for the

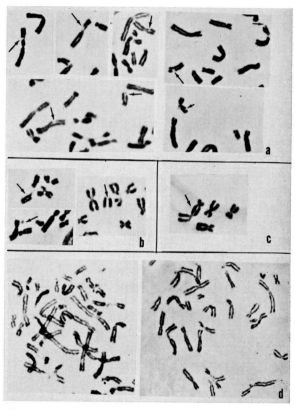

FIGURE 2. Chromosomal aberrations induced by streptonigrin: a—chromatid breaks; b—isochromatid breaks resulting in acentric fragments; c—dicentric chromosome; d—cells exhibiting multiple abnormalities.

TABLE 3.   *Chromosome Damage Induced by 1.0 µg/ml Mitomycin C (MC) in Combination with 1 × 10⁻⁵ м of the Lysosomal Stabilizers Cortisone Acetate (CA) and Chloroquine Dihydrochloride (CL)*

Treatment*	Breaks	Gaps	No. of quadriradials	Total cells	Mean breaks/cell
Control	0.020	0.060	0	450	0.020
MC	2.618	0.878	20	131	2.924
CA + MC	0.967	0.400	19	110	1.309
MC + CA	2.136	1.049	8	81	2.333
CA + MC	0.991	0.609	10	110	1.173
CL + MC	1.222	0.911	21	135	1.533
MC + CL	1.413	0.870	13	92	1.696
CL + MC	1.284	1.716	5	102	1.382

* First drug added 24 hours prior to harvest; second drug added 18 hours prior to harvest.

final 24 hours of incubation. Figure 2 illustrates SN-induced chromosomal damage. The addition of either stabilizing agent (CA or CL) six hours prior to the SN resulted in a decrease of chromosome damage, but yielded frequencies of breaks still significantly elevated when compared to the controls (0.336 and 0.344 breaks per cell, respectively). It is interesting to note that an even greater decrease in chromosome damage was achieved by adding the stabilizer six hours after the addition of SN (0.256 breaks per cell for CA and 0.208 breaks per cell for CL). The most "protective" treatment was observed when either CA or CL was added simultaneously with the SN at 24 hours prior to harvest (0.192 breaks per cell in both cases). Although some decrease in chromosomal damage was obtained with the addition of lysosomal stabilizers, it apparently mattered little whether the drugs were added before, after, or at the same time as the SN. There was no evidence for absolute protection against chromosomal damage since great differences were still observed between the control and treated cells in all cases.

Mitomycin C (MC)

Table 3 illustrates the effect of MC alone and in combination with CA and CL on leukocyte chromosomes. The control rate of chromosome damage was 0.020 breaks per cell as compared with 2.924 breaks per cell for a concentration of 1.0 μg MC/ml in a 24-hour exposure. As with SN, there was a reduction in chromosome breakage when MC was combined with the lysosomal stabilizers CA and CL. Also similar to the SN experiment, the greatest "protection" was achieved when MC and the stabilizers were added simultaneously (CA + MC = 1.173 breaks per cell and CL + MC = 1.382 breaks per cell).

It is perhaps easier to assess the chromosomal effect of MC than that of SN because of the ability of MC to induce remarkable QR's with relatively high frequency (Figure 3) (Cohen and Shaw, 1964; Shaw and Cohen, 1965). In Table 3, it is shown that MC alone produced 20 QR's in 131 cells; 15.27 per cent of cells contained this readily discernible cytologic landmark. There was no obvious protection by lysosomal stabilizers against QR formation since these rearrangements were present in all

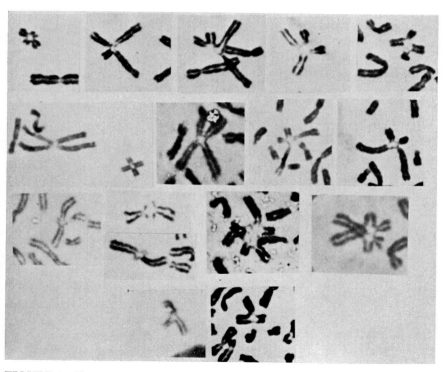

FIGURE 3. Chromatid exchanges induced by mitomycin C. Both quadriradial (QR) and triradial (TR) configurations are depicted. Most formations are single two-chromosome exchanges, but several are complex and involve more than two chromosomes.

treated cultures regardless of the time of addition of CA or CL. In point of fact, there was no reduction of frequency when the cells were pre-treated with CA or CL six hours before MC addition.

LYSOSOMAL ENZYME ASSAYS

The above results indicate relatively little protective ability of lysosomal stabilizers against chromosome damage. This finding poses the question of whether the particular chromosome-breaking agents being investigated acted via the destruction of lysosomal membranes and subsequent enzyme release. To further investigate this problem, various concentrations of MC and SN were incubated with rabbit liver cells, and assays were determined on isolated lysosomes for the release of the lysosomal enzymes β-glucuronidase and acid phosphatase. The amount of enzyme released (rendered nonsedimentable) under these conditions was then determined. Neither SN nor MC caused an increase in free lysosomal enzymes when compared with the water-treated control cells (Table 4). This was apparent regardless of the concentrations tested. Therefore, it would appear that neither of these chromosome-breaking agents demonstrated a lytic effect on the integrity of the lysosomal membrane of rabbit liver cells.

VITAMIN A ALCOHOL

Chromosome Damage

The various vitamin A compounds are known lysosomal labilizers

TABLE 4. *Effect of Mitomycin C (MC) and Streptonigrin (SN) on the Release of the Lysosomal Enzymes β-Glucuronidase and Acid Phosphatase from Rabbit Liver Cells In Vitro. Values Expressed as Percentages of Enzyme Activity Released by 0.1 Per Cent Triton X–100*

Mitomycin C			Streptonigrin		
Concentration (μg MC/ml)	β-glucuronidase	Acid phosphatase	Concentration (μg SN/ml)	β-glucuronidase	Acid phosphatase
5.0	8.0	5.7	0.050	9.6	5.5
2.5	8.6	5.3	0.025	9.9	3.9
1.0	8.9	5.3	0.010	9.2	5.0
0.5	8.7	5.0	0.005	10.3	5.5
0.1	8.7	5.2	0.001	9.2	5.8
Water	9.2	6.0	Water	9.5	5.4

TABLE 5. *Chromosomal Damage Induced by Vitamin A Alcohol*

Treatment	Breaks per cell Hours prior to harvest			Total cells	Mean
	4	24	48		
Control					
Breaks	0.072	0.056	0.060	375	0.063
Gaps	0.072	0.080	0.096		0.083
Vitamin A					
10^{-7} M					
Breaks	0.048	0.064	0.016	375	0.043
Gaps	0.056	0.056	0.032		0.048
10^{-5} M					
Breaks	0.040	0.048	0.048	375	0.045
Gaps	0.056	0.056	0.032		0.048
10^{-4} M					
Breaks	0.048	0.072	0.060	375	0.060
Gaps	0.052	0.063	0.074		0.063

(Weissmann, 1968) and their presence in the lymphocyte cultures should induce chromosomal breakage if the lysosomal mechanism is indeed operative. Table 5 illustrates the chromosomal breaking potential of three concentrations of vitamin A alcohol (10^{-4} M, 10^{-5} M, 10^{-7} M) for 48-, 24-, and 4-hour exposures. It is obvious from comparison of these data to that from control cultures that vitamin A alcohol, in this particular treatment regimen, does not induce chromosomal abnormalities.

Effect on Mitosis

Figure 4 illustrates the effect of vitamin A alcohol on the mitotic rate of leukocyte cultures. Contrary to the finding with most other exogenous agents, vitamin A alcohol apparently does not cause a suppression of mitosis. In point of fact, in some cases, there actually appears to be an enhancement of cell division following vitamin A treatment. This is evident particularly in treatments of 10^{-5} and 10^{-7} M.

ELECTRON MICROSCOPIC STUDIES

The effects of MC, SN, and vitamin A alcohol on the frequency and contents of the lysosomes and the integrity of their membranes is shown in Table 6. There was a remarkable decrease in the mean number of lysosomes per cell in the vitamin A alcohol-treated cells. However, there

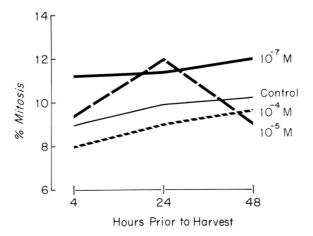

FIGURE 4. The effect of vitamin A alcohol on the mitotic rate of cultures of lymphocytes from human beings.

were no apparent differences in the number of lysosomes in the controls when compared with the MC or SN treatments. Similarly, an increase in lysosomal membrane disintegration or rupture was observed after the vitamin A alcohol treatment in comparison to the other drugs. In all cases, the appearance of the lysosomal contents was granular. In addition, some of the control cells also contained vesicular lysosomes. These results confirm the findings of the enzyme release studies (Table 4), namely, that MC and SN do not affect lysosomal integrity. Vitamin A alcohol, however, did labilize lysosomes and cause disintegration of their membranes (Figures 5, 6, and 7).

TABLE 6. *Electron Microscopic Study of Frequency of Lysosomes and Integrity of Membranes in Lymphocytes Treated with Various Agents*

Treatment	No. cells	Mean no. lysosomes/cell	Lysosomal content	Membrane integrity
Control	152	1.91	Granular or vesicular	Intact
1.0 μg/ml MC	100	1.80	Granular	Generally intact; few disintegrating
0.0 μg/ml SN	100	1.92	Granular	Some disintegrating
10^{-5} M vitamin A alcohol	100	1.15	Granular	Frequent rupturing

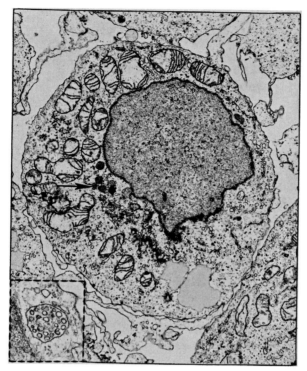

FIGURE 5. Electron micrograph of human leukocyte. Arrow indicates cluster of vesicular lysosomes. Reduced from × 17,500. Inset depicts high power of vesicular lysosome. Note intact lysosomal membrane. Reduced from × 52,500.

Discussion

The role of lysosomes in a variety of the normal metabolic activities of the cell has been extensively investigated during the past several years. Additionally, it has been suggested that these organelles, containing acid hydrolytic enzymes, may be involved in pathologic processes such as the induction of chromosomal damage (Allison and Paton, 1965; Venuat, Theron, Bresson, and Catton, 1968). It has been noted that several agents capable of causing chromosomal aberrations, such as ultraviolet and X-irradiation and some viruses, also bring about the release of enzymes from lysosomes. In order to test this hypothesis, Allison and Paton (1965) attempted to selectively rupture lysosomes by the addition of vital dyes such as acridine orange and neutral red, which are concentrated in lysosomes. Upon photoactivation of these concentrated dyes, the lysosomal

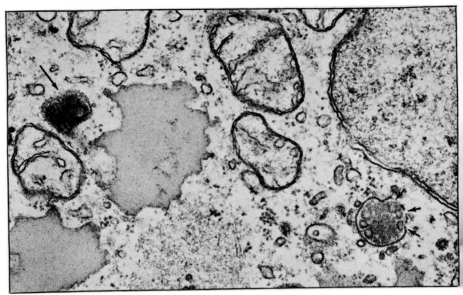

FIGURE 6. Electron micrograph of vitamin A-treated lymphocyte. Arrows denote distinct breaks in lysosomal membrane and disintegrating lysosomes. Reduced from × 45,500.

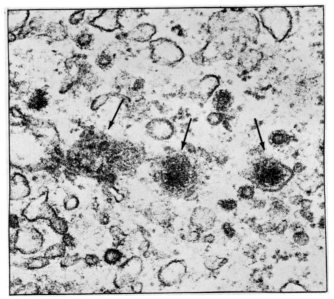

FIGURE 7. Electron photomicrograph of vitamin A-treated lymphocyte illustrating stages of lysosomal degeneration. Reduced from × 70,000.

membrane is preferentially damaged. An increase in chromatid breaks was found following such treatment and it was therefore suggested that chromosome damage may be induced by the release of lysomal enzymes.

The possible involvement of this mechanism in virus-induced chromosomal damage was investigated by Aula and Nichols (1968). Both measles virus and human adenovirus 12 were studied in human leukocytes as well as in heteroploid tissue culture lines. An attempt was made to protect against chromosome damage by the addition of a lysosomal stabilizer (CA), but in no case was protection evident. Additional experiments using adenovirus 12 in five different cell lines of human, rodent, and marsupial origins suggested that chromosomal damage inflicted by the virus is probably under the control of the viral genome and is not likely to involve the activation of cellular lysosomal enzymes (zur Hausen, 1968). Therefore, the involvement of lysosomal rupture and enzyme release was not suggested as integral to the mechanism of chromosome damage induced by these viruses.

The present investigations have attempted to evaluate the possible role of lysosomes in chemically induced chromosome breakage. Previous work would suggest that mitomycin C, when injected into sarcoma-bearing animals, causes a labilization of lysosomes in the sarcoma cells (Nitani, Suzuki, Shimoyama, and Kimura, 1966). However, the possibility of intraperitoneal admixture with cell types other than sarcoma cells must be considered as an alternative explanation for the apparent change in lysosomal enzyme distribution.

The results of direct enzyme assays on isolated rabbit lysosomes (Table 4) indicate that these compounds do not directly cause lysosomal membranes to rupture in this particular system. Their effect on human lymphocyte lysosomes could conceivably be different, but such is not expected. This consideration is currently under investigation. Similarly, the electron microscopic study of human lymphocytes (Table 6) did not reveal any obvious degeneration or reduction in the frequency of lysosomes in the mitomycin- and streptonigrin-treated cells, suggestive of a direct interaction between these drugs and the lysosome.

Although no direct evidence for lysosomal damage by SN and MC was obtained, there was an apparent decrease in chromosomal damage when these drugs were combined with the lysosomal stabilizers (Tables 2 and 3). It is obvious that the greatest decrease in damage was achieved by adding the stabilizer and the chromosomal breaker simultaneously. Addition of the stabilizer six hours after the breaker also reduced cytogenetic damage. The least protective regimen was that which would be expected to protect the greatest, *i.e.* the pretreatment of cells with the stabilizer. Although the mechanisms of lysosomal labilization may be active in this particular case, several additional explanations are also possible for these observations. Both MC and SN have previously been shown to suppress mitosis remarkably (Cohen, Shaw, and Craig, 1963; Cohen and Shaw, 1964). The present study indicates a similar mitotic inhibition for the lysosomal stabilizers tested (Figure 1). If those cells which are chromosomally damaged by MC or SN are still further inhibited from dividing by the presence of the lysosomal stabilizers, it may well be that only those cells which are relatively undamaged or slightly damaged survive to mitosis. In other words, those cells with gross chromosomal damage may be less capable of sustaining the further mitotic inhibition of the lysosomal stabilizing agent. This would have the effect of reducing the amount of obvious chromosomal damage in those mitotic cells observed in the combination treatments regardless of the sequence in which the drugs are added.

Additionally, a situation of competitive inhibition may exist. It has been suggested that both SN and MC interact with the DNA moiety of the cell (Radding, 1963; Iyer and Szybalski, 1963). Similar observations have been made with chloroquine (Parker and Irvin, 1952; Cohen and Yielding, 1965). If such be the case and both the breakers and stabilizers compete for the same active sites, over-all chromosomal damage may be reduced since the stabilizers alone do not break chromosomes (Table 1). A third explanation lies in the possibility that a direct interaction may occur between the chromosome-breaking agent and the lysosomal stabilizer, rendering the MC or the SN inactive and thereby lowering the over-all frequency of chromosomal damage. Even though these suggestions have not been proved, other explanations besides the stabilization of lysosomal membranes may readily explain the decrease in chromosome damage upon addition of the stabilizer.

The investigations with vitamin A alcohol, however, a known lysosomal labilizer, also failed to yield evidence in support of this hypothesis. Enzymatic assays in various systems (Weissman, 1968) and the present electron microscopic study (Table 6, and Figures 5, 6, and 7) demonstrate that the lysosomes are indeed ruptured following vitamin A treatment. However, there is no suggestion of increased chromosomal damage induced by vitamin A (Table 5). If indeed the original hypothesis (Allison and Paton, 1965) holds, vitamin A as well as other lysosomal labilizers should cause chromosomal breaks. Several other labilizers, namely streptolysin S and staphylococcus alphatoxin, are currently under investigation from this standpoint.

Summary

The possibility that chemically induced chromosomal damage is mediated through the mechanism of lysosomal labilization was investigated. The utilization of the known chromosome-breaking agents mitomycin C and streptonigrin showed no effect on lysosomal membranes as evidenced by both enzymatic and electron microscopic studies. The combination of these drugs with known lysosomal stabilizing agents reduced the frequency of chromosome damage somewhat, although other possible explanations for this observation are discussed. The known lysosomal labilizer vitamin A alcohol did not increase the frequency of chromosome breakage in peripheral lymphocytes. Therefore, these studies yield no evidence to support the hypothesis that the destruction of lysosomal membranes and the subsequent release of hydrolytic enzymes are instrumental in the induction of chromosomal damage.

ACKNOWLEDGMENTS

The technical assistance of Mrs. Elizabeth Kovi and Mrs. Clara Lockwood is greatly appreciated. We are also indebted to Dr. Kurt Hirschhorn for his helpful discussions during the course of this study and for his critical reading of the manuscript. This investigation was supported in part by a grant from the United States Children's Bureau (Project No. 417).

ABBREVIATIONS

AdR—2'-adenine deoxyriboside
ATP—adenosine triphosphate
CA—cortisone acetate
CL—chloroquine dihydrochloride
DMSO—dimethyl sulfoxide
FUdR—5-fluorodeoxyuridine
HY—hydrocortisone 21-(dihydrogen phosphate)
MC—mitomycin C
PR—prednisolone acetate
SN—streptonigrin

REFERENCES

Allison, A. C., and L. Mallucci. 1965. Histochemical Studies of Lysosomes and Lysosomal Enzymes in Virus Infected Cell Cultures. *Journal of Experimental Medicine*, 121:463–476.

Allison, A. C., and G. R. Paton. 1965. Chromosome Damage in Diploid Cells Following Activation of Lysosomal Enzymes. *Nature*, 207:1170–1173.

Aula, P., and W. W. Nichols. 1968. Lysosomes and Virus Induced Chromosome Breakage. *Experimental Cell Research*, 51:595–601.

Cohen, M. M. 1963. The Specific Effects of Streptonigrin Activity on Human Chromosomes in Culture. *Cytogenetics*, 2:271–279.

Cohen, M. M., and M. W. Shaw. 1964. Effects of Mitomycin C on Human Chromosomes. *Journal of Cell Biology*, 23:386–395.

————. 1965. "Specific Effects of Viruses and Antimetabolites on Mammalian Chromosomes." *The Chromosome: Structural and Functional Aspects (In Vitro*, Publication of the Tissue Culture Association, Vol. 1). Baltimore, Maryland: The Williams and Wilkins Co. Pp. 50–66.

Cohen, M. M., M. W. Shaw, and A. P. Craig. 1963. The Effects of Streptonigrin on Cultured Human Leukocytes. *Proceedings of The National Academy of Sciences of the U.S.A.*, 50:16–24.

Cohen, S. N., and K. L. Yielding. 1965. Inhibition of DNA and RNA Polymerase Reactions by Chloroquine. *Proceedings of The National Academy of Sciences of the U.S.A.*, 54:521–527.

Elliott, W. H. 1963. The Effects of Antimicrobial Agents on Deoxyribonucleic Acid Polymerase. *Biochemical Journal*, 86:562–567.

Gibbons, I. R., and J. R. Bradfield. 1957. "Experiments on Staining Thin-Sections For Electron Microscopy," *Electron Microscopy: Proceedings of The Stockholm Conference*, F. S. Sjostrand and J. Rhodin, Eds., New York, New York: Academic Press. Pp. 121–124.

Hausen, H. zur. 1968. Association of Adenovirus Type 12 Deoxyribonucleic Acid With Host Cell Chromosomes. *Journal of Virology*, 2:218–223.

Hirschhorn, R., K. Hirschhorn, and G. Weissmann. 1967. Appearance of Hydrolase Rich Granules in Human Lymphocytes Induced by Phytohemagglutinin and Antigens. *Blood, The Journal of Hematology*, 30:84–102.

Humphrey, R. M., and W. C. Dewey. 1965. Radiosensitivity of Normal and 5-Bromodeoxyuridine Treated Mammalian Cells During Different Phases of the Cell Cycle. *Experimental Cell Research*, 39:483–495.

Iyer, V. N., and W. Szybalski. 1963. A Molecular Mechanism of Mitomycin Action. Linking of Complementary DNA Strands. *Proceedings of The National Academy of Sciences of the U.S.A.*, 50:355–362.

Kersten, H. 1962. Action of Mitomycin C on Nucleic Acid Metabolism in Tumor and Bacterial Cells. *Biochimica et biophysica acta*, 55:558–560.

Kersten, H., W. Kersten, G. Leopold, and B. Schnieders. 1964. Effect of Mitomycin C on DNAase and RNA in *Escherichia coli. Biochimica et biophysica acta*, 80:521–523.

Kihlman, B. A. 1961. Biochemical Aspects of Chromosome Breakage. *Advances in Genetics*, 10:1–51.

————. 1966. *Actions of Chemicals on Dividing Cells*. Englewood Cliffs, New Jersey: Prentice-Hall, Inc., 260 pp.

Lea, D. E. 1955. *Actions of Radiations on Living Cells*. Cambridge, England: Cambridge University Press, 2nd edition, 416 pp.

Luft, J. H. 1961. Improvements in Epoxy Resin Embedding Methods. *Journal of Biophysical and Biochemical Cytology*, 9:409–414.

MacGregor, H. C., and H. G. Callan. 1962. The Actions of Enzymes on Lampbrush Chromosomes. *Quarterly Journal of Microscopic Science*, 103:172–203.

Mallucci, L., and A. C. Allison. 1965. Lysosomal Enzymes in Cells Infected with Cytopathic and Non-cytopathic Viruses. *Journal of Experimental Medicine*, 121:477–485.

Moorhead, P. S., P. C. Nowell, W. J. Mellman, D. M. Battips, and D. A. Hungerford.

1960. Chromosome Preparations of Leukocytes Cultured From Human Peripheral Blood. *Experimental Cell Research*, 20:613–616.

Nitani, H., A. Suzuki, M. Shimoyama, and K. Kimura. 1966. The Role of Lysosomes in Cancer Chemotherapy. II. Effect of Mitomycin C Injection on Lysosomal Enzymic Activities of Yoshida Ascites Sarcoma Cells. *Gann*, 57:193–200.

Ostertag, W. 1966. Chemische Mutagenese an Menschlichen Zellen in Kultur. *Abhandlungen der Mathematisch-Naturwissenschaftlichen Klasse*, NR 1:1–124.

Parker, F. S., and J. L. Irvin. 1952. The Interaction of Chloroquine with the Albumin of Bovine Plasma. *Journal of Biological Chemistry*, 199:889–895.

Radding, C. M. 1963. "Incorporation of H^3-thymidine by K12(X) Induced by Streptonigrin," *Genetics Today*, S. J. Geerts, Ed. Oxford, England: Pergamon Press. P. 22.

Reich, E. 1964. Actinomycin: Correlation of Structure and Function of Its Complexes with Purines and DNA. *Science*, 143:684–689.

Revell, S. H. 1953. Chromosome Breakage by X-Rays and Radiomimetic Substances in Vicia. *Heredity*, 6(Supplement on Chromosome Breakage): 107–124.

Reynolds, E. S. 1963. The Use of Lead Citrate at High pH as an Electron-Opaque Stain in Electron Microscopy. *Journal of Cell Biology*, 17:208–213.

Schwartz, H. S., J. E. Sodergren, and F. S. Philips. 1963. Mitomycin C: Chemical and Biological Studies on Alkylation. *Science*, 142:1181–1183.

Shaw, M. W., and M. M. Cohen. 1965. Chromosome Exchanges in Human Leukocytes Induced by Mitomycin C. *Genetics*, 51:181–190.

Somers, C. E., and R. M. Humphrey. 1963. A Chromosome Study of Radiation Sensitization by 5-Bromodeoxyuridine. *Experimental Cell Research*, 30:208–217.

Stacey, K. A., M. Cobb, S. F. Cousens, and P. Alexander. 1958. The Reactions of the "Radiomimetic" Alkylating Agents with Macromolecules in Vitro. *Annals of The New York Academy of Sciences*, 72:682–701.

Talalay, P., W. H. Fishman, and C. Huggins. 1946. Chromogenic Substrates. II. Phenolphthalein Glucuronic Acid as Substrate for the Assay of Glucuronidase Activity. *Journal of Biological Chemistry*, 166:757–772.

Ts'o, P. O. P., G. K. Helkamp, and C. Sander. 1962. Interaction of Nucleosides and Related Compounds with Nucleic Acids as Indicated by the Change of Helix-Coil Transition Temperature. *Proceedings of The National Academy of Sciences of the U.S.A.*, 48:686–698.

Ts'o, P. O. P., and P. Lu. 1964. Interaction of Nucleic Acids. I. Physical Binding of Thymidine, Adenine, Steroids, and Aromatic Hydrocarbons to Nucleic Acids. *Proceedings of The National Academy of Sciences of the U.S.A.*, 51:17–24.

Venuat, A. M., M. C. Theron, M. L. Bresson, and A. Cattan. 1968. Induction d'Anomalies Chromosomiques chez la Souris par Injection a l'Animal de Lysosomes Isogeniques Resultats Preliminaires. *Revue Francais Clinical et Biologique*, 13: 707–709.

Waring, M. J. 1964. Complex Formation with DNA and Inhibition of *Escherichia coli* RNA Polymerase by Ethidium Bromide. *Biochimica et biophysica acta*, 87: 358–361.

Weissmann, G. 1968. "Effect on Lysosomes of Drugs Useful in Connective Tissue Disease," *The Interaction of Drugs and Subcellular Components of Animal Cells*, P. N. Campbell, Ed. London, England: J. & A. Churchill, Ltd. Pp. 203–217.

Wolff, S. 1960. Radiation Studies on the Nature of Chromosome Breakage. *American Naturalist*, 94:85–93.

Wolff, S., and H. E. Luippold. 1955. Metabolism and Chromosome Break Rejoining. *Science*, 122:231–232.

Discussion

Dr. Louis Fink, Columbia University, New York, New York: Dr. Takahashi, have you performed nucleotide analysis after reaction with 4HAQO? Also, is there any further information concerning the loss of fluorescence of treated DNA after denaturation? Do you find preferential binding to nucleotides?

Dr. Taijo Takahashi, Aichi Cancer Center Research Institute, Nagoya, Japan: The fluorescent material binds to nucleotides after enzymatic digestion of DNA; however, it is rather difficult to detect which nucleotides bind preferentially with 4HAQO.

Dr. Martin Griffin, Oklahoma Medical Research Foundation, Oklahoma City, Oklahoma: Dr. Cohen, have you noted in the literature that Dr. Marion Zuelzer has already detected both in vivo and in vitro binding of radioactive cortisone to rat liver histones? In other words, a direct interaction, both in the test tube and in the rat injected with radioactive hydrocortisone (this was followed by isolating the chromatin and extracting histones from it), allowed her to estimate that a significant percentage of cortisone is bound directly to the histone fraction. This has been confirmed in our laboratory using radioactive hydrocortisone and HeLa cells. After incubating HeLa cells with radioactive steroid, the chromatin was shown to contain radioactivity. The exact nature of the chromatin sites which bind the steroid is unknown. Although we haven't subfractionated chromatin, the presence of radioactive cortisone on the chromatin is, I believe, well established. If there is a direct interaction between cortisone and chromatin, the mechanism of protecting chromosomes against streptolysin-induced breakage may be occurring directly at the chromatin level.

Dr. Maimon M. Cohen, State University of New York, Buffalo, New York: I wasn't aware of this, but it is interesting and we will look into it.

Dr. L. D. Samuels, Children's Hospital, Columbus, Ohio: A year ago our group at Columbus reported on work with the antibiotic daunomycin (sometimes called rubidomycin) done in conjunction with Dr. B. K. Vig and others. Actinomycin is a cancer therapeutic drug that, when used in the proper concentrations, stops DNA protein synthesis. However, a small concentration in human leukocytes in culture causes fragmentation and interchanges in patterns similar to those produced by streptonigrin. Further, when arginine was added to the mixture, we got an increased number of aberrations and an increase in the mitotic index.

The susceptibility to induction of aberrations apparently varies among individuals. We found up to a twofold difference in susceptibility in samples from healthy technicians, medical students, etc. In some persons, it takes twice as much daunomycin to produce the same number of aberrations as it does in others. I can think of no reason to account for this other than genetic susceptibility. By timed exposure, we found that these aberrations are probably produced in the late G1 period.

We have speculated that this might involve an interaction of the protein backbone with the DNA break. I agree that stabilizers such as hydrocortisone may work at the level of the histone backbone. I think our work gives some support to this because I believe that arginine has some effect on this same site. We found in other experiments that arginine interacts with divalent calcium and that divalent calcium may be involved in stabilizing the histone backbone, as inferred by Dr. Cole in his analysis of chromosome ultrastructure. Thus, we found that by stripping the calcium from DNA, we can increase the susceptibility of chromatin to disintegration. Therefore, any agent which would stabilize the histone backbone would allow breaks in DNA to be held in continuity and would allow repair to take place so that no aberrations would be produced. To the contrary, anything that disturbs the integrity of the histone backbone would allow dispersion of the DNA breaks and, thus, allow fragmentation and aberrant cross linking.

Dr. W. Sly, Washington University School of Medicine, St. Louis, Missouri: I wonder, for the sake of argument, whether Dr. Cohen has chosen the proper experimental model. Cortisone and steroids, as I understand them, cause lympholysis with a considerable loss of cytoplasm in treated lymphocytes. Is this not an unduly complicated model? Would it not be wiser to use a simpler system for cortisone exposure for this kind of study, such as fibroblasts in culture, rather than lymphocytes?

Dr. Cohen: It might be simpler from the standpoint of the steroids. However, we find it much more difficult to work with fibroblasts than with lymphocytes as far as chromosome preparations are concerned.

Dr. Sly: Have you any idea what cortisone treatment does to the electron microscopic morphology of lysosome structure?

Dr. Cohen: No, we haven't looked at this yet.

Dr. Sly: It would seem important to establish this in connection with effects you wish to attribute to lysosomal stabilization.

Dr. Raymond G. Hall, Jr., Loma Linda University, Loma Linda, California: Do you know whether hydrocortisone changes the permeability of the cell membrane to breaking agents? Do you think this might be a likely effect?

Dr. Cohen: Anything is likely until tested. All I can say is we have no information relative to permeability at this point.

Dr. Sly: Dr. Takahashi, do you know whether the agent that you used is mutagenic in bacteria or induces temperate bacteriophage in bacteria?

Dr. Takahashi: It has already been shown that 4HAQO or 4NQO has a mutagenic effect on bacteria and an inducible effect on temperate bacteriophage.

Dr. Fink: Dr. Cohen, I'd like to know a little bit more about the effect of DMSO on chromosomal stabilization or breakage.

Dr. Cohen: We could demonstrate no increase in chromosomal breakage with DMSO and we saw no mitotic inhibition.

Dr. Fink: Did you increase the concentration?

Dr. Cohen: Yes, we went up to about 6 or 7 per cent final concentration and still saw no increase in chromosomal breakage.

Dr. D. G. Harnden, Western General Hospital, Edinburgh, Scotland: Some time ago it was reported from our laboratory that exposure in vivo to benzene in a factory caused chromosome damage or was at least associated with chromosome damage in the workers. We have now studied chromosomes of men from a second factory where the conditions were similar to those at the first one. Again we found an increased number of aberrations in exposed individuals, but our controls showed the same increase. The only difference between the two observations is that controls were matched for age in the second group, but not in the first. We have reassessed control data from normal populations and find an increase in yield of both stable and unstable aberrations with increasing age. I do not suggest that benzene plays no part, but I would like to suggest that in such studies age be taken into account. I wonder if Dr. Cohen has considered this matter of age and if he has any evidence on changes in lysosomes with the age of individuals.

Dr. Cohen: The individuals used in these studies are always in a very narrow age group; I do not believe age has anything to do with this particular study. We have also found an increase in aberrations, particularly in aneuploidy, with age and in certain age groups. However, we have not studied changes in lysosomes with age, and I know of no one who has.

Dr. R. W. Teel, Loma Linda University, Loma Linda, California: Dr. Cohen, have you employed solvents other than DMSO in your work?

Dr. Cohen: Yes, when we did the work with streptonigrin, the compound was dissolved initially in acetone. We used several concentrations of acetone, and within the concentrations we saw no effect of acetone. We have no experience with other solvents.

Dr. T. C. Washburn, Sinai Hospital, Baltimore, Maryland: Dr. Cohen, have you had any experience with mothers who have taken LSD (lysergic acid diethylamide) during pregnancy? Geneticists have been looking for multiple congenital anomalies in the offspring, but I understand that a certain number of patients have developed leukemia. Have you had any experience with this?

Dr. Cohen: So far as I know, there has only been one published case suggesting that a congenital malformation was the direct result of LSD ingestion. This was an article emanating from the University of Iowa and published in *Lancet*. There are studies of abortion material showing chromosomal abnormalities as well as structural abnormalities. Probably the largest series of this sort has not yet been published. It is now in progress at George Washington University under the direction of Dr. C. B. Jacobson.

A case was reported in the *Journal of the American Medical Association* several months ago of a Philadelphia-like chromosome seen in an individual with subacute leukemia who was also an LSD user. There was another case which cannot be reported since the individual subsequently died and did not release permission for the use of his material in a scientific report.

At this point, all we can say is that there does not seem to be an over-all increase in the obvious congenital malformations that pediatricians would normally pick up in routine screening of infants born to mothers who had ingested LSD. There are various reasons for this. The animal work seems to suggest that in inducing teratogenesis this drug works at a very early time in pregnancy. If we make a calculation to human gestational time, this comes out to be the sixteenth to twenty-second day of pregnancy. In other words, the dangerous period occurs before a woman even knows she is pregnant.

Dr. Milan Macek, Baylor College of Medicine, Houston, Texas: May I say that in the last year we have analyzed various tissue cultures from two embryos whose mothers took large doses of LSD during the first months of pregnancy. We found an increase of chromosomal abnormalities in cultures of fibroblasts from various tissues. We observed enlargement of secondary constrictions and similar abnormalities, including polyploidy, just as Dr. Cohen has observed in his studies.

The Virus Genome and Transformation of Mammalian Cells

FRED RAPP* AND JANET S. BUTEL

Department of Virology and Epidemiology, Baylor College of Medicine, Houston, Texas

It is widely recognized that the cancer cell represents one of the greatest biological challenges confronting man today. In his quest to understand and control neoplastic cells, the attention of the oncologist has turned more and more to viruses. There are now over 25 different viruses known to cause tumorous growths in at least one species of animal. Therefore, oncogenic animal viruses have become important model systems for the study of the neoplastic process.

Intensive efforts during the last decade have been concerned with (1) isolation of additional viruses capable of causing tumors in animals, (2) isolation of viruses from human tumors, and (3) elucidation of the molecular events underlying the transformation of mammalian cells by viruses. Of these, a continuation of the first effort would appear to be needless, the second goal has not achieved significant results, and the third approach has been only partially successful. From the long-range point of view, translation of this success will afford rapid progress in such related fields as embryology, mnemonology, and geriatrics.

The virus selected for study by many investigators is simian papovavirus 40 (SV40). The primary reason for this selection is the limited amount of genetic information carried by SV40. For the purpose of studying transformation, it is clearly a better candidate than the deoxyribonucleic acid (DNA)-containing adenoviruses or the ribonucleic acid (RNA)-containing sarcoma and leukemia viruses. This paper will review the extensive studies done with SV40 since its discovery by Sweet and Hilleman (1960) and the demonstration of its oncogenicity in newborn hamsters by Eddy (1962) and by Girardi, Sweet, Slotnick, and Hilleman (1962).

As defined by Melnick (1962), SV40 is a papovavirus containing

---
* American Cancer Society Professor of Virology. Present address: Department of Microbiology, The Milton S. Hershey Medical Center, Pennsylvania State University, Hershey, Pennsylvania 17033.

DNA as its genetic material. The viral genome is estimated to code for about 10 average-sized proteins. Therefore, if these few viral genes were characterized, it should be possible to determine what is necessary to effect the transformation of a normal cell into a cancer cell. Another advantage of using SV40 as a model tumor virus is that it can be propagated in tissue culture. The events in the replicative cycle can, therefore, be analyzed and compared to their expression in a transformed cell. It is this achievement, made possible by the contributions of many investigators, that sets SV40 apart from other tumor viruses in 1969. It also makes mandatory a careful analysis of the results obtained thus far and a delineation of problems remaining to be solved. That is the purpose of this paper.

Chemical and Physical Properties of the Virus Particle

The mature virus particle is estimated to be from 41 (Koch *et al.*, 1967) to 45 (Mayor, Jamison, and Jordan. 1963) mμ in diameter. The full particle bands at a density of 1.32 g/ml in rubidium chloride (Black, Crawford, and Crawford, 1964) and at 1.34 g/ml in cesium chloride (Yoshiike, 1968b). It has been reported to have a sedimentation coefficient of 240 (Black, Crawford, and Crawford, 1964) and 219 (Koch *et al.*, 1967). This discrepancy may be caused by the use of different buffers in the sedimentation experiments. The number of capsomeres comprising the virus capsid has been evaluated as 42 (Mayor, Jamison, and Jordan, 1963), a figure supported by Howatson and Crawford (1963) for the other papovaviruses, or 72 (Klug, 1965). Recent data (Anderer *et al.*, 1967), however. strongly support the 72-subunit concept.

SV40 contains double-stranded DNA, variously estimated to weigh 4.0×10^6 daltons (Mayor, Jamison, and Jordan, 1963), 2.6×10^6 and 3.2×10^6 daltons (Crawford and Black, 1964), and 2.2×10^6 daltons (Anderer *et al.*, 1967). The discrepancy in these values undoubtedly results from the use of diverse biophysical techniques of varying sensitivities. This amount of DNA is sufficient to code for approximately 10 average-sized proteins. The DNA may be in either circular or linear configurations and contains 41 per cent guanine plus cytosine (Crawford and Black, 1964). This base composition closely resembles that of the mammalian host cell. In fact, nearest neighbor base-sequence analyses revealed that the doublet patterns for SV40 and mammalian cell DNA's were remarkably similar (Morrison, Keir, Subak-Sharpe, and Crawford, 1967). The significance of this in regard to the oncogenic potential of SV40 is currently unknown.

An elegant series of experiments has recently revealed that there are three different polypeptide chains in the protein moiety of SV40 (Anderer *et al.*, 1967; Anderer, Koch, and Schlumberger, 1968; Schlumberger, Anderer, and Koch, 1968). The molecular weights are reportedly 16,400 for the A chains, 16,900 for the B chains, and 16,800 for the C chains; the ratio of the individual components is 45:45:10 for A:B:C. Of interest is the fact that the C component is located inside the mature viral particles, with the A and B chains comprising the protein shell. Antiserum against SV40 did not react with purified preparations of C polypeptide. It might also be mentioned that antiserum against the SV40 tumor antigen (T-antigen) did not react with C either. As Schlumberger, Anderer, and Koch noted (1968), these three polypeptide chains, containing a total of about 450 amino acids, account for more than one third of the coding capacity of the SV40 genome.

Replicative Cycle of the Virus

The virus cytolytic cycle, which culminates in the production of progeny virus, can be analyzed and subdivided into a series of distinct events. Since transformed cells do not produce virus, the replicative cycle of the virus is obviously blocked somewhere. The individual events in the growth cycle must be known before the location of this block can be determined.

SV40 replicates well in kidney cells derived from African green monkeys. The different events known to occur during the virus replicative cycle are presented in Table 1. Temporal data are not indicated because the events are dependent upon the multiplicity of infection, the state of the cell at time of infection, and the time the investigators chose to take samples. Because of these factors, the temporal data presented by various investigators do not correlate well, but the sequence of events

TABLE 1. *Steps in the Replication of SV40*

1. Attachment
2. Penetration and uncoating
3. Synthesis of early RNA
4. Induction of enzymes
5. Synthesis of T-antigen
6. Synthesis of DNA
7. Synthesis of late RNA
8. Synthesis of capsid antigen
9. Maturation
10. Release of progeny virus

remains the same. Of course, once the synthesis of a product of infection has been initiated (such as T-antigen), it can be detected at later times throughout the cycle.

Initially, the virus must attach to a cell. Attachment occurs equally well at both 4 C and 37 C. After 1.5 hours at 37 C, 64 per cent of the virus had adsorbed to green monkey kidney (GMK) cells (Carp and Gilden, 1966). In parallel experiments, these same investigators found that over 90 per cent of the virus adsorbed to a stable GMK cell line (BSC-1) after one hour at either 4 or 37 C. Following adsorption, the virus enters into eclipse. About 50 per cent of the virus eclipses within two hours after attachment to either primary GMK or stable BSC-1 cells (Carp and Gilden, 1966).

The uncoating of the viral genome during eclipse is followed by synthesis of messenger RNA (mRNA). The early mRNA, formed before viral DNA synthesis, represents only a small portion (about 37 per cent) of the viral genome (Aloni, Winocour, and Sachs, 1968). Relatively small amounts of this early RNA are synthesized. The precise function of this mRNA is not known, but it undoubtedly plays a role in the ensuing induction of enzymes in the infected cell.

Thymidine kinase (Kit, Dubbs, Frearson, and Melnick, 1966; Hatanaka and Dulbecco, 1967), thymidine synthetase (Kit, Dubbs, Frearson, and Melnick, 1966), DNA polymerase (Kit, Piekarski, and Dubbs, 1967), and dihydrofolate reductase (Frearson, Kit, and Dubbs, 1966) all show increased activity in GMK cells following infection by SV40. The increase in the levels of thymidine kinase activity is the most notable, sometimes being ten- to twentyfold greater than in the uninfected cells. The other three enzymes generally increase only slightly (two- to fivefold). The increases in enzyme levels are generally first detected 12 to 16 hours after virus infection. The enzyme inductions do not require DNA synthesis, but are dependent upon protein synthesis, according to experiments employing metabolic inhibitors. There have been contradictory reports regarding the effect of SV40 infection on deoxycytidylate deaminase levels in monkey cells (Kit, de Torres, and Dubbs, 1967; Hatanaka and Dulbecco, 1966). It is generally believed that these elevated enzyme levels are caused by stimulation of host cell enzymes by the virus. However, thymidine kinase may be an exception. Kit (1967) concluded that the formation of thymidine kinase is controlled, either directly or indirectly, by the virus genome. Hatanaka and Dulbecco (1967) went further and concluded that there is an SV40-specific thymidine kinase. The induction of synthesis of these host cell enzymes indicates that SV40 is able to overcome the normal regulatory mechanism of the cell.

At approximately the same time enzyme induction occurs, T-antigen is being formed in the infected cells. This early antigen can be detected by both complement-fixation and immunofluorescence techniques using sera from hamsters bearing tumors induced by SV40 (Rapp, Kitahara, Butel, and Melnick, 1964; Sabin and Koch, 1964; Hoggan, Rowe, Black, and Huebner, 1965). The latter technique localizes the tumor antigen in the nucleus of infected cells. The synthesis of T-antigen does not require DNA synthesis (Rapp, Melnick, and Kitahara, 1965; Rapp et al., 1965; Butel and Rapp, 1965). The T-antigen has been extensively purified and shown to be distinct from nuclear exoribonuclease based on elution profiles from diethylaminoethyl (DEAE)-cellulose (Lazarus, Sporn, Smith, and Henderson, 1967). Despite the time at which it is synthesized, T-antigen does not appear to be one of the DNA biosynthetic enzymes mentioned above (Kit et al., 1967). Neither does it appear to be a constituent of the mature virus particle (Gilden, Carp, Taguchi, and Defendi, 1965), although the extraction procedures might have degraded a labile antigen. The T-antigen is important because it serves as a specific identifiable marker of SV40 and is easy to detect.

An immunologically identical antigen is synthesized in most SV40-induced tumors and transformed cells; this will be discussed in greater detail in a following section. Although the T-antigen has been vitally important in the study of SV40, its biological function is still obscure.

Following the induction of enzymes and T-antigen, viral DNA which will be incorporated into progeny virions is synthesized in the infected cells. However, it appears that the synthesis of cellular DNA is also stimulated by SV40 (Hatanaka and Dulbecco, 1966; Kit, de Torres, Dubbs, and Salvi, 1967), although there have been some contradictory reports (Gershon, Sachs, and Winocour, 1966; Sauer, Fischer, and Munk, 1966). These conflicting data might be caused by differences in the monkey cell lines used by the various laboratories. Cellular DNA and viral DNA have nearly the same buoyant densities, so it is difficult to separate the two nucleic acids. This is generally accomplished by first boiling the DNA and then passing it through either a nitrocellulose or methylated albumin-kieselguhr (MAK) column. The heat treatment denatures cellular DNA and it is retained by the column; the closed circular viral DNA is not denatured and passes through the column. It is not clear at this time whether the stimulation of cellular DNA involves a different viral gene than the one responsible for synthesis of virus DNA.

RNA synthesized any time after viral DNA has been condensed is considered "late" RNA. This RNA represents at least 76 per cent of the virus genome. Approximately 40 times more late RNA than early RNA is made in an infected culture (Aloni, Winocour, and Sachs, 1968).

The late RNA undoubtedly codes for, among other things, the three different polypeptides involved in capsid protein. The synthesis of capsid antigen depends on prior DNA synthesis, because metabolic inhibitors which interfere with DNA replication prevent the formation of capsid protein (Rapp et al., 1965; Butel and Rapp, 1965).

The DNA and capsid protein are then assembled together, and the mature particles are released from the cell. Before this release, the typical vacuolating cytopathology of SV40 becomes apparent (Mayor et al., 1962; Sweet and Hilleman, 1960). Interestingly, addition of protein inhibitors such as puromycin or fluorophenylalanine late in the growth cycle will allow virus particles to form, but will almost completely prevent the vacuolization of the cytoplasm (Mayor, Jamison, Jordan, and McGregor, 1966). Therefore, capsid antigen per se does not appear to be responsible for the specific viral effects observed. The nature of the initiating protein is not known.

Attention has recently been drawn to the fact that SV40 is able to complement the growth of human adenoviruses in GMK cells. This has been reviewed in detail (Rapp and Melnick, 1966; Rapp, 1967, 1968). The salient features of the system are outlined in Table 2. Adenoviruses proceed through the replicative cycle in GMK cells only to the point of synthesis of viral DNA. Then the infection is aborted and no capsid antigen is formed. When SV40 is present, the adenovirus completes its replicative cycle and produces infectious progeny as a consequence of complementation between the two unrelated viruses. Phenotypic mixing and recombination are probably not involved, for the progeny viruses formed are genetically identical to the two parental viruses. The actual factor provided by SV40 is not clear, but it has recently been shown

TABLE 2. *Complementation of SV40 and Human Adenoviruses in Simian Cells*

Property detected	Single infection		Mixed infection	
	SV40	Adenovirus	SV40	Adenovirus
T-antigen	+	+	+	+
Messenger RNA	+	+	+	+
Viral DNA	+	+	+	+
Capsid protein	+	0	+	+
Virus particles	+	0	+	+
Infectious progeny virus	+	0	+	+

Abbreviations: +, present; 0, absent.

(Jerkofsky and Rapp, 1969) that this complementation is cell dependent. SV40 is able to grow in BSC-1 cells, but fails to enhance the growth of human adenoviruses. Since this enhancement is probably an indirect effect, the phenomenon of complementation probably is not mediated by a separate SV40 cistron.

The foregoing section has described the various steps in the replicative cycle of SV40. There are a number of specific events involved, including the synthesis of T-antigen, the induction of enzymes, the induction of DNA synthesis, synthesis of early and late virus-specific RNA, synthesis of capsid protein, and complementation of human adenoviruses. These cannot be coded for by separate genes in the small complement of SV40 DNA. Whether the code for a specific event is actually contained in the viral genome or is a cell codon which is derepressed by the invading virus cannot be determined until a variety of cell and virus mutants have been obtained. A great deal has been learned about what the virus does, but not much about how it performs these functions. Therefore, it is not possible at this time to know with surety how many of the viral genes have been accounted for. The T-antigen remains an enigma. When its biological function is unravelled, a great deal may be clarified, especially if it is found to possess properties leading to regulation or derepression of the host cell genome.

Defective SV40

It is important to take note of the defective forms of SV40 known to exist because of the influence they have had on our thinking regarding tumor induction. In addition, defective mutants will undoubtedly play a major role in future studies concerning mechanisms of action by the virus.

One defective form of SV40 (PARA [particle aiding replication of adenovirus]), unable to induce the synthesis of capsid protein, was originally found associated with a strain of adenovirus 7 thought to be adapted to growth in GMK cells. The key observation that pinpointed the presence of SV40 genetic information was that adenovirus 7 caused SV40-like tumors in hamsters and induced the synthesis of SV40 T-antigen in tissue culture (Huebner, Chanock, Rubin, and Casey, 1964; Rowe and Baum, 1964; Rapp, Melnick, Butel, and Kitahara, 1964). Subsequent experiments revealed a mixed population. One component was a human adenovirus which could replicate singly in human cells but could grow in monkey cells only in the presence of SV40. The second particle (PARA) was the defective SV40 genome encased in an adenovirus capsid. It could multiply in GMK cells only in the presence of an adenovirus, which was required to provide the coat protein (Boeyé, Melnick, and Rapp, 1965, 1966; Rowe and Baum, 1965). Plaque kinetics can be used to characterize such a mixed population. When increasing dilutions are plated and the titer of the original stock calculated, the calculated titer will fall with each increasing dilution. If excess amounts of helper virus are added to the assay plates so that each cell which gets infected with a defective particle is assured of containing a helper virus, the calculated titer will be the same at all dilutions. The defective SV40 can be transferred to a heterologous adenovirus population if it is present during the replicative cycle (Rapp, Butel, and Melnick, 1965; Rowe, 1965; Butel and Rapp, 1966b). This transfer is termed "transcapsidation" (Rapp, Butel, and Melnick, 1965).

The actual amount of SV40 genetic material in PARA is not clear. Both components of the population share similar biophysical properties (Butel and Rapp, 1966a), so that PARA has not been obtained separately from the adenovirus. When DNA is extracted, it is a mixture of adenovirus and SV40 DNA with a buoyant density typical of the helper adenovirus and no separate peak suggestive of a distinct PARA DNA (Rapp and Khare, 1967). However, techniques which readily separated artificial mixtures of SV40 and adenovirus DNA's failed to achieve separation of the adenovirus and SV40-hybridizable DNA's from a mixture extracted from PARA-adenovirus 7 (Baum et al., 1966). This observation suggests that the SV40 DNA may be linked to some adenovirus DNA.

In addition to the T-antigen marker, PARA also contains the genetic information required to induce SV40 transplantation immunity in weanling hamsters (Rapp, Tevethia, and Melnick, 1966; Rapp, Butel, Tevethia, and Melnick, 1967). One very important observation is that when PARA is transcapsidated to nononcogenic human adenovirus populations such as type 2, that adenovirus then becomes tumorigenic (Rapp et al., 1966; Rapp, Jerkofsky, Melnick, and Levy, 1968). Plaque-purification of the parental PARA-adenovirus 7 stock has recently yielded a variety of clones of varying oncogenicity (Table 3). The explanation for this variation is

TABLE 3. *Variation in Oncogenic Ability of PARA Plaque Progeny*

Oncogenicity	Plaque progeny no.	Per cent tumor induction
Tumors	104	81
No tumors	24	19
Total	128	

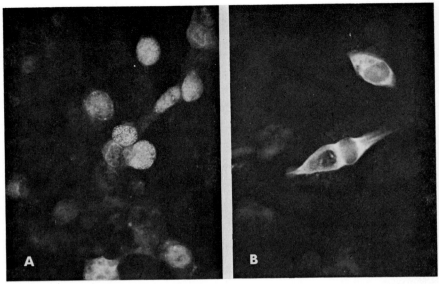

FIGURE 1. Localization of SV40 T-antigen after inoculation of human embryonic kidney cell cultures with plaque progeny of PARA (defective SV40)-adenovirus type 7. a—Normal intranuclear localization of T-antigen. b—Cytoplasmic localization of T-antigen. Reduced from × 400.

not known although it was not merely caused by differences in the titer of PARA in the different preparations. Plaque-purification also yielded at least one PARA mutant which induces the synthesis of SV40 T-antigen in the cytoplasm of GMK cells (Butel, Guentzel, and Rapp, 1969) (Figure 1). This atypical localization of the T-antigen may be caused by either a defective virus-controlled transfer mechanism or an altered effect upon a host transfer system. Further characterization of the mutant is required before the effect of the altered location of T-antigen synthesis on the properties of the virus can be determined.

Recent reports indicate that SV40 stocks contain a certain number of defective particles (Uchida, Watanabe, and Kato, 1966; Uchida, Yoshiike, Watanabe, and Furuno, 1968; Sauer, Koprowski, and Defendi, 1967; Altstein, Sarycheva, and Dodonova, 1967). These particles possess SV40 capsids, but are recognized because they induce the synthesis of T-antigen, and sometimes virus(V-) antigen, and do not initiate plaque formation. These particles are slightly lighter in CsCl (Uchida, Yoshiike, Watanabe, and Furuno, 1968; Yoshiike, 1968a, b) and have been found to contain a significantly shorter molecule of DNA (Yoshiike, 1968a, b).

Little is known about the biological properties of these defective particles. It has not been reported whether they can induce SV40 transplantation immunity, stimulate DNA synthesis, or complement human adenoviruses in simian cells. Of note is the finding that these defective particles were found to be as tumorigenic as reference, nondefective SV40 (Uchida and Watanabe, 1968). The presence of these defective particles has important implications regarding tumor induction because it has been postulated that perhaps only defective viruses are oncogenic. It is important to determine whether these particles are genetically stable or whether they are produced randomly anew during each replicative cycle. If these defective particles are produced randomly during each replicative cycle, no stock of SV40 would be free from them and plaque purification of a stock would not eliminate such particles.

Reported properties of the two types of defective SV40 particles are compared in Table 4. This does not imply that all the defective particles produced by undiluted passage are the same. In fact, they probably are not, and inspection of Table 4 will reveal that any conclusions comparing the two types of particles would be premature at this time because of the lack of sufficient data.

Transformation by SV40

SV40 was first reported to be tumorigenic in newborn hamsters in 1962 by Eddy, Borman, Grubbs, and Young and by Girardi, Sweet, Slotnick, and Hilleman. Ashkenazi and Melnick (1963) and Black and Rowe (1964) quickly confirmed this. The virus will not produce tumors in adult animals (Girardi, Sweet, and Hilleman, 1963). The SV40-

TABLE 4. *Comparison of Properties of Types of Defective SV40*

Property	Type of defective SV40	
	PARA	Undiluted passage
SV40 capsid	0	+
Adenovirus capsid	+	0
Induce SV40 T-antigen	+	+
Induce SV40 capsid antigen	0	0, +
Buoyant density in CsCl	1.34	1.33
Oncogenic	+	+
Induce SV40-transplant immunity	+	NK
Genetically stable	+	NK
Complement adenovirus	+	NK

Abbreviations: 0, absent; +, present; NK, not known.

induced tumors can be removed, trypsinized or minced, and the cells readily transplanted into recipient weanling hamsters.

Prior immunization of the weanling hamsters with SV40 will render them resistant to challenge with the tumor cells (Melnick and Ashkenazi, 1963; Khera, Ashkenazi, Rapp, and Melnick, 1963; Habel and Eddy, 1963; Koch and Sabin, 1963; Defendi, 1963). This resistance is termed transplantation immunity and is believed to indicate a virus-specific antigen on the surface of the tumor cell. The antigen is virus specific because only SV40 will immunize hamsters against SV40 tumor cells.

A typical transplantation rejection test is performed as follows: A group of weanling hamsters are inoculated two or three times with SV40. The control (uninoculated) and inoculated groups are subdivided and challenged with tenfold dilutions of tumor cells. The dose of cells required to produce tumors in 50 per cent of the animals (TPD_{50}) in each group is calculated after 12 weeks of observation for tumor development. When using the SV40 system, it is not unusual to observe a thousand-fold difference in TPD_{50} between the control and immunized animals. The transplantation rejection test requires a highly oncogenic challenge cell ($\leq 10^2$ cells/TPD_{50}) to detect significant immunity readily.

It is postulated that the immunizing virus infects a few cells in the adult animal and transforms them. These cells are promptly rejected by the host; this process immunizes the host against further challenge with homologous virus-transformed cells. At present, there is no unequivocable proof either for or against this hypothesis. It appears that transplantation immunity is cell-mediated because treatment of weanling hamsters with antihamster thymocyte serum (AHTS) during the period of inoculation with SV40 prevented the immunization of the animals to virus-induced antigens (Tevethia, Dreesman, Lausch, and Rapp, 1968). Animals treated with AHTS were not able to resist challenge with SV40 tumor cells (Figure 2).

Unfortunately, there is no in vitro test which measures the transplantation antigen-antibody reaction. However, the colony-inhibition test (Hellström and Sjögren, 1966) and the mixed hemagglutination technique (Häyry and Defendi, 1968) may detect the transplantation antigen. Tevethia, Katz, and Rapp (1965) detected a surface (S)-antigen on SV40 tumor cells by the indirect immunofluorescence test using sera from hamsters which had resisted tumor transplants. Hamster isoantigens were ruled out as the cause of this reaction (Tevethia, Couvillion, and Rapp, 1968) by inoculating newborn hamsters with SV40 and reinoculating the animals with virus during the latent period before the appearance of the tumors. This procedure prevented tumor development, but

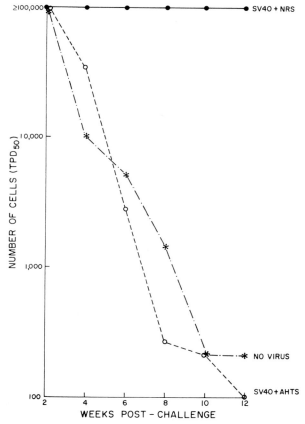

FIGURE 2. Effect of antihamster thymocyte serum (AHTS) on SV40-induced transplantation immunity. ●——● animals inoculated with SV40 and then challenged with cells transformed by the same virus; these animals also received four inoculations of normal rabbit serum (NRS) before challenge. O----O animals inoculated with SV40 and then challenged with cells transformed by the same virus; these animals received four inoculations of AHTS before challenge. *—.—.—* animals challenged with cells transformed by SV40. (From Tevethia, D r e e s m a n, Lausch, and Rapp, 1968.)

the hamsters still made S-antibody. This experiment ruled out hamster isoantigens because the hamsters had not been exposed to any hamster cells. Unfortunately, recent experiments (Tevethia, Diamandopoulos, Rapp, and Enders, 1968) have indicated that the S-antigen detected by immunofluorescence and the transplantation antigen detected by transplantation rejection tests in hamsters are probably not identical because cells which contained only the S-antigen (and no T-antigen) did not carry the SV40-specific transplantation antigen.

Nevertheless, the S-antigen does appear to be under virus control; there is one unconfirmed report (Kluchareva et al., 1967) that a similar antigen was detected in human and hamster embryo cells soon after infection with SV40. However, the high multiplicities of virus used and the very early appearance of antigen suggest that adsorbed virus may have been detected at the cell surface. The transplantation and S-antigens may be new antigens coded for by the virus genome or they may be derepressed cellular antigens. At this time, no direct evidence supports either alternative.

A second distinct antigen present in most SV40-induced tumor cells is the T-antigen. It is detected using sera from tumor-bearing hamsters in either the complement-fixation (Black, Rowe, Turner, and Huebner, 1963) or immunofluorescence test (Rapp, Butel, and Melnick, 1964; Pope and Rowe, 1964). Immunofluorescence reveals that this antigen is present in the nuclei of all SV40 tumor cells. The source of antisera readily distinguishes between the T- and the S-antigens. Tumor-bearing hamsters yield antibody against T-antigen, whereas animals which have rejected tumor transplants provide S-antibody. Antibody against SV40 capsid antigen does not react with either S- or T-antigen. The tumor antigen was directly related back to SV40 when it was found to be synthesized during the virus replicative cycle in monkey cells. This was described in detail in a preceding section.

SV40 readily transforms cells in tissue cultures. This in vitro transformation of cells recently has been reviewed in detail (Black, 1968). Several species have been shown susceptible to cellular transformation in vitro by SV40. However, most attention will be paid to experiments involving hamster cells since that species is susceptible to tumor induction in vivo by SV40. Both hamster embryo (Ashkenazi and Melnick, 1963) and newborn hamster kidney (Rabson and Kirschstein, 1962; Black and Rowe, 1963b; Shein, Enders, Levinthal, and Burket, 1963) cells were used originally. Cells from separate organs have since been transformed (Diamandopoulos and Enders, 1965). Cells transformed in vitro were tumorigenic and were found to contain the intranuclear tumor antigen in most instances.

However, some hamster cells exposed to SV40 became oncogenic but did not contain SV40 T-antigen (Diamandopoulos and Enders, 1965). Two of the cell lines carried the S-antigen, demonstrating that its synthesis may occur independently of the synthesis of T-antigen (Diamandopoulos, Tevethia, Rapp, and Enders, 1968). Only those cell lines positive for both S- and T-antigens carried the SV40 transplantation antigen (Tevethia, Diamandopoulos, Rapp, and Enders, 1968). Also, exposure of BHK 21 cells to SV40 DNA increased their malignant potential in the absence of persistent T-antigen (Black and Rowe, 1965). The cells were not characterized for other virus-specific antigens.

All investigators have observed that, although tumor cells contained the tumor antigen, they did not contain any detectable virus capsid anti-

TABLE 5. *Phenotypic Expression of SV40 Markers*

Property	Cytolytic cycle	Transformed cells
Synthesis of T-antigen	+	+
Induction of enzymes	+	NK
Stimulation of cell DNA synthesis	+	NK
Synthesis of virus capsid antigen	+	0
Formation of virus particles	+	0
Cell death	+	0
Synthesis of transplantation antigen	NK	+
Synthesis of surface (S) antigen	NK	+

Abbreviations: +, present; NK, not known; 0, absent.

gen and only rarely was any infectious virus released. Such observations suggest that the virus replicative cycle is blocked in the transformed cells. A comparison of events which occur during the virus cytolytic cycle in monkey cells with those events expressed in transformed cells is given in Table 5. In conjunction with the idea that the virus undergoes an incomplete growth cycle during transformation, it is noteworthy that the defective SV40 particle (PARA) associated with a helper adenovirus is also able to transform cells in tissue culture (Black and Todaro, 1965; Rabson, Malmgren, and Kirschstein, 1966; Diamond, 1967). The use of PARA, defective for capsid protein, effectively rules out that antigen as having any role in malignant transformation by SV40.

PARA is just one example of transformation by defective SV40. It was mentioned in the preceding section that the defective SV40 produced by undiluted passage is oncogenic. SV40 greatly inactivated by hydroxylamine was shown to still be oncogenic and capable of transforming hamster cells in vitro (Altstein *et al.*, 1967). Somewhat unexpectedly, it was found that inactivation of SV40 with ultraviolet light or cobalt-60 irradiation actually enhanced the oncogenicity of the preparation (Defendi and Jensen, 1967). All these results indicate that only a portion of the virus genome is required to initiate cell transformation.

Hamster tumor and transformed cells rarely release detectable levels of infectious virus. Various manipulations have been reported to "induce" the release of infectious virus. One manipulation was the plating of tumor cells onto monolayers of susceptible GMK cells (Gerber and Kirschstein, 1962; Black and Rowe, 1963a; Sabin and Koch, 1963; Black, 1966). Treatment with metabolic inhibitors was reported to induce some tumor cells to release virus (Gerber, 1964; Burns and Black, 1968). The most recent innovation is to fuse the tumor cells with susceptible indicator cells by using Sendai virus to form heterokaryons. The object of this procedure is to ensure more intimate contact between the two cell types. It has been successful in some cell lines which had previously failed to yield virus (Gerber, 1966; Koprowski, Jensen, and Steplewski, 1967; Watkins and Dulbecco, 1967; Dubbs and Kit, 1968). Under any of the preceding conditions, the yield of virus is still very low and the occurrence of a virus-yielding cell very rare. Indeed, some cell lines will not yield virus at all (Melnick, Khera, and Rapp, 1964; Westphal and Dulbecco, 1968).

Fusion of two different nonvirus-yielding transformed cell lines, sometimes in the presence of GMK cells, has been reported to yield infectious SV40 (Knowles, Jensen, Steplewski, and Koprowski, 1968). However, no quantitative data were presented regarding the frequency of such release, the amount of virus released, or the characteristics of the released virus. If confirmed, this will be a very important finding because it suggests that defective portions of the SV40 genome are present in transformed cells, that the defective portion varies from one transformed cell line to the next, and that these defective regions can complement one another in a susceptible cell. Recombination of different genome segments also might be involved.

The failure of induction experiments to meet with convincing success brings us to the next important point—what is the state of the viral genome in the transformed cell? Viral DNA can be detected in the tumor cells (Reich, Black, and Weissman, 1966; Westphal and Dulbecco, 1968). Westphal and Dulbecco (1968) were able to estimate the number of virus DNA equivalents per cell from reconstruction experiments; the number varied from five to 60, depending on the cell line tested. There was no relationship between the number of DNA copies per cell and the ability of that cell line to release infectious virus. The viral DNA was located in the nuclei of the transformed cells. Subsequent experiments (Sambrook, Westphal, Srinivasan, and Dulbecco, 1968) provided evidence that the viral DNA molecules were actually linked to the cellular DNA by covalent bonds. It was not possible to determine whether the multiple copies are attached at one site or at many sites on the host cell chromosome.

A different type of experiment supports these conclusions. Somatic hybrids between mouse cells and SV40-transformed human cells were formed and a series of clones isolated. T-antigen originally was expressed in the hybrid cells but seemed to be lost from the cells concurrently with human chromosomes (Weiss, Ephrussi, and Scaletta, 1968). In fact, all or nearly all the human chromosomes had to be lost for a cell to become T-antigen negative. Whether multiple copies of the virus genome are attached to different chromosomes or whether the "integrated" chromosome is the last to be lost in the cell hybrid experiment remains to be determined.

Although both biophysical evidence and formation of virus-specific antigens indicate the presence of SV40 DNA in transformed cells, infectious DNA cannot be isolated (Sabin and Koch, 1963; Kit, Kurimura, Salvi, and Dubbs, 1968). However, infectious DNA can be detected following the fusion of certain transformed cell lines with monkey kidney cells (Kit, Kurimura, Salvi, and Dubbs, 1968) after a lag comparable to that seen in the eclipse period during the replicative cycle.

In view of this evidence that viral DNA is present in the transformed cells in association with host chromosomes, apparently some mechanism must be operative for the insertion of the genome(s). Conversely, there must be another active mechanism which excises the viral DNA following the fusion of transformed and susceptible cells in order to release infectious virus. This "excision enzyme" must be a normal component of the monkey (susceptible) cell and might be the reason those cells are not easily transformed by the virus. Those rare instances in which monkey kidney cells have been transformed by SV40 (Fernandes and Moorhead, 1965; Wallace, 1967; Rapp, unpublished data) are probably the result of transformation of an excision enzyme-negative cell.

Whatever its integrated configuration, viral DNA is partially transcribed in the tumor cells. Virus-specific RNA can be detected (Benjamin, 1966; Aloni, Winocour, and Sachs, 1968; Oda and Dulbecco, 1968). Only about one third of the SV40 genome appears to be transcribed, but the RNA is not identical to either the "early" or "late" RNA formed during the virus replicative cycle. It appears that at least one late gene is transcribed in the tumor cell, but its identity is not known. Obviously, it is not the gene coding for capsid protein. It would be fascinating to know the control mechanism which regulates the selective transcription of the integrated viral genome(s).

Discussion and Extrapolation to Cancer in Man

It was stated earlier that a small papovavirus such as SV40 might be a useful model system to help in the elucidation of basic mechanisms operative in cases of neoplasia in human beings. A vast amount of information has been gathered since SV40 was discovered in 1960. Unfortunately, the many pieces have not yet fallen into a clear-cut pattern. Nevertheless, certain lines of thinking seem rational at this time and bear extrapolation to investigations on cancer in man.

Attempts to isolate infectious virus from solid tumors would appear to have a low probability for success. Many SV40 tumors are virus-free, and those which do release virus yield only very small amounts. The release of even these minimal amounts of virus requires various manipulations of tumor cells and sensitive indicator cells. In the case of tumors in man, this would involve an unknown indicator cell and an unknown assay system. These difficulties relegate virus isolation to a low place on the list of probable approaches.

Serology would appear to be a better approach than virus isolation. Immunological tests have revealed the key antigens known to be associated with virus-induced tumors. One would expect that serum from a cancer patient would react with a T-antigen present in the cancer cells. Twenty different specimens were tested, and none of the sera reacted in any way with antigens in tumor cells from the homologous patient (Rapp, Melnick, Kitahara, and Sheppard, 1965). These negative results can be explained in several ways. Only a few samples, at most, of a particular type of tumor were obtained. Since not all SV40 tumor-bearing animals form T-antibody, these few samples might have been obtained from such negative individuals merely by chance. Furthermore, SV40 T-antigen is relatively easy to detect. The polyoma and adenovirus T-antigens are apparently not as antigenic since fewer tumor-bearing animals in those systems make antibody. The human system(s) might be antigenically weak also. S-antigen is detected using sera from immune animals (those which have rejected tumor cells). This would be difficult to duplicate in a human study, because it would be impossible to know against which tumor cells to test the normal (hopefully immune) sera. Transplantation rejection tests are obviously impossible to perform, but in vitro tests which duplicate the in vivo test will be logical to try as they are developed.

Biochemical techniques are being used in attempts to detect other virus markers in human tumors. For example, mRNA can be extracted and tested for ability to hybridize with DNA from known groups of viruses. This approach may yield results where other approaches have failed. Success depends on the availability of a related virus to provide nucleic acid for the hybridization tests. However, it might be expected that, if enough virus-specific RNA is produced to detect, translation of the RNA will occur and will result in a more readily detectable protein or antigen.

All available evidence suggests that tumor cells contain new antigens. One then wonders why these cells are not recognized as foreign by the host's immunological system and immediately destroyed. Perhaps the great majority of initiated tumors are destroyed in this fashion, and the clinical cases which do occur arise at a time when the host's immune defense system is temporarily impaired. It is known that persons with certain immunological deficiencies are more prone to develop neoplastic disease. One can also postulate that the virus-transformed cells grow rapidly and overwhelm the defenses of the host or that the virus-transformed cells are hardy and resist the killing effects of the body's defense mechanisms. Resolution of this key problem awaits advancement by immunologists in their studies of tumor immunity.

More and more evidence indicates that defective virus genomes can effect transformation. Whether only defective viruses can do so remains to be determined. The description of the PARA-adenovirus association reveals that defective genomes can be carried by unrelated helper viruses and that the helper viruses then become oncogenic. The defective genome would be undetected in the helper virus population unless key reagents were available to recognize it. What is more, the defective genome would be transferred from one helper virus to the next by transcapsidation during a joint infection. Defective cancer virus genomes would thereby have a vehicle for spread throughout a population "disguised" in a variety of protein coats. One can visualize a variety of epidemiological characteristics depending on the helper virus with which the defective genome happened to be associated at a given time. This might be one reason epidemiological studies of cancer in man have failed to yield any definite pattern.

The study of the replicative cycle of cancer viruses has allowed one very significant conclusion. The viruses appear to be able to alter the cell's regulatory mechanisms. Cell enzyme levels are elevated and cellular DNA is synthesized. Obviously, loss of regulatory control is a prominent feature of an invading, rapidly growing cancer cell. The key step, still unknown, must be a derepression of one or more cell regulatory genes. Possibly it is a repression of a regulatory gene, thereby allowing for continual function of certain synthetic activities. The new antigens might be a result of derepression also. Considering that each cell in the body contains a total complement of human genetic information, the transplantation antigen could easily be coded for somewhere in the mass of genetic information that is normally repressed in the adult. What appears clear is that the key to neoplasia is the regulatory mechanism(s) operative in the host cell and the effect of a cancer virus genome upon that mechanism.

ACKNOWLEDGMENTS

The authors are grateful to Dr. Joseph L. Melnick for his support and to Dr. S. S. Tevethia, Dr. R. L. Lausch, and Dr. M. A. Jerkofsky for their collaboration.

This research was supported in part by Public Health Service grants

CA 04600 and CA 10036 from the National Cancer Institute, National Institutes of Health.

REFERENCES

Aloni, Y., E. Winocour, and L. Sachs. 1968. Characterization of the Simian Virus 40-Specific RNA in Virus-Yielding and Transformed Cells. *Journal of Molecular Biology,* 31:415–429.

Altstein, A. D., G. I. Deichman, O. F. Sarycheva, N. N. Dodonova, E. M. Tsetlin, and N. N. Vassilieva. 1967. Oncogenic and Transforming Activity of Hydroxylamine-Inactivated SV40 Virus. *Virology,* 33:746–748.

Altstein, A. D., O. F. Sarycheva, and N. N. Dodonova. 1967. Detection of Defective (T-Antigen Inducing, but Noninfectious) Particles in Preparations of SV40 Virus. *Virology,* 33:744–746.

Anderer, F. A., M. A. Koch, and H. D. Schlumberger. 1968. Structure of Simian Virus 40. III. Alkaline Degradation of the Virus Particle. *Virology,* 34:452–458.

Anderer, F. A., H. D. Schlumberger, M. A. Koch, H. Frank, and H. J. Eggers. 1967. Structure of Simian Virus 40. II. Symmetry and Components of the Virus Particle. *Virology,* 32:511–523.

Ashkenazi, A., and J. L. Melnick. 1963. Tumorigenicity of Simian Papovavirus SV40 and of Virus-Transformed Cells. *Journal of the National Cancer Institute,* 30:1227–1265.

Baum, S. G., P. R. Reich, C. J. Hybner, W. P. Rowe, and S. M. Weissman. 1966. Biophysical Evidence for Linkage of Adenovirus and SV40 DNA's in Adenovirus 7-SV40 Hybrid Particles. *Proceedings of the National Academy of Sciences of the U.S.A.,* 56:1509–1515.

Benjamin, T. L. 1966. Virus-Specific RNA in Cells Productively Infected or Transformed by Polyoma Virus. *Journal of Molecular Biology,* 16:359–373.

Black, P. H. 1966. An Analysis of SV40-Induced Transformation of Hamster Kidney Tissue In Vitro. III. Persistence of SV40 Viral Genome in Clones of Transformed Hamster Cells. *Journal of the National Cancer Institute,* 37:487–493.

———. 1968. The Oncogenic DNA Viruses: A Review of In Vitro Transformation Studies. *Annual Review of Microbiology,* 22:391–426.

Black, P. H., E. M. Crawford, and L. V. Crawford. 1964. The Purification of Simian Virus 40. *Virology,* 24:381–387.

Black, P. H., and W. P. Rowe. 1963a. An Analysis of SV40-Induced Transformation of Hamster Kidney Tissue In Vitro. I. General Characteristics. *Proceedings of the National Academy of Sciences of the U.S.A.,* 50:606–613.

———. 1963b. Transformation in Hamster Kidney Monolayers by Vacuolating Virus, SV40. *Virology,* 19:107–109.

———. 1964. Viral Studies of SV40 Tumorigenesis in Hamsters. *Journal of the National Cancer Institute,* 32:253–265.

———. 1965. Increase of Malignant Potential of BHK-21 Cells by SV40 DNA Without Persistent New Antigen. *Proceedings of the National Academy of Sciences of the U.S.A.,* 54:1126–1133.

Black, P. H., W. P. Rowe, H. C. Turner, and R. J. Huebner. 1963. A Specific Complement-Fixing Antigen Present in SV40 Tumor and Transformed Cells. *Proceedings of the National Academy of Sciences of the U.S.A.,* 50:1148–1156.

Black, P. H., and G. J. Todaro. 1965. In Vitro Transformation of Hamster and Human Cells with the Adeno 7-SV40 Hybrid Virus. *Proceedings of the National Academy of Sciences of the U.S.A.*, 54:374–381.

Boeyé, A., J. L. Melnick, and F. Rapp. 1965. Adenovirus-SV40 "Hybrids": Plaque Purification into Lines in Which the Determinant for the SV40 Tumor Antigen is Lost or Retained. *Virology*, 26:511–512.

———. 1966. SV40-Adenovirus "Hybrids": Presence of Two Genotypes and the Requirement of Their Complementation for Viral Replication. *Virology*, 28:56–70.

Burns, W. H., and P. H. Black. 1968. Analysis of Simian Virus 40 Induced Transformation of Hamster Kidney Tissue In Vitro. V. Variability of Virus Recovery from Cell Clones Inducible with Mitomycin C and Cell Fusion. *Journal of Virology*, 2:606–609.

Butel, J. S., M. J. Guentzel, and F. Rapp. 1969. Variants of Defective Simian Papovavirus 40 (PARA) Characterized by Cytoplasmic Localization of Simian Papovavirus to Tumor Antigen. *Journal of Virology*, 4:632–641.

Butel, J. S., and F. Rapp. 1965. The Effect of Arabinofuranosylcytosine on the Growth Cycle of Simian Virus 40. *Virology*, 27:490–495.

———. 1966a. Inactivation and Density Studies with PARA-Adenovirus 7 (SV40-Adenovirus "Hybrid" Population). *Journal of Immunology*, 97:546–553.

———. 1966b. Replication in Simian Cells of Defective Viruses in an SV40-Adenovirus "Hybrid" Population. *Journal of Bacteriology*, 91:278–284.

Carp, R. I., and R. V. Gilden. 1966. A Comparison of the Replication Cycles of Simian Virus 40 in Human Diploid and African Green Monkey Kidney Cells. *Virology*, 28:150–162.

Crawford, L. V., and P. H. Black. 1964. The Nucleic Acid of Simian Virus 40. *Virology*, 24:388–392.

Defendi, V. 1963. Effect of SV40 Virus Immunization on Growth of Transplantable SV40 and Polyoma Virus Tumors in Hamsters. *Proceedings of the Society for Experimental Biology and Medicine*, 113:12–16.

Defendi, V., and F. Jensen. 1967. Oncogenicity by DNA Tumor Viruses: Enhancement after Ultraviolet and Cobalt-60 Radiations. *Science*, 157:703–705.

Diamandopoulos, G. T., and J. F. Enders. 1965. Studies on Transformation of Syrian Hamster Cells by Simian Virus 40 (SV40): Acquisition of Oncogenicity by Virus-Exposed Cells Apparently Unassociated with the Viral Genome. *Proceedings of the National Academy of Sciences of the U.S.A.*, 54:1092–1099.

Diamandopoulos, G. T., S. S. Tevethia, F. Rapp, and J. F. Enders. 1968. Development of S and T Antigens and Oncogenicity in Hamster Embryonic Cell Lines Exposed to SV40. *Virology*, 34:331–336.

Diamond, L. 1967. Transformation of Simian Virus 40-Resistant Hamster Cells with an Adenovirus 7-Simian Virus 40 Hybrid. *Journal of Virology*, 1:1109–1116.

Dubbs, D. R., and S. Kit. 1968. Isolation of Defective Lysogens from Simian Virus 40-Transformed Mouse Kidney Cultures. *Journal of Virology*, 2:1272–1282.

Eddy, B. E. 1962. Tumors Produced in Hamsters by SV40. *Federation Proceedings*, 21:930–935.

Eddy, B. E., G. S. Borman, G. E. Grubbs, and R. D. Young. 1962. Identification of the Oncogenic Substance in Rhesus Monkey Kidney Cell Cultures as Simian Virus 40. *Virology*, 17:65–75.

Fernandes, M. V., and P. S. Moorhead. 1965. Transformation of African Green

Monkey Kidney Cultures Infected with Simian Vacuolating Virus (SV40). *Texas Reports on Biology and Medicine*, 23 (Supplement 1):242–258.

Frearson, P. M., S. Kit, and D. R. Dubbs. 1966. Induction of Dihydrofolate Reductase Activity by SV40 and Polyoma Virus. *Cancer Research*, 26:1653–1660.

Gerber, P. 1964. Virogenic Hamster Tumor Cells: Induction of Virus Synthesis. *Science*, 145:833.

―――. 1966. Studies on the Transfer of Subviral Infectivity from SV40-Induced Hamster Tumor Cells to Indicator Cells. *Virology*, 28:501–509.

Gerber, P., and R. L. Kirschstein. 1962. SV40-Induced Ependymomas in Newborn Hamsters. I. Virus-Tumor Relationships. *Virology*, 18:582–588.

Gershon, D., L. Sachs, and E. Winocour. 1966. The Induction of Cellular DNA Synthesis by Simian Virus 40 in Contact-Inhibited and in X-irradiated Cells. *Proceedings of the National Academy of Sciences of the U.S.A.*, 56:918–925.

Gilden, R. V., R. I. Carp, F. Taguchi, and V. Defendi. 1965. The Nature and Localization of the SV40-Induced Complement-Fixing Antigen. *Proceedings of the National Academy of Sciences of the U.S.A.*, 53:684–692.

Girardi, A. J., B. H. Sweet, and M. R. Hilleman. 1963. Factors Influencing Tumor Induction in Hamsters by Vacuolating Virus, SV40. *Proceedings of the Society for Experimental Biology and Medicine*, 112:662–667.

Girardi, A. J., B. H. Sweet, V. B. Slotnick, and M. R. Hilleman. 1962. Development of Tumors in Hamsters Inoculated in the Neonatal Period with Vacuolating Virus SV40. *Proceedings of the Society for Experimental Biology and Medicine*, 109:649–660.

Habel, K., and B. E. Eddy. 1963. Specificity of Resistance to Tumor Challenge of Polyoma and SV40 Virus-Immune Hamsters. *Proceedings of the Society for Experimental Biology and Medicine*, 113:1–4.

Hatanaka, M., and R. Dulbecco. 1966. Induction of DNA Synthesis by SV40. *Proceedings of the National Academy of Sciences of the U.S.A.*, 56:736–740.

―――. 1967. SV40-Specific Thymidine Kinase. *Proceedings of the National Academy of Sciences of the U.S.A.*, 58:1888–1894.

Häyry, P., and V. Defendi. 1968. Use of Mixed Hemagglutination Technique in Detection of Virus-Induced Antigen(s) on SV40-Transformed Cell Surface. *Virology*, 36:317–320.

Hellström, I., and H. O. Sjögren. 1966. Demonstration of Common Specific Antigen(s) in Mouse and Hamster Polyoma Tumors. *International Journal of Cancer*, 1:481–489.

Hoggan, M. D., W. P. Rowe, P. H. Black, and R. J. Huebner. 1965. Production of "Tumor-Specific" Antigens by Oncogenic Viruses During Acute Cytolytic Infections. *Proceedings of the National Academy of Sciences of the U.S.A.*, 53:12–19.

Howatson, A. F., and L. V. Crawford. 1963. Direct Counting of the Capsomeres in Polyoma and Papilloma Viruses. *Virology*, 21:1–6.

Huebner, R. J., R. M. Chanock, B. A. Rubin, and M. J. Casey. 1964. Induction by Adenovirus Type 7 of Tumors in Hamsters Having the Antigenic Characteristics of SV40 Virus. *Proceedings of the National Academy of Sciences of the U.S.A.*, 52:1333–1340.

Jerkofsky, M. A., and F. Rapp. 1969. Cell-Mediated Complementation of Human Adenoviruses by Simian Papovavirus. *Proceedings of the Society for Experimental Biology and Medicine*, 132:987–992.

Khera, K. S., A. Ashkenazi, F. Rapp, and J. L. Melnick. 1963. Immunity in Hamsters to Cells Transformed In Vitro and In Vivo by SV40. Tests for Antigenic Relationship Among the Papovaviruses. *Journal of Immunology*, 91:604–613.

Kit, S. 1967. "Induction of Enzymes of DNA Metabolism by Simian Virus 40," *Subviral Carcinogenesis* (First International Symposium on Tumor Viruses), Y. Ito, Ed. Nagoya, Japan: Research Institute, Aichi Cancer Center, and The Japanese Cancer Association. Pp. 116–141.

Kit, S., D. R. Dubbs, P. M. Frearson, and J. L. Melnick. 1966. Enzyme Induction in SV40-Infected Green Monkey Kidney Cultures. *Virology*, 29:69–83.

Kit, S., T. Kurimura, M. L. Salvi, and D. R. Dubbs. 1968. Activation of Infectious SV40 DNA Synthesis in Transformed Cells. *Proceedings of the National Academy of Sciences of the U.S.A.*, 60:1239–1246.

Kit, S., J. L. Melnick, M. Anken, D. R. Dubbs, R. A. de Torres, and T. Kitahara. 1967. Nonidentity of Some Simian Virus 40-Induced Enzymes with Tumor Antigen. *Journal of Virology*, 1:684–692.

Kit, S., L. J. Piekarski, and D. R. Dubbs. 1967. DNA Polymerase Induced by Simian Virus 40. *Journal of General Virology*, 1:163–173.

Kit, S., R. A. de Torres, and D. R. Dubbs. 1967. Deoxycytidylate Deaminase Activity of Simian Virus 40-Infected Cell Cultures. *Cancer Research*, 27:1907–1914.

Kit, S., R. A. de Torres, D. R. Dubbs, and M. L. Salvi. 1967. Induction of Cellular Deoxyribonucleic Acid Synthesis by Simian Virus 40. *Journal of Virology*, 1:738–746.

Kluchareva, T. E., K. L. Shachanina, S. Belova, V. Chibisova, and G. I. Deichman. 1967. Use of Immunofluorescence for Detection of Specific Membrane Antigen in Simian Virus 40-Infected Nontransformed Cells. *Journal of the National Cancer Institute*, 39:825–832.

Klug, A. 1965. Structure of Viruses of the Papilloma-Polyoma Type. II. Comments on Other Work. *Journal of Molecular Biology*, 11:424–431.

Knowles, B. B., F. C. Jensen, Z. Steplewski, and H. Koprowski. 1968. Rescue of Infectious SV40 After Fusion Between Different SV40-Transformed Cells. *Proceedings of the National Academy of Sciences of the U.S.A.*, 61:42–45.

Koch, M. A., H. J. Eggers, F. A. Anderer, H. D. Schlumberger, and H. Frank. 1967. Structure of Simian Virus 40. I. Purification and Physical Characterization of the Virus Particle. *Virology*, 32:503–510.

Koch, M. A., and A. B. Sabin. 1963. Specificity of Virus-Induced Resistance to Transplantation of Polyoma and SV40 Tumors in Adult Hamsters. *Proceedings of the Society for Experimental Biology and Medicine*, 113:4–12.

Koprowski, H., F. C. Jensen, and Z. Steplewski. 1967. Activation of Production of Infectious Tumor Virus SV40 in Heterokaryon Cultures. *Proceedings of the National Academy of Sciences of the U.S.A.*, 58:127–133.

Lazarus, H. M., M. B. Sporn, J. M. Smith, and W. R. Henderson. 1967. Purification of T Antigen from Nuclei of Simian Virus 40-Induced Hamster Tumors. *Journal of Virology*, 1:1093–1095.

Mayor, H. D., R. M. Jamison, and L. E. Jordan. 1963. Biophysical Studies on the Nature of the Simian Papovavirus Particle (Vacuolating SV40 Virus). *Virology*, 19:359–366.

Mayor, H. D., R. M. Jamison, L. E. Jordan, and S. McGregor. 1966. The Influence of p-Fluoro-phenylalanine, Puromycin, and Actinomycin on the Development of Simian Papovavirus (SV40). *Experimental and Molecular Pathology*, 5:245–262.

Mayor, H. D., S. E. Stinebaugh, R. M. Jamison, L. E. Jordan, and J. L. Melnick. 1962. Immunofluorescent, Cytochemical, and Microcytological Studies on the Growth of the Simian Vacuolating Virus (SV-40) in Tissue Culture. *Experimental and Molecular Pathology*, 1:397–416.

Melnick, J. L. 1962. Papova Virus Group. *Science*, 135:1128–1130.

Melnick, J. L., and A. Ashkenazi. 1963. Protection in Hamsters Immunized with Simian Papovavirus When Challenged with SV40-Induced Tumor Cells. (Abstract) *Federation Proceedings*, 24:438.

Melnick, J. L., K. S. Khera, and F. Rapp. 1964. Papovavirus SV40: Failure to Isolate Infectious Virus from Transformed Hamster Cells Synthesizing SV40-Induced Antigens. *Virology*, 23:430–432.

Morrison, J. M., H. M. Keir, H. Subak-Sharpe, and L. V. Crawford. 1967. Nearest Neighbour Base Sequence Analysis of the Deoxyribonucleic Acids of a Further Three Mammalian Viruses: Simian Virus 40, Human Papilloma Virus and Adenovirus Type 2. *Journal of General Virology*, 1:101–108.

Oda, K., and R. Dulbecco. 1968. Regulation of Transcription of the SV40 DNA in Productively Infected and in Transformed Cells. *Proceedings of the National Academy of Sciences of the U.S.A.*, 60:525–532.

Pope, J. H., and W. P. Rowe. 1964. Detection of Specific Antigen in SV40-Transformed Cells by Immunofluorescence. *Journal of Experimental Medicine*, 120:121–128.

Rabson, A. S., and R. L. Kirschstein. 1962. Induction of Malignancy In Vitro in Newborn Hamster Kidney Tissue Infected with Simian Vacuolating Virus (SV40). *Proceedings of the Society for Experimental Biology and Medicine*, 111:323–328.

Rabson, A. S., R. A. Malmgren, and R. L. Kirschstein. 1966. Induction of Neoplasia In Vitro in Hamster Kidney Tissue by Adenovirus 7-SV40 "Hybrid" Strain (LLE46). *Proceedings of the Society for Experimental Biology and Medicine*, 121:486–489.

Rapp, F. 1967. "Viral Oncogenesis," *Methods in Cancer Research*, H. Busch, Ed. New York, New York: Academic Press, Inc. Vol. I. Pp. 451–544.

———. 1968. "Dependence and Complementation Among Animal Viruses Containing Deoxyribonucleic Acid," *The Molecular Biology of Viruses* (18th Symposium of the Society of General Microbiology), L. V. Crawford and M. G. P. Stoker, Eds. Cambridge, England: The University Press. Pp. 273–293.

———. 1969. Unpublished data.

Rapp, F., J. S. Butel, L. A. Feldman, T. Kitahara, and J. L. Melnick. 1965. Differential Effects of Inhibitors on the Steps Leading to the Formation of SV40 Tumor and Virus Antigens. *Journal of Experimental Medicine*, 121:935–944.

Rapp, F., J. S. Butel, and J. L. Melnick. 1964. Virus-Induced Intranuclear Antigen in Cells Transformed by Papovavirus SV40. *Proceedings of the Society for Experimental Biology and Medicine*, 116:1131–1135.

———. 1965. SV40-Adenovirus "Hybrid" Populations: Transfer of SV40 Determinants from One Type of Adenovirus to Another. *Proceedings of the National Academy of Sciences of the U.S.A.*, 54:717–724.

Rapp, F., J. S. Butel, S. S. Tevethia, M. Katz, and J. L. Melnick. 1966. Antigenic Analysis of Tumors and Sera from Animals Inoculated with PARA-Adenovirus Populations. *Journal of Immunology*, 97:833–839.

Rapp, F., J. S. Butel, S. S. Tevethia, and J. L. Melnick. 1967. Comparison of Ability of Defective Foreign Genomes (PARA and MAC) Carried by Human Adenoviruses to Induce SV40 Transplantation Immunity. *Journal of Immunology*, 99:386–391.

Rapp, F., M. A. Jerkofsky, J. L. Melnick, and B. Levy. 1968. Variation in the Onco-genic Potential of Human Adenoviruses Carrying a Defective SV40 Genome (PARA). *Journal of Experimental Medicine*, 127:77–90.

Rapp, F., and G. P. Khare. 1967. DNA Biosynthesis in Monkey Kidney Cells Infected with PARA (SV40)-Adenoviruses. *Proceedings of the Society for Experimental Biology and Medicine*, 126:491–496.

Rapp, F., T. Kitahara, J. S. Butel, and J. L. Melnick. 1964. Synthesis of SV40 Tumor Antigen During Replication of Simian Papovavirus (SV40). *Proceedings of the National Academy of Sciences of the U.S.A.*, 52:1138–1142.

Rapp, F., and J. L. Melnick. 1966. Papovavirus SV40, Adenovirus and Their Hybrids: Transformation, Complementation and Transcapsidation. *Progress in Medical Virology*, 8:349–399.

Rapp, F., J. L. Melnick, J. S. Butel, and T. Kitahara. 1964. The Incorporation of SV40 Genetic Material into Adenovirus 7 as Measured by Intranuclear Synthesis of SV40 Tumor Antigen. *Proceedings of the National Academy of Sciences of the U.S.A.*, 52:1348–1352.

Rapp, F., J. L. Melnick, and T. Kitahara. 1965. Tumor and Virus Antigens of Simian Virus 40: Differential Inhibition of Synthesis by Cytosine Arabinoside. *Science*, 147:625–627.

Rapp, F., J. L. Melnick, T. Kitahara, and R. Sheppard. 1965. Search for Virus-Induced Antigens in Human Tumors Using the SV40-Hamster System as a Model. *Proceedings of the Society for Experimental Biology and Medicine*, 118:573–576.

Rapp, F., S. S. Tevethia, and J. L. Melnick. 1966. Papovavirus SV40 Transplantation Immunity Conferred by an Adenovirus-SV40 Hybrid. *Journal of the National Cancer Institute*, 36:703–708.

Reich, P. R., P. H. Black, and S. M. Weissman. 1966. Nucleic Acid Homology Studies of SV40 Virus-Transformed and Normal Hamster Cells. *Proceedings of the National Academy of Sciences of the U.S.A.*, 56:78–85.

Rowe, W. P. 1965. Studies of Adenovirus-SV40 Hybrid Viruses. III. Transfer of SV40 Gene Between Adenovirus Types. *Proceedings of the National Academy of Sciences of the U.S.A.*, 54:711–717.

Rowe, W. P., and S. G. Baum. 1964. Evidence for a Possible Genetic Hybrid Between Adenovirus Type 7 and SV40 Viruses. *Proceedings of the National Academy of Sciences of the U.S.A.*, 52:1340–1347.

―――. 1965. Studies of Adenovirus SV40 Hybrid Viruses. II. Defectiveness of the Hybrid Particles. *Journal of Experimental Medicine*, 122:955–966.

Sabin, A. B., and M. A. Koch. 1963. Behavior of Noninfectious SV40 Viral Genome in Hamster Tumor Cells: Induction of Synthesis of Infectious Virus. *Proceedings of the National Academy of Sciences of the U.S.A.*, 50:407–417.

―――. 1964. Source of Genetic Information for Specific Complement-Fixing Anti-gens in SV40 Virus-Induced Tumors. *Proceedings of the National Academy of Sciences of the U.S.A.*, 52:1131–1138.

Sambrook, J., H. Westphal, P. R. Srinivasan, and R. Dulbecco. 1968. The Integrated State of Viral DNA in SV40-Transformed Cells. *Proceedings of the National Academy of Sciences of the U.S.A.*, 60:1288–1295.

Sauer, G., H. Fischer, and K. Munk. 1966. The Effect of SV40 Infection on DNA Synthesis in *Cercopithecus* Kidney Cells. *Virology*, 28:765–767.

Sauer, G., H. Koprowski, and V. Defendi. 1967. The Genetic Heterogeneity of Simian

Virus 40. *Proceedings of the National Academy of Sciences of the U.S.A.*, 58: 599–606.

Schlumberger, H. D., F. A. Anderer, and M. A. Koch. 1968. Structure of Simian Virus 40. IV. The Polypeptide Chains of the Virus Particle. *Virology*, 36:42–47.

Shein, H. M., J. F. Enders, J. D. Levinthal, and A. E. Burket. 1963. Transformation Induced by SV40 in Newborn Syrian Hamster Renal Cell Cultures. *Proceedings of the National Academy of Sciences of the U.S.A.*, 49:28–34.

Sweet, B. H., and M. R. Hilleman. 1960. The Vacuolating Virus, SV40. *Proceedings of the Society for Experimental Biology and Medicine*, 105:420–427.

Tevethia, S. S., L. A. Couvillion, and F. Rapp. 1968. Development in Hamsters of Antibodies Against Surface Antigens Present in Cells Transformed by Papovavirus SV40. *Journal of Immunology*, 100:358–362.

Tevethia, S. S., G. T. Diamandopoulos, F. Rapp, and J. F. Enders. 1968. Lack of Relationship Between Virus-Specific Surface and Transplantation Antigens in Hamster Cells Transformed by Simian Papovavirus SV40. *Journal of Immunology*, 101:1192–1198.

Tevethia, S. S., G. R. Dreesman, R. N. Lausch, and F. Rapp. 1968. Effect of Anti-Hamster Thymocyte Serum on Papovavirus SV40-Induced Transplantation Immunity. *Journal of Immunology*, 101:1105–1110.

Tevethia, S. S., M. Katz, and F. Rapp. 1965. New Surface Antigen in Cells Transformed by Simian Papovavirus SV40. *Proceedings of the Society for Experimental Biology and Medicine*, 119:896–901.

Uchida, S., and S. Watanabe. 1968. Tumorigenicity of the Antigen-Forming Defective Virions of Simian Virus 40. *Virology*, 35:166–169.

Uchida, S., S. Watanabe, and M. Kato. 1966. Incomplete Growth of Simian Virus 40 in African Green Monkey Kidney Culture Induced by Serial Undiluted Passages. *Virology*, 28:135–141.

Uchida, S., K. Yoshiike, S. Watanabe, and A. Furuno. 1968. Antigen-Forming Defective Viruses of Simian Virus 40. *Virology*, 34:1–8.

Wallace, R. 1967. Viral Transformation of Monkey Kidney Cell Cultures. *Nature*, 213: 768–770.

Watkins, J. F., and R. Dulbecco. 1967. Production of SV40 Virus in Heterokaryons of Transformed and Susceptible Cells. *Proceedings of the National Academy of Sciences of the U.S.A.*, 58:1396–1403.

Weiss, M. C., B. Ephrussi, and L. J. Scaletta. 1968. Loss of T-Antigen from Somatic Hybrids Between Mouse Cells and SV40-Transformed Human Cells. *Proceedings of the National Academy of Sciences of the U.S.A.*, 59:1132–1135.

Westphal, H., and R. Dulbecco. 1968. Viral DNA in Polyoma- and SV40-Transformed Cell Lines. *Proceedings of the National Academy of Sciences of the U.S.A.*, 59:1158–1165.

Yoshiike, K. 1968a. Studies on DNA from Low-Density Particles of SV40. I. Heterogeneous Defective Virions Produced by Successive Undiluted Passages. *Virology*, 34:391–401.

———. 1968b. Studies on DNA from Low-Density Particles of SV40. II. Noninfectious Virions Associated with a Large-Plaque Variant. *Virology*, 34:402–409.

Virus Effects on Host Chromosomes

PAUL S. MOORHEAD*

The Wistar Institute of Anatomy and Biology, Philadelphia, Pennsylvania

Since 1961, when the first report appeared on chromosome breakage following virus infection with herpes simplex of cells in culture (Hampar and Ellison, 1961), at least 20 viruses have been implicated in the induction of abnormalities in mammalian chromosomes. Viruses known to be oncogenic which have been thoroughly studied from the standpoint of karyology are: simian virus 40 (SV40) (Yerganian, Shein, and Enders, 1962; Moorhead and Saksela, 1963), Rous sarcoma virus (RSV) (Nichols, 1963), polyoma virus (Vogt and Dulbecco, 1963; Defendi and Lehman, 1965), Shope papilloma virus (Palmer, 1959; McMichael, Wagner, Nowell, and Hungerford, 1963), and human adenovirus type 12 (Stich, van Hoosier, and Trentin, 1964). Other viruses known to induce chromosomal lesions and mitotic abnormalities are: herpes zoster (Benyesh-Melnick, Stich, Rapp, and Hsu, 1964); Sendai virus (Saksela, Aula, and Cantell, 1965); vaccinia virus (zur Hausen and Lanz, 1966); rubella virus (Boué, Boué, Moorhead, and Plotkin, 1964; Chang et al., 1966); hemadsorption virus, type 2 (Homma, Ohira, and Ishida, 1968); human adenoviruses 2, 4, 7, and 18 (Cooper, Stich, and Yohn, 1967); Newcastle disease virus (Cantell, Saksela, and Aula, 1966); influenza virus (ter Meulen and Love, 1967); and poliomyelitis virus (Bartsch, Habermehl, and Diefenthal, 1967).

Further, a number of viruses have been shown to be capable of producing abnormalities of the metaphase chromosomes in circulating lymphocytes during some natural infections of man, *i.e.*, measles virus (Nichols, Levan, and Östergren, 1962; Tanzer, Stoitchkov, Harel, and Boiron, 1963; Aula, 1965), chicken pox and mumps viruses (Aula, 1965; Gripenberg, 1965), and hepatitis virus (Aya, 1965; El-Alfi, Smith, and Biesele, 1965). However, this cataloguing of viruses with a demonstrated capacity for direct or indirect production of effects on metaphase chromosomes is most certainly incomplete. (For a thorough review, see article

* Present Address: Department of Medical Genetics, University of Pennsylvania School of Medicine, Philadelphia, Pennsylvania.

by Stich and Yohn [in press].)

In most of the studies to date, there was little attempt to do more than link the basic fact of infection with the anomalies produced. Further, the variety of possible combinations of host cells with a particular virus has resulted in numerous reports, of which only a few represent independent assessments of the same cell-virus combination. Therefore, mutually supporting studies should not be neglected.

Cell and Virus Interactions

The interaction of host cells with virus is usually termed "lytic" or "nonlytic," a dichotomy which may arbitrarily be applied to an individual cell. However, the characterization of a certain species of cells as lytic or nonlytic (relative to virus infection) can be misleading. In transforming or abortive infections, only a small proportion of the cells infected may produce viral tumor antigen (T-antigen), which is regarded as the indicator of abortive infection. An even smaller proportion of these cells are committed to any change in growth which will produce a visible focus, such as in the Todaro test system (Todaro and Martin, 1967; Todaro, Green, and Swift, 1966), as discussed by Dr. Miller (1970, see pages 78 to 84, this volume).

Abortive infection can even be obtained in cell populations which are considered permissive cells, *i.e.*, in the species of cell which lyses easily on infection with the virus in question. A complete transformation can be obtained by infection of green monkey cells with SV40 by introducing a very low multiplicity of virus (Fernandes and Moorhead, 1965).

There are several important factors to consider in making generalizations regarding lytic systems or transforming cell-virus systems. For example, infection at the time of maximum cell division causes a significantly greater proportion of cells to become abortively infected with SV40, as measured by the production of T-antigen, an induced complement-fixing antigen (ICFA) (Girardi and Jensen, 1966). Other factors involved are the age of the culture and the effective multiplicity. It has long been known that the culture age of human diploid fibroblast cells (total number of times a cell population doubles in vitro)—can be directly correlated with the susceptibility to transformation with SV40 (Jensen, Koprowski. and Pontén, 1963). This correlation has been confirmed quantitatively by the test of transformation efficiency already mentioned (Todaro and Martin, 1967; Todaro, Green, and Swift, 1966). Age effect and multiplicity or virus input effect are both illustrated in Figure 1. The underlying factor of the genetic constitution of the cells themselves has been discussed by Dr. Miller (1970, see pages 78 to 84, this volume); different frequencies of susceptible cells or differing rates of production of obvious foci of growth-altered human cells are characteristic for cells from certain individuals. It is of interest that for both factors, the age of the culture (cumulative divisions in vitro) and genetic predisposition, the incidence of chromatid and chromosome breaks already present is abnormally elevated (Todaro and Martin, 1967; Saksela and Moorhead, 1963).

With such factors in mind concerning the course of response of infected cells, especially as examined in experimental systems in vitro, let us review some of the findings concerning infection. We will then examine the nature of the sequential chromosomal changes occurring in a transforming system and discuss the various interpretations available to us of the cytological types of aberrations produced. Hampar and Ellison (1961) infected Chinese hamster cell cultures with herpes simplex virus and obtained a variety of classes of chromosome damage with little interruption to cell growth; heat-inactivated virus, however, did not cause

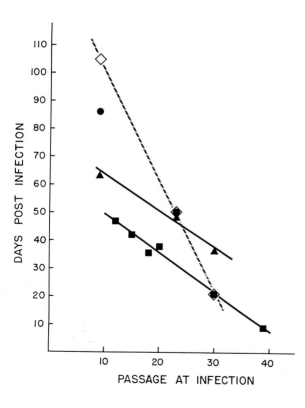

FIGURE 1. Effect of in vitro age (cumulative doublings of population) at time of infection with SV40 virus on the earliest appearance of loss of inhibition of cell division and on chromosomal abnormalities. Dicentrics, □; significant increases in tetraploidy, ● (no line shown); loss of inhibition of cell division following infections at low multiplicities, ▲; loss of inhibition of cell division following infections at high viral multiplicities, ■ (performed by Dr. A. Girardi).

damage. Using Chinese hamster cells infected with herpes simplex, Rapp and Hsu (1965) also concluded that there was a dependence upon viral replication for the production of increased levels of chromosome abnormalities. Further, monkey kidney cells infected with herpes simplex virus preparations which had been inactivated by heat, antibodies, or ultraviolet irradiation failed to induce increased aberration levels (Tanzer *et al.*, 1964).

Regarding instances in which the virus does not naturally replicate in the species of infected cells, there have been contrary reports. Significant, if not extensive, increases in the frequency of chromosome breaks and achromatic gaps have been observed in rabbit cells which are unable to support the replication of measles virus (Mauler and Hennessen, 1965). Human adenovirus 12 does not replicate in Syrian hamster cells (Kitamura *et al.*, 1964), but the observation of chromosome aberrations following infection supports the position that the maturation of infectious viral particles is not necessary for damage (zur Hausen, 1968). Also in this work, an inverse correlation between aberration frequency and cloning efficiency could be demonstrated, indicating that cellular death was primarily the result of the genetic damage itself, there being little contribution to lysis from virus replication. Comparative studies of two types of cells, each responding differently to infection with human adenovirus 12, revealed that an array of aberrations, including breaks, occurred in newborn Syrian hamster cells without the synthesis of viral structural antigens or of mature virus (MacKinnon, Kalnins, Stich, and Yohn, 1966). In the human amnion line, complete synthesis of virus and cessation of cell growth occurred. Although nuclear abnormalities were obvious, no important increase in metaphase chromosomal aberrations was seen. Similarly, a significant reduction in mitotic rate was obtained by infection of Chinese hamster cell lines with human adenovirus 12 (Stich, van Hoosier, and Trentin, 1964), but chromatid and chromosome breaks, exchanges, and formation of new marker chromosomes were extensive.

All of the aforementioned work, as well as that of zur Hausen (1967), clearly demonstrates that the production of chromosome and chromatid aberrations and of forms deriving from breakage is not dependent upon the later phases of virus infection or viral maturation. Chromosome damage is apparently produced as the result of some early function of virus interaction with the host cell, possibly a function involving coat stripping or other early enzymes coded for or induced by viral deoxyribonucleic acid (DNA).

Oncogenic DNA Viruses

In recent years, the results of research on DNA virus-induced tumors have led to the view that the period during which initial virus infection occurs is transient and involves a fundamental change in the relation of the virus DNA and host cell DNA in a fraction of target cells (Black, 1968). In vitro models of infection and transformation and also experimental tumor systems supporting this view indicate that an abortive infection is critical in the potentiation of a cell toward a new course of behavior within the host cell population (Defendi and Lehman, 1966). Infections leading to cell destruction are, therefore, largely irrelevant; however, if infection and reinfection persist for a time or lysis occurs in even a fraction of the population, integration of virus DNA can occur and is most likely to be the fundamental step toward neoplasia.

Evidence that viral DNA actually is integrated into the cell's DNA has been obtained by the demonstration of increased hybridization between DNA extracted from a virus-transformed cell line and specific viral ribonucleic acid (RNA) (Sambrook, Westphal, Srinivasan, and Dulbecco, 1968). The capacity of viral RNA produced in vitro upon an SV40 template to hybridize with DNA from SV40-transformed cells was greater than the capacity to hybridize with DNA from similar cell lines transformed by another DNA virus, polyoma. Various techniques for isolation of DNA from the transformed lines were used, including the prior isolation of chromosomes en masse. In each case, the amount of DNA-RNA hybridization obtained was specifically greater for the appropriate DNA source. Sambrook, Westphal, Srinivasan, and Dulbecco (1968) estimated that from five to 60 viral DNA equivalents persist in each cell of the various transformed cell lines investigated.

In long-term cytological studies of the SV40 transformation of human diploid fibroblast cells in vitro, it was noted that the period of most extensive chromosomal damage is delayed considerably (up to weeks following infection) and is closely associated with the general occurrence of the loss of contact inhibition of cell division (Moorhead and Saksela, 1965). Very little virus replication occurs (Carp and Gilden, 1966). In early studies on the effects on chromosomes produced by this DNA virus, a variety of damage was observed, including achromatic gaps, true breaks, dicentric formation, polyploidy, and exaggerations of the known secondary constrictions (Yerganian, Shein, and Enders, 1962; Koprowski et al., 1962). Sequential studies of transforming populations of human cells showed a slight but significant increase in breakage, followed by a striking increase in dicentric formation or other exchanges and in tetraploidy. The sequence of appearance of significant levels of breakage, of dicentrics, and of apparent loss of contact inhibition of division, was similar, but not the same, in the experiment using the more susceptible aged cells. Although these events were generally reproducible, their relative positions in time of occurrence were shifted in the more rapid transformation system.

In a later, more detailed study (Girardi, Weinstein, and Moorhead, 1966) of the SV40 transformation of human diploid cells involving periodic assessment of net cell production over a standard period of growth, we saw the following changes:

(1) There was an increment in net growth, which was not associated with any increase in mitotic frequency. This increment approximately coincided with gross changes observed in the culture itself and is attributable to increased cell division through loss of inhibition of division.

(2) A second increment in cell growth rate occurred which was associated in time with an increased mitotic index.

(3) Between the two changes in cell growth capacity, there occurred the first significant increase in chromosome aberrations, mostly dicentrics.

The transformed cultures continue active cell division accompanied by numerous exchanges, dicentrics, polyploidy, and also extensive cell death for a number of weeks. The comment made earlier by Mary Gaulden (1970, see page 74, this volume) in regard to mitotic delay is also quite important in this cell-virus system. We have some evidence of extensive cell death accompanied by rapid cell division plus mitotic delay. These simultaneous changes make it difficult for us to account for the total economy of cell production. Eventually, in nearly all cultures, rapid cell division ceases. Survivors from such transformations then may lie quiescent for many weeks before regrowth occurs. These recovered cell lines have been, in every case, permanent in their propagation thereafter, *i.e.* as established cell lines. This establishment as a permanent line is, therefore, the third distinct growth property acquired by the dominant element of the population; two of these growth properties are preceded by extensive chromosomal changes. Thus, we have a mixture of selective forces acting upon a great range of chromosomal restructuring.

We have tried to stabilize such recovered transformed lines, which are in every case capable of continued propagation. Although there is little chromosome breakage or rearrangement occurring above control values, we have been unable to obtain a monotype cell by repeated serial

cloning (Weinstein and Moorhead, 1965). An examination of 20 karyotypes after two successive clonings yielded more than a dozen different
karyotypes, primarily with numerical differences at a near-diploid level.
Similar results have been shown by Cooper and Black (1964) using SV40-
transformed hamster cells. They reported persistence of breaks and rearrangements and surmised that by unknown mechanisms the integrated
viral genome might cause this persistence. Such an instability is not confined to culture systems because Stoltz, Stich, and Yohn (1967) observed
it in adenovirus 12-induced tumors. If the onset of chromosome changes
makes no contribution to tumor initiation, in the context of our model, we
should then be able to clone out some lines which are karyologically normal but which show all the novel growth characteristics which are
acquired reproducibly in these experiments.

In an attempt to do this, we examined material in a mass culture
immediately after the loss of inhibition of division (Weinstein and Moorhead, 1967); the event correlates most closely with tumorigenicity
(Aaronson and Todaro, 1968). We monitored infected cultures daily, and
within hours of the first significant increase in mitotic rate (signifying
loss of contact inhibition of division), we prepared similar material for
chromosome studies. More than half of such cells had abnormal chromosomes (Figures 2 and 3). However, the number of normal karyotypes
often exceeded the statistical expectations based on the very small percentage of normal cell divisions which occurred as a background, entirely
apart from virus-stimulated divisions in these cells with high density conditions. These findings seem to support the belief that chromosomally
normal transformed cells do exist; however, so far we have not obtained
any. A predilection for the loss of acrocentric D and G chromosomes from
the karyotypes of these cells was again observed, although such loss is
probably a selective phenomenon.

A subclone of cells, all having lost one arm of chromosome No. 1,
was formed, indicating origin in breakage at the near-centromeric constriction. However, such a subclone may represent only the result of
strong selective forces rather than of a viral affinity for any particular
chromosome, or it may represent a regional predisposition to breakage. In
either case, the chromosome changes probably do not precede the time of
loss of contact inhibition of division.

The possibility that viral agents which produce chromosomal breakage also produce numerous gene mutations, or at least produce crypto-
structural deletions, is a most interesting question which was raised years
ago by Albert Levan (1956). This possibility has not yet been excluded
by anyone's work as a basis for accepting the Boverian hypothesis of

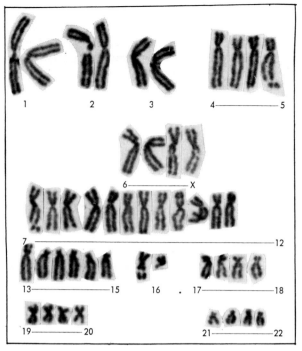

FIGURE 2. Earliest effects of SV40 virus infection on metaphase chromosomes during transformation of human diploid cell WI-38. Material providing this karyotype was fixed on the same day that the first significant increase in mitosis occurred in sister cultures. Note displaced, or true, break in No. 7 (?) and isolocus breaks in No. 2, No. 5, and No. 16.

FIGURE 3. Karyotype of human diploid cell from similar experiments as noted in Figure 2. Note constrictions in long arm of No. 17, a dicentric, and isolocus breaks.

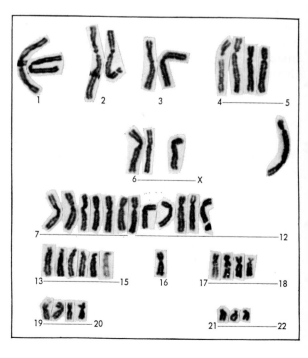

neoplasia. Burdette and Yoon (1967) produced mutations (lethal factors, visibles, and structural changes) by introduction of the Schmidt-Ruppin strain of RSV (SR-RSV) into drosophila. Similar studies with well-marked mammalian cells would be most valuable.

Nichols, Levan, Heneen, and Peluse (1965) have proposed a plausible linkage between a virus mechanism for break induction and the effects of a nucleoside triphosphate. Cytidine triphosphate (CTP) and SR-RSV were found to produce similarities in the morphology of the aberrations and in the nonrandom distribution of these breaks. Both agents produced in human leukocytes (1) isolocus breaks, (2) rare reunions of broken ends, and (3) a significant localization of breaks at centromeres.

Thus, few general correlates are available to us at present concerning viruses and chromosome damage. Both RNA and DNA viruses are oncogenic, and both cause some of the same types of abnormalities in chromosomes. However, the RNA viruses seem notably less effective, both in causing early chromosomal effects and in the karyology of the resultant tumors. This lack of rules regarding classifications of virus groups is well exemplified by the fact that oncogenic and nononcogenic strains of RSV, SR-RSV and Bryan (B-RSV) strains exist. These may be distinguished by their respective capacity or noncapacity to produce chromosome breaks in human cells (Nichols *et al.*, 1964).

Convincing hypotheses for the arrangement of the DNA within the mammalian metaphase chromosome and the complexities of relations between an agent's primary effect and secondary ones mediated through the cell's metabolism upon both chromosome and mitotic apparatus are urgently needed. The fact that so many viruses as well as other agents induce both breakage and disruption of normal function of mitosis has no satisfactory explanation, except in the surmise that it could be caused by point mutation which controls cell division.

Effects on Chromosomes

BREAKAGE

In general, the aberrations induced by virus appear to be morphologically indistinguishable from those of chemical and irradiation origin. Perhaps more achromatic gaps than open breaks occur in the viral material (Figures 2 and 3).

A range of morphological types of breaks occurs, suggesting from appearances no physical rupture but only a stretching of the major coils to complete breakage and physical displacement of parts. This range of expression can also be observed in a single lesion, *i.e.* in two apparently homologous sites of one chromosome (Figures 2 and 3). Such lesions are termed isolocus breaks and are a common finding in various cell-virus systems (Östergren and Wakonig, 1954). Difficulties of determining whether a true loss of genetic material would have occurred during subsequent anaphase have been relatively minor problems in most virus studies since the frequency of achromatic gaps increases in conjunction with increases in the open breaks. Further, there is no question that many viruses can produce genetic losses because they are apparent at anaphase (Figure 4) and in later generations as deletions. Breakage is also impli-

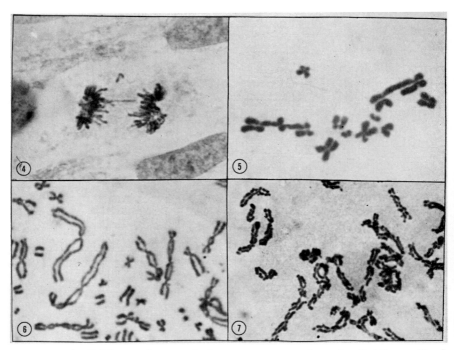

FIGURE 4. Bridge and acentric fragment at anaphase in dividing cell of human diploid cell line WI-38 during transformation of culture induced by SV40 virus infection.

FIGURE 5. Dicentrics at metaphase in SV40-infected culture of human diploid cell line WI-38.

FIGURE 6. Bizarre rearrangements produced in WI-38 human cells by in vitro infection with mycoplasma. (Courtesy of Eric Stanbridge.)

FIGURE 7. Fragmented appearance of a WI-38 cell during transformation with SV40. This is similar to pulverization but is rarely observed in SV40-infected human cell cultures.

cated in the many restructured forms dependent upon reunion. Reunion or capacity for healing may be affected differently by different viruses. Some have noted that structural rearrangements such as dicentrics (Figure 5) are more common in animal cells damaged by SV40 infection, and we have noted the same in human diploid fibroblasts.

Observations of apparent exchanges involving half-chromatids or some lesser strand level are absent or rare in most reports on virus-induced damage. These cases cannot, in any case, be distinguished from so-called stickiness.

It is probably correct to consider most chromosomal damage and breakage as a rather general form of pathology of the cell. Clearly, cellular death occurs with most of the severe exchange examples. Chromosomal breaks and restructuring have been found to be associated also with several nononcogenic factors: mycoplasma infection (Paton, Jacobs, and Perkins, 1965) (Figure 6), low temperature (Hampel and Levan, 1964), exposure to irradiated glucose (Moutschen and Matagne, 1965), or even low calcium levels (Basrur and Baker, 1963). No indication of a growth transformation occurred in cells as a result of any of these factors.

Although there is no firm evidence that chromosome breakage is at all significant for the oncogenic process, the many fundamental connections between these phenomena deserve explanation.

PULVERIZATION

The frequent occurrence of what appear to be finely minced chromosomes associated with virus infections has led to the separation of this aberration from other forms of breakage or derangements of dividing cells (Nichols, Levan, Aula, and Norrby, 1965). The morphological appearance of this virus-induced abnormality is suggestive of a loss of integrity of the chromosome (Figure 7) rather than merely a high incidence of breaks in one cell. This pulverized appearance can be induced by chemicals (D'Amato, 1952), by several viruses other than measles (Stich, Hsu, and Rapp, 1964; Saksela, Aula, and Cantell, 1965), and by virus vaccine (Harnden, 1964). This pulverized appearance has been described as "fragmented," "shattered," or "reduced to fine powder-like particles." Using measles and Sendai viruses, Nichols et al. (1967) studied the DNA synthesis of cells displaying this type of aberration. They pointed out that pulverized chromosomes were usually part of a syncytial cell which also contained intact metaphase chromosomes (Figure 8). Autoradiography indicated that the pulverized chromosomes actually represented nuclei actively engaged in DNA synthesis. Uptake of tritiated

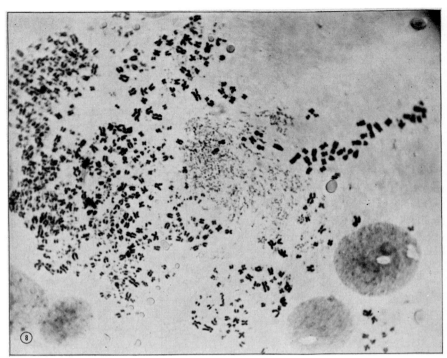

FIGURE 8. Pulverization of chromosomes observed in a syncytial cell following infection with measles virus. (Courtesy of Warren Nichols.)

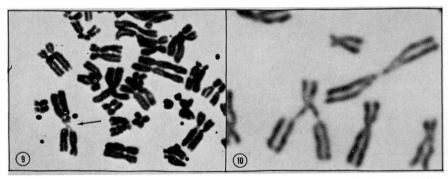

FIGURE 9. Diplochromosomes produced in WI-38 human cells by SV40 infection in vitro. In this portion of a metaphase cell, an attenuation of the puff-like secondary constriction of chromosome No. 1 is apparent.

FIGURE 10. An example of selective endoreduplication during metaphase in a leukocyte from an adult. (Courtesy of André Boué.)

thymidine (^{3}H-TdR) could be demonstrated before 1 hour had elapsed from access to ^{3}H-TdR to fixation. Intact groups of chromosomes, with a normally condensed metaphase appearance, failed to reveal any label. Preparations of measles virus which retain hemolytic activity but are noninfectious also produce the effect of pulverization (Norrby, Levan, and Nichols, 1965). In the latter work, various treatments of the virus which destroyed its infectivity failed to eliminate pulverization, except where such treatment also destroyed the hemolytic or syncytium-forming activity. Thus, pulverization seems to be an effect of the virus which is dependent upon cell fusion. Such virus-induced fusions permit dyssynchrony of DNA synthesis between the nuclei involved and eventually result in pulverization. Conceivably, this could be the result of an induction by one nucleus of chromosomal condensation in the other during the latter's period of DNA synthesis. Such interpretations concerning pulverized or disintegrated chromatin masses produced in binucleate cells by Colcemid treatment have been offered by Kato and Sandberg (1967).

NUMERICAL ABNORMALITIES

Disturbances in the function of the spindle apparatus and in the process of cytokinesis which lead to duplications and losses of chromosomes from the daughter cells are commonplace for viruses. Although there is the possibility that cell fusions produced through the virus may contribute to duplication, the duplication of the entire chromosomal complement usually occurs by endoreduplication, a process involving two successive rounds of chromosomal replication with only one cytoplasmic division. Endoreduplication is indicated at metaphase by the appearance of side-by-side association of the chromosomal products (Figure 9). Presumably, tandem periods of DNA synthesis may also be restricted to one chromosome or chromosome region (Lejeune et al., 1968). This selective endoreduplication may be much more important in nondisjunctive changes involving the gain or loss of chromosomes than was previously recognized (Figure 10).

Dyssynchrony of DNA synthesis may also be implicated within certain chromosomes as reflected in despiralized or pulverized portions of chromosomes. Apparent despiralization occurred extensively in several cultures of cell lines derived from the blood of leukemic patients (zur Hausen, 1967a) (Figure 11). In this study, chromosomes could be observed lagging at anaphase, which correlated with the general frequency of cells containing such despiralized chromosomes. A similar decoiled morphology reminiscent of the pulverized appearance has also been

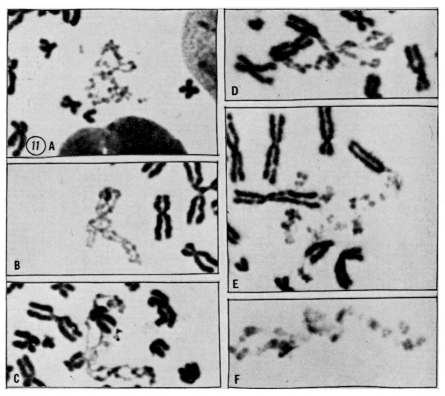

FIGURE 11. Examples of incompletely condensed chromosomes during SK-Ll metaphases. The following chromosomes are involved: a, No. 16; b, a large chromosome of the C group; c through f, incomplete condensations of the No. 1 chromosome. (Reprinted from zur Hausen, 1967a.)

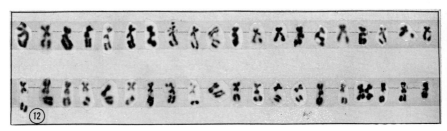

FIGURE 12. Examples of specific breakage produced by infection with adenovirus 12 at the site of a secondary constriction in the long arm of chromosome No. 17 of cells from a human being. (Courtesy of H. zur Hausen.)

reported for a late-labeling ring chromosome (Gripenberg, 1967). Thus, losses of chromosomes may be a result of virus-induced dyssynchrony, acting either through effects on the synthesis period or on the timing of condensation.

The Question of Specific Effects

Attempts to localize virus in terms of a site on the chromosomes representing a hot spot of viral integration have not been successful to date. Association of silver grains with chromosomes after introduction of virus heavily labeled with ^{3}H-TdR has been observed by some researchers, but one cannot conclude that this represents a preferred site of virus or is not an artifact involving the degradation of labeled material. In studies of adenovirus 12 infection, a high proportion of the breaks produced occurred at the midpoint of the long arm of No. 17, but chromosome-associated silver grains failed to localize at this very specific site of breakage (zur Hausen, 1968) (Figure 12).

The question of specific site reactions to breaking agents has been raised often, and clearly there is still much to learn about the specialized regions of the chromosome which are common to all such mammalian cells (Hsu, 1963). We can list telomeres, centromeres, and various secondary constrictions (SC).

The term "secondary constriction" includes at least three morphologically distinct differentiated regions. The primary constriction involves a constriction only in appearance. A whitish sphere or mass of nonstaining material which may represent specific uncondensed chromatin is often evident on each side of the centromeric region of mammalian chromosomes; therefore, the word "constriction" is to some degree an accepted misnomer. SC's of the stalk type occur in human cells on the short arms of the five pairs of acrocentric chromosomes. These stalks and the satellites are associated with nucleolus formation. SC's of a puff-like or fuzzy appearance occur near the centromeric region of chromosomes No. 1, No. 9, and No. 16, and perhaps No. 4; these definitely can be seen to involve a despiralization. At least some of these puff-like regions are late in labeling and share their negative heteropyknosis with the late-labeling X of female cells (Schmid, 1963; Saksela and Moorhead, 1962). A number of examples of the stretching or breakage of the puff-like SC of chromosome No. 1 in human cells are available from various viral infections (Boué, Boué, and Lazar, 1967) (Figures 13 and 14; also see Figure 9).

SC's of a third type which are similar to achromatic gaps are less

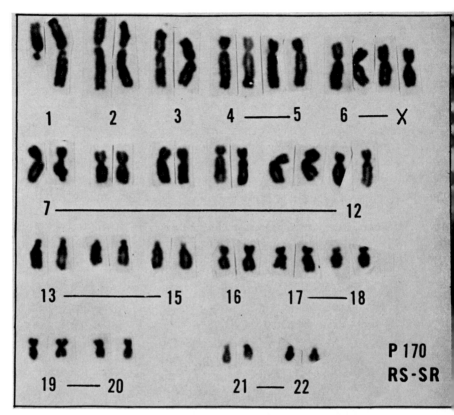

FIGURE 13. An example of breakage at the site of the diffuse (fuzzy) secondary constriction of chromosome No. 1 observed after infection of human cells with SR-RSV.

consistently observed. In several reports such gap-like SC's have been mentioned, such as in the middle of the long arm of a D chromosome and at the midpoint of the long arm of No. 17. These are indistinguishable from achromatic gap lesions produced by virus infections, except by the apparent consistency of their karyotypic location. The region on No. 17 affected with such high frequency by adenovirus 12 infection is a case in point of this kind of infrequent but identifiable SC (Figures 3 and 12). We had noted this SC on No. 17 to be more pronounced in the SV40-infected human cell cultures, and Miles and O'Neill (1966) reported its presence in a pseudodiploid permanent human cell line. A gap-type SC occurring at the midpoint of the long arm of a D chromosome was often observed in our SV40 material and was frequently apparent in cell lines derived from the blood of leukemic patients (zur Hausen, 1967a). In zur Hausen's work, the puff-like SC of No. 1 was stretched, and attenuation of the primary constriction of No. 16 chromosome was noted. Only those chromosomes of the human karyotype which bear SC's—whether stalk-like, puff-like, or gap-like—were preferentially affected. These specialized regions are thus observed to be exaggerated, attenuated, broken, or de-spiralized in various virus infections and in certain neoplastic cells.

An intriguing example of a viral effect on a specific region has evolved from studies on cell lines in cultivation obtained from patients with African (Burkitt's) lymphoma. Miles and O'Neill (1967) first reported the occurrence of a faint constriction near the tip of the long arm of a C-group chromosome in cells from the Epstein-Barr (EB)-2 line. Independently, we had noted this same constriction in 20 to 30 per cent of the cells of this line (Figure 15). Dr. Gertrude Kohn undertook a study of independently derived cell lines from patients with Burkitt's lymphoma and found this same marker in a percentage of the cells in four of five lines examined (Figure 16). The fifth line, SK-1, had a translocation which involved a No. 2 and a C chromosome, which conceivably could have obscured the marker (Kohn *et al.*, 1967).

Virological studies have recently implicated the EB particles often observed by electron microscopy in these lines with some agent which is present in European and American populations (Henle and Henle, 1965; Henle and Henle, 1968). This was indicated by the occurrence of an

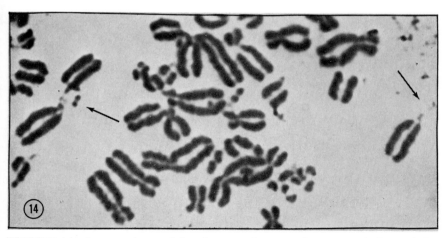

FIGURE 14. Attenuation and breakage at the secondary constrictions of the No. 1 chromosomes of a human embryonic cell infected in vitro with measles. This metaphase, of which only a part is shown, also includes strongly pul-verized chromatin material. (Reproduced from Boué, Boué, and Lazar, 1967.)

indirect immunofluorescent reaction of sera from 30 per cent of children and 90 per cent of adults to Burkitt's lymphoma cell antigens. Individual cells were chosen for direct examination; all cells showing immunofluorescence had particles, whereas nonimmunofluorescent cells did not (zur Hausen *et al.*, 1967). Through such approaches, the same relations were established for continuous lines derived from both malignant and nonmalignant tissues of American patients. Attempts to transfer a detectable virus to other cells failed, and cocultivation experiments were initi-

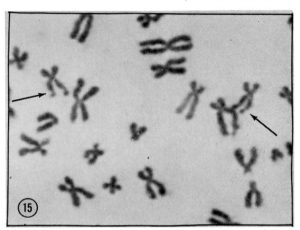

FIGURE 15. A part of a metaphase cell from a Burkitt's lymphoma cell line (EB-2) showing both No. 10 (?) chromosomes with the specific secondary constriction or lesion.

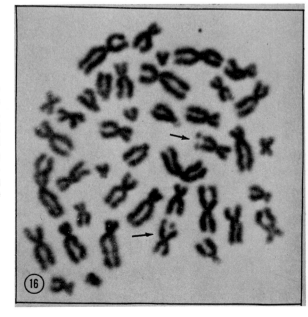

FIGURE 16. A more obvious example of the specific marker chromosomes as observed at metaphase in cell line JIYOYE, a line also derived from a patient with Burkitt's lymphoma. (Courtesy of Gertrude Kohn.)

ated using irradiated Burkitt's lymphoma cell lines and normal blood cells. Nine cell lines could be established by this procedure; each of the nine was found to contain the marker chromosome in some proportion, and all showed some immunofluorescent cells. Sera of three of the infants contributing leukocytes to this production of cell lines were tested, and none was positive.

Later, a technician who had contributed cells to the above experiment became ill with infectious mononucleosis, and her serum was then found to have become positive. The leukocytes she had contributed had failed to proliferate, but after natural infection, her cell cultures grew successfully and these cells were positive for the EB factor (1 to 3 per cent immunofluorescence at four weeks).

Prospective determinations on sera from students, made by the Henles in collaboration with workers at Yale University, revealed that only after the occurrence of infectious mononucleosis did their sera become positive to the EB factor.

Dr. Diehl of this group (Diehl, Henle, Henle, and Kohn, 1968) then initiated cell lines from patients with infectious mononucleosis; all examined by Kohn (1968) showed some cells with the specific C-group marker. The SC of the presumed No. 10 was also seen in cell lines from persons without a history of infectious mononucleosis, but the incidence of this was extremely low (<1 per cent).

In all such lines studied, the chromosome number was 46, or occasionally 47 or 48, with extra C-group chromosomes. Breakage was minimal or normal, about 1 to 3 per cent. In currrent work by these researchers (zur Hausen et al., 1967; Kohn, 1968; and Diehl, Henle, Henle, and Kohn, 1968), EB-2 cells have been cloned and each of 24 clones reveals a similar low frequency of cells with EB-specific immunofluorescence. Also, the C-10 marker chromosome occurs in each clone.

Very recently, Pope, Horne, and Scott (1968) have given support to the conclusion that these herpes-like particles are associated with a definite promotion of proliferation, a true growth transformation. They have demonstrated proliferative stimulation and long-term culture of leukocytes as a result of the inoculation into the culture of filtrates from cells carrying such herpes-like particles. As in the work discussed above (Kohn, 1968; Diehl, Henle, Henle, and Kohn, 1968), all the transformed continuous cultures thereby obtained reveal the same presumed No. 10 marker constriction as well as a diploid or near-diploid chromosome constitution.

It should be noted that this specific lesion was not observed in direct studies on Burkitt's tumors (Jacobs, Tough, and Wright, 1963; Rabson *et al.*, 1966). However, its specific association with cultures bearing the herpes-like bodies, the association with infectious mononucleosis, and the promotion of cell growth in vitro certainly suggest that this constriction or lesion is induced by the presence of the virus or that it may reflect specific activation of a region normally associated with cell proliferation in this cell type, the lymphoblast.

Certain reports of very specific chromosome changes do exist in the literature; in the light of this more thoroughly studied case of a specific lesion in the EB type of cell, these other reports might be given more attention and credence. Wald, Upton, Jenkins, and Borges (1964) reported a stickiness, a pale region on a mouse chromosome, which they postulated might tend to produce nondisjunction of chromatids at anaphase. They induced this lesion in fresh cells with a filtrate from mouse leukemic cells. In this case, both irradiation and a virus were implicated, and in the leukemia itself, aneuploidy with one extra chromosome was observed. Tsuchida and Rich (1964) found an increased incidence of SC's which were "coincident with the early *preleukemic* period of splenic hyperplasia." More recently, there have been two published reports of the specific and reproducible gain or loss of certain chromosomes; one case concerns Shope papilloma virus on rabbit cells (Prunieras and Delascluse, 1967), and the other involves the infection of a triploid HeLa cell line with hemadsorption virus, type 2 (Homma, Ohira, and Ishida, 1968). Independent confirmation of these remarkable findings would be most interesting.

According to Melander (1963), nondisjunction, lagging at anaphase, and elimination of specific chromosomes, as well as ". . . allocycly . . . expressed as positive heteropycnosis (the appearance of a chromocenter) during interphase and sometimes as negative heteropycnosis (the appearance of a constriction) during mitosis" are the consequences of pseudochiasmata or stickiness at specific loci and are part of differentiation in some lower forms. Whether disturbances of condensation or of DNA synthesis timing or specific activations of new SC regions are involved, the attention of cytologists and of others might well be directed to these specialized regions of the mammalian chromosome and their associations with virus and other agents which induce neoplasia.

ACKNOWLEDGMENTS

Gertrude Kohn, Harald zur Hausen, and Hans Stich kindly permitted me to read their unpublished material in the preparation of this paper. Grateful acknowledgment is hereby made to these researchers and to Warren Nichols, Eric Stanbridge, André Boué, and Joëlle Boué for permission to use their photographic material.

The author was the recipient of Research Career Development Award 5-K3-CA-18372 from the National Cancer Institute. Unpublished research reported here was supported by United States Public Health Service Contract PH43–62–157 from the Viral Carcinogenesis Branch, National Cancer Institute, and the Damon Runyon Memorial Fund Grant DRG-978AT.

REFERENCES

Aaronson, S. A., and G. J. Todaro. 1968. Basis for the Acquisition of Malignant Potential by Mouse Cells Cultivated In Vitro. *Science,* 162:1024–1026.

Aula, P. 1965. Virus-Associated Chromosome Breakage. A Cytogenetic Study of Chickenpox, Measles and Mumps Patients and of Cell Cultures Infected with Measles Virus. *Annales Academiae Scientiarum Fennicae Series A (IV Biology),* 89:5–75.

Aya, T. 1965. A Chromosome Study in Leucocyte Cultures from Serum Hepatitis Patients. *Journal of the Faculty of Science, Hokkaido University, Series VI (Zoology),* 15:699–705.

Bartsch, H. D., K.-O. Habermehl, and W. Diefenthal. 1967. Chromosomal Damage after Infection with Poliomyelitis Virus. *Experimental Cell Research,* 48:671–675.

Basrur, V. R., and D. G. Baker. 1963. Human Chromosome Breakage in Low-Calcium Cultures. *Lancet,* 1:1106–1107.

Benyesh-Melnick, M., H. F. Stich, F. Rapp, and T. C. Hsu. 1964. Viruses and Mammalian Chromosomes. III. Effect of Herpes Zoster Virus on Human Embryonal Lung Cultures. *Proceedings of the Society for Experimental Biology and Medicine,* 117:546–549.

Black, P. H. 1968. The Oncogenic DNA Viruses: A Review of In Vitro Transformation Studies. *Annual Review of Microbiology,* 22:391–426.

Boué, J. G., A. Boué, and P. Lazar. 1967. Altérations Chromosomiques Induites par le Virus de la Rubéole et par le Virus de la Rougeole dans les Cellules Diploïdes Humaines Cultivées In Vitro. *Pathologie et Biologie,* 15:997–1007.

Boué, J. G., A. Boué, P. S. Moorhead, and S. A. Plotkin. 1964. Altérations Chromosomiques Induites par le Virus de la Rubéole dans les Cellules Embryonnaires Diploïdes Humaines Cultivées In Vitro. *Comptes Rendus Hebdomadaires des Séances de l'Académie des Sciences série D (Sciences Naturelles),* 259:687–690.

Burdette, W. J., and J. S. Yoon. 1967. Mutations, Chromosomal Aberrations, and Tumors in Insects Treated with Oncogenic Virus. *Science,* 155:340–341.

Cantell, K., E. Saksela, and P. Aula. 1966. Virological Studies on Chromosome Damage of HeLa Cells Induced by Myxoviruses. *Annales Medicinae Experimentalis et Biologiae Fenniae,* 44:255–259.

Carp, R. I., and R. V. Gilden. 1966. A Comparison of the Replication Cycles of Simian Virus 40 in Human Diploid and African Green Monkey Kidney Cells. *Virology,* 28:150–162.

Chang, T. H., P. S. Moorhead, J. G. Boué, S. A. Plotkin, and J. M. Hoskins. 1966. Chromosome Studies of Human Cells Infected In Utero and In Vitro with Rubella Virus. *Proceedings of the Society for Experimental Biology and Medicine,* 122:236–243.

Cooper, H. L., and P. H. Black. 1964. Cytogenetic Studies of Three Clones Derived from a Permanent Line of Hamster Cells Transformed by SV40. *Journal of Cellular and Comparative Physiology,* 64:201–219.

Cooper, J. E. K., H. F. Stich, and D. S. Yohn. 1967. Viruses and Mammalian Chromosomes. VIII. Dose Response Studies with Human Adenovirus Types 18 and 4. *Virology*, 33:533–541.

D'Amato, F. 1952. Further Investigations on the Mutagenic Activity of Acridines (XXXIII-LI). *Caryologia*, 4:388–413.

Defendi, V., and J. M. Lehman. 1965. Transformation of Hamster Embryo Cells In Vitro by Polyoma Virus: Morphological, Karyological, Immunological and Transplantation Characteristics. *Journal of Cellular and Comparative Physiology*, 66:351–410.

Defendi, V., and J. M. Lehman. 1966. Biological Characteristics of Primary Tumors Induced by Polyoma Virus in Hamsters. *International Journal of Cancer*, 1:525–540.

Diehl, V., G. Henle, W. Henle, and G. Kohn. 1968. Demonstration of a Herpes Group Virus in Cultures of Peripheral Leukocytes from Patients with Infectious Mononucleosis. *Journal of Virology*, 2:663–669.

El-Alfi, O. S., P. M. Smith, and J. J. Biesele. 1965. Chromosomal Breaks in Human Leucocyte Cultures Induced by an Agent in the Plasma of Infectious Hepatitis Patients. *Hereditas*, 52:285–295.

Fernandes, M. V., and P. S. Moorhead. 1965. Transformation of African Green Monkey Kidney Cultures Infected with Simian Vacuolating Virus (SV40). *Texas Reports on Biology and Medicine*, 23 (Supplement 1):242–258.

Gaulden, M. 1970. "Discussion," *Genetic Concepts and Neoplasia* (The University of Texas M. D. Anderson Hospital and Tumor Institute at Houston, 23rd Annual Symposium on Fundamental Cancer Research, 1969). Baltimore, Maryland: The Williams & Wilkins Co. P. 74.

Girardi, A. J., and F. C. Jensen. 1966. "Transformation of Human Cells by Oncogenic Virus SV40," *Recent Results in Cancer Research. VI. Malignant Transformation by Viruses*, W. H. Kirsten, Ed. New York, New York: Springer-Verlag. Pp. 126–134.

Girardi, A. J., D. Weinstein, and P. S. Moorhead. 1966. SV40 Transformation of Human Diploid Cells. A Parallel Study of Viral and Karyological Parameters. *Annales Medicinae Experimentalis et Biologiae Fenniae*, 44:242–254.

Gripenberg, U. 1965. Chromosome Studies in Some Virus Infections. *Hereditas*, 54:1–18.

Gripenberg, U. 1967. The Cytological Behavior of a Human Ring-Chromosome. *Chromosoma*, 20:284–289.

Hampar, B., and S. A. Ellison. 1961. Chromosomal Aberrations Induced by an Animal Virus. *Nature*, 192:145–147.

Hampel, K. E., and A. Levan. 1964. Breakage in Human Chromosomes Induced by Low Temperature. *Hereditas*, 51:315–343.

Harnden, D. G. 1964. Cytogenetic Studies on Patients with Virus Infections and Subjects Vaccinated against Yellow Fever. *American Journal of Human Genetics*, 16:204–213.

Hausen, H. zur. 1967a. Chromosomal Changes of Similar Nature in Seven Established Cell Lines Derived from the Peripheral Blood of Patients with Leukemia. *Journal of the National Cancer Institute*, 38:683–696.

———. 1967b. Induction of Specific Chromosomal Aberrations by Adenovirus Type 12 in Human Embryonic Kidney Cells. *Journal of Virology*, 1:1174–1185.

———. 1968. Chromosomal Aberrations and Cloning Efficiency in Adenovirus Type 12-Infected Hamster Cells. *Journal of Virology*, 2:915–917.

Hausen, H. zur, W. Henle, K. Hummeler, V. Diehl, and G. Henle. 1967. Comparative Study of Cultured Burkitt Tumor Cells by Immunofluorescence, Autoradiography, and Electron Microscopy. *Journal of Virology*, 1:830–837.

Hausen, H. zur, and E. Lanz. 1966. Chromosomale Aberratonen bei L-Zellen nach Vaccinin-Virus-Infektion. *Zeitschrift für Medizinische Mikrobiologie und Immunologie*, 152:60–65.

Henle, G., and W. Henle. 1965. Evidence for a Persistent Viral Infection in a Cell Line Derived from Burkitt's Lymphoma. *Journal of Bacteriology*, 89:252–258.

Henle, W., and G. Henle. 1968. "Present Status of the Herpes-Group Virus Associated with Cultures of the Hematopoietic System," *Perspectives in Virology*, M. Pollard, Ed. New York, New York: Academic Press, Inc. Vol. VI. Pp. 105–124.

Homma, M., M. Ohira, and N. Ishida. 1968. Specific Chromosome Aberrations in Cells Persistently Infected with Type 2 Hemadsorption Virus. *Virology*, 34:60–68.

Hsu, T. C. 1963. Longitudinal Differentiation of Chromosomes and the Possibility of Interstitial Telomeres. *Experimental Cell Research*, Suppl. 19:73–85.

Jacobs, P. A., I. M. Tough, and D. H. Wright. 1963. Cytogenetic Studies in Burkitt's Lymphoma. *Lancet*, 2:1144–1146.

Jensen, F., H. Koprowski, and J. A. Pontén. 1963. Rapid Transformation of Human Fibroblast Cultures by Simian Virus. *Proceedings of the National Academy of Sciences of the U.S.A.*, 50:343–348.

Kato, H., and A. A. Sandberg. 1967. Chromosome Pulverization in Human Binucleate Cells Following Colcemid Treatment. *Journal of Cell Biology*, 34:35–46.

Kitamura, I., G. van Hoosier, Jr., L. Sample, G. Taylor, and J. J. Trentin. 1964. Characteristics of Human Adenovirus Type 12-Induced Hamster Tumor Cells in Tissue Culture. *Proceedings of the Society for Experimental Biology and Medicine*, 116:563–568.

Kohn, G., V. Diehl, W. J. Mellman, W. Henle, and G. Henle. 1968. C-Group Chromosome Marker in Long-Term Leukocyte Cultures. *Journal of the National Cancer Institute*, 41:795–804.

Kohn, G., W. J. Mellman, P. S. Moorhead, J. Loftus, and G. Henle. 1967. Involvement of C-Group Chromosomes in Five Burkitt Lymphoma Cell Lines. *Journal of the National Cancer Institute*, 38:209–222.

Koprowski, H., J. A. Ponten, F. Jensen, R. G. Ravdin, P. Moorhead, and E. Saksela. 1962. Transformation of Cultures of Human Tissue Infected with Simian Virus SV40. *Journal of Cellular and Comparative Physiology*, 59:281–292.

Lejeune, J., B. Dutrillaux, J. Lafourcade, R. Berger, D. Abonyi, and M. O. Rethore. 1968. Endoréduplication Selective du Bras Long du Chromosome 2 chez une Femme et sa Fille. *Comptes Rendus Hebdomadaires des Séances de l' Académie des Sciences Série D (Sciences Naturelles)*, 266:24–26.

Levan, A. 1956. Chromosomes in Cancer Tissue. *Annals of the New York Academy of Sciences*, 63:774–789.

MacKinnon, E., V. I. Kalnins, H. F. Stich, and D. S. Yohn. 1966. Viruses and Mammalian Chromosomes. V. Comparative Karyologic and Immunofluorescent Studies on Syrian Hamster and Human Amnion Cells Infected with Human Adenovirus Type 12. *Cancer Research*, 26:612–618.

Mauler, R., and W. Hennessen. 1965. Virus Induced Alterations of Chromosomes. *Archiv für die Gesamte Virusforschung*, 16:175–181.

McMichael, H., J. E. Wagner, P. C. Nowell, and D. A. Hungerford. 1963. Chromosome Studies of Virus-Induced Rabbit Papillomas and Derived Primary Carcinomas. *Journal of the National Cancer Institute*, 31:1197–1215.

Melander, Y. 1963. Cell Differentiation and Delayed Separation of Anaphase Chromosomes. *Hereditas*, 49:277–284.

Miles, C. P., and F. O'Neill. 1966. Prominent Secondary Constrictions in a Pseudo-Diploid Human Cell Line. *Cytogenetics*, 5:321–324.

———. 1967. Chromosome Studies of 8 In Vitro Lines of Burkitt's Lymphoma. *Cancer Research*, 27:392–402.

Miller, R. W. 1970. "The Association Between Congenital Malformations and Cancer," *Genetic Concepts and Neoplasia* (The University of Texas M. D. Anderson Hospital and Tumor Institute at Houston, 23rd Annual Symposium on Fundamental Cancer Research, 1969). Baltimore, Maryland: The Williams & Wilkins Co. Pp. 78–84.

Moorhead, P. S., and E. Saksela. 1963. Non-Random Chromosomal Aberrations in SV40-Transformed Human Cells. *Journal of Cellular and Comparative Physiology*, 62:57–83.

———. 1965. The Sequence of Chromosome Aberrations During SV40 Transformation of a Human Diploid Cell Strain. *Hereditas*, 52:271–284.

Moutschen, J., and R. Matagne. 1965. Cytological Effects of Irradiated Glucose. *Radiation Botany*, 5:23–28.

Nichols, W. W. 1963. Relationships of Viruses, Chromosomes and Carcinogenesis. *Hereditas*, 50:53–80.

Nichols, W. W., P. Aula, A. Levan, W. Heneen, and E. Norrby. 1967. Radioautography with Tritiated Thymidine in Measles and Sendai-Induced Chromosome Pulverizations. *Journal of Cell Biology*, 35:257–262.

Nichols, W. W., A. Levan, P. Aula, and E. Norrby. 1965. Chromosome Damage Associated with the Measles Virus In Vitro. *Hereditas*, 54:101–118.

Nichols, W. W., A. Levan, L. L. Coriell, H. Goldner, and C. G. Ahlström. 1964. Chromosome Abnormalities In Vitro in Human Leukocytes Associated with Schmidt-Ruppin Rous Sarcoma Virus. *Science*, 146:248–250.

Nichols, W. W., A. Levan, W. K. Heneen, and M. Peluse. 1965. Synergism of the Schmidt-Ruppin Strain of the Rous Sarcoma Virus and Cytidine Triphosphate in the Induction of Chromosome Breaks in Human Leucocytes. *Hereditas*, 54:213–236.

Nichols, W. W., A. Levan, B. Hall, and G. Östergren. 1962. Measles-Associated Chromosome Breakage. (Preliminary Communication) *Hereditas*, 48:367–370.

Norrby, E., A. Levan, and W. W. Nichols. 1965. The Correlation Between the Chromosome Pulverization Effect and Other Biological Activities of Measles Virus Preparations. *Experimental Cell Research*, 41:483–491.

Östergren, G., and T. Wakonig. 1954. True or Apparent Subchromatid Breakage and the Induction of Labile States in Cytological Chromosome Loci. *Botaniska Notiser*, 4:357–373.

Palmer, C. G. 1959. The Cytology of Rabbit Papillomas and Derived Carcinomas. *Journal of the National Cancer Institute*, 23: 241–249.

Paton, G. R., J. P. Jacobs, and F. T. Perkins. 1965. Chromosome Changes in Human Diploid Cell Cultures Infected with Mycoplasma. *Nature*, 207:43–45.

Pope, J. H., M. K. Horne, and W. Scott. 1968. Transformation of Foetal Human Leukocytes In Vitro by Filtrates of a Human Leukaemic Cell Line Containing Herpes-Like Virus. *International Journal of Cancer*, 3:857–866.

Prunieras, M., and C. Delescluse. 1967. Études sur les Rapports Virus-Chromosomes. VII. Nouvelles Récherches Caryologiques sur les Cultures de Cellules Dérivées de Papillomes de Shope. *Annales de l'Institut Pasteur*, 5:680–697.

Rabson, A. S., G. T. O'Conor, S. Baron, J. J. Whang, and F. Y. Legallais. 1966. Morphologic, Cytogenetic and Virologic Studies In Vitro of a Malignant Lymphoma from an African Child. *International Journal of Cancer*, 1:89–106.

Rapp, F., and T. C. Hsu. 1965. Viruses and Mammalian Chromosomes. IV. Replication of Herpes Simplex Virus in Diploid Chinese Hamster Cells. *Virology*, 25: 401–411.

Saksela, E., P. Aula, and K. Cantell. 1965. Chromosomal Damage of Human Cells Induced by Sendai Virus. *Annales Medicinae Experimentalis et Biologiae Fenniae*, 43:132–136.

Saksela, E., and P. S. Moorhead. 1962. Enhancement of Secondary Constrictions and the Heterochromatic X in Human Cells. *Cytogenetics*, 1:225–244.

Saksela, E., and P. S. Moorhead. 1963. Aneuploidy in the Degenerative Phase of Serial Cultivation of Human Cell Strains. *Proceedings of the National Academy of Sciences of the U.S.A.*, 50:390–395.

Sambrook, J., H. Westphal, P. R. Srinivasan, and R. Dulbecco. 1968. The Integrated State of Viral DNA in SV40-Transformed Cells. *Proceedings of the National Academy of Sciences of the U.S.A.*, 60:1288–1295.

Schmid, W. 1963. DNA Replication Patterns of Human Chromosomes. *Cytogenetics*, 2:175–193.

Stich, H. F., T. C. Hsu, and F. Rapp. 1964. Viruses and Mammalian Chromosomes. I. Localization of Chromosome Aberrations after Infection with Herpes Simplex Virus. *Virology*, 22:439–445.

Stich, H. F., G. L. van Hoosier, and J. J. Trentin. 1964. Viruses and Mammalian Chromosomes. Chromosome Aberrations by Human Adenovirus Type 12. *Experimental Cell Research*, 34:400–403.

Stich, H. F., and D. S. Yohn. Viruses and Chromosomes. *Progress in Medical Virology*. (in press.)

Stoltz, D. B., H. F. Stich, and D. S. Yohn. 1967. Viruses and Mammalian Chromosomes. VII. The Persistence of a Chromosomal Instability in Regenerating Transplanted and Cultured Neoplasms Induced by Human Adenovirus Type-12 in Syrian Hamsters. *Cancer Research*, 27:587–598.

Tanzer, J., Y. Stoitchkov, P. Harel, and M. Boiron. 1963. Chromosomal Abnormalities in Measles. *Lancet*, 2:1070–1071.

Tanzer, J., M. Thomas, Y. Stoitchkov, M. Boiron, and J. Bernard. 1964. Altérations Chromosomiques Observées dans des Cellules de Rein de Singe Infectées In Vitro par le Virus de l'Herpes. *Annales de l'Institut Pasteur*, 107:366–373.

Ter Meulen, V., and R. Love. 1967. Virological, Immunochemical and Cytochemical Studies of Four HeLa Cell Lines Infected with Two Strains of Influenza Virus. *Journal of Virology*, 1:626–639.

Todaro, G. J., H. Green, and M. R. Swift. 1966. Susceptibility of Human Diploid Fibroblast Strains to Transformation by SV40 Virus. *Science*, 153:1252–1254.

Todaro, G. J., and G. M. Martin. 1967. Increased Susceptibility of Down's Syndrome Fibroblasts to Transformation by SV40. *Proceedings of the Society for Experimental Biology and Medicine*, 124:1232–1236.

Tsuchida, R., and M. A. Rich. 1964. Chromosomal Aberrations in Viral Leukemogenesis. I. Friend and Rauscher Leukemia. *Journal of the National Cancer Institute*, 33:33–47.

Vogt, M., and R. Dulbecco. 1963. Steps in the Neoplastic Transformation of Hamster Embryo Cells by Polyoma Virus. *Proceedings of the National Academy of Sciences of the U.S.A.*, 49:171–179.

Wald, N., A. C. Upton, V. K. Jenkins, and W. H. Borges. 1964. Radiation-Induced Mouse Leukemia: Consistent Occurrence of an Extra and a Marker Chromosome. *Science*, 143:810–813.

Weinstein, D., and P. S. Moorhead. 1965. Karyology of Permanent Human Cell Line W-18 VA2, Originated by SV40 Transformation. *Journal of Cellular and Comparative Physiology*, 65:85–92.

———. 1967. The Relation of Karyotypic Change to Loss of Contact Inhibition of Division in Human Diploid Cells after SV40 Infection. *Journal of Cellular Physiology*, 69:367–376.

Yerganian, G., H. M. Shein, and J. F. Enders. 1962. Chromosomal Disturbances Observed in Human Fetal Renal Cells Transformed In Vitro by Simian Virus 40 and Carried in Culture. *Cytogenetics*, 1:314–324.

Discussion

Dr. André Boué, Centre International de l'Enfance, Paris, France: I would like to comment on the sequence of chromosomal aberrations observed in a clone of human diploid cells infected with and transformed by Rous sarcoma virus (Schmidt-Ruppin). After incubation for 1 hour, the cells were suspended in soft agar in petri dishes. Colonies of transformed cells appeared in two or three weeks. From these colonies, clones were initiated. The cells of these clones were morphologically transformed (vacuolated cells, tridimensional growth). In no case was infectious virus recovered from these cultures. However, when these cells were grown together with chicken embryo fibroblasts, infectious virus was recovered. These cells gave colonies in soft agar. When inoculated onto the chorioallantoic membrane of embryonated eggs, tumors developed.

These clones had a shorter in vitro lifetime than did control cells. They remained diploid, and even when maintained in vitro for months, no established cell lines were obtained. One clone, 809/SR2, had a longer lifetime and chromosomal changes were observed (Figure 1). For 80 days, the cells remained diploid, but there was an increase in the percentage of breaks (25 to 50 per cent, in contrast to less than 10 per cent in the control cells). At day 80, a ring chromosome was observed in the D group. From that time, we had two cell populations. The percentage of cells with this marker chromosome increased and represented 65 per cent of the cells at day 123.

Between day 80 and day 90, changes in the number of chromosomes were observed in both cell populations (with and without ring chromosomes). Trisomic cells appeared with an extra chromosome in different groups (C, D, and F), but only trisomic C cells were observed later and their percentage increased. At day 109, cells with a double trisomy were observed (trisomy C + C, C + D, C + F), but later, only cells with two C chromosomes were observed. At day 123, cells with 46 chromosomes

HUMAN DIPLOID CELLS TRANSFORMED BY ROUS SARCOMA VIRUS

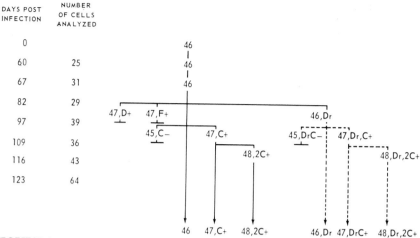

FIGURE 1.

represented 40 per cent of the total cell population, cells with trisomy C, 40 per cent, and cells with double trisomy C, 20 per cent. After day 133, no mitoses were observed. No established cell lines were obtained.

As cells from this clone were frozen, different cultures of thawed cells could be studied and the same sequence of chromosomal aberrations was observed. A careful analysis of metaphases of the chromosomal preparations in which the first trisomic C cells appeared has shown cells with 45 chromosomes and one group C chromosome lacking. It may be postulated that the formation of trisomic cells is the result of nondisjunction. Later a nondisjunction occurring in a cell which already had 47 chromosomes gave a cell with a double trisomy and one with 46 chromosomes, which is apparently normal. The percentage of cells with 46 chromosomes decreased sharply when the cells with trisomy C appeared, but remained stable when cells with 48 chromosomes were detected.

The analysis of the sequence of chromosomal changes showed that the modifications of the number of chromosomes are the result of nondisjunction and that there is a selection of the different types of cells with chromosomal aberrations, some cells being more competitive and outnumbering the other chromosomally abnormal cells and even the population of cells with 46 chromosomes.

Dr. Charles Miles, University of Utah, Salt Lake City, Utah: Dr. Moorhead, I wonder if the effect on chromosome No. 1 may not be a highly specific one. There is a kind of fragmentation or pulverization that appears to involve specifically the long arm of No. 1, especially in the leukocyte lines, so that it's a different kind of fragmentation. This effect cannot be accounted for by cell fusion nor on the basis of selection.

Also, Dr. Moorhead, I assume you have been looking at short-term cultures, lymphocytes from patients with infectious mononucleosis. Have you found a No. 10 marker in those patients?

Dr. Paul S. Moorhead, Wistar Institute of Anatomy and Biology, Philadelphia, Pennsylvania: No, but we've not been looking at that. The material I was presenting was done by Dr. Kohn and the people in the Henles' laboratory. Your first remark concerns the point I was trying to make. Zur Hausen, in examining cell lines derived from seven leukemic patients, found just what you described in all seven. The long arm of chromosome No. 1, from the secondary constriction down to the telomere, is completely despiralized, fragmented, pulverized. His pictures are very clear, and he can associate this with anaphase losses. He also found parts of other chromosomes completely pulverized. In addition zur Hausen has evidence of deoxyribonucleic acid (DNA) synthesis in these parts during the G2 period, which is a parallel to the pulverization phenomenon involving syncytia with two nuclei. All of his observations involved chromosomes No. 1, 9, and 16, the ones carrying the three major secondary constrictions, and also one entire chromosome in the C group, which could possibly be the late-labeling X. However, I don't know whether all these cases were female. I think the effect on DNA synthesis is connected with the condensation pattern or timing. There are a number of suggestions of this in the literature; certain Swedish workers have proposed this theory for some time. Such a mechanism might have more importance in virus work than we have realized before this.

Dr. Gertrude Kohn, Children's Hospital, Philadelphia, Pennsylvania: I would like to answer Dr. Miles. We have examined chromosomes from patients with acute infectious mononucleosis and found that there seem to be two cell strains. One divides spontaneously and does not need stimulation with phytohemagglutinin (PHA); the other does need the PHA. We have looked at the chromosomes of both of these populations. The population which needs PHA does not have the marker chromosomes in the C group. The one which divides spontaneously does not have the marker in most of the cells, but we have found two metaphases in which there is a suggestion that the marker chromosome is there. I don't quite know what that means because in long-term leukocyte lines from these patients and in the Burkitt's tumor cell lines, we don't have the marker chromosome in all the metaphases. However, in our cloning experiments in a Burkitt's tumor cell line, we find that every cloned line contains the marker chromosome in a certain percentage of the cells, which means that from this line, even a cell which does not have the marker will, when cloned out, produce cells which do have the marker.

Dr. William Sly, Washington University School of Medicine, St. Louis, Missouri: Dr. Rapp, is it correct that cells can be transformed in lines which are capable of permitting the lytic cycle to occur?

Dr. Fred Rapp, Baylor College of Medicine, Houston, Texas: Yes.

Dr. Sly: When these transformed cells are superinfected with simian virus 40 (SV40), is it known whether the virus is adsorbed? Also, is it known whether late gene expression can occur in these cells which carry the SV40?

Dr. Rapp: It is possible to transform cells that are lytic for the virus, but this happens only in rare instances. We have been working with such a cell line in our laboratory. It is a BSC-1 (a stable line of green monkey kidney cells) culture transformed by SV40 in which all the usual virus markers generally present in the transformed cell have been identified. This cell cannot be superinfected with SV40. Miss Trilock, a graduate student in our laboratory, has been attempting to determine why. The prime reason for lack of susceptibility is that SV40 does not adsorb to the cells, although the virus will absorb, penetrate, and replicate in the parental cells. This may represent selection, of course.

Dr. Gerald L. Van Hoosier, Baylor College of Medicine, Houston, Texas: Dr. Rapp, as you know, there appears to be quite a bit of variation among the adenoviruses, and perhaps in the inverse variation between the strains of the transplant antigen and the oncogenicity of the virus. For example, one could take simian adenovirus 7 (SA7), one of the most oncogenic adenoviruses and yet one of the weakest transplant antigens. At the other extreme, one might take human adenovirus type 7 which is very weakly oncogenic yet can immunize better against adenovirus 12-induced tumors in a transplant test. Since you found variation in the fluorescent T-antigen, do you have any evidence that the differences you found in oncogenicity may be the result of either quantitative or qualitative differences in the transplant antigens that this pair of particles might absorb?

Dr. Rapp: I do not agree with your statement that SA7 is a weak virus concerning transplant immunity. We have some evidence that it is probably as effective as other adenoviruses, but fairly precise quantitation is required to show the effect. Concerning your second comment, we have tested some of these progeny in transplant-rejection tests. In some, even the nononcogenic variants produce transplantation resistance against cells transformed by the parental strain of the virus. We have not tested each plaque-derived strain as yet. However, thus far, all variants tested have induced transplant-rejection immunity.

Dr. K. Taylor, San Diego State College, San Diego, California: Dr. Moorhead, I observed in a leukocyte culture from a three-year-old boy with trisomy G that about one third of the cells showed isochromatid gaps or breaks and even terminal deletions at the same place in the long arm of chromosome No. 16. Also, there was one dicentric chromosome whose size and symmetry suggested origin from No. 16, breaking at the same point, with sister-strand fusion. These were more than halfway distal in the long arm of No. 16. Have you seen breaks in such a place?

Dr. Moorhead: I have not personally. I tried today to present a survey of this but it is not complete. I'm sure there may be some in the literature, but offhand I don't know of any. In some reports, specific effects involve only chromosome No. 1, and in others specific effects involve chromosomes No. 16 and No. 1 without ever involving No. 9, except in the case of zur Hausen's work, so I do think there is something strange about these regions. At least two laboratories, our own and Schmidt's, have shown that these regions label late, just as one of the X's in female cells.

Dr. B. R. Brinkley, The University of Texas M. D. Anderson Hospital and Tumor Institute at Houston, Houston, Texas: Dr. Moorhead, we are interested in the ultrastructure of specialized chromosome regions such as the nucleolus organizer. You defined tertiary constrictions as nonnucleolus organizer constrictions. What is the evidence for this?

Dr. Moorhead: The evidence that the stalk-like regions on the acrocentrics are involved with nucleolus formation is from work done here in Houston. The classification I'm giving is purely morphological and I think it is reasonably consistent. Pufflike regions on chromosomes No. 1, 9, 16, and perhaps another at the base of one of the B chromosomes are very similar and could be put in one class. Then you would have the type such as is seen in the middle of one of the D chromosomes, which is like a very thin achromatic gap. We observed it in SV40-treated material and some people have reported it in normal material. Miles reported it in the pseudodiploid line he studied. I think it has been reported too often not to be true. But these are only morphologic classifications which should serve until its real nature is known.

Dr. Donald Ruchnagel, University of Michigan Medical School, Ann Arbor, Michigan: Dr. Moorhead, much of the discussion yesterday seemed to imply that the Philadelphia chromosome in chronic granulocytic leukemia patients is believed to be more or less etiological in the leukemic process. Today you have shown that viruses seem to cause specific breaks in chromosomes. What are the implications of these observations with respect to the question of whether the Philadelphia chromosome is a primary or secondary phenomenon?

Dr. Moorhead: I have not worked with the leukemias at all. However, I think it is the only outstanding specific lesion that exists which can be completely confirmed preceding clinical evidence of disease. This chromosome also may be involved in some kind of specific reaction to an agent which is as yet unknown.

Dr. Joseph Lynn, Baylor University Medical Center, Dallas, Texas: I would like to concur with Dr. Stich's earlier comment that chromosomal abnormalities are not necessary antecedents to neoplasia. We have worked with Dr. J. B. Howell on the electron microscopy of tissue samples from patients with the nevoid basal cell carcinoma syndrome, which was referred to briefly yesterday. I am not aware of any chromosomal abnormalities in this syndrome. In patients with this disorder, basal cell carcinomas appear at a very early age. In addition, there is a peculiar lack of differentiation of keratinocytes on the palms and soles, which contain "dark cells." These dark cells have been described in patients with carcinoma of the breast and other tumors. In the approximately 250 tumors from human beings that we have studied ultrastructurally, dark cells are found consistently. Also, perichromatin granules are present in increased numbers in these specimens.

Before we became biased in looking for these intranuclear particles, we studied 102 tumors and 65 miscellaneous nonneoplastic biopsy specimens which were graded for the presence of perichromatin granules. These particles increased in frequency during viral infections. The granules were originally described by Watson and Swift. Monevon studied them using glycolmethacrylate-embedded tissues for enzyme digestion; he thinks the particles are proteins. On the basis of study of 20 glycolmethacrylate-embedded human tumors subjected to various enzyme digestions, we concluded that human granules are not DNA but probably protein, primarily with some ribonucleic acid (RNA). Microincineration indicates that some inorganic materials are present in these particles.

Dr. Rapp's reference to the loss of control of G1 and cell differentiation, which is Prescott's definition or description of the molecular lesion that is cancer, represents the kind of unifying concept of carcinogenesis with which all cancer researchers can live. The induction of a particular enzyme-forming system by viruses or other agents or chemicals may be the only critical factor in malignant transformation.

Dr. Rapp, have you looked ultrastructurally at the cytoplasmic tumor antigens and, if so, where are they located? In methylcholanthrene-induced carcinoma of the cervix in mice, Schmidt and Foreman have shown dense mitochondrial granules of the same size and electron density as perichromatin granules. With DNA being present in mitochondria and perichromatin granules inside the nucleolus containing some RNA protein and possibly divalent cations, we are wondering about a milieu-induced feedback mechanism for chemical carcinogenesis. This mechanism might be short circuited by DNA or RNA oncogenic viruses.

Have you looked at cytoplasmic tumor antigens with Dr. Stich's ferritin immunoelectron microscopy technique? Slow virus infections seem to have been neglected at this symposium, as they possibly are in the area of cancer research. The association of various "autoimmune" diseases and cancers in man has been pointed out, however. The similarities between NZB mouse disease, Aleutian mink disease, and Scrapie and systemic lupus erythematosus, polyarteritis, and subacute sclerosing leukoencephalitis in man are but a few intriguing and provocative possible analogies.

Dr. Rapp: We have not studied this question. Other investigators have looked at a variety of cells to determine the localization of tumor antigens by electron microscopy. They have found that adenovirus type 12-transformed cells have this material in the cytoplasm. To my knowledge, no one has found the SV40 tumor antigen or anything resembling it in the cytoplasm by ultrastructural methods.

You mentioned the slow viruses. There is increasing evidence from a number of laboratories that suggests not slow viruses but slow diseases. The viruses replicate quite effectively, going through their regular cycle as rapidly as do some of our faster viruses; they are somewhat harder to detect. The diseases, however, take a long time to develop and are complicated by virus-antibody complexes which circulate and are often infectious. It is, therefore, hard to distinguish antibodies in those systems and it is also difficult to isolate viruses. I agree with you completely that this area needs much more study.

Dr. Ernest H. Y. Chu, Oak Ridge National Laboratories, Oak Ridge, Tennessee: Dr. Moorhead, in SV40-transformed cells from man, have you isolated clones which retain all properties of transformed cells and yet have the normal karyotype?

Dr. Moorhead: We tried to do this with considerable effort, but for technical reasons, we failed to get enough clones. We obtained about 20 clones, trying to clone them as early as possible—at about the time of loss of contact inhibition of division. In all clones, there was complete instability of karyotype, which was a surprise. If we could catch karyologically normal clones early enough, perhaps they would not be pushed aside in the competition within a mass culture. There must be normal karyotype cells present, cells that have acquired at least the first step in their growth transformation. All clones seem persistently unstable.

Dr. Lynn: I would like to recount a particular case of a 15-year-old boy who had progressive mental and motor deterioration over an 8-month period. A brain biopsy was done in desperation after no viral agent was identified on serological examination or culture attempts. Neutralization was insignificant at a dilution of 1:32 against adenovirus. Increased numbers of perichromatin granules were found in the initial biopsy, which was not diagnostic on light microscopy. Another biopsy showed a typical picture of a viral encephalitis but with no mature viruses and no titers, but many perichromatin granules. This isn't too surprising if one recalls reports of heart studied at autopsy using fluorescent antiviral antibody techniques. These reveal myocardial viral antigens in the absence of serological or other evidence of viral disease.

Ultrastructural Aspects of Chromosome Damage

B. R. BRINKLEY AND MARGERY W. SHAW

Department of Biology, The University of Texas M. D. Anderson Hospital and Tumor Institute at Houston, Houston, Texas

A number of mutagenic agents are known to induce damage and structural rearrangement of mitotic and meiotic chromosomes. The mechanisms of damage and the possible relationships to mutation and tumorigenesis are discussed in this volume.

The structural basis of chromosome damage and the types of aberrations produced have been determined entirely from studies with the light microscope. Although most aberrations are detectable by this means, interpretation of damage in relationship to the macromolecular structure of the chromosome can be achieved only by extending the observations to finer levels of organization, such as that which can be achieved with electron optics.

Unfortunately, methods used for chromosome study with the light microscope have generally not been amenable to ultrastructural investigations. However, methods recently developed in our laboratories now permit the evaluation of damage to selected chromosomes with both light and electron microscopy.

In this report, we will describe the fine structure of chromosome aberrations in mammalian cells which either occurred spontaneously or were induced by X rays, mitomycin C, or tritiated thymidine (^{3}H-TdR). Particular emphasis will be placed on the comparative aspects of damage as observed with light and electron microscopy.

Materials and Methods

CELL CULTURES

Human Lymphocytes

Phytohemagglutinin-stimulated lymphocytes from human beings were cultured in chromosome medium 1A (Grand Island Biological Company) for 72 to 96 hours. Cells in metaphase were collected by the addition of colchicine or Colcemid (CIBA). Harvesting procedures followed the method of Moorhead *et al.* (1960) with slight modifications. The cells were then flame-dried on collodion-coated slides. Suitable cells in metaphase were photographed with the light microscope using phase objective magnifications of 25 or 40; the cells then were transferred to a grid by the method of Shaw, Brinkley, and Schwab (in preparation) for examination with the electron microscope. The chromosomes were unsectioned and unstained.

Rat Kangaroo Cells

Cells derived from the kidney of the rat kangaroo were used. The cell line PtK_2 (American Type Culture Collection No. CCL) was grown as a monolayer on a modified McCoy's 5a medium supplemented with 20 per cent fetal calf serum. For the experiments, 1×10^6 cells were seeded into plastic 30 mm petri dishes (Falcon Plastics) and incubated overnight at 37 C. The dishes were removed from the incubator and exposed to X rays.

SPECIAL TREATMENTS

Mitomycin C

Mitomycin C was dissolved in culture medium and was added to lymphocyte cultures 24 hours before harvest at a final concentration of 1.0 μg/ml.

Tritiated Thymidine

^{3}H-TdR was added to lymphocyte cultures for 4 to 6 hours before harvest in a concentration of 0.3 μc/ml media (specific activity 6.7 c/mmole).

Irradiation Procedures

Cell monolayers growing in plastic petri dishes were exposed to X rays produced by a Maxitron X-ray unit (General Electric). The conditions of irradiation were 250 kev (peak) at 15 ma, filtered with 0.5 mm of copper and 1.0 mm of aluminum, giving a half-value layer of 1.26 mm of copper. The dose rate was 180 rads/min. One set of dishes received 250 rads and another set, 500 rads. Immediately after irradiation, the flasks were returned to the incubator. A single flask from each treatment was fixed at half-hour intervals for a total of 8 hours. Control cultures were treated in the same way, except that they were not irradiated.

ELECTRON MICROSCOPY

Whole Mount Preparation of Human Chromosomes

The details of the whole mount procedure are given in a separate communication (Shaw, Brinkley, and Schwab, in preparation). Briefly, the method is as follows:

Suitable metaphase cells noted on the collodion-coated slides were photographed with phase optics. A copper electron-microscope grid was positioned over a selected cell and anchored to the slide with a small drop of collodion applied to one edge. A small aluminum foil disc was placed over the grid, and a strip of Scotch tape was placed over the grid and foil. With a scalpel or razor blade, the collodion film was scored around the Scotch tape. The tape was then carefully pulled up with forceps. A drop of water applied to the edge of the tape as it was being stripped off permitted the collodion strip with the cell attached to come off onto the copper grid. The grid then was examined directly in a Hitachi HU-11C electron microscope using a 20-μ objective aperture and operating at 50 kv.

Thin Section Analysis of Rat Kangaroo Chromosomes

Cell monolayers were fixed in situ by the method of Brinkley, Murphy, and Richardson (1967). Briefly, this method consists of decanting the growth medium and adding 3 per cent Millonig's phosphate-buffered glutaraldehyde for 1 hour followed by a buffer rinse and post-fixation in 1 per cent OsO_4 for 1 hour. The monolayers were washed two times in distilled water and prestained with 2 per cent aqueous uranyl acetate for 20 minutes. Alcohol dehydration was done at room temperature with a graded series of ethanol up to 90 per cent. The cells then were dehydrated further in a graded series of hydroxypropyl methacrylate (HPMA) and embedded by covering the monolayer with a thin layer of Epon 812 mixture. After polymerization at 60 C for 48 hours, the petri dishes were snapped free of the hardened Epon. The cells embedded in the Epon disc then were viewed with the oil immersion objective ($\times 100$). Chromosome aberrations were scored and selected cells were marked with a sharp needle or diamond marker. The marked area was cut out with a no. 2 cork borer and glued, with the cell side up, to an Epon block for sectioning. Serial sections were cut with a diamond knife on an LKB Ultratome III. Silver to gray sections were collected on collodion-coated copper slotted grids (Busby, Turner, and Roberts, 1967). With care, up to 15 contiguous sections could be collected on a single grid. These sections were stained in uranyl acetate and lead citrate and stabilized with carbon before examination with the electron microscope.

Results and Discussion

ULTRASTRUCTURAL FEATURES OF NORMAL MAMMALIAN CHROMOSOMES

Unsectioned Human Chromosomes

The methanol-acetic acid fixative used in the whole mount method has the advantage of preserving chromosome structures which are familiar to light microscopists accustomed to observing squash or air-dried preparations. Unfortunately, however, the method is extremely harsh in its effects on other cell structures; spindle tubules and other achromatic elements of the mitotic apparatus are destroyed, as are membrane-bound organelles. Undoubtedly, the fixative also removes basic chromosomal proteins while preserving acidic protein, deoxyribonucleic acid

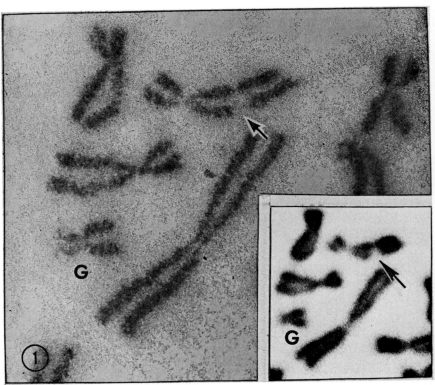

FIGURE 1. Light and electron micrographs of a group of chromosomes from human beings. Note the greater detail evident in the arms of the G chromosome in the electron micrograph. Arrows indicate a break in the B chromosome.

(DNA), and ribonucleic acid (RNA). Even with its shortcomings, however, the method permits direct observation of unsectioned, unstained chromosomes with the electron microscope. It is, therefore, possible to extend the resolution limits from that achieved with light optics (0.1 to 0.2 μ) to the intermediate range of electron microscopy (0.2 to 0.005 μ).

The usual morphological features of human chromosomes are readily detectable in the electron microscope. Figure 1 shows a composite light and electron micrograph of several metaphase chromosomes. In the light micrograph, the kinetochore (or centromere) region appears fuzzy and indistinct. In the electron micrograph, the same region is seen to consist of distinct fibrillar components extending across the kinetochore region. The short arms of the small G-group chromosome in the light micrograph can be seen with great detail in the electron micrograph. Major coiling of the chromatids in the long arms is also evident. In the same figure, the long arm of the B chromosome in the light micrograph contains an erosion or wedge-shaped gap in one chromatid (arrow). When the same region is examined in the electron microscope, it is seen as a clean break. Furthermore, the same locus on the sister chromatid also appears to be damaged.

The preservation and resolution achieved in whole mount preparation does not permit a detailed analysis of the strandedness of human chromosomes. Perhaps the Langmuir trough procedure (Wolfe, 1965; Dupraw, 1965; Ris, 1967) for spreading intact chromosomes is better suited for studies of strandedness. Nevertheless, occasional thin preparations reveal that fibrils 200 to 300 A in diameter compose the chromatid arms. Occasionally, these appear to be composed of finer fibrils arranged in supercoils (Figure 2). One consistent observation in many preparations is the apparent division of chromatids into half-chromatids.

A hitherto undescribed structure which has been seen consistently in our electron microscope preparations is a series of fibers which appear to connect or cross-link sister chromatids. (Examples of these fibers, which we call "interchromatid connections," are shown later in this paper in Figures 8, 9, and 20.)

The kinetochore region is visible as a primary constriction in all preparations. Usually, at least two strands are visible in each chromatid. Occasionally, there are suggestions of cross-linking or chiasma-like strands in the kinetochore region; this observation supports the conclusion of Cuevas-Sosa (1967) that sister chromatid crossing-over can occur in the centromere.

The clear vacuole, which occasionally can be observed with the light microscope at the primary constriction in chromosomes treated with colchicine, is seen frequently in electron microscope preparations (Figure

3). This translucent area is generally devoid of any structure. Occasionally, 200- to 300-A fibrils are seen to extend around or through the clear area.

As seen in the electron microscope, the secondary constriction and satellite-bearing regions were similar to the images observed with the light microscope, but were much clearer in detail. Figure 3 shows autosome No. 9 with its typical secondary constriction in the proximal region of the long arm and a D-group autosome with prominent stalks and satellites.

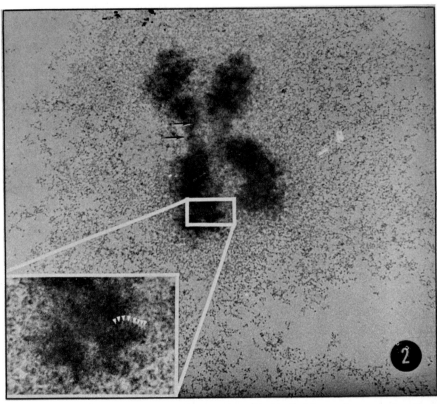

FIGURE 2. Electron micrograph showing fibrils in kinetochore region (arrows). Inset shows substructures arranged in supercoils within the fibrils.

FIGURE 3. No. 9 chromosome showing kinetochore (K) and secondary constriction (SC). Note the detailed satellites in the D chromosome.

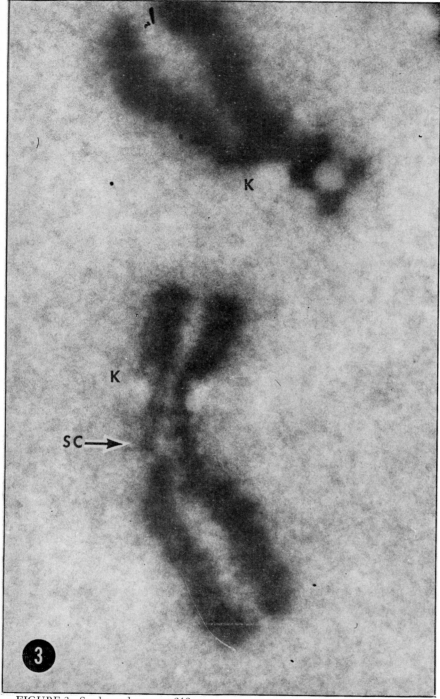

FIGURE 3: See legend on page 318.

The telomeres or terminal regions of human chromosomes exhibited no unusual structure. In some preparations, fine threads appeared to loop out at the telomere region; occasionally, telomeric association was seen to involve fine strands extending from the tip of one chromosome to constrictions, breaks, or telomeres of other chromosomes.

Thin Sections of Rat Kangaroo Chromosomes

Ultrathin sections of rat kangaroo chromosomes fail to show detailed

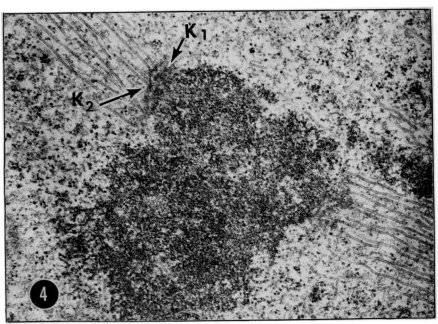

FIGURE 4. Thin section of rat kangaroo chromosome showing spindle tubules attached to the kinetochore elements (K_1 and K_2). (Courtesy of Brinkley and Stubblefield, 1969.)

FIGURE 5. Thin section of a rat kangaroo cell during metaphase. Note nucleolus organizer (NO), or secondary constriction, on the X chromosome; also note the kinetochore (K) and centriole (C). (Courtesy of Hsu, Brinkley, and Arrighi, 1967.)

FIGURE 6. Higher magnification of nucleolus organizer seen in Figure 5. Axial elements (A), less dense fibrous loops (F), and spindle tubules (S) are evident. (Courtesy of Hsu, Brinkley, and Arrighi, 1967.)

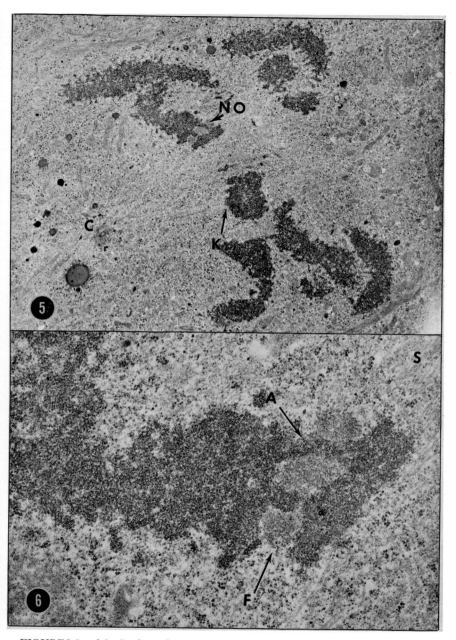

FIGURES 5 and 6: See legends on page 320.

structural organization in the more condensed regions of the chromosome arms. In most sections, coarse fibers 800 to 1,000 A in diameter appear to be the most consistent component. However, in special regions such as the kinetochore and nucleolus organizer, fibers 50 to 70 A, 200 to 300 A, and 400 to 500 A can be seen. Although sectioned chromosomes appear multistranded, there seems to be little order to the strandedness; the division of chromatids into half-chromatids or smaller units is not readily apparent in sectioned metaphase preparations. Frequently, an indication of major coiling is evident along the outer surface of the chromatids.

In addition to the fibrillar components of the arms, numerous granules often are seen embedded in the chromosome arms. These measure 250 to 500 A in diameter and are similar to perichromatin granules seen in nuclei in interphase. In addition, 150- to 180-A granules (assumed to be ribosomes) often are found in close apposition to the chromosome.

The Primary Constriction (Kinetochore). The kinetochores in rat kangaroo cells, clearly defined by the attachment of chromosomal spindle fibrils, are structurally identical to those described in HeLa cells (Robbins and Gonatas, 1964), Chinese hamster cells (Brinkley and Stubblefield, 1966), and mouse embryonic cells (Jokelainen, 1967). Essentially, they consist of two components: a densely stained axial element and less dense lateral loops (Figure 4). Each axial element consists of a pair of microfibrils, each 50 to 80 A in diameter, which extends along the chromosome for a distance of up to 0.5 μ. As in Chinese hamster cells, serial section analysis indicates that two axial elements (K_1 and K_2) (Figure 4) exist on each chromatid. The lateral loops extend perpendicularly from the axial elements to form a lampbrush-type organization. The spindle fibrils extend from the axial elements toward the centrioles at the poles (Figure 4). Details concerning the formation and fate of the kinetochore throughout mitosis in rat kangaroo cells is the subject of a review by Brinkley and Stubblefield (1969).

Except for the specialized structures described above, all other structures seen in the kinetochore region, or primary constriction, consisted of fibrils and granules like those described in the chromosome arms.

The Secondary Constriction (Nucleolus Organizer). The secondary constriction, or nucleolus organizer, in the rat kangaroo cell is located near the kinetochore on the long arm of the submetacentric X chromosome (Shaw and Krooth, 1964). Hsu, Brinkley, and Arrighi (1967) have recently described the ultrastructure of this region in a combined phase and electron microscope study. Figure 5 shows the secondary constriction in a cell at metaphase. Like the kinetochore, it also consists of a dense axial core and less dense fibrils. The axial core, however, is much thicker in the secondary constriction, measuring 800 to 1,000 A in greatest diameter. The less dense fibrils form a spherical "puff" on all sides of the axial core. A higher magnification of the secondary constriction seen in Figure 5 is shown in Figure 6. This region can be identified from prophase to telophase and serves as an excellent ultrastructural marker for the X chromosome in these cells.

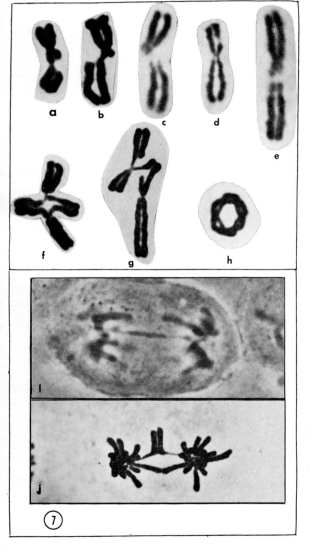

FIGURE 7. Light microscopy i m a g e s of chromatid breaks (a and b), isochromatid breaks (c), gaps (d and e), exchanges (f and g), rings (h), dicentric bridge (i), and side-arm bridge (j). The anaphase bridges are from rat kangaroo fibroblasts.

Telomeres. The telomeres of sectioned rat kangaroo chromosomes exhibit no unusual structural characteristics. Nucleolus organizer-like bodies seen on the ends of some Chinese hamster chromosomes (see Figure 8 in Hsu, Brinkley, and Arrighi, 1967) were not observed in rat kangaroo chromosomes.

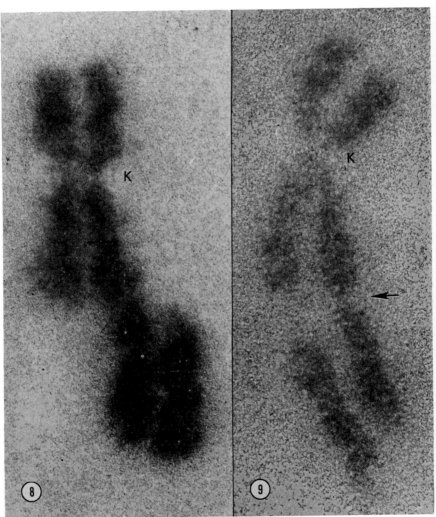

FIGURE 8. Unaligned chromatid break. Note prominent kinetochore (K).

FIGURE 9. Aligned chromatid break. Arrow points to weak point in sister chromatid.

THE ULTRASTRUCTURE OF CHROMOSOME ABERRATIONS

The most common types of induced or spontaneous aberrations seen by light microscopy are shown in Figure 7. These include breaks (Figure 7a, b, and c), gaps (Figure 7d and e), exchanges (Figure 7f and g), rings (Figure 7h), and bridges (Figure 7i and j). It was possible to examine most of the same types of aberrations in both whole chromosomes and ultrathin sections with the electron microscope.

Breaks

Figures 8, 9, and 10 show three typical breaks viewed with the electron microscope in unsectioned, unstained chromosomes from human beings. Ultrathin sections of broken fragments of rat kangaroo chromosomes are shown in Figures 11 and 16. In every case, there is a complete lack of structural continuity between the broken ends. Figures 8 and 10 are examples of unaligned breaks. In Figure 8, the terminal fragment is broken and "flipped over," but still in proximity to the sister chromatid. The distal fragments usually appear to be attached to the isologous region of the sister chromatid by the same interchromatid connections which bind undamaged chromatids. Unfortunately, the broken ends are not characterized by any observable structural features which might distinguish them from the telomeres of undamaged chromosomes. However, we know from genetic analysis that broken ends are unstable and "sticky" and tend to restitute (heal) or combine with other broken ends, whereas telomeres do not attach to broken ends or to other telomeres.

An aligned break is shown in Figure 9. In such damage, the broken ends remain aligned, but no fibers traverse the intervening broken region. Using the light microscope, such aberrations probably would be considered gaps.

Figure 11 is a phase and electron micrograph of a cultured rat kangaroo cell which received 500 rads of X-irradiation eight hours before fixation. Numerous acentric fragments resulting from chromatid and isochromatid deletions are seen on the equatorial plate. One fragment of the X chromosome (Figure 11a, arrow) is broken at the secondary constriction. A small portion of the nucleolus organizer is seen at the broken end (Figure 11b). Four serial sections of this region show both the axial element and the less dense fibrous material which surrounds the axial element, which is also present in the normal nucleolus organizer.

It was evident in many micrographs, such as the one shown in Figure 11, that acentric fragments were still somewhat aligned on the metaphase plate although the cell was already in anaphase. Their inability to move to the poles is generally thought to be caused by the absence of a kineto-chore. In this study, numerous deleted fragments were examined in serial sections. All were truly acentric in that they lacked a kinetochore and were not attached to spindle fibers in any way. The manner in which

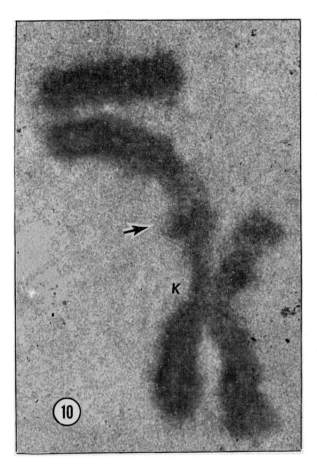

FIGURE 10. A break in chromosome C. As in Figure 9, arrow points to damaged area in the sister chromatid.

FIGURE 11. a—Rat kangaroo cell in anaphase after 500 rads of X-irradiation. Note numerous fragments still aligned on metaphase plate. Arrow points to a fragment of the X chromosome. b—Electron micrograph of the same cell. Arrow points to X chromosome fragment containing a piece of the nucleolus organizer. c through f—Serial sections of the same region which show both the axial element and the less dense fibrous material which surround the axial element. (Courtesy of Humphrey and Brinkley, 1969.)

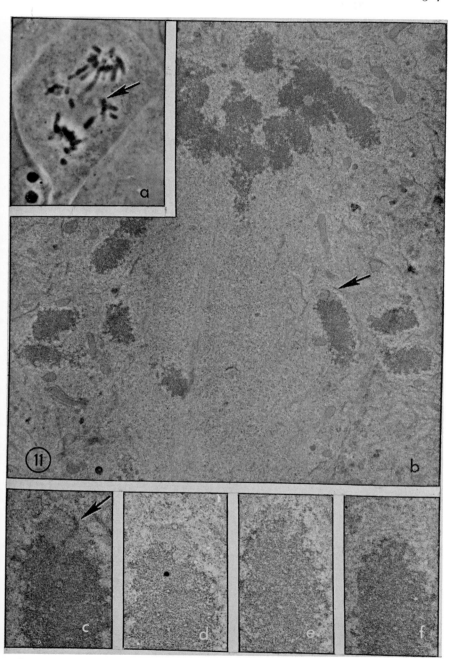

FIGURE 11: See legend on page 326.

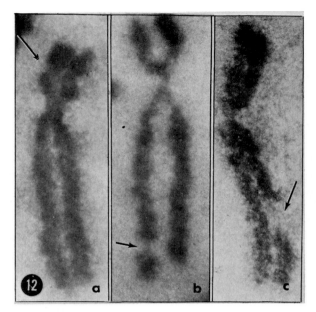

FIGURE 12. a-c — Chromatid gaps (arrows) in chromosomes from three human beings. The gap in c may have been scored as a break in the light microscopy analysis since one broken end appears unaligned.

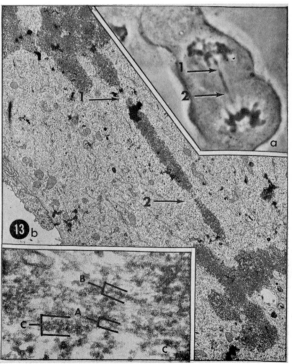

FIGURE 13. An anaphase bridge seen with both the phase (a) and electron microscopes (b-c). Arrows 1 and 2 point to gaps in the bridge. A higher magnification of the gap indicated by arrow 1 is shown in c. Microfibrils ranging from 50 to 70 A (A), 200 to 250 A (B), and 500 to 800 A (C) are indicated. (Courtesy of Humphrey and B r i n k l e y, 1969.)

the fragment arrives at the metaphase plate during metakinesis is not understood since prometaphase movement requires kinetochore function (Bajer, personal communication; Harris, 1965). It is possible that interchromatid connections serve to guide a chromatid fragment to the equatorial plate, but there is no simple explanation in the case of an isochromatid or of a chromosome break.

Gaps or Achromatic Lesions

Numerous gaps were evident in the chromosomes of both human lymphocytes and rat kangaroo fibroblasts after treatment with mitomycin C, ^{3}H-TdR, and ionizing radiation. In the light microscope, these lesions may or may not show structural continuity. When the same regions were viewed in the electron microscope, some were seen to be clean breaks (Figure 1) whereas others were structurally continuous but had eroded regions in the chromatids.

Figure 12 shows chromatid gaps of differing intensities. In Figure 12a, a weak isolocus gap is present on the short arm of a B group chromosome. Such a faint region may or may not be detectable with the light microscope. In Figure 12b, a B chromosome exhibits a more typical chromatid gap in the terminal region of the long arm. A fine strand appears to connect the two segments across the gap. The gap in Figure 12c is perhaps more instructive. Here the criterion of light microscopy for a break is met (*i.e.* unalignment), but fibrous connections are still seen between the two broken ends. Even though the distance between the involved element is great and one of the broken ends appears unaligned, fibrous connections exist.

Serial section analysis of gaps provides suggestive evidence that the chromosome is multistranded. Figure 13a-c shows gaps in bridges formed during anaphase. Two gaps are shown in both phase (Figure 13a) and electron (Figure 13b) micrographs (arrows). The gap indicated by arrow 1 consists of three classes of microfibrils when examined at higher magnification (Figure 13c). Class A fibrils measured 50 to 80 A in diameter, whereas class B fibrils measured 200 to 250 A. A third, coarser fibril, C, measured 500 to 800 A. These measurements suggest that the B and C fibrils may be second and third order supercoils of the A fibril. Alternate types of organization also can be proposed. Experiments are now underway to determine the organization and molecular composition of the microfibrils.

In greatly attenuated gaps such as those shown in Figure 14, the chromosome often appears double. Doubleness of the chromatid has been reported in numerous light microscope studies, but chromatid substructure rarely is seen in electron micrographs of sectioned material.

Figure 15 shows a near-tetraploid rat kangaroo cell in which nu-

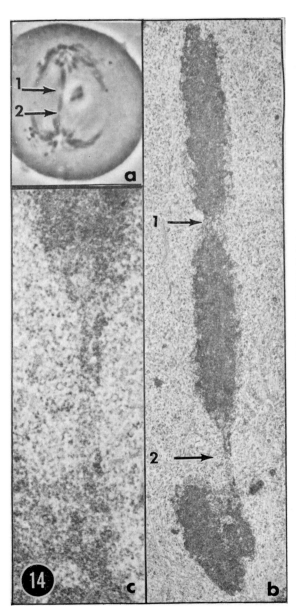

FIGURE 14. Light (a) and electron (b and c) micrographs of an anaphase bridge showing two gaps (arrows 1 and 2). The gap indicated by arrow 2 appears bipartite (b and c). (Courtesy of Humphrey and Brinkley, 1969.)

merous chromatid and isochromatid lesions are evident (arrows). This cell was treated with mitomycin C, but did not receive colchicine or Colcemid before fixation. The cell is also tetrapolar, and the positions of

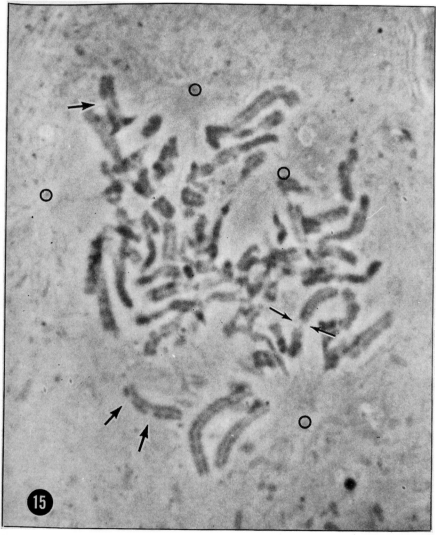

FIGURE 15. Near-tetraploid rat kangaroo cell after treatment with mito-mycin C. The cell is also tetrapolar (circles indicate centriole position). Both chromatid gaps (large arrows) and isochromatid gaps (small arrows) are seen in the preparation which was fixed and embedded in situ.

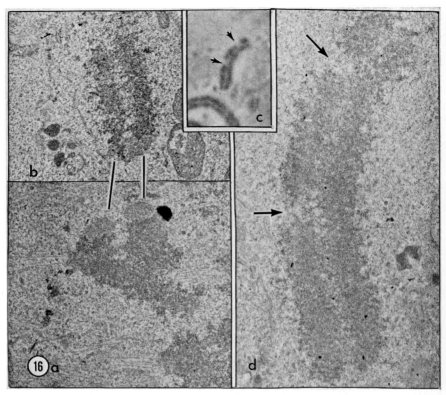

FIGURE 16. X chromosome in a rat kangaroo cell broken by mitomycin C, as shown by electron (a, b, and d) and light (c) microscopy. Chromatid gaps (arrows) are also evident on the acentric fragment (c and d). The black and white bars (a and b) indicate region of break showing part of the nucleolus organizer.

the centrioles are indicated by circles. The damaged chromosomes in Figure 15 are shown after ultrathin sectioning in Figures 16 through 19. In Figure 17, microfibrils 50 to 80 A (class A) and 400 to 800 A (class C) in size are seen extending across the gap; these are seen in greater detail in Figure 18. Analysis of 10 serial sections indicated that the two chromatid gaps in Figure 13 contained microfibrils similar to those in Figures 17 and 18.

Serial sections of the chromosome shown in Figures 15 and 16 also indicated that the damage to this chromosome was actually an acentric fragment or isochromatid deletion of the long arm of the X chromosome. The break passed through the secondary constriction. The kinetochore-bearing short arm containing a small portion of the secondary constriction was found several microns away from the long acentric fragment of the long arm. The microtubular attachment of the kinetochores of the short arm fragment to the spindle is evident in Figure 16a. The deleted long arm was free of spindle attachment. Again, as in Figure 11, the fine structure of the nucleolus organizer appears the same as in undamaged

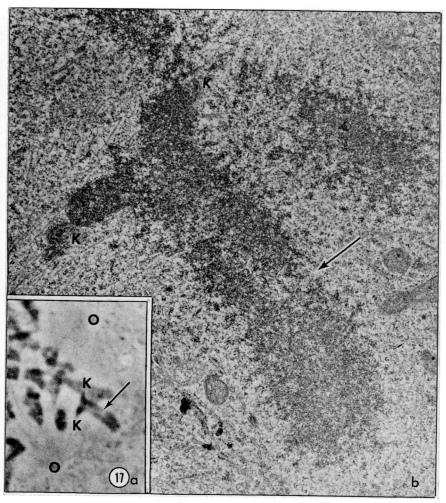

FIGURE 17. Light (a) and electron (b) micrographs of a chromatid gap (arrows) in a rat kangaroo chromosome. Kinetochores (K) are seen in both micrographs. Circles indicate centriole position.

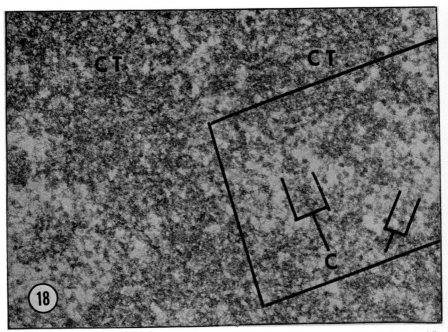

FIGURE 18. Higher magnification of the chromosome shown in Figure 17. Both A and C fibrils are seen in the region near the gap. Chromatids are indicated by CT.

chromosomes even though the break passed through the middle of the structure.

An isochromatid gap is shown in Figure 19a and b (arrows). The arms of the chromosome are continuous across the gap because of fine fibrous connections. Although a constriction is produced, it is unlike the nucleolus organizer constriction (compared with Figures 5, 6, 24, 25, and 26). In the light microscope, isolocus gaps often resemble nucleolus organizers. Both, however, are structurally weak areas in comparison with the more condensed regions of the arms. This weakness may account for the fact that both isolocus gaps and secondary constrictions are broken easily during slide preparation (Evans, 1961).

Exchanges and Anaphase Bridges

A chromatid exchange induced by mitomycin C is shown in Figure 20. The exchange occurred between the chromatids of two homologous chromosomes and could be considered an "alternate symmetrical" or "class I" exchange as proposed by Shaw and Cohen (1965). The exceptionally clear interchromatid connections argue convincingly for the occurrence of true exchange of genetic material rather than homolog association. In the regions of the exchange, some breaks remained open

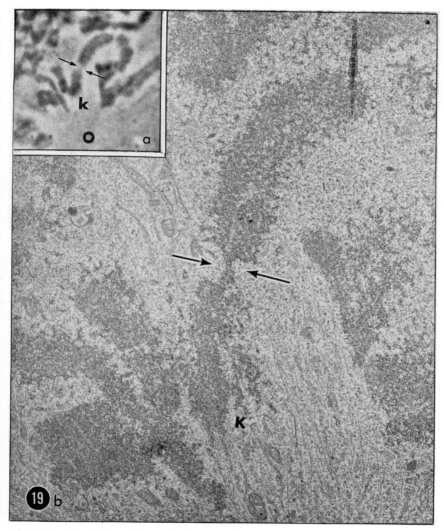

FIGURE 19. Light (a) and electron (b) micrographs of an isolocus gap (arrows) in a rat kangaroo chromosome treated with mitomycin C. Circle indicates centriole position.

while others were healed. The isolocus unexchanged regions frequently showed erosions or weak spots.

Breaks followed by proximal chromatid reunion result in dicentric formation, whereas distal chromatid healing leads to acentric fragments. These aberrations produce bridges and fragments during anaphase,

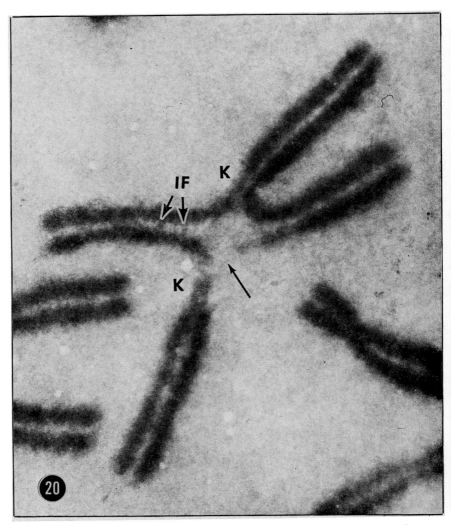

FIGURE 20. A quadriradial exchange between two No. 1 human chromosomes. Arrow points to broken region. Interchromatid connections (IF) and kinetochores (K) can also be identified.

whether the exchange is between sister chromatids (intrachange) or between chromatids of different chromosomes (interchange). The latter refers to both homologous and nonhomologous exchanges. Anaphase bridges are shown in Figures 13 and 14.

A second type of anaphase bridge is shown in Figures 21 and 22. These are the so-called "side-arm" bridges which have been reported in both plant (Crouse, 1954; La Cour and Rutishauser, 1954; Heddle, in preparation) and animal cells (Whissel-Buechy, personal communication; Brinkley and Humphrey, 1969). These configurations occur most frequently in cells which received radiation in the late G2 period or the beginning of prophase. In our own study, 39 of 100 rat kangaroo cells in anaphase fixed 30 minutes after irradiation with 250 rads exhibited one to three side-arm bridges (Brinkley and Humphrey, 1969).

Although a bridge or connection is implied by the abrupt bending of the chromosome arms, such connections are seldom evident in the light microscope. Nevertheless, several investigators have interpreted side-arm bridges to indicate an exchange involving subunits of the chromatids (see discussion by Evans, 1962). Such an interpretation favors the multi-stranded hypothesis of chromosome structure.

Although the difficulty of demonstrating the physical existence of side-arm bridges in thin sections is obvious because of their delicate nature, Mr. Joiner Cartwright, Jr., of our laboratory, has been successful in serially sectioning several such bridges. Figures 21 and 22 show phase and electron micrographs of side-arm bridges. In each case, a definite strand not visible in the phase image is evident in the electron micrographs. The bridge obviously is made up of a strand smaller than the chromatid. In fact, in Figure 23b, an unstretched bridge appears to be continuous with a fibrous component approximately half the diameter of the chromatid. The bridge shown in Figures 21a and 23a is considerably more attenuated than the one seen in Figures 22a and 23b.

Damage to Special Regions

The kinetochore, nucleolus organizer, and telomeres are genetically and structurally differentiated regions on the chromosome which often are damaged by physical, chemical, and viral agents. For this reason, we were particularly interested in the ultrastructure of these regions and the damage which could be detected with the electron microscope.

Figures 24 and 25 show greatly attenuated nucleolus organizers of the X chromosome in the rat kangaroo following X-irradiation with 250 rads. For comparison, the same region of an untreated chromosome is

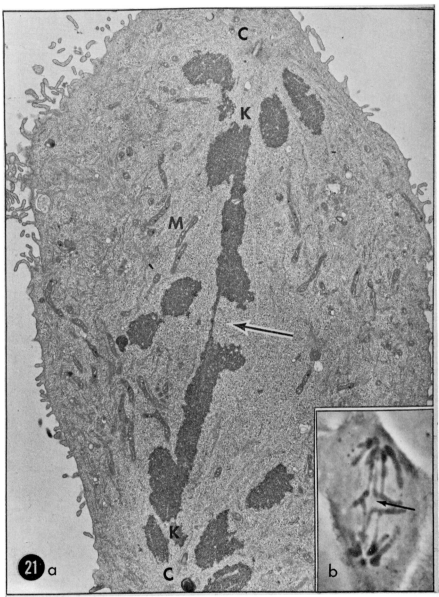

FIGURE 21. Electron (a) and light (b) micrographs of anaphase cell showing a side-arm bridge (arrows). Also seen are centrioles (C), kinetochores
(K), and mitochondria (M). (Courtesy of Brinkley and Humphrey, 1969.)

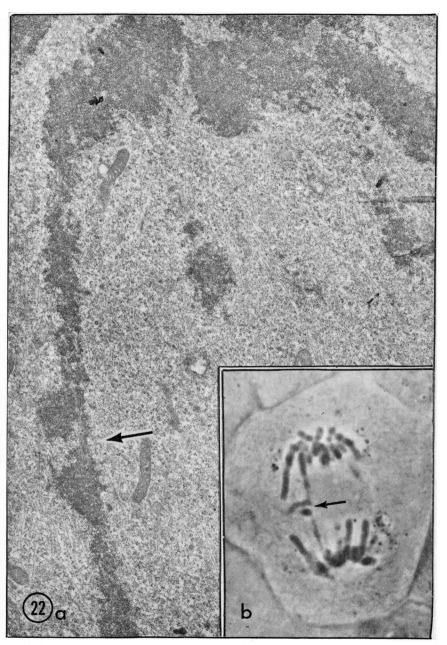

FIGURE 22. Electron (a) and light (b) micrographs of side-arm bridge (arrows). (Courtesy of Brinkley and Humphrey, 1969.)

shown in Figure 26. Breaks in the secondary constriction (as shown in Figures 11 and 16) already have been mentioned.

The kinetochore region, as suggested previously by Nowell (1964) from light microscope studies, often appears damaged after treatment with mitomycin C. A normal kinetochore is shown in Figure 27. Figure 28 shows a higher magnification of a kinetochore in which the axial ele-

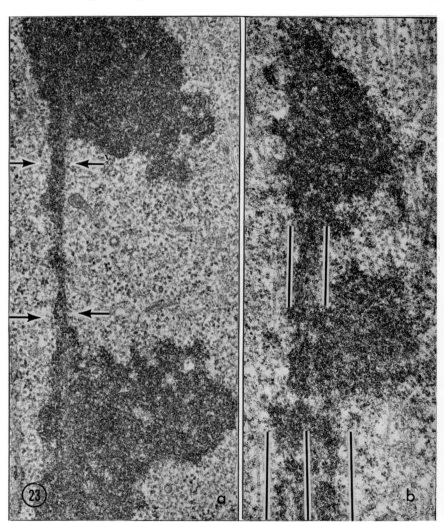

FIGURE 23. Higher magnifications of the subchromatid bridges shown in Figures 21 and 22. The three black and white bars in b indicate two half-chromatids, one of which appears to be continuous with the bridge.

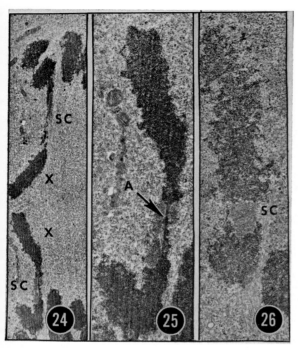

FIGURES 24 and 25. X chromosomes of a rat kangaroo cell in anaphase which were X-irradiated with 250 rads. Note attenuated secondary constriction (SC) showing both axial element (A) and less dense filaments. (Courtesy of Humphrey and B r i n k l e y, 1969.)

FIGURE 26. The same region as seen in Figures 24 and 25 of an untreated chromosome which has a normal secondary constriction. (Courtesy of Humphrey and B r i n k l e y, 1969.)

ments (K_1 and K_2) are extended from the chromosome body. Serial sections of this chromosome indicate that the axial elements are broken and greatly distorted. It is interesting that numerous spindle tubules appear to be associated with the kinetochore, even though it has been damaged.

Summary

The present study has extended the observations of the more common chromosome aberrations to the electron microscope level. The results are summarized in Table 1. Although some aspects of damage observed in this manner were in agreement with descriptions derived from light microscope studies, the following important exceptions were noted:

1. Some aberrations which would have been considered breaks with the light microscope were found to be structurally continuous. This was true even of so-called "aligned" breaks.
2. Perhaps of lesser importance was the observation that structures which would have been scored as gaps with the light microscope were in fact clean breaks. (Together, the first two observations suggest that it may be hazardous to quantitate chromosome damage in metaphase-arrested cells with the light microscope.)

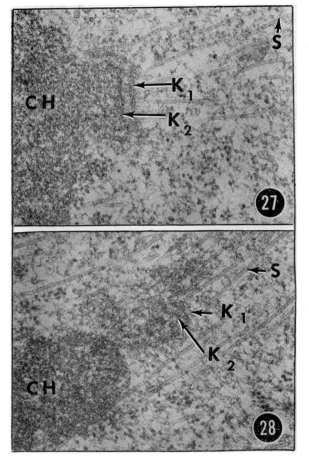

FIGURE 27. Normal kinetochore structure at metaphase showing spindle tubules (S) and axial elements (K_1 and K_2). The chromosome is indicated by CH.

FIGURE 28. Kinetochore damaged by mitomycin C treatment. The axial elements (K_1 and K_2) are distorted and pulled away from the chromosome (CH). Spindle tubules (S) are still associated with the kinetochore.

3. Serial section analysis of gaps suggests that chromosome fibrils are composed of three orders of supercoiling. The smallest fibrils measured 50 to 80 A and could not be composed of more than two DNA-histone complexes.
4. Division of chromatids into bipartite units, or half-chromatids, was evident in some gaps.
5. The existence of side-arm bridges or subchromatid exchanges was confirmed by thin section analysis, and their relationship to chromosome strandedness was discussed.

We conclude, therefore, that the chromosome is multistranded with each chromatid divided into at least half-chromatids. These, in turn, may consist of class A microfibrils (50 to 70 A) supercoiled into class B fibrils (200 to 250 A). Class B fibrils may be supercoiled further to form class C fibrils (500 to 800 A). Further investigations concerning the structure and chemical composition of chromatid subunits are under way.

ACKNOWLEDGMENTS

This work was supported in part by United States Public Health Service Grants GM-15887 and GM-15361. The authors would like to thank Mr. Joiner Cartwright, Jr., Mrs. B. A. Sedita, Miss Patricia Murphy, Miss Muriel Melcher, and Miss Ann Craig for their technical assistance.

TABLE 1. *Comparative Aspects of Chromosome Damage Observed with Light and Electron Microscopy*

Type of damage	Light microscope	Electron microscope
I. Breaks		
A. Aligned	Apparent structural discontinuity, broken ends aligned	1. True structural discontinuity, broken ends aligned, sister chromatid connections 2. True structural continuity
B. Unaligned	Apparent structural discontinuity, broken ends unaligned	1. True structural discontinuity, broken ends unaligned, sister chromatid connections 2. True structural continuity
II. Gaps		

A. Chromatid	Achromatic lesions with apparent structural continuity	1. True structural continuity
		  a. 50–80 A fibrils
		  b. 200–250 A fibrils
		  c. 500–800 A fibrils
		2. True structural discontinuity

B. Isochromatid	Achromatic with apparent structural continuity; may appear like exaggerated secondary constrictions or nucleolus organizer regions	True structural continuity, but not like nucleolus organizers
III. Bridges		
A. Chromosome	Dicentric with chromosome stretched across metaphase plate	Same as light microscope except stretched regions often double revealing half-chromatids
B. Side-arm	Stickiness at sharply bent regions of anaphase arms; apparent structural continuity between associated arms	Same as light microscope except true structural continuity of half-chromatid

REFERENCES

Bajer, A. Personal communication.

Brinkley, B. R., and R. M. Humphrey. 1969. Evidence for Subchromatid Organization in Mammalian Chromosomes. I. Light and Electron Microscopy of X-Ray Induced Side-Arm Bridges. *Journal of Cell Biology*, 42:827–831.

Brinkley, B. R., P. Murphy, and L. C. Richardson. 1967. Procedure for Embedding In Situ Selected Cells Cultured In Vitro. *Journal of Cell Biology*, 35:279–283.

Brinkley, B. R., and E. Stubblefield. 1966. The Fine Structure of the Kinetochore of Chinese Hamster Cells In Vitro. *Chromosoma*, 19:28–43.

———. 1969. "The Kinetochore and Centriole in Mitosis and Meiosis," *Advances in Cell Biology*, D. Prescott, Ed. New York, New York: Appleton-Century-Crofts. Pp. 119–185.

Busby, N., R. A. Turner, and D. K. Roberts. 1967. A Serial Sectioning Method for Electron Microscopy. (Abstract) *Journal of Cell Biology*, 35:19A.

Crouse, H. V. 1954. X-Ray Breakage of Lily Chromosomes at First Meiotic Metaphase. *Science*, 119:485–487.

Cuevas-Sosa, A. 1967. Crossing-Over and the Centromere. *Cytogenetics*, 6:331–341.

Dupraw, E. J. 1965. The Organization of Nuclei and Chromosomes in Honeybee Embryonic Cells. *Proceedings of the National Academy of Sciences of the U.S.A.*, 53:161–168.

Evans, H. J. 1961. Chromatid Aberrations Induced by Gamma Irradiation. I. The Structure and Frequency of Chromatid Interchanges in Diploid and Tetraploid Cells of *Vicia faba*. *Genetics*, 46:257–275.

Evans, H. J. 1962. "Chromosome Aberrations Induced by Ionizing Radiations," *International Review of Cytology*, G. H. Bourne and J. F. Danielli, Eds. New York, New York: Academic Press, Inc. Pp. 221–321.

Harris, P. J. 1965. Some Observations Concerning Metakinesis in Sea Urchin Eggs. *Journal of Cell Biology*, 25 (Supplement on Mitosis): 73–77.

Heddle, J. A. 1968. The Strandedness of Chromosomes: Evidence from Chromosomal Aberrations. (in preparation.)

Hsu, T. C., B. R. Brinkley, and F. A. Arrighi. 1967. The Structure and Behavior of the Nucleolus Organizers in Mammalian Cells. *Chromosoma*, 23:137–153.

Humphrey, R. M., and B. R. Brinkley. 1969. Ultrastructural Studies of Radiation-Induced Chromosome Damage. *Journal of Cell Biology*, 42:745–753.

Jokelainen, P. T. 1967. The Ultrastructure and Spatial Organization of the Metaphase Kinetochore in Mitotic Rat Cells. *Journal of Ultrastructure Research*, 19:19–44.

La Cour, L. F., and A. Rutishauser. 1954. X-Ray Breakage Experiments with Endosperm. I. Sub-Chromatid Breakage. *Chromosoma*, 6:696–709.

Moorhead, P. S., P. C. Nowell, W. J. Mellman, D. M. Battips, and D. A. Hungerford. 1960. Chromosome Preparations of Leukocytes Cultured from Human Peripheral Blood. *Experimental Cell Research*, 20:613–616.

Nowell, P. C. 1964. Mitotic Inhibition and Chromosome Damage by Mitomycin in Human Leukocyte Cultures. *Experimental Cell Research*, 33:445–449.

Ris, H. 1967. "Ultrastructure of the Animal Chromosome," *Regulation of Nucleic Acid and Protein Biosynthesis*, V. V. Koningsberger and L. Bosch, Eds. Amsterdam, The Netherlands: Elsevier Publishing Co.; New York, New York: American

Elsevier Publishing Co., Inc.; and London, England: Elsevier Publishing Co., Ltd. Pp. 11–21.

Robbins, E., and N. K. Gonatas. 1964. The Ultrastructure of a Mammalian Cell During the Mitotic Cycle. *Journal of Cell Biology*, 21:429–463.

Shaw, M. W., B. R. Brinkley, and L. E. Schwab. 1969. Electron Microscopy of Human Chromosomes: General Methods. (in preparation.)

Shaw, M. W., and M. M. Cohen. 1965. Chromosome Exchanges in Human Leukocytes Induced by Mitomycin C. *Genetics*, 51:181–190.

Shaw, M. W., and R. S. Krooth. 1964. The Chromosomes of the Tasmanian Rat-Kangaroo (*Potorous tridactylis apicalis*). *Cytogenetics*, 3:19–33.

Whissel-Buechy, D. Y. E. Personal communication.

Wolfe, S. L. 1965. The Fine Structure of Isolated Chromosomes. *Journal of Ultrastructure Research*, 12:104–112.

Discussion

Dr. Ernest H. Y. Chu, Oak Ridge National Laboratory, Oak Ridge, Tennessee: Dr. Brinkley's study certainly extends chromosome aberration analysis to a new level of sophistication. However, his implication that such analysis under the light microscope is inadequate is not entirely true. Certain types of aberrations such as exchanges are recognizable unmistakably even with the light microscope. Also, Dr. Brinkley's study illustrates only too well what Revell would have called "gaps" instead of chromatid breaks as Dr. Brinkley labeled them. Further, one can sometimes see the connecting strand within a gap under the light microscope.

Effects of Radiation and Other Agents on the Molecular Structure and Organization of the Chromosome

ARTHUR COLE, PETER M. CORRY,* AND
RUTHANN LANGLEY

Department of Physics, The University of Texas M. D. Anderson Hospital and Tumor Institute at Houston, Houston, Texas

A model of metaphase chromosome structure based on light micro-scopic, electron microscopic, and ultracentrifugation studies (Somers, Cole, and Hsu, 1963; Cole and Somers-Cronenwett, 1964; Cole and Langley, 1965, 1966; Cole, 1967; Corry and Cole, 1968) has been pro-posed by one of the authors (Cole, 1967). The model suggests that two double-stranded deoxyribonucleic acid (DNA) molecules associate with histone protein and twist around each other to produce an 80- to 100-A fiber; two such fibers then cohelically associate to form a 200-A fiber. Possibly, a further association of specific protein with an elemental fiber, as described above, leads ultimately to the condensed structure of the metaphase chromatid; the packing arrangement for the condensed struc-ture could be similar to that produced by a doubling over-twisting up sequence of a single fiber.

Although these suggestions are considered tentative, they have proved useful in the planning of various investigations, including a study on the effects of various agents on chromosome structure and function. One objective of these studies is to achieve an understanding of the type or size of elemental units (mainly DNA and proteins) that make up the chromosome, the types of associations or molecular bonds involved in basic arrangements, and the form of the three-dimensional architecture involved in the complete structure. A second objective is to understand more fully the mechanism of action of the various agents, particularly radiation.

Materials and Methods

Intact mitotic chromosomes used in these studies were isolated from

---

* Present Address: Department of Radiology, Royal Victoria Hospital, Montreal, Quebec, Canada.

Chinese hamster B14 and Don C cells using methods reported previously (Somers, Cole, and Hsu, 1963; Corry and Cole, 1968). In brief, cells grown in culture were subjected to two- to three-hour Colcemid mitotic arrest, shaken off the glass culture vessels, washed, suspended in a hypotonic lysing solution containing mainly 0.005 M Mg^{++} SO_4, and ruptured by some 10 strokes of a Dounce homogenizer. The suspended metaphase chromosomes were partially purified by low-speed sedimentation of the lysate through a sucrose gradient and collection of the middle fractions.

In the ultracentrifuge sedimentation studies (Corry and Cole, 1968), the original cells were grown for 16 to 20 hours in media containing tritiated thymidine (^{3}H-TdR) to label the chromosomes. Subsequently, the purified chromosome fraction was layered carefully on top of a sucrose density gradient containing mainly 5 M NaCl (pH 9.6) to dissociate the protein from the DNA components. Sedimentation was done for 14 to 18 hours at 24,000 rpm at 20 C. Subsequently, fractions of the gradient were collected and the measured radioactivity was utilized to specify the distribution of the DNA.

In light and electron microscope studies, drops of the chromosome preparation were placed either on formvar-covered specimen grids on glass slides or directly on glass slides for light microscope work. The chromosomes were allowed to settle for at least 10 minutes and subsequently were subjected to a treatment sequence consisting of (1) temporarily fixing a cover slip over the specimen and flushing various solutions between the glass slide and cover slip while observing the effects by light microscopy or (2) carrying the specimen grid directly through a series of treatment baths. In the work reported in this paper, final treatments for electron microscopic studies consisted of 0.2 per cent uranyl acetate staining followed by Anderson's critical point drying (T. F. Anderson, 1956). Most of the electron microscope work was done using a stereo technique which utilizes a specially built tilting specimen holder. A Hitachi HU-11A electron microscope was used in these studies.

Ultracentrifuge Studies

Only a brief description of the ultracentrifuge studies will be given in this paper since most of this work has been presented elsewhere (Corry and Cole, 1968).

Figure 1 illustrates a typical sedimentation pattern for native DNA isolated from intact chromosomes. The basic gradient contained 5 M NaCl, 0.1 M Na_2SO_4, 0.025 M ethylenediaminetetraacetate (EDTA), and 5 to 28 per cent sucrose concentration by weight. The pH was adjusted to 9.6.

These conditions were selected to inhibit deoxyribonuclease activity. The sucrose gradient was prepared as an exponential constant sedimentation velocity type (Noll, 1967). The sedimentation velocity corresponding to the peak of the DNA distribution for 26 similar controls was found at 68.2 ± 3.5 Svedberg units. Using Studier's relationship (Studier, 1965), the corresponding molecular weight was $224 \times 10^6 \pm 32 \times 10^6$ daltons. This corresponds to a length of about 120 μm for double-stranded DNA. Figures 2 and 3 illustrate sedimentation patterns obtained when either 0.1 M mercaptoethanol, which reduces S-S bonds (Figure 2), or 0.05 M hydroxylamine, which cleaves amino acid ester linkages (Figure 3), was included in the gradient. Since the control patterns were not altered significantly by these reagents, it appears that the sedimented DNA strands cannot be made up of smaller subunits which are joined by S-S, ester, or salt linkages (salt or ionic linkages would be dissociated by the 5 M salt present in all gradients). Based on these and other studies, it appears that the DNA molecules in the hamster chromosome consist mainly of segments from 10 to several hundred microns long. If large numbers of longer molecules normally exist in the chromosome as has been reported by other workers (Lett, Caldwell, Dean, and Alexander, 1967; Cairns, 1966; Sasaki and Norman, 1966), such molecules must be unstable in the experimental conditions used in our studies.

Depending on the particular experimental situation, from five to 50 per cent of the DNA activity sedimented to the bottom of the centri-

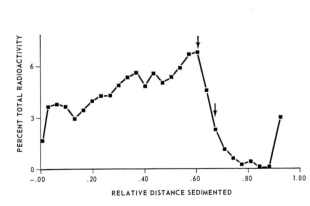

FIGURE 1. Typical sedimentation pattern for double-stranded DNA from metaphase chromosomes. The sedimentation was performed for 14 hours at 24,000 rev/min at 20 C in a Beckman SW 25.1 rotor using an exponential sucrose gradient (5 to 28 per cent by weight) containing 5 M NaCl, 0.1 M Na_2SO_4, 0.025 M EDTA at pH 9.6. The sedimentation constant ($S_{20,w}$) at the peak of the distribution was 65.4.

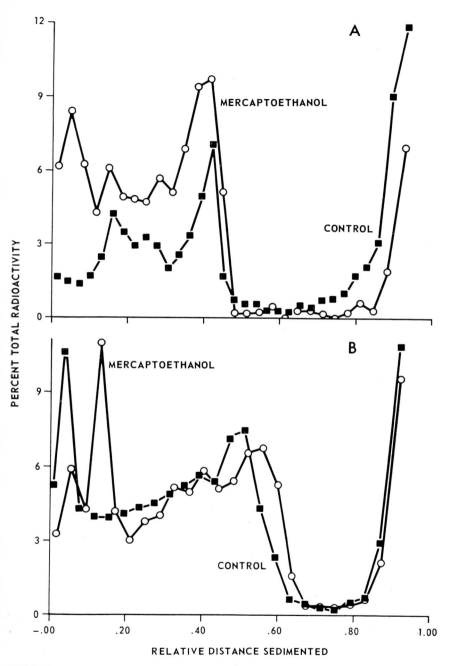

FIGURE 2. DNA sedimentation patterns with and without 0.1 M mercaptoethanol included in the gradients. Sedimentation time was 8 hours in a and
12 hours in b.

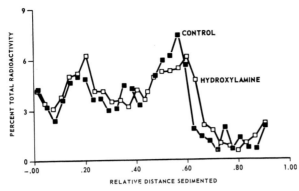

FIGURE 3. The DNA sedimentation patterns with and without 0.05 M hydroxylamine included in the gradients. Sedimentation time was 14 hours.

fuge tube; this would implicate associated molecular weights greater than 3×10^9 daltons. It is believed, however, that this material consists largely of entangled or loosely associated DNA strands of a molecular weight of about 100 to 200×10^6 daltons. This belief is based on the fact that, when part of this DNA was prevented from sedimenting to the bottom (e.g., when mercaptoethanol was included in the gradient or in the radiation studies which will be described later in this paper), the corresponding activity always reappeared in the region of the original peak of 68 Svedberg units. No appreciable activity was observed in the region between 75 and 90 Svedberg units. A detailed computer analysis of the way in which radiation degraded the distributions (and eliminated sedimentation to the bottom) implied that most of the total DNA activity could be approximated by a molecular weight distribution with a mean value of 200×10^6 daltons and a standard deviation of 50×10^6 daltons (Corry and Cole, 1968).

If the chromosomes contain long linear DNA fibers (the total DNA molecular weight in an average chromosome of about 6×10^{10} daltons corresponds to a length of some 3 cm), it is obvious that an appreciable number of molecules 0.01 cm long (200×10^6 daltons) must be joined in some way. The form of this linking arrangement is uncertain at present although Dounce and Hilgartner (1964) have proposed that protein S-S linkages are involved.

Figure 4 illustrates the effect of ^{137}Cs gamma radiation on the molecular weight distribution when isolated metaphase chromosomes are irradiated (in 0.1 M Na_2SO_4, 0.05 M EDTA, 10 per cent sucrose, pH 9.6) before sedimentation. Detailed analyses of such degraded distributions yield a value of 1.05×10^{11} double strand breaks per gram rad which corresponds to about 600 ev energy absorbed in the DNA per double strand break. This is some 10 times the energy required for inducing

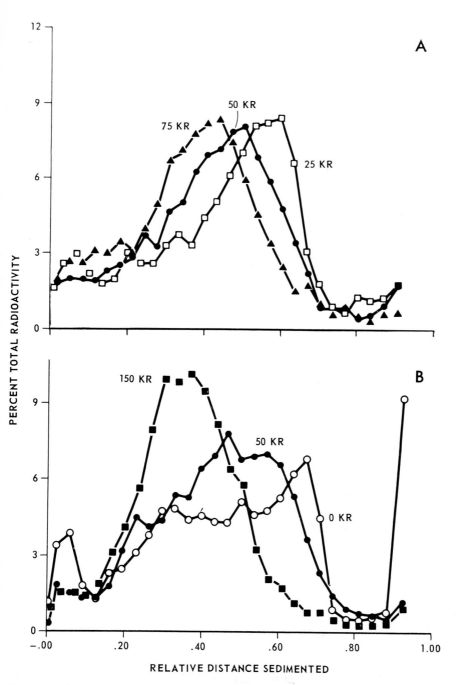

FIGURE 4. Sedimentation patterns for DNA from metaphase chromosomes irradiated with ^{137}Cs gamma rays. Sedimentation time was 14 hours.

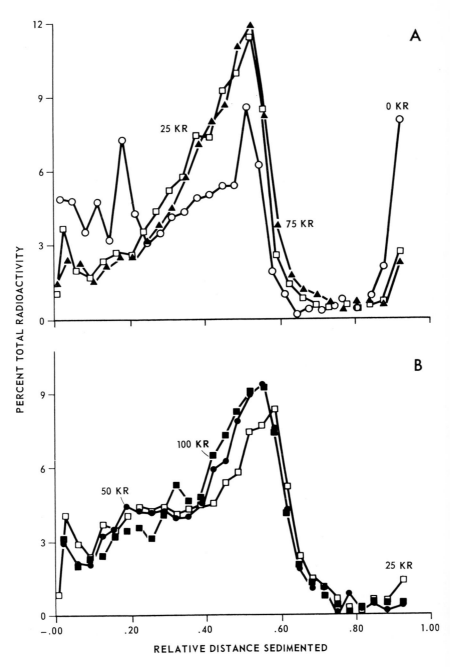

FIGURE 5. Sedimentation patterns for DNA from metaphase chromosomes irradiated in the presence of 0.05 м cystamine. Sedimentation time was 12 hours in a and 14 hours in b.

single strand breaks (Lett and Alexander, 1961). Very similar distributions were observed when metaphase chromosomes were irradiated within the cell (in Hanks' balanced salt solution, pH 6.8) before isolation. Hence, within experimental error, double strand breakage occurred with equal efficiency whether the chromosomes were irradiated intra- or extracellularly. The salt concentration, pH, and degree of chromosomal swelling were significantly different in the two situations. One interpretation of these results is that double strand scission is induced by a direct radiation interaction in the DNA molecule and is not mediated by indirect action of the environment.

Figure 5 illustrates that when isolated chromosomes were irradiated in the presence of 0.05 M cystamine, very little double strand scission could be induced; there appears to have been at least a sevenfold protective (*i.e.* dose reduction) effect. Cystamine and cysteamine are known to be very effective radiation protective agents (Jellum, 1966; Sinclair, 1968); these agents belong to the general class of protective agents containing sulfhydryl (SH) or S-S groups.

As described subsequently in this paper in the section on electron microscope studies, there is reason to believe that specific deoxyribonuclease and ligase activity may be present during cell mitosis. This belief is based on the possibility that sister chromatid strands may be interlocked during metaphase and must be separated enzymatically. To investigate this possibility, a study has been initiated on the dependence of DNA sedimentation patterns on the phase of mitosis. A preliminary result for the DNA distribution from chromosomes isolated from cells 40 minutes after reversing the Colcemid metaphase block by washing and incubating the cells in fresh media can be seen in Figure 6. Such chromosomes may be considered to be grouped as postmetaphase, preanaphase, and anaphase. This initial result suggests that there is an increase in the amount

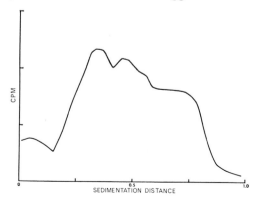

FIGURE 6. Sedimentation pattern for DNA from mitotic chromosomes isolated 45 minutes after reversal of Colcemid metaphase block. Sedimentation time was 14 hours.

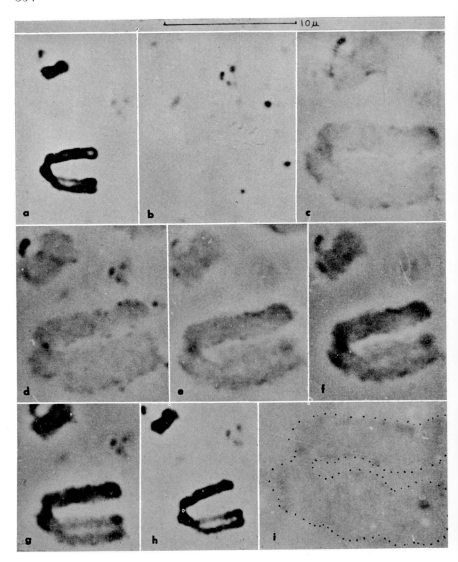

FIGURE 7. The effect of $Mg^{++}Cl_2$ concentration on chromosome size (pH = 7.2). The Mg concentrations were: a—3 mM, chromosome fully condensed; b—0, chromosome fully swollen and invisible; c—0.005 mM; d—0.016 mM; e—0.05 mM; f—0.166 mM; g—0.55 mM; h—1.66 mM; and i—0, pH 5.6, dots outline swollen chromosome.

of both high-molecular weight ($> 10^8$ daltons) and low molecular weight material compared with the metaphase chromosomes. Although this result might be considered to conform to expection if deoxyribonuclease and ligase activity occurred, it must be considered tentative until further studies are completed.

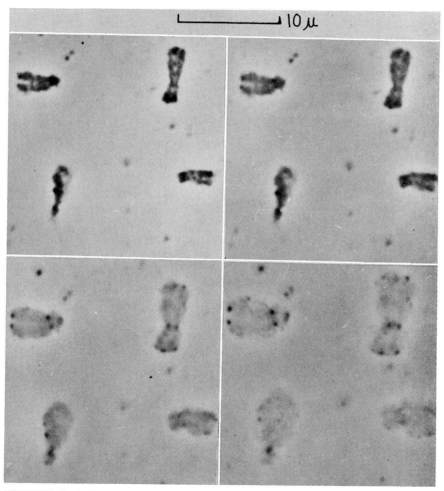

FIGURE 8. Effect of LiCl concentration on chromosome size (pH = 7.0). The lithium concentrations were: top left—100 mM; top right—40 mM; bottom left—10 mM; and bottom right—0.1 mM. Centromeric and telomeric structures are evident in the swollen chromosomes.

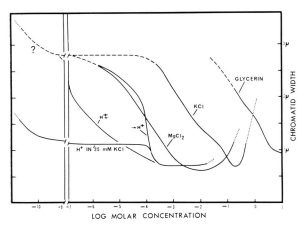

FIGURE 9. Effect of various agents on chromatid width. The dashed lines indicate regions where measurements were difficult because of low optical contrast. Dotted lines indicate regions of irreversible damage.

Light Microscope Studies

The effects of a large number of agents on the morphology and the swelling and condensation properties of isolated chromosomes have been observed using phase and interference contrast light microscopy. Typical reversible effects which illustrate effects of divalent and monovalent cations are shown in Figures 7 and 8. Figure 9 is a plot of the measured dependence of chromatid width on the concentration of various reagents. The swelling-condensation phenomenon is reversible, *i.e.*, the chromosomes may be carried through many cycles of swelling and condensation without apparent loss of structure, providing excessively high reagent concentrations are not used. Table 1 lists concentrations for a number of agents that will induce reversible or irreversible effects. There is a rather notable effect of pH on condensation in that a drop of less than one-half pH unit from pH 4.2 to pH 3.8 causes a seemingly "implosive" condensation. This sharp dependence suggests that cooperative phenomena may be involved in the mechanism. One of the authors (Cole, 1967) has suggested that condensation may involve an increase in ionic association of protein with DNA, resulting in neutralization of charge and a consequent relaxation or collapse of the DNA molecules, combined with a transition of a part of the protein from an extended β form to a condensed α-helical form.

In the studies of radiation effects on chromosomes as observed with the light microscope, 250 kvp X rays (G. E. Maxitron-250 without filter) were utilized. Large doses (> 25,000 rads) are required to produce obvious effects. Although these dosages may preclude direct comparison of the results with in vivo systems, interesting quantitative and qualitative differences in the response have been observed, depending on the physical state or chemical environment of the chromosome during irradiation. The work presented here was done at room temperature in solutions of pH $\approx$ 7.0. Thermoluminescent dosimetry was used to determine the radiation dose.

Figure 10-1a shows a chromosome condensed in 3 mM $MgSO_4$. In Figure 10-1b, the chromosome was swollen to double its contracted width in 0.5 M KCl. This salt concentration represents the highest value tolerated without inducing observable damage. It was thought that some (reversible) dissociation of the nuclear protein and the DNA would occur in this condition; consequently, the radiation response might be

TABLE 1. *Effects of Various Agents on the Functional (Reversible Swelling) Integrity of Isolated Chromosomes*

Agent	Concentration	
	Reversible (no damage)	Irreversible (damaged)
H^+	$>1.5 \times 10^{-11}$ M	$<1.5 \times 10^{-11}$ M
	$<1.5 \times 10^{-2}$ M	$>1.5 \times 10^{-2}$ M
Mg^{2+}, Ca^{2+}	$<1.5 \times 10^{-1}$ M	$>1.5 \times 10^{-1}$ M
K^+, Na^+, Li^+	$<5 \times 10^{-1}$ M	$>5 \times 10^{-1}$ M
Na_2-EDTA	0–0.15 M	(?)
Uranyl acetate	In pH >7.0	In pH <7.0
Glycerin	0–10 M	
Sucrose	0–2 M	
Urea	<4 M	8 M
Thiourea	~1 M	(?)
Mercaptoethanol	(?)	>1 mM
Sodium dodecyl sulfate	$\overset{\sim}{<}0.003\%$	$\overset{\sim}{>}0.01\%$
Diocytyl sodium sulfosuccinate (Colace)	$\overset{\sim}{<}0.03\%$	$\overset{\sim}{>}0.1\%$
Ribonuclease	0.5%	
Lysozyme	0.1%	
Phospholipase	$\overset{\sim}{<}0.1\%$	$\overset{\sim}{>}0.1\%$ (?)
Deoxyribonuclease		0.5%
Trypsin		0.01%
Pepsin		0.1%
Colcemid	0.6 λ/ml	(?)
Glutaraldehyde		2.5%

From Cole (1967).
Abbreviation: EDTA, ethylenediaminetetraacetate.

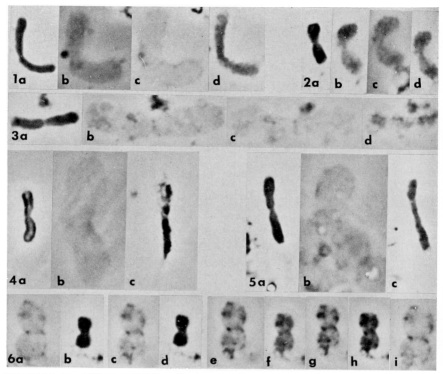

FIGURE 10. Effects of X-irradiation on chromosome morphology and swelling properties (pH = 7 at 25 C).

1a—Chromosome condensed in 3 mM $MgSO_4$; b—swollen in 0.5 M KCl; c—swollen in 1 mM KCl immediately after 150 krads X ray; and d—recondensed in 3 mM $MgSO_4$ and showing some damage.

2a—Chromosome condensed in 3 mM $MgSO_4$; b—swollen in 0.5 M KCl; c—swollen in 1 mM KCl immediately after 150 krads X ray; and d—recondensed in 3 mM $MgSO_4$ and showing obvious damage.

3a—Chromosome condensed in 3 mM $MgSO_4$; b—swollen in 1 mM KCl; c—swollen in 1 mM KCl immediately after 150 krads X ray; and recondensed in 3 mM $MgSO_4$ and showing extensive damage.

4a—Chromosome condensed in 3 mM $MgSO_4$; b—swollen in 0.5 mM Na_2EDTA + 0.5 mM KCl; and c—recondensed in 3 mM $MgSO_4$ after exposure to 75 krads X ray in 0.5 mM Na_2EDTA + 0.5 mM KCl.

5a—Chromosome condensed in 3 mM $MgSO_4$; b—swollen in 0.5 mM Na_2EDTA + 0.5 mM KCl + 1 mM cysteine; and c—recondensed in 3 mM $MgSO_4$ after exposure to 75 krads X ray in 0.5 mM Na_2EDTA + 0.5 mM KCl + 1 mM cysteine.

6a—Chromosome swollen in 1 mM KCl; b—condensed in 3 mM $MgSO_4$, then irradiated with 150 krads X ray; no change observed in condensed state;

(Continued on page 359)

different from that of a fully associated state. Figure 10-1c shows the chromosome still in 0.5 M KCl immediately after about 45 krads of X-radiation; little change can be noted. However, when the chromosome is recondensed in 3 mM MgSO$_4$ (Figure 10-1d), some damage is apparent; a possible loss of organization and recondensation to a measured width 33 per cent greater than the initial compact state has occurred. One should note that, if radiation is omitted in all these studies, the chromosome always recondenses to a state which is indistinguishable from the initial condensed state. The sequence in Figure 10-2 is similar to that in Figure 10-1 except that about 75 krads of X-radiation were delivered between the observations shown in Figures 10-2b and 10-2c. In Figure 10-2d, a more obvious alteration of organization and a recondensation again to 1.3 times the initial width is shown. Greater doses show greater damage; however, little change could be noted for exposures of less than about 25 krads to chromosomes in 0.5 M KCl.

The effects produced in 0.5 M KCl were compared with those produced in a low ionic strength medium which also induces chromosomal swelling but would not be expected to induce dissociation of protein and DNA. The condensed chromosome shown in Figure 10-3a was swollen in 1 mM KCl in Figure 10-3b. Immediately after about 150-krad X-radiation, the chromosome, still swollen in 1 mM KCl, exhibited obvious damage (Figure 10-3c). This damage was very apparent after the chromosome was recondensed in 3 mM MgSO$_4$ (Figure 10-3d). There appears to have been a loss of material and disruption of the organization which left various stringy remnants and resulted in failure to condense fully. In general, the results of various studies on chromosomes swollen in 1 mM KCl and 0.5 M KCl have been qualitatively similar; at present, no significant effect can be attributed to a possible dissociation of protein and DNA at the higher salt concentration. Instead, the extent of swelling appears to be the determining factor which leads to the observed radiation

---

(Continued from page 358)

c—reswollen in 1 mM KCl (swells to 90 per cent the width of 6a); d—recondensed in 3 mM MgSO$_4$, then irradiated again with 150 krads (300 krads total); no change observed in condensed state; e—reswollen in 1 mM KCl (swells to 84 per cent the width of 6a); f—placed in 0.5 M KCl and irradiated with 75 krads (375 krads total); g—chromosome swollen 10 per cent in width in 0.5 M KCl just after irradiation; h—in 3 mM MgSO$_4$, chromosome no longer condensing properly, *i.e.* it shows damage; chromosome width is about 33 per cent larger than in 6b or 6d; and i—again in 1 mM KCl, chromosome swollen to the same size as originally in 6a.

damage (this will be discussed subsequently).

A series of studies was made to determine whether the response could be altered by removing polyvalent cations, which may be complexed in the chromosome structure, with EDTA. Figure 10-4a shows a typical condensed chromosome which was swollen in 0.5 mM Na_2 EDTA plus 0.5 mM KCl (Figure 10-4b) and then irradiated with 75 krads. The chromosome exhibits obvious damage after recondensation in 3 mM $MgSO_4$, as shown in Figure 10-4c. However, this damage was comparable to that produced in 1 mM KCl, so that the removal of loosely complexed polyvalent cations did not appear to alter the radiation effect greatly. In fact, higher concentrations of Na_2 EDTA yield lesser damage which can be attributed to the fact that the chromosome is less swollen at the higher salt (Na_2 EDTA) concentrations.

Some studies were made on the possible protective effects of SH-containing compounds. A chromosome (condensed in Figure 10-5a) was swollen in 0.5 mM Na_2 EDTA + 0.5 mM KCl with 1 mM cysteine (Figure 10-5b) and then irradiated in this swollen condition; upon recondensation in 3 mM $MgSO_4$ (Figure 10-5c), the chromosome appeared to exhibit less damage than that illustrated in Figure 10-4c for irradiation in the medium without cysteine. These differences have not been large so that, at present, a positive statement of the protection afforded isolated structures cannot be made.

The radiation response of a compact chromosome is considerably different from that of a swollen one. A summary of various observations is presented by the study illustrated in Figure 10-6. A chromosome was swollen in 1 mM KCl (Figure 10-6a), condensed in 3 mM $MgSO_4$ (Figure 10-6b), and then irradiated with about 150 krads. No change was observed in the condensed structure. After reswelling in 1 mM KCl (Figure 10-6c), no gross damage was apparent (such as that seen in Figure 10-3c) although the measured reswollen width was only 0.90 that of the initial swollen width. Recondensation was normal (Figure 10-6d), and subsequent irradiation with 150 krads (300 krads total) again did not change the condensed structure. Reswelling a third time in 1 mM KCl (Figure 10-6e) did not expose any apparent damage except that the swollen width was now about 0.84 that of the initial value. The chromosome then was exposed to 0.5 M KCl (Figure 10-6f). An additional 75 krads (375 krads total) appeared to cause some swelling of the structure (Figure 10-6g) and to produce damage since subsequent exposure to 3 mM $MgSO_4$ (Figure 10-6h) produced incomplete condensation with the chromosome width 1.33 times larger than it had been previously (Figures 10-6b and 10-6d). A subsequent reswelling in 1 mM KCl (Figure 10-6i) yielded a structure which was quite similar to the original swollen state (Figure 10-6a), that is, the previous effect of the restriction of swelling resulting from irradiation during the compact state appeared to be reversed by irradiation during the swollen state.

A number of conclusions may be based on these studies. (1) Damage to chromosome structure can be observed with the light microscope by (a) the loss of the integrity of the normal swelling-condensation responses, (b) apparent changes in organization, and (c) loss of material and rupture or degradation of the structure. (2) Radiation-induced damage (as defined in [1]) apparently depends on the degree of swelling of the chromosome. Compact chromosomes are relatively radioresistant. Part (or all?) of this effect may be attributed to a relatively greater contribution of indirect effects in swollen structures. (3) SH compounds may show protection against radiation damage as defined in [1]. (4) Damage induced in compact structures is qualitatively different from damage induced in swollen structures. A cross-linking or aggregation type of damage (which restricts subsequent swelling) may predominate in compact structures whereas a degradation or disruptive type of damage may predominate in swollen structures (Lett, Caldwell, Dean, and Alexander, 1967). All the effects require large doses in the order of 10^5 rads, which corresponds to about 6×10^5 ev/energy deposited in the DNA of a chromosome. On the basis of studies done at our laboratories and elsewhere

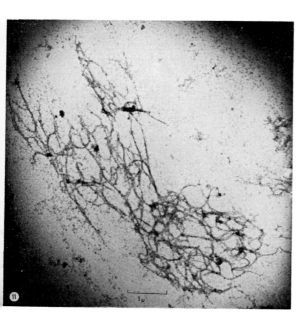

FIGURE 11. Electron micrograph of metaphase chromosome after trypsin treatment (0.1 per cent trypsin in 3 mM $MgSO_4$ for 20 min at 37 C) showing fibers 300 to 500 A across.

(Lett and Alexander, 1961; Lett, Caldwell, Dean, and Alexander, 1967; Humphrey, Steward, and Sedita, 1968; Corry and Cole, 1968), this energy would be expected to induce about 1,000 double strand breaks and 10,000 single strand breaks in the DNA of a chromosome. The degree and type of interactions expected in the protein component are poorly defined but must certainly contribute to the effects observed in this study. It is believed that the complex structural arrangement of the metaphase chromosome, which contains about 86 per cent protein and 14 per cent DNA (Cantor and Hearst, 1966; Huberman and Attardi, 1966), inhibits the expression of this damage at the level of observation reported in this paper.

Electron Microscope Studies

A brief review of the effects of various agents on chromosome structure as observed by two-dimensional electron microscopy has been published (Cole, 1967). Figure 11 shows one form of swollen metaphase structure observed after trypsin treatment. More recent studies using stereo electron microscopy have been limited mainly to the irreversible effects of 0.0025 per cent to 0.1 per cent (by weight) trypsin (Worthington Biochemical Corporation, code TRL) in solution A (isotonic salts and glucose) for treatment times from 15 seconds to about one hour at room temperature. In most cases, pretreatment with 10 mM EDTA was used to remove associated divalent cations. Although various levels of action were observed on a single specimen grid, the average effect increased with treatment time.

Stereo electron microscopic pairs are best seen by direct binocular viewing of transparencies. Projected images of carefully processed transparencies yield a reasonable quality. Although a good deal of detail and information is lost in the printed presentation of stereo pairs, a useful picture is still retained. The micrographs presented in this paper may be observed directly by focusing the right eye on the right picture and the left eye on the left picture. Inexperienced observers tend to see three images, the central one being three-dimensional; however, the nonstereo side images are quickly removed from the consciousness. A slight rocking motion of the pictures about a perpendicular axis between the pairs will help in aligning the eyes. Viewing should be done with adequate, if not bright, lighting. Placing a dark divider between the image pair is sometimes helpful. Use of a simple 1.5- to 3-power binocular viewer or loupe will generally bring the stereo image into focus immediately for the unpracticed viewer. The crossed-eye technique (right eye on left picture, left eye on right picture) gives the effect of viewing the object from the rear.

Figures 12 and 13 are stereo illustrations of pairs of chromosomes which are somewhat swollen by a salt or trypsin effect. These structures are generally similar in appearance to untreated chromosomes except for size (a fully condensed chromatid measures about 0.5 μ in diameter) and for the somewhat open telomeric regions which expose organized fibers measuring from 400 to 800 A across. The fibers in the telomeric regions usually appear to loop back rather than to end abruptly.

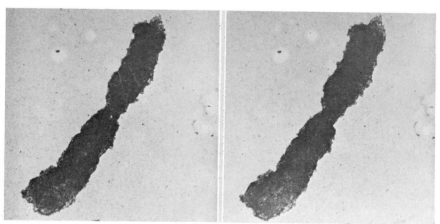

FIGURE 12. Stereo electron micrographic pair of a metaphase chromosome after a 0.5 M KCl treatment. The appearance is similar to untreated chromosomes. Magnification ×6,000.

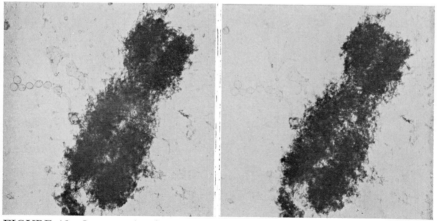

FIGURE 13. Stereo pair of a trypsin-treated metaphase chromosome (0.025 per cent trypsin in solution A for 10 min at 37 C) showing adjacent sister chromatids. The finer fibers measure about 400 A across. Magnification ×6,500.

Figures 14 and 15 illustrate a more disrupted structure after trypsin digestion. Partly disorganized fibers which measure from about 100 to 400 A across are seen to extend over several microns in length. These

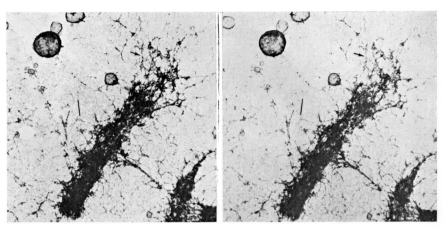

FIGURE 14. Stereo pair of trypsin-treated chromosome (0.0025 per cent trypsin in solution A for 15 minutes at 37 C) illustrating more open structure. Fibers of 100 to 400 A in diameter which are several microns long extend above the substrate up to about a micron. The bar near the center of the field indicates a vertical and depth dimension of 0.5 μ, that is, it slopes 45° with respect to the plane of the substrate. The arrow refers to a region shown at higher magnification in Figure 16. Magnification ×9,000.

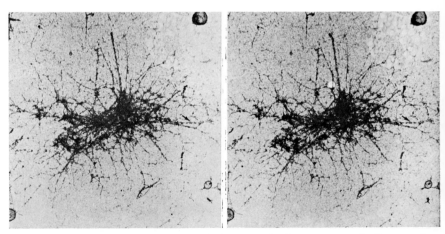

FIGURE 15. Stereo pair of a trypsin-treated chromosome similar to that shown in Figure 14. The arrow indicates a region shown at higher magnification in Figures 20 and 23. Magnification ×9,000.

structures are similar to those shown by other investigators (Trosko and Wolff, 1965; Wolfe and Martin, 1968). In these figures, most of the material is in free space, the high points being 0.5 to 1 μ above the substrate. This fact attests to the effectiveness of the critical point drying technique (T. F. Anderson, 1956) in maintaining three-dimensional structures.

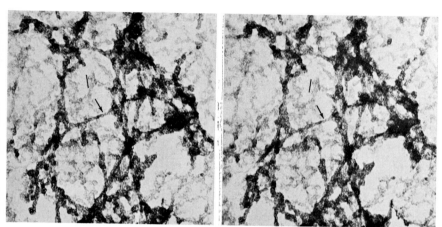

FIGURE 16. Higher magnification stereo pair of the upper right region of the chromosome shown in Figure 14. The bar indicates a vertical and depth dimension of 500 A. In various places, the fine structure of the 100-A fibers appears to consist of a twisted pair of 20-A fibers (arrow). Magnification ×75,000.

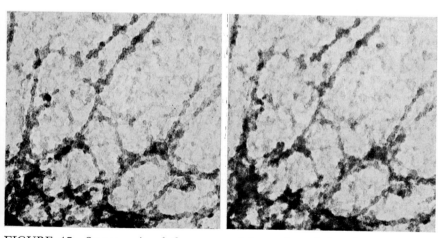

FIGURE 17. Stereo pair of the upper right region of the chromosome of Figure 15 showing fine structure of 100-A fibers. Magnification ×75,000.

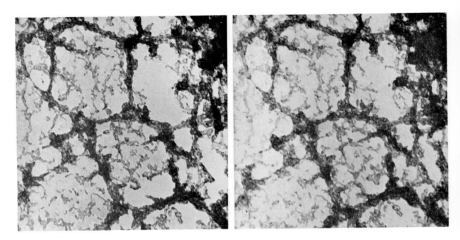

FIGURE 18. Higher magnification stereo pair of finer structure of the pre-dominant 100-A fibers found after trypsin treatment which appear to consist of various kinked and twisted arrangements of 20-A fibers. Magnification ×135,000.

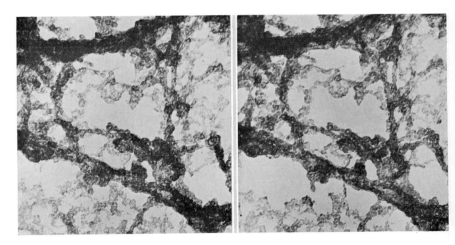

FIGURE 19. Stereo pair of the upper right region of the chromosome seen in Figure 14 showing fine fibers of 20 to 30 A and larger groups from 100 to 400 A. Magnification ×135,000.

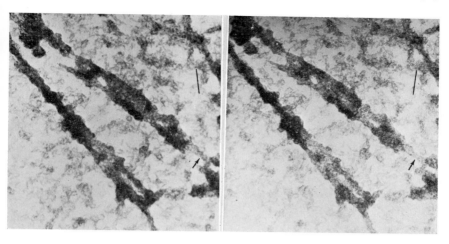

FIGURE 20. Stereo pair of the right region of the chromosome seen in Figure 15 (arrow) showing several 400-A fiber groupings which contain fibrous structures from 7 to 200 A. The bar measures a vertical and depth dimension of 500 A. The arrow indicates the region shown at higher magnification in Figure 23. Magnification ×135,000.

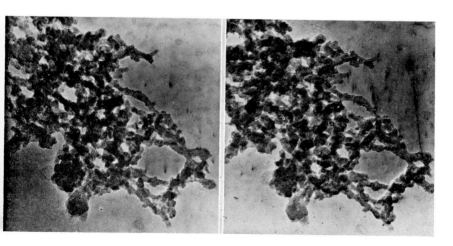

FIGURE 21. Stereo pair of chromosome fibers at telomeric region of a chromosome after X-irradiation (210 krads in 10 and 1 mM KCl, no EDTA treatment). The predominant fibers measure about 200 A in diameter. Magnification ×67,000.

At higher magnification, the fibers of trypsin-treated chromosomes exhibit a twisted, knobby, or loosely organized structure (Figures 16 through 20). The finest structures visible in these micrographs are about 7 A across while the predominant fibers measure about 100 A in diameter

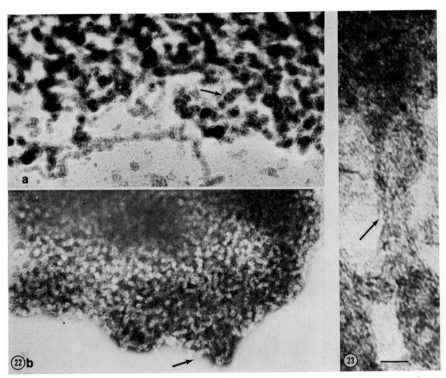

FIGURE 22. a—Positively stained 200-A fibers from an untreated chromosome. A finer structure containing perhaps four dense 20-A fibers enmeshed in a less dense matrix is apparent (arrow). Magnification ×140,000. b— Negatively stained (phosphotungstic acid) 200-A fibers from telomeric region of an untreated chromosome. A finer structure of 25-A fibers is apparent (arrow). Magnification ×44,000.

FIGURE 23. Higher magnification (nonstereo) image of a region of the suspended fibers of Figures 15 and 20 showing fine structure containing 7-A fibers which, in certain regions (arrow), appear to be cohelically twisted into a 20-A fiber with about a 40-A pitch length. Bar indicates 100 A. Visualization of such detail can be considered a result of a free space image enhanced by phase contrast since the objective lens was adjusted to about 500 A underfocus at the level of the suspended fiber and close to focus at the level of the substrate. Magnification ×840,000.

(Figures 16, 17, and 18) and the larger groupings of fibers measure up to about 400 A across (Figures 19 and 20). A possible interpretation of these structures (consistent with Figures 16 through 20 and many similar electron micrographs) is that two 20-A fibers are cohelically twisted to form the 100-A fiber (Figures 16 and 17) and that two 100-A fibers are cohelically twisted to form a 200-A fiber. It is proposed that this arrangement is not observed consistently because of damage to and loss of the organization in the normal untreated condensed chromosomes. This loss of organization may be the result of the removal or hydrolysis of a large amount of the protein which comprises most of the condensed structure and may lead to a kinked arrangement similar to the kinking of a twisted taut rubber band when the tension is relaxed. The structures shown in Figures 16 through 20 are similar in appearance to electron micrographs of interphase chromatin as demonstrated by Ris (1967, 1968). It was noted also that, for chromosome treatments which were less harsh and did not involve EDTA pretreatment, the predominant fiber observed was 200 A in diameter (Figures 21 and 22). The latter figure appears to show a substructure apparently containing four densely stained 20-A fibers (believed to be double-stranded DNA molecules) within a less dense matrix (believed to be a protein component). Ris has proposed that the 100-A fiber contains a single DNA (double-stranded) molecule and that two 100-A fibers associate in the presence of divalent cation to form the 200-A fiber (Ris, 1967, 1968).

In many micrographs, the 20-A fibers exhibit a finer structure containing two 7-A fibers (Figure 23) which apparently are twisted cohelically. Figure 23 is a higher magnification (nonstereo) image of a region of one of the suspended fibers shown in Figure 20. The fine (cohelical) structure shown has been observed in many samples and for various treatment and staining conditions; it is believed to represent slightly open regions of the double-stranded cohelical DNA molecule, although this has not been verified.

Figures 24, 25, and 26 illustrate swollen structures exhibiting typical centromeric regions. In Figure 24, a damaged chromosome (in this case, treated in 1 M KCl) is partly separated or stretched in the centromeric region, exposing a limited number (perhaps only two per chromatid) of 400- to 800-A fibers which appear continuous across this region. A study of a number of such stretched centromeric regions indicates that there is probably a minimum of two and a maximum of four 400-A fiber groupings associated with each chromatid. Figures 25 and 26 illustrate the multiple kinetochore structures usually observed. Two kinetochores are found for each chromatid (four in the whole chromosome). Each

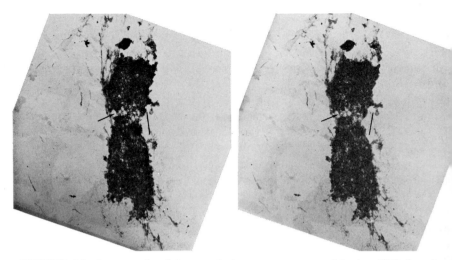

FIGURE 24. Stereo pair of damaged chromosome treated in 1 м KCl showing stretched centromeric region exposing a limited number of fibers of 400 to 800 A in diameter (arrow). The bar refers to a vertical and depth dimension of 1 μ. Magnification ×6,700.

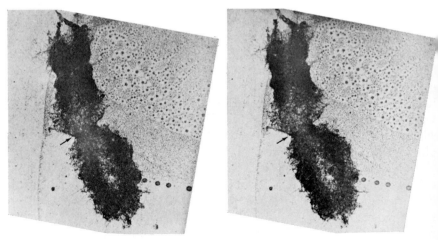

FIGURE 25. Stereo pair of chromosome after three sequences of 10 mM MgSO₄, 10 mM EDTA, and 0.5 м KCl treatments. The open lacy areas consist mainly of 100-A fibers. Four kinetochore structures, each consisting of a pair of 400-A fibers (arrow) (believed to be swollen 200-A fibers), are suggested in this micrograph, although the two kinetochores on the right are not clear. Magnification ×6,000.

kinetochore on the left of the picture is seen to be a double structure consisting of two 400-A fibers which appear to extend deep into the chromosome. Since the chromosome has swollen some two and one-half times its condensed dimension, the 400-A fibers may represent swollen 200-A fibers. Although it may be difficult to see in the final printed stereo pairs, the two kinetochores on the left are not in parallel orientation; the lower one moves up while the top one moves down toward the left of the picture. There is an indication that the individual 400-A fibers are twisted cohelically. These kinetochore structures, which cannot be seen in whole condensed chromosomes, are very similar to the structure reported in sectioned material by Brinkley and Stubblefield (1966).

The previous micrographs are representative of metaphase structures with poorly separated chromatids. Chromosomes with separated chromatids always exhibit connecting interchromatid fibers which appear identical to the intrachromatid fibers (Figures 27, 28, and 29). In Figure 27, the upper chromosome arm has a relatively condensed nonseparated structure and the lower, separated structure contains 100- to 400-A diameter strands which apparently connect across the two chromatids. Figure 28 shows a typical chromosome with well-separated chromatids in both arms. The significance of the inevitable presence of interchromatid strands is not understood at present but suggests the following conditions: (1) Metaphase chromatids are independent separated structures which, however, always tend to stick together in the variety of experimental conditions used and, consequently, leave residue connecting

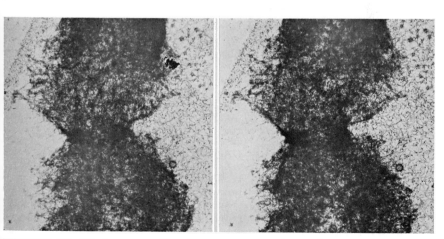

FIGURE 26. Higher magnification stereo pair of the kinetochore region of Figure 25. Magnification ×15,000.

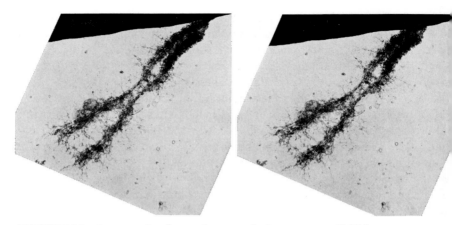

FIGURE 27. Stereo pair of trypsin-treated chromosome (0.025 per cent trypsin in solution A for 10 minutes at 37 C) showing attached chromatids at top right and separated chromatids at bottom left where various interchromatid fibers of 100 to 800 A in diameter can be seen. The upper part of the chromosome can be seen to be completely detached from the substrate. Magnification ×5,000.

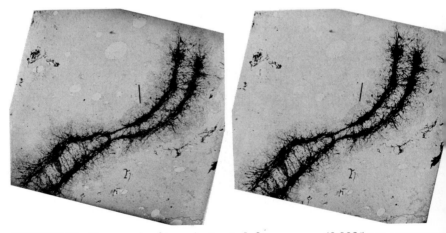

FIGURE 28. Stereo pair of trypsin-treated chromosome (0.0025 per cent trypsin in solution A for 15 minutes at 37 C) showing well-separated chromatids and interchromatid fiber groupings 100 A and larger in diameter. Fine material is seen to surround and outline the whole chromosome. Magnification ×2,500.

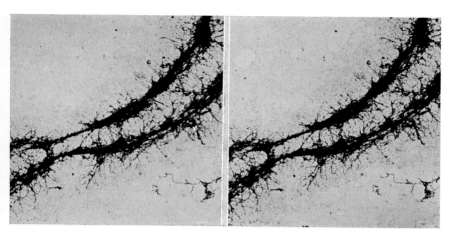

FIGURE 29. Higher magnification of centromeric region of Figure 28. Magnification ×5,700.

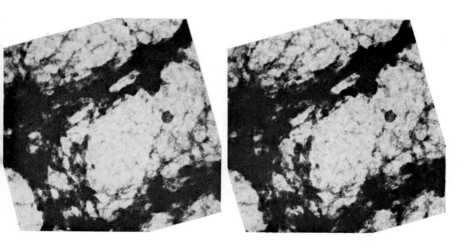

FIGURE 30. Higher magnification of lower left region of Figure 29. The fine material is visible as short fibers 20 A and larger in diameter. Magnification ×41,000.

strands after swelling or partial dissociation or digestion. (2) Metaphase chromatids are not truly separated structures but have a number of inter-locked strands which must be reorganized (broken and repaired) during segregation of the chromatids after metaphase. The interlocked, or cate-

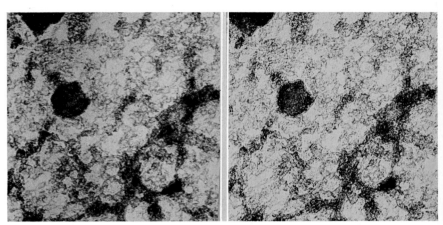

FIGURE 31. Higher magnification of right region of Figure 30. Fragmented and twisted fibers about 20 A in diameter are visible. Magnification ×125,000.

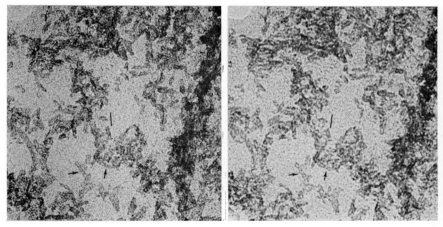

FIGURE 32. Higher magnification of region similar to that of Figure 30. The fragments 20 A in diameter are seen to consist of two finer 7- to 8-A diameter fibers which appear cohelically twisted in some places (arrows). Magnification ×350,000. Bar indicates vertical and depth dimension of 100 A.

nated, structure might be the inevitable result of chromosomal replication (Norman, personal communication). Interchromatid strands are specific (undefined) structures not identical to the chromatid structure.

To better understand these possibilities, studies are being directed to investigate changes in structure observed when chromosomes are isolated from cells in various stages of mitosis.

Figures 28 through 32 illustrate another feature commonly found after partial trypsin digestion of chromosomes, *i.e.*, the presence of a coat of apparently degraded or fractured material which uniformly surrounds the prominent chromosome structure (Figure 29). These figures show this residue material at increasingly higher magnification. In Figure 31, the material is seen to consist of short fragments of 10- to 20-A wide fibers, in Figure 32, the 20-A wide material is seen to consist largely of two associated 8-A fibers which, in certain regions, appear to be twisted cohelically (arrow). It is believed that this material consists of uranyl acetate-stained and broken protein and DNA molecules of the chromosome.

Discussion

The results of the various studies are consistent with interpretations of chromosome structure presented previously (Cole, 1967). In particular, the predominant 100-A fiber is believed to consist of two double-stranded DNA molecules which are associated cohelically. A possible mechanism for producing this structure consists of a cross-linking association by histone molecules to the negatively charged hydrated phosphate groups of the two DNA molecules. The resulting preferential neutralization of the centrally facing charged groups could lead to a reciprocal central collapse of the two DNA double molecules because of (1) a reduction of the stiffness of the DNA molecules in this region which would be imposed normally by mutual repulsion of nearby anionic sites (Alexander and Hitch, 1952; N. G. Anderson, 1956) or (2) a loss of bound water caused by the reduction of water binding anionic sites (Cole, 1962). The reciprocal central collapse would lead to a cohelical structure of about 80 to 100 A in diameter because of restrictions imposed by the flexibility of the DNA molecule (Cole, 1962, 1967). Assuming, for example, that the structure of the DNA molecules tended toward the B form on the exterior and toward the A form on the interior, such a structure might be termed an A-B hybrid rotation isomer of DNA.

Much effort has been made to establish the structure of the kinetochore and the centromeric region because it was believed that this region should reflect the continuity of a basic structure rather than that of a higher order packing involved in forming the condensed metaphase configuration. Micrographs such as those of Figures 25 and 26 definitely show four kinetochore structures per chromosome, or two per chromatid. This fact implies that a kinetochore structure is associated with each chromatid arm.

Brinkley and Stubblefield (1966) suggest that the chromosomal fibers from each chromatid arm are continuous through the kinetochore; however, Figures 25 and 26 suggest that the fibers may end at the kinetochore and that the two chromatid arms are maintained as a unit by virtue of an association of the related kinetochores. This suggestion is relevant to interpretation of various facets of chromosome structure and function, including condensation, aberration, and multiple or diffuse centromeres.

The various studies suggest that a basic element of the metaphase chromatid consists of at least one and, perhaps, two or four 200-A fibers. Such interpretations obviously tend to favor a polyneme concept (two or more identical DNA double molecules make up the basic genetic or replicating fiber) rather than a unineme concept of mammalian chromosome structure. Such may be the case even if the 100-A fiber were the basic element since our studies suggest that two DNA molecules are involved at this level. The authors are aware of the difficulties imposed by a polyneme concept and suggest that considerable additional work is necessary before an interpretation of chromosome structure can be confidently accepted.

It appears that the effects of various agents, particularly radiation, are not well understood at present. The connections between single or double strand breaks in DNA and subsequent chromosomal aberration or cell death are probably indirect and complex, considering the complexity of chromosome structure and replication. Recent studies on DNA repair processes as reported in this volume (Hanawalt, 1970, see pages 528 to 547, this volume; Gellert, Little, Oshinsky, and Zimmerman, 1970, see pages 548 to 554, this volume; Setlow, Boling, and Beattie, 1970, see pages 555 to 568, this volume; Humphrey, Steward, and Sedita, 1970, see pages 570 to 592, this volume; Painter, 1970, see pages 593 to 600, this volume) appreciably expand our appreciation of this problem.

ACKNOWLEDGMENTS

Mrs. Nancy Flatt contributed to the recent studies on the molecular weight distribution of DNA from postmetaphase chromosomes.

The authors wish to thank Mr. Eldridge F. Dorsey for his help in preparing the electron micrographic stereo pairs for publication. This work was supported in part by funds from the United States Atomic Energy Commission, contract AT-(40–1)-2832.

REFERENCES

Alexander, P., and S. F. Hitch. 1952. A Comparative Study of the Anomalous Viscosity of a High Molecular Weight Polyelectrolyte and Thymus Nucleic Acid. *Biochimica et biophysica acta*, 9:229–236.

Anderson, N. G. 1956. Cell Division. Part One. A Theoretical Approach to the Primeval Mechanism, the Initiation of Cell Division and Chromosomal Condensation. *Quarterly Review of Biology*, 31:169–199.

Anderson, T. F. 1956. "Electron Microscopy of Microorganisms," *Physical Techniques in Biological Research*, G. Osten and A. W. Pollister, Eds. New York, New York: Academic Press, Inc. Vol. III. Pp. 177–240.

Brinkley, B. R., and E. Stubblefield. 1966. The Fine Structure of the Kinetochore of a Mammalian Cell In Vitro. *Chromosoma*, 19:28–43.

Cairns, J. 1966. Autoradiography of HeLa Cell DNA. *Journal of Molecular Biology*, 15:372–373.

Cantor, K. P., and J. E. Hearst. 1966. Isolation and Partial Characterization of Metaphase Chromosomes of a Mouse Ascites Tumor. *Proceedings of the National Academy of Sciences of the U.S.A.*, 55:642–649.

Cole, A. 1962. A Molecular Model for Biological Contractility: Implications in Chromosome Structure and Function. *Nature*, 196:211–214.

———. 1967. "Chromosome Structure," *Theoretical and Experimental Biophysics*, A. Cole, Ed. New York, New York: Marcel Dekker, Inc. Vol. I. Pp. 305–375.

Cole, A., and C. Somers-Cronenwett. 1964. "Electron Microscopic Studies of Isolated Mammalian Metaphase Chromosomes," *Abstracts: Biophysical Society, Eighth Annual Meeting* (February 26–28, 1964, Chicago, Illinois). Abstract WC3.

Cole, A., and R. Langley. 1965. "Studies on the Structure of Mammalian Chromosomes," *Abstracts: Biophysical Society, Ninth Annual Meeting* (February 24–26, 1965, San Francisco, California). P. 166.

———. 1966. "Studies on the Structure of Mammalian Chromosomes," *Abstracts: Biophysical Society, Tenth Annual Meeting* (February 23–25, 1966, Boston, Massachusetts). P. 46.

Corry, P. M., and A. Cole. 1968. Radiation-Induced Double-Strand Scission of the DNA of Mammalian Metaphase Chromosomes. *Radiation Research*, 36:528–543.

Dounce, A. L., and C. A. Hilgartner. 1964. A Study of DNA Nucleoprotein Gels and the Residual Protein of Isolated Cell Nuclei. *Experimental Cell Research*, 36:228–241.

Gellert, M., J. W. Little, C. K. Oshinsky, and S. B. Zimmerman. 1970. "Studies on the Enzymatic Joining of DNA Strands," *Genetic Concepts and Neoplasia* (The University of Texas M. D. Anderson Hospital and Tumor Institute at Houston, 23rd Annual Symposium on Fundamental Cancer Research, 1969). Baltimore, Maryland: The Williams & Wilkins Co. Pp. 548–554.

Hanawalt, P. C. 1970. "Repair Replication of Damaged DNA In Vivo," *Genetic Concepts and Neoplasia* (The University of Texas M. D. Anderson Hospital and Tumor Institute at Houston, 23rd Annual Symposium on Fundamental Cancer Research, 1969). Baltimore, Maryland: The Williams & Wilkins Co. Pp. 528–547.

Huberman, J. A., and G. Attardi. 1966. Isolation of Metaphase Chromosomes from HeLa Cells. *Journal of Cell Biology*, 31:95–105.

Humphrey, R. M., D. L. Steward, and B. A. Sedita. 1968. DNA Strand Breaks and Rejoining Following Exposure of Synchronized Chinese Hamster Cells to Ionizing Radiation. *Mutation Research*, 6:459–465.

———. 1970. "DNA Strand Scission and Rejoining in Mammalian Cells," *Genetic Concepts and Neoplasia* (The University of Texas M. D. Anderson Hospital and Tumor Institute at Houston, 23rd Annual Symposium on Fundamental Cancer Research, 1969). Baltimore, Maryland: The Williams & Wilkins Co. Pp. 570–592.

Jellum, E. 1966. The Role of Cystamine-Nucleic-Acid Interactions in Protection Against X-Ray-Induced Damage of DNA. *International Journal of Radiation Biology*, 10:577–594.

Lett, J. T., and P. Alexander. 1961. Crosslinking and Degradation of Deoxyribonucleic Acid Gels with Varying Water Contents When Irradiated with Electrons. *Radiation Research*, 15:159–173.

Lett, J. T., I. Caldwell, C. J. Dean, and P. Alexander. 1967. Rejoining of X-Ray Induced Breaks in the DNA of Leukaemia Cells. *Nature*, 214:790–792.

Noll, H. 1967. Characterization of Macromolecules by Constant Velocity Sedimentation. *Nature*, 215:360–363.

Norman, A. Personal communication.

Painter, R. B. 1970. "Nonconservative Replication of Damaged DNA in Mammalian Cells," *Genetic Concepts and Neoplasia* (The University of Texas M. D. Anderson Hospital and Tumor Institute at Houston, 23rd Annual Symposium on Fundamental Cancer Research, 1969). Baltimore, Maryland: The Williams & Wilkins Co. Pp. 593–600.

Ris, H. 1967. "Ultrastructure of the Animal Chromosome," *Regulation of Nucleic Acid and Protein Biosynthesis*, V. V. Koningsberger and L. Bosch, Eds. Amsterdam, The Netherlands: Elsevier Publishing Co.; New York, New York: American Elsevier Publishing Co., Inc.; and London, England: Elsevier Publishing Co., Ltd. Pp. 11–21.

Ris, H. Personal communication.

Sasaki, M. S., and A. Norman. 1966. DNA Fibers from Human Lymphocyte Nuclei. *Experimental Cell Research*, 44:642–645.

Setlow, J. K., M. E. Boling, and K. L. Beattie. 1970. "Repair of DNA in *Haemophilus influenzae*. III. Excision and Recombination Defects and the Site of Repair of Ultraviolet-Irradiated Transforming DNA," *Genetic Concepts and Neoplasia* (The University of Texas M. D. Anderson Hospital and Tumor Institute at Houston, 23rd Annual Symposium on Fundamental Cancer Research, 1969). Baltimore, Maryland: The Williams & Wilkins Co. Pp. 555–568.

Sinclair, W. K. 1968. The X-Ray Protective Effect of Cysteamine During the Cell Cycle of Chinese Hamster Cells. (Abstract) *Radiation Research*, 35:565.

Somers, C. E., A. Cole, and T. C. Hsu. 1963. Isolation of Chromosomes. *Experimental Cell Research*, 9:220–234.

Studier, F. W. 1965. Sedimentation Studies of the Size and Shape of DNA. *Journal of Molecular Biology*, 11:373–390.

Trosko, J. E., and S. Wolff. 1965. Strandedness of *Vicia faba* Chromosomes as

Revealed by Enzyme Digestion Studies. *The Journal of Cell Biology*, 26:125–135.
Wolfe, S. L., and P. G. Martin. 1968. The Ultrastructure and Strandedness of Chromosomes from Two Species of *Vicia. Experimental Cell Research*, 50:140–150.

Modifications in Transfer RNA During Chemical Carcinogenesis

I. BERNARD WEINSTEIN

Institute of Cancer Research and Department of Medicine, Columbia University College of Physicians and Surgeons, and Francis Delafield Hospital, New York, New York

The Concept of Cancer as an Aberration in Differentiation

At the present time, the cancer cell can be defined only in terms of certain gross biologic properties. These include an escape from normal regulation of cell replication, a progressive dedifferentiation, and an impairment in intercellular coordination (Weinstein, 1968). From a genetic point of view, the most intriguing aspect of the process is that, once established, the neoplastic state is stable in the sense that, with the rare exceptions discussed below, the progeny of tumor cells are always tumor cells.

Since Boveri first proposed the somatic mutation theory of cancer in 1914, there has been a tendency to interpret this stable aspect of the neoplastic trait as evidence that neoplastic transformation involves a permanent and irreversible change in the genetic material (deoxyribonucleic acid [DNA]) of the cell. Despite extensive genetic and biochemical studies, however, there is no direct evidence for the somatic mutation theory of cancer. We know that the normal process of differentiation leads to the derivation of cell lines with highly unique patterns of gene expression which become stabilized and are transmitted to progeny cells. It is conceivable, therefore, that certain tumors (and perhaps all tumors in their initial stages) represent aberrations in differentiation which do not involve permanent changes in the host DNA. Several examples (Table 1) of the production by tumor cells of gene products not synthesized by the normal tissue of origin are consistent with the concept of aberrant differentiation. These examples provide direct evidence for a gross disturbance in gene expression in tumor cells. The uncontrolled cellular replication often emphasized in tumor biology may represent merely one facet of this aberration. Some of the examples listed in Table 1 indicate that the disturbance in gene expression may include a "switching-on" of genes normally expressed only in the fetus. This aspect is

TABLE 1. *Evidence for Aberrant Gene Expression in Cancer Cells*

Findings	References
1. Ectopic hormone production by tumors (human)	Bower and Gordan, 1965
2. Hepatomas (human and rodent) make a fetal alpha$_1$ globulin	Alpert, Uriel, and de Nechaud, 1968
3. Colon cancers (human) produce embryonic colon antigen	Gold and Freedman, 1965
4. Hepatomas (rodent) may produce embryonic and other organ-specific antigens	Ivanov, Fel, and Olenov, 1968
5. Hepatomas (human and rodent) may produce muscle type aldolase	Matsushima, Kawabe, Shibuya, and Sugimura, 1968; Nordmann and Schapira, 1966

reminiscent of the "embryonal arrest" theory of cancer proposed by Cohnheim in 1870. Abundant experimental data (particularly in vitro transformation studies) indicate, however, that in most cases cancer probably does not arise from embryonal arrests, but from differentiated cells which are converted to cancer cells. It is intriguing that this conversion may result in the reexpression of fetal genes; further comparative biochemical studies between tumor and fetal tissues should be rewarding.

The concept of cancer as an aberration in differentiation has profound implications in terms of our approach to therapy, since it implies that the neoplastic state of a cell is potentially reversible (Gellhorn, 1966). Table 2 lists several examples of the apparent reversion or redifferentiation of tumor cells. Although at present this appears to be a relatively rare event, its occurrence in several species and cell lines indicates that the phenomenon may be more general than is realized and may be exploitable for cancer therapy. The studies of Macpherson (1965), indicating that hamster cells transformed to tumor cells by the Rous sarcoma virus may spontaneously revert to normal, and those of Sanders and Burford (1968), suggesting that this reversion can be enhanced by N-nitrosomethylurea (a compound which under other circumstances is a carcinogen), are particularly provocative. It could be argued that neoplasia is the result of a somatic mutation and that the examples of redifferentiation of tumor cells (Table 2) are a result of an additional mutation which corrects the original defect. This explanation seems unlikely in the case of the nuclear transplantation studies of McKinnell (1962). Nor can it be invoked to explain the redifferentiation of neuroblastomas (Everson and Cole, 1966) since the entire cell population of a tumor would have to undergo simultaneously a similar type of mutation.

The biochemical mechanisms underlying the normal control of gene expression during differentiation are poorly understood, but it is clear that they do not operate via somatic mutation (Gurdon, 1967). It is important, therefore, in considering mechanisms by which exogenous agents produce cancer, to keep our minds open to the possibility that they do so by changing the cytoplasmic environment of a cell in a way which induces an altered and self-sustaining pattern of gene expression.

Role of Transfer Ribonucleic Acid (tRNA) in Cell Regulation and Differentiation

In view of the findings cited above, we cannot necessarily assume that the primary target of chemical carcinogens is cellular DNA or the chromosomes. There is extensive evidence that several carcinogens have the capacity to react with ribonucleic acid (RNA), either in vivo or in vitro, to an extent which is equal to or greater than their capacity to react with DNA. (For a review of this subject see Farber [1968], Miller and Miller [1967], and Magee, Craddock, and Swann, [1967].) At the same time, we cannot ignore the abundant evidence of in vivo interaction

TABLE 2. *Examples of Reversion or Redifferentiation of Tumor Cells*

Reversion or redifferentiation	References
1. Crowngall tumor (plant)—grafted onto normal plant yields normal seeds	Braun and Wood, 1961
2. Lucké renal carcinoma (frog)—nuclei transplanted into enucleated egg yield embryos with well-differentiated tissues	McKinnell, Deggins, and Labat, 1969
3. Rous sarcoma virus-transformed cells (hamster) —yield normal tissue culture cells either spontaneously or after treatment with N-nitrosomethylurea	Macpherson, 1965; Sanders and Burford, 1968
4. Anaplastic embryonal carcinoma (mouse)— converts to highly differentiated teratoma	Kleinsmith and Pierce, 1964
5. Polyoma virus-transformed cells (hamster)— yield tissue culture clones with increased contact inhibition and decreased tumor-producing ability	Pollack, Green, and Todaro, 1968
6. Neuroblastoma (man)—may regress or convert to ganglioneuromas	Everson and Cole, 1966
7. Endometrial carcinoma (man)—progesterone induces formation of decidua and secretory glands in the tumor	Kistner, Griffiths, and Craig, 1965

of several chemical carcinogens with cell proteins, lipids, and carbohydrates (Farber, 1968; Miller and Miller, 1967; Magee, Craddock, and Swann, 1967). The crucial problem, of course, is to find which of these interactions is responsible for converting a normal cell to a tumor cell and which are merely side reactions.

My interest in the possibility that tRNA might be the critical target during carcinogenesis was first aroused by the studies of Dr. Emmanuel Farber, which indicated that the hepatic carcinogen, ethionine, results in extensive in vivo ethylation of rat liver tRNA (Farber et al., 1967; Axel, Weinstein, and Farber, 1967). The central role of tRNA in the translation of the genetic code has suggested to several investigators the possibility that changes in the abundance and specificity of individual tRNA's might play an important role in metabolic regulation and cellular differentiation (Ames and Hartman, 1963; Stent, 1964; Sueoka, Kano-Sueoka, and Gartland, 1966; Weinstein, Friedman, and Ochoa, 1966). Changes in the tRNA population have been demonstrated in bacteria after T2 phage infection (Sueoka, Kano-Sueoka, and Gartland, 1966), after infection with an RNA phage (Hung and Overby, 1968), during sporulation (Kaneko and Doi, 1966; Lazzarini, 1966), and as a consequence of changes in the growth media (Doi, Kaneko, and Goehler, 1966; Yegian and Stent, 1969a, b). Recently, changes in the tRNA profiles of mammalian cells have been described after infection with herpes virus (Subak-Sharpe et al., 1966), and in hamster cells transformed with adenovirus 7 or simian virus 40 (SV40) (Taylor, Buck, Granger, and Holland, 1968). In addition, the total tRNA of certain tumors has a higher content of methylated bases than the tRNA of the corresponding normal tissue (Bergquist and Matthews, 1962; Viale et al., 1967). Borek and his colleagues have amassed evidence for an increase in the tRNA methylases of several tumors, a finding confirmed by others (see Tsutsui, Srinivasan, and Borek, [1966] and Baliga, Borek, Weinstein, and Srinivasan [1969] for a review of this subject). In collaboration with Dr. Emmanuel Farber, we found that liver tRNA obtained from rats which were fed ethionine for one month (prior to the appearance of hepatomas) was deficient in a minor leucine tRNA, presumably as a result of ethylation (Axel, Weinstein, and Farber, 1967). Additional effects of ethylation of liver tRNA during hepatic carcinogenesis are discussed in this volume by Dr. Novelli (1970, see pages 409 to 426, this volume).

In an extensive study of mammalian tissues, Taylor, Buck, Granger, and Holland (1968) found that the methylated albumin-kieselguhr (MAK) column elution profiles of tRNA's from different normal organs were usually similar. The elution profiles of phenylalanyl-, seryl-, gly-

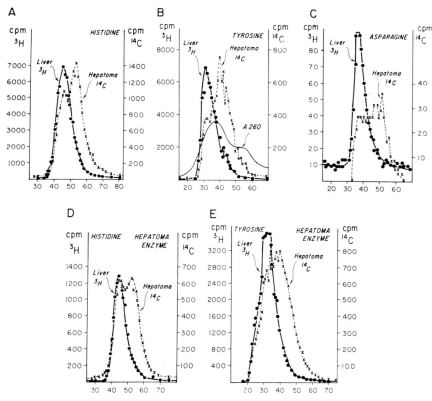

FIGURE 1. MAK column elution profiles of aminoacyl-tRNA's of normal rat liver and Novikoff hepatoma. Hepatoma enzymes were used to charge the tRNA's in D and E, while normal liver enzymes were used for all other profiles. A gradient of 0.3 to 0.7 M NaCl was used in A, B, and D; 0.35 to 0.6 M NaCl was used in C and E. A typical optical density (A_{260}) profile is shown in B. For additional details see Baliga, Borek, Weinstein, and Srinivasan (1969).

FIGURE 2. DEAE-Sephadex A-50 column chromatography of rat liver tRNA. The column (1 cm × 150 cm) was preequilibrated with 0.02 M Tris-HCl (pH 7.5), 0.0075 M $MgCl_2$ and 0.375 M NaCl. Three milliliters of rat liver tRNA in water (total 3,802 A_{260} units) were diluted to 12 ml with the starting buffer, and applied to the column. A linear gradient elution was carried out using 1 liter of 0.02 M Tris-HCl (pH 7.5), 0.016 M $MgCl_2$ and 0.525 M NaCl in the reservoir, and 1 liter of 0.02 M Tris-HCl (pH 7.5), 0.0075 M $MgCl_2$ and 0.375 M NaCl in the mixing chamber. The flow rate was 10 ml/hr. Each fraction contained 7 ml.

Fractions were assayed for amino acid-accepting activity using a crude

(Continued on page 385)

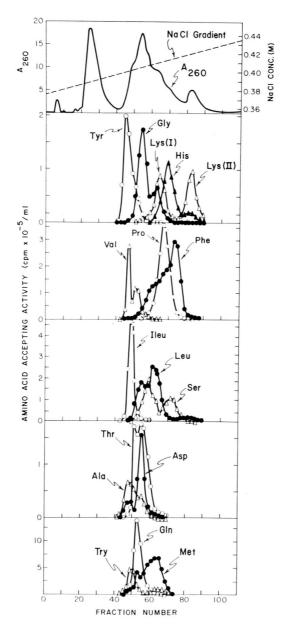

(Continued from page 384)

mixture of aminoacyl-tRNA synthetases obtained from rat liver. (For a complete description of the methods used, see Nishimura and Weinstein, 1969.)

cyl-, and tyrosyl-tRNA's from Ehrlich ascites tumor, however, differed appreciably from those of the corresponding normal mouse organ tRNA's. Yang and Novelli (1968) have described differences in the seryl-tRNA elution profiles between two mouse plasma cell tumors while Mushinski and Potter (1969) find variations in the abundance of different leucyl-tRNA's in a series of mouse plasma cell tumors.

In collaboration with Drs. Baliga, Borek, and Srinivasan, (Baliga, Borek, Weinstein, and Srinivasan, 1969), we have studied the elution profiles on MAK columns of aminoacyl tRNA's for 18 amino acids, comparing tRNA's obtained from the Novikoff hepatoma to those present in normal rat liver. Histidine, tyrosine, and asparagine showed the most notable differences in tRNA profiles (Figure 1). It appears that, in addition to the peaks present in normal liver, the tumor contains tRNA's for each of these amino acids which eluted at higher salt concentrations than the corresponding normal tRNA's. These changes were also apparent when the ^{14}C- and ^{3}H-labeling of hepatoma and liver tRNA's were reversed. The increased heterogeneity of Novikoff tyrosine tRNA also was confirmed by reverse-phase, benzoylated diethylaminoethyl (BD)-cellulose, and diethylaminoethyl (DEAE)-Sephadex A-50 column chromatography. In addition to the changes shown in Figure 1, the elution profiles of seryl-, arginyl-, isoleucyl-, lysyl-, methionyl-, and tryptophanyl-tRNA's of the hepatoma were generally broader and eluted later than the corresponding components in normal liver (Baliga, Borek, Weinstein, and Srinivasan, 1969). The tRNA's for nine other amino acids were studied also, but these revealed no major differences between the hepatoma and liver.

It is apparent, therefore, that extensive changes in the tRNA population accompany physiological or developmental changes, viral infection, and tumor formation, although at the present time it is difficult to separate cause from effect.

The tRNA Profile of Normal Rat Liver and Patterns of Codon Recognition

Despite rapid advances in the purification and sequence analysis of bacterial and yeast tRNA's, there are relatively few studies on the characterization of individual mammalian tRNA's. As a background to our studies on changes in tRNA which might occur during hepatic carcinogenesis, it was, therefore, necessary to obtain a detailed profile of the tRNA's present in normal rat liver. These studies were done in collaboration with Dr. Susumu Nishimura of the National Cancer Center in

Tokyo, while he was a visiting scientist in our laboratory, and the findings are summarized here (for a more detailed description, see Nishimura and Weinstein [1969]).

Figure 2 indicates the results obtained when approximately 200 mg of normal rat liver tRNA were chromatographed on a DEAE-Sephadex A-50 column and the fractions assayed for amino acid-accepting activity for 16 amino acids. An optical density peak (fractions 20 to 40) which eluted prior to the tRNA region appears to be a low molecular weight contaminant. The significance of this material is not known. Individual tRNA's were eluted as rather sharp peaks, and the presence of multiple forms of tRNA for a given amino acid was readily apparent (Figure 2). The DEAE-Sephadex procedure resulted in a ten- to twentyfold purification of tRNA's for tyrosine, phenylalanine, valine, serine, and lysine. Selected regions of this column were further fractionated on reverse phase columns of the types described by Kelmers, Novelli, and Stulberg (1965), and Weiss and Kelmers (1967), or on the BD-cellulose column described by Gillam et al. (1967). In this way, it was possible to obtain relatively pure samples of rat liver tRNA's specific for tyrosine, valine, serine, and phenylalanine. More recently, Drs. Fink and Goto in my laboratory (Fink, Nishimura, and Weinstein, 1968; Fink, Goto, and Weinstein, 1969) have used a simple two-step purification method which y:elds rat liver phenylalanine tRNA of greater than 95 per cent purity. This tRNA is of interest since it contains an unidentified fluorescent nucleoside similar to that present in the phenylalanine tRNA's of yeast (RajBhandary, Faulkner, and Stuart, 1968) and wheat germ (Dudock and Katz, 1969). Comparative studies on the structures of phenylalanine tRNA's obtained from yeast, rat liver, and hepatic tumors are currently in progress (Fink, Goto, and Weinstein, 1969).

The availability of isolated rat liver tRNA's made it possible to determine whether certain patterns of specificity by which a tRNA molecule recognizes codons in mRNA, previously established with *Escherichia coli* and yeast tRNA's, also apply to higher organisms. Degeneracy of the genetic code, *i.e.* the existence of multiple codons for the same amino acid, is a prominent feature in both microbial (Crick, 1966b) and mammalian systems (Weinstein, 1963; Marshall, Caskey, and Nirenberg, 1967; Caskey, Beaudet, and Nirenberg, 1968). Studies with *E. coli* and yeast tRNA's indicate that this is the result of the existence of multiple types of tRNA for the same amino acid, with each type recognizing a distinct codon (Weisblum, Gonano, von Ehrenstein, and Benzer, 1965; von Ehrenstein and Dais, 1963; Gonano, 1967), as well as the ability of individual tRNA's to recognize multiple codons (Kellogg, Doctor, Loebel, and Nirenberg, 1966; Söll, Cherayil, and Bock, 1967; Söll and RajBhandary, 1967).

The latter mechanism is explained by the wobble hypothesis of Crick (1966a). Table 3 summarizes the results obtained when isolated rat liver tRNA's were charged with their corresponding radioactive amino acids and tested for codon recognition in the Nirenberg and Leder (1964) ribosomal binding assay. The right side of this table indicates the predicted base in the 5' position of the anticodon of each of these tRNA's, based on the wobble hypothesis. Both rat liver lysine tRNA's, Lys$_I$ and Lys$_{II}$, responded to AAA and AAG; all three tyrosine tRNA's, Tyr$_{I-A}$, Tyr$_{I-B}$ and Tyr$_{I-C}$, responded to UAU and UAC; the two phenylalanine tRNA's, Phe$_I$ and Phe$_{II}$, both responded to UUU and UUC; and one of the serine tRNA's, Ser$_{II}$, responded to AGU and AGC (Table 3). These results are entirely consistent with the wobble mechanism. The apparent response of a separate serine tRNA, Ser$_I$, to the four codons UCU, UCC, UCA and UCG does not fit the wobble mechanism, but experiments in progress indicate that Ser$_I$ separates into two components on a reversed phase chromatography (RPC)-freon column. It is likely that one of these components recognizes the three codons UCU, UCC and UCA. The latter pattern of recognition is seen with a purified yeast serine tRNA and is explained by the presence of inosine in the anticodon (Zachau et al., 1966). Consistent with this formulation are recent results of Staehelin et al. (1968) indicating that a serine tRNA purified from rat liver does contain inosine in the 5' end of the anticodon. The results obtained with three liver valine tRNA's, Val$_{I-A}$, Val$_{I-B}$, and Val$_{I-C}$, are difficult to interpret since these subfractions differed in their relative responses to similar codons and the subfractions may not be completely separate from each other. The response of Val$_{II}$ to GUA, GUG, and, to a lesser extent, GUU, does not fit the wobble mechanism. Mirzabekov et al. (1967) have reported a similar pattern of codon recognition for a purified yeast valine tRNA, and Kellogg, Doctor, Loebel, and Nirenberg (1966) had similar results with an E. coli valine tRNA. These findings suggest that an unusual base in the 5' position of the anticodon, perhaps pseudouridine (Kellogg, Doctor, Loebel, and Nirenberg, 1966; Mirzabekov et al., 1967) can pair with either A, G, or U. Should this prove to be true, an additional base-pairing rule would be added to the wobble hypothesis. I must emphasize that the interpretations for serine and valine tRNA's discussed above and presented in Table 3 are preliminary. Alternative explanations have not been excluded, and further fractionation and codon recognition studies are required to clarify these points.

With phenylalanine, tyrosine, and lysine, we observed multiple

TABLE 3. *Codon Responses of Isolated Rat Liver tRNAs**

tRNA	Actual codon response			Predicted base in 5' position of anticodon
Lys$_I$; Lys$_{II}$	AAA ● AAG ●			Uracil
Tyr$_I$; Tyr$_{II}$	UAU ● UAC ●			Guanine
Phe$_I$; Phe$_{II}$	UUU ● UUC ●			Guanine
Ser$_I$	UCU ● UCC UCA	● ●		Inosine
	UCG ●	●		Cytidine
Ser$_{II}$	AGU ● AGC ●			Guanine
Val$_{I-A}$; Val$_{I-B}$; Val$_{I-C}$	GUU ● GUC GUA	● ●		Inosine
	GUG ●	●		Cytidine
Val$_{II}$	GUA ● GUG GUU ●			Pseudouridine?

* Isolated rat liver tRNA's were obtained by fractionation on DEAE Sephadex A-50 and reverse phase columns. Multiple tRNA's were obtained for a given amino acid and these are designated by the subscripts. They were charged with their corresponding radioactive amino acids and tested for codon responses in the Nirenberg and Leder (1964) ribosomal binding assay, using synthetic RNA triplets. The right-hand column is "predicted" from the wobble hypothesis (Crick, 1966a). Additional details are described in the text and in Nishimura and Weinstein (1969).

Abbreviations: A, adenine; C, cytidine; G, guanine; Lys, lysine; Phe, phenylalanine; Ser, serine; Tyr, tyrosine; U, uracil; Val, valine.

tRNA fractions for the same amino acid which appear to be identical with respect to codon recognition. The functional significance of this apparent redundancy in tRNA's is not known, and our data do not completely exclude the possibility that it reflects an in vitro artifact. However, redundancy for tRNA's apparently exists also in *E. coli* (Söll, Cherayil, and Bock, 1967) and in a haploid strain of yeast (Söll *et al.*, 1966). It has been postulated that the redundant copies may provide a source of tRNA suppressors (Söll *et al.*, 1966; Bergquist, Burns, and

Plinston, 1968). Hybridization studies done with drosophila DNA suggest that there may also be redundancy of the cistrons for tRNA on the DNA (Ritossa, Atwood, and Spiegelman, 1966). We believe, therefore, that certain cases of redundancy seen in the present study also exist in vivo. Further studies are necessary to determine whether or not these redundant copies play a role in cell regulation and differentiation in mammalian systems.

Modifications of tRNA by Acetylaminofluorene

I would like to describe recent experiments done by Drs. Louis Fink, Susumu Nishimura and Manjul Agarwal in our laboratory using acetylaminofluorene (AAF) and its derivatives. AAF is a potent hepatic carcinogen for rats which binds to liver RNA, as well as DNA and protein, when administered in vivo (Marroquin and Farber, 1965; Henshaw and Hiatt, 1963; Kriek, 1968; Miller and Miller, 1967; Kriek, Miller, Juhl, and Miller, 1967). This carcinogen, as do certain other aromatic amides, requires metabolic activation as a prerequisite for combination with macromolecules (Miller, 1968; King and Phillips, 1968). The primary step in this activation is N-hydroxylation (Miller, 1968). The final metabolite, or proximate carcinogen, has not been identified in vivo. The Millers have suggested (1968) that it may be an ester of N-OH-AAF and they have demonstrated that a synthetically prepared ester, N-acetoxy-AAF, complexes directly with RNA and DNA at neutral pH in vitro. Hydrolysis of these nucleic acids indicated that the major nucleoside derivative is 8-(N-2-fluorenylacetamido) guanosine (Miller and Miller, 1967; Kriek, Miller, Juhl, and Miller, 1967). This reaction is shown in Figure 3. N-acetoxy-AAF and 9-^{14}C-N-acetoxy-AAF (960 dpm/μg) were generously supplied to us by Dr. James Miller of the University of Wisconsin. This permitted us to examine the effects of in vitro modification of E. coli tRNA by N-acetoxy-AAF with respect to amino acid-acceptance capacity, ribosomal binding, and chromatographic behavior. I would now like to present evidence that in this model system the carcinogen selectively modifies the function of specific types of tRNA. A preliminary report of some of these results has been published (Fink, Nishimura, and Weinstein, 1968).

N-acetoxy-AAF in water has absorption maxima at 274 mμ and 301 mμ. The tRNA previously reacted with N-acetoxy-AAF, after being repurified, revealed absorption in the 300 to 310 mμ region, reflecting the presence of bound AAF (Figure 4). This absorption provides a convenient method for detecting AAF on nucleic acids (as described by Miller, Juhl, and Miller, 1966). With increasing concentrations of N-

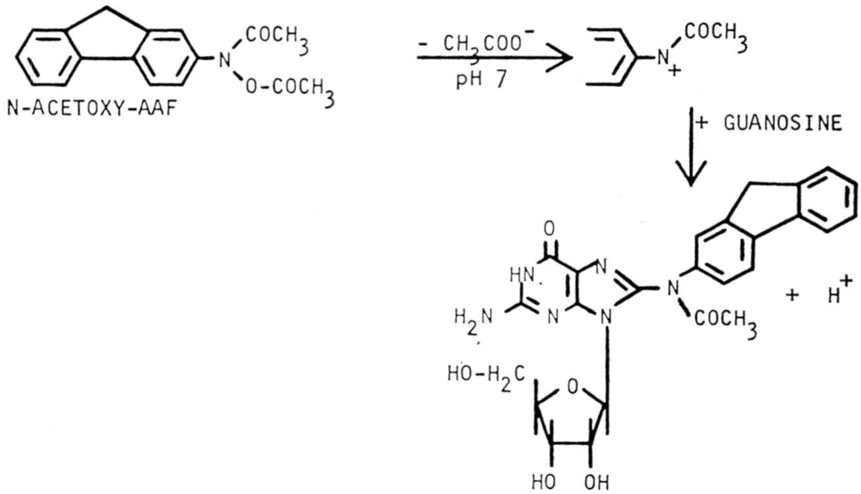

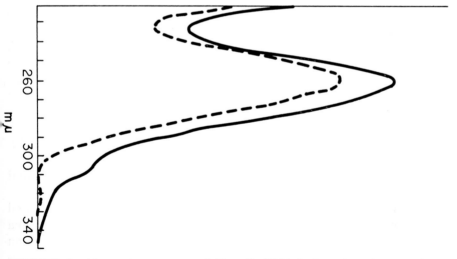

FIGURE 3. The in vitro reaction of N-acetoxy-AAF with guanosine. Modified from Kriek, Miller, Juhl, and Miller (1967).

ABSORBANCE

FIGURE 4. Absorption spectra of E. coli tRNA before (– – –) and after (——) reaction with 3×10^{-2} M N-acetoxy-AAF. Reaction conditions were similar to those described by Miller and Miller (1967).

acetoxy-AAF in the reaction mixture, there was an increase in the 310/260 ratio of the reisolated tRNA, indicating increasing amounts of bound AAF. More quantitative studies using ^{14}C-N-acetoxy-AAF indicated that at 1.5×10^{-3} M N-acetoxy-AAF there was approximately 1 mole of AAF bound per mole of tRNA, and at 3.0×10^{-4} M N-acetoxy-AAF, there were approximately 3 moles of AAF per mole of tRNA. These calculations assume a uniform distribution of AAF among the tRNA's. Subsequent studies (see below), however, indicate that this is probably not the case. Time-course studies indicated that maximum binding of AAF to tRNA occurred by 3 hours of incubation. Therefore, a 3.5-hour incubation period was chosen for the preparation of all subsequent batches of AAF tRNA.

The first functional property tested was the amino acid-acceptance capacity of the modified tRNA in the aminoacyl-tRNA synthetase reaction. To be certain that we were measuring total acceptance capacity, these studies were done in the range of limiting tRNA concentration (0.12 to 1.2 $A_{260}/0.1$ ml assay system). In addition, samples were incubated for 10 min at 37 C, since time-course studies indicated that by this time the charging reaction had reached a plateau in both control and AAF tRNA. The acceptance capacity for 15 amino acids of control tRNA and of tRNA previously reacted with 1.5×10^{-3} M N-acetoxy-AAF is shown in Table 4. The activity of arginine and lysine tRNA's showed the greatest extent of inhibition; there was less or no inhibition for several other tRNA's; there was actual stimulation (136 to 231 per cent) of valine and alanine tRNA acceptance, when compared to equivalent amounts of control tRNA. Both the inhibition of the acceptance capacity of tRNA for arginine and lysine and the stimulation for valine and alanine were reproducible with repeated batches of AAF tRNA and were apparent when the tRNA concentration in the reaction mixture was varied over a threefold range. In contrast to the selective effects obtained with 1.5×10^{-3} M N-acetoxy-AAF, there was extensive inactivation of the acceptance capacity of tRNA for all amino acids when the tRNA was reacted with high concentrations (10^{-2} M) of drug.

The functional properties of AAF tRNA with respect to ribosomal binding and codon response are shown in Table 5. When AAF tRNA was aminoacylated with lysine, both the poly A- and the poly AG-stimulated ribosomal binding of this tRNA were less than 40 per cent of that obtained with control lysyl-tRNA. Conversely, no significant differences between AAF and control tRNA were observed in the binding of phenylalanyl-tRNA stimulated by poly U, of methionyl-tRNA stimulated by poly UG or poly UGA, or of tyrosyl-tRNA stimulated by poly UA. A significant

TABLE 4. *Amino Acid Acceptance Capacity of* E. Coli *tRNA After Treatment with N-Acetoxy-AAF (1.5 × 10⁻³ M)**

Amino acid	Amino acid acceptance ($\mu\mu$moles/assay system)		
	Control tRNA	AAF tRNA	% Control†
Arginine	35	12	34
Lysine	17	9	52
Leucine	63	36	57
Isoleucine	15	9	60
Threonine	19	12	62
Glycine	17	11	62
Histidine	6	4	63
Phenylalanine	18	12	65
Proline	17	12	69
Aspartic	20	15	74
Tyrosine	21	17	80
Serine	9	8	88
Methionine	45	41	91
Valine	37	51	136
Alanine	8	18	231

* All tRNAs were tested at a limiting concentration, *i.e.* 0.61 A_{260} units/0.1 ml assay system. The preparation of the AAF tRNA was similar to that described in Figure 3. The preparation of *E. coli* aminoacyl-tRNA synthetases and additional details of the assay system are similar to those described by Nishimura, Harada, Narushima, and Seno (1967).
† Acceptance AAF tRNA × 100/acceptance control tRNA.

decrease in the binding of the AAF tRNA was observed, however, with tyrosyl tRNA and poly UAC. Additional codons and tRNA's remain to be tested, but it is already apparent that AAF produces selective modifications in the ability of certain tRNA's to recognize their normal codons.

When AAF tRNA was chromatographed on DEAE-Sephadex, there was a discordance between the 260-mμ and 310-mμ elution profiles, suggesting that molecules of tRNA carrying AAF were delayed in their elution from the column (Figure 5). Previous studies (Nishimura, Harada, Narushima, and Seno, 1967) have indicated that *E. coli* methionine tRNA (which includes a mixture of formylmethionine and methionine tRNA's) normally elutes as a single peak at the beginning of the A_{260} profile. After AAF modification, we observed three methionine tRNA peaks (Figure 5). The first is eluted at a position which is identical to that of control methionine tRNA. Peaks 2 and 3 are eluted later and are in the region of 310-mμ absorption. These results suggest that peaks 2 and 3 might be derived from peak 1 by AAF modification, or that AAF had brought about modifications of other tRNA's which allowed them to

TABLE 5. *Codon Response of AAF tRNA**

| Template | Aminoacyl-tRNA bound to ribosomes | |
	Control tRNA	AAF tRNA
[14]C-Lys-tRNA	$\Delta\mu\mu$moles	
Poly A	1.58	0.61
Poly AG (3:1)	2.06	0.45
	$\mu\mu$moles	
None	0.28	0.21
[14]C-Phe-tRNA	$\Delta\mu\mu$moles	
Poly U	2.80	2.55
	$\mu\mu$moles	
None	0.14	0.27
[14]C-Met-tRNA	$\Delta\mu\mu$moles	
Poly UG (5:1)	0.88	1.05
Poly UGA (10:3:1)	0.94	0.98
	$\mu\mu$moles	
None	0.41	0.58
[14]C-Tyr-tRNA	$\Delta\mu\mu$moles	
Poly UA (5:1)	0.86	0.70
Poly UAC (1:1:1)	0.87	0.39
	$\mu\mu$moles	
None	0.18	0.59

* *E. coli* control tRNA and *E. coli* tRNA previously reacted with N-acetoxy-AAF (1.5×10^{-3} M) were charged with the indicated ^{14}C-amino acids and tested at comparable concentrations in the Nirenberg and Leder (1964) ribosomal binding assay. Reaction mixtures contained 1.0 A_{260} unit of *E. coli* ribosomes and 0.1 A_{260} units of the indicated polynucleotides as templates. Remaining details of the assay system are described by Nishimura and Weinstein (1969).

Abbreviations: A, adenine; AAF, acetylaminofluorene; C, cytosine; G, guanine; Lys, lysine; Met, methionine; Phe, phenylalanine; Tyr, tyrosine; U, uracil.

accept methionine. To investigate these two possibilities, previously purified methionine tRNA was reacted with N-acetoxy-AAF and then chromatographed on DEAE-Sephadex. Again, three methionine tRNA peaks were obtained (Figure 6), indicating that peaks 2 and 3 are derived from peak 1 as a result of AAF modification. Consistent with this was an increase in 310:260 ratio of peaks 2 and 3, when they were compared to peak 1.

The fact that BD-cellulose has a strong affinity for lipophilic residues (Gillam *et al.*, 1967) suggested that it might give even better resolution between AAF tRNA and control tRNA. When control tRNA was chromatographed on BD-cellulose, 95 per cent of the A_{260} material was eluted during the NaCl gradient and the remaining 5 per cent was eluted with 10 per cent ethanol; methionine tRNA eluted as a single peak in the early

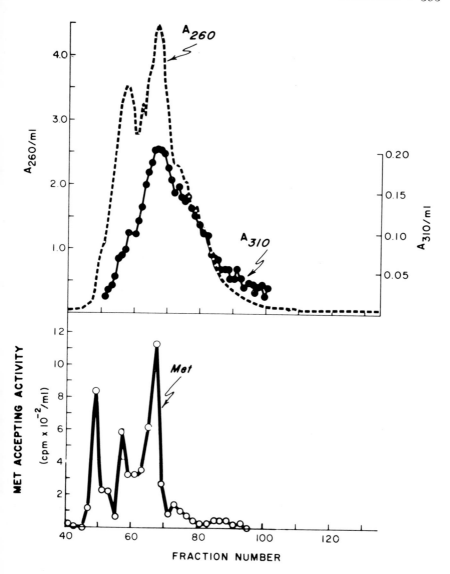

FIGURE 5. Chromatography of *E. coli* AAF tRNA on a DEAE-Sephadex A-50 column. The column (0.5 × 100 cm) was prepared as described by Nishimura, Harada, Narushima, and Seno (1967), 220 A_{260} of *E. coli* tRNA, previously reacted with 1.5 × 10⁻³ M N-acetoxy-AAF, was diluted to 10 ml with initial buffer and loaded on the column. A linear gradient elution was carried out using 250 ml of 0.525 M NaCl, 0.016 M $MgCl_2$, 0.02 M Tris-HCl

(Continued on page 396)

portion of the salt (NaCl) gradient (Figure 7). In contrast to these results, when AAF tRNA was chromatographed on BD-cellulose, only 25 per cent of the A_{260} material eluted with the NaCl gradient; the remaining 75 per cent required 10 to 20 per cent ethanol for elution. Figure 8 indicates the results obtained when purified methionine tRNA was reacted with ^{14}C-N-acetoxy-AAF (1.5×10^{-3}M) and chromatographed on BD-cellulose and the fractions were assayed for methionine tRNA with

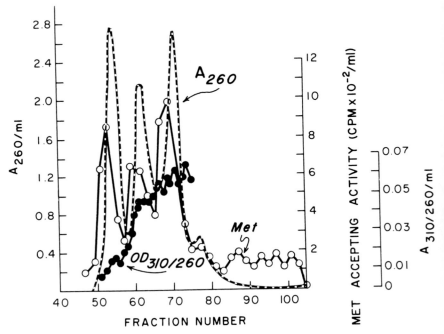

FIGURE 6. Fractionation of purified *E. coli* methionine tRNA, which had been previously reacted with 1.5×10^{-3} M N-acetoxy-AAF, on a DEAE-Sephadex A-50 column. The column was prepared and run as described in Figure 5. The tRNA (83 A_{260}) was applied in 3 ml of the initial buffer. The recovery was 70 per cent; fraction aliquots of 0.02 ml were assayed for ^{14}C-methionine acceptance.

(Continued from page 395)
(pH 7.5) in the reservoir and 250 ml 0.375 M NaCl, 0.0075 M MgCl$_2$, 0.02 M Tris-HCl (pH 7.5) in the mixing chamber. The flow rate was 10 ml/hr. Each fraction contained 2 ml of eluate. The recovery was 85 per cent. Fraction aliquots of 0.02 ml were assayed for ^{14}C-methionine acceptance using *E. coli* aminoacyl tRNA synthetase.

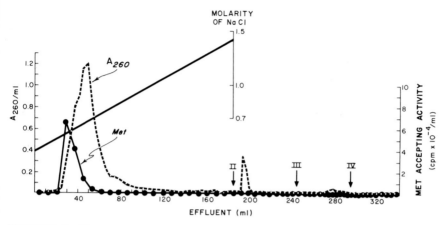

FIGURE 7. Chromatography of unfractionated *E. coli* tRNA on a BD-cellulose column (Gillam *et al.*, 1968) at 4 C. The column (29 × 0.5 cm) was
equilibrated with 0.4 M NaCl, 0.05 M sodium acetate (pH 5.0) and 37 A_{260} of
control tRNA was applied. The elution sequence was: (1) a linear gradient
of 100 ml 0.4 M NaCl, 0.05 M sodium acetate (pH 5.0) in the mixing chamber
and 100 ml of 1.5 M NaCl in 0.05 M sodium acetate (pH 5.0) in the reservoir;
(2) 75 ml of 1.5 M NaCl, 0.05 M sodium acetate containing 10 per cent
ethanol; (3) 75 ml of the latter buff but containing 15 per cent ethanol;
and (4) 75 ml of the latter but containing 20 per cent ethanol. The flow rate
was .7 ml/min. Aliquots of 0.05 ml were assayed for ^{3}H-methionine acceptance.

^{3}H-methionine. Three major A_{260} and methionine tRNA peaks were observed. The first peak eluted at the beginning of the NaCl gradient and
contained no ^{14}C-AAF, the second eluted with 10 per cent ethanol and
contained ^{14}C-AAF, and the third eluted with 20 per cent ethanol and
also contained ^{14}C-AAF. The specific activities of peaks 2 and 3 indicated
that both contained approximately 1 mole of bound AAF per mole of
tRNA.

It appears, therefore, that, under these conditions, approximately
one third of *E. coli* methionine tRNA does not react with N-acetoxy-AAF
and the remaining two thirds form at least two derivates. These results
may be explained by recent evidence indicating that our methionine
tRNA was actually a mixture of three components: tRNA^{Met_1}, tRNA^{Met_2},
and tRNA^{fMet} (Seno, Kobayashi, and Nishimura, 1968; Cory, Marcker,
Dube, and Clark, 1968). In addition, *E. coli* tRNA^{fMet} can apparently
exist in two different forms. Further studies are required to determine
the relative reactivities of these subfractions with N-acetoxy-AAF, and
alternative explanations have not been excluded.

The high resolving power of the BD-cellulose column suggested its use to separate those tRNA's that react with AAF during in vivo carcinogenesis from those that do not (Agarwal and Weinstein, 1969). Figure 9 indicates results obtained when normal rats were injected with ^{14}C-N-hydroxy-AAF and the tRNA fractionated on a BD-cellulose col-

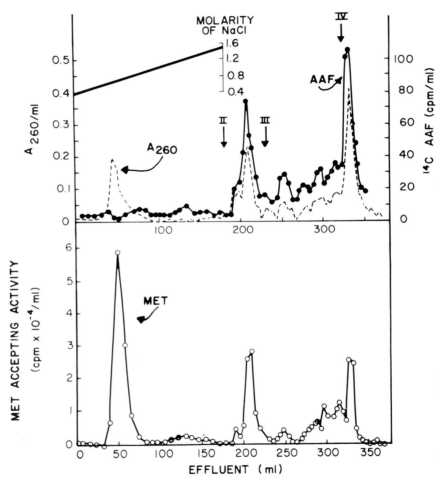

FIGURE 8. Chromatography of purified *E. coli* methionine tRNA (16 A_{260}), which had been previously reacted with 1.5×10^{-3} M ^{14}C-N-acetoxy-AAF, on a BD-cellulose column. The elution scheme was similar to that described in Figure 7. The A_{260} recovery was 90 per cent. Two ml of each fraction was counted directly in Bray's solution to determine the distribution of ^{14}C-AAF and 0.05 ml was assayed for ^{3}H-methionine acceptance.

umn. Whereas approximately 90 per cent of the RNA is eluted during the NaCl gradient, almost all of the radioactivity remains tightly bound to the column and is eluted only with ethanol. The ethanol region, therefore, provides a highly enriched source of the RNA's which reacted with AAF. Similar results were obtained when rats were injected with ^{14}C-AAF. The high affinity of AAF tRNA for the BD-cellulose column thus makes it possible to isolate and characterize the specific types of tRNA which react with the carcinogen during prolonged feeding. Such studies are now in progress.

Regarding the molecular basis for specificity of interaction between derivatives of AAF and tRNA's and possible consequences of this interaction, previous studies have established that the major nucleic acid target for this carcinogen is the 8 position of guanosine (Miller, Juhl, and Miller, 1966; Kriek, Miller, Juhl, and Miller, 1967). The sensitivity of a given tRNA to modification by this agent will depend, therefore, on the number of guanosine residues it contains, the degree to which secondary and tertiary structures of the tRNA influence the reactivity of these residues, and whether or not the residues occupy positions in the tRNA which are critical for its function. The unusual sensitivity of *E. coli* lysine tRNA to inactivation by N-acetoxy-AAF cannot be explained at present, since the structure of this tRNA is not known. It is of interest that this tRNA is also unusually sensitive to inactivation by other agents (Miura, 1967), and it is tempting to relate this to the possible presence of thio bases (Weiss, Hsu, Foft, and Scherberg, 1968) in this tRNA. The fact that reaction of *E. coli* tRNA with N-acetoxy-AAF actually enhanced the acceptance capacities for valine and alanine might be explained by assuming that: (1) AAF modification permits other tRNA's to become "mischarged" with valine or alanine; (2) AAF residues enhance the affinity of valine and alanine tRNA's for their corresponding aminoacyl-tRNA synthetases; or, (3) AAF converts a portion of valine and alanine tRNA's from a denatured to a renatured conformation. The latter explanation is the most likely, since renaturation of tRNA with both magnesium (Adams, Lindahl, and Fresco, 1967; Sueoka, Kano-Sueoka, and Gartland, 1966) and chloroquine (Muench, 1966) has been described. Enhancement of acceptance activity for certain tRNA's also has been described as a consequence of 5-fluorouracil incorporation (Giege, Heinrich, Weil, and Ebel, 1969; Kaiser, 1969) and as a result of in vitro methylation with dimethyl sulfate (Borek, 1969).

How might the presence of an AAF residue on a tRNA molecule alter its functional properties? Attachment to the 8 position of guanosine would not directly interfere with hydrogen bonding. In contrast to

the effects of alkylation of nitrogen 7 of this base (Brookes and Lawley, 1964), it does not greatly increase acidic ionization of nitrogen 1 or cause depurination resulting from secondary cleavage of the glycoside bond (Kriek, Miller, Juhl, and Miller, 1967). A clue to the mechanism can be found, however, in recent studies by A. N. Michelson (personal communication) on the conformation of 8-bromoguanosine and studies by Ward and Reich (1968) on the conformation of polyformycin. The

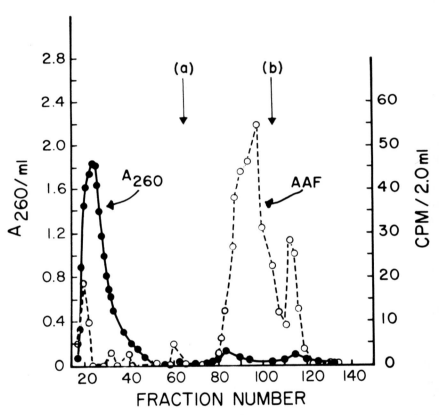

FIGURE 9. Chromatography on BD-cellulose of rat liver tRNA obtained 18 hr after injection of ^{14}C-N-hydroxyacetylaminofluorene (specific activity 6 mc/mM; 33 μc intraperitoneally [150 g rat]). The sample (220 A_{260}) was applied to a 1 × 32 cm column. The elution sequence at 20 C was: a linear gradient of 200 ml of 0.4 M NaCl, 0.05 M sodium acetate, 0.01 M MgCl in the mixing chamber and 200 ml of 1.5 M NaCl, 0.05 M sodium acetate, 0.01 M MgCl in the reservoir; then (a) a 200 ml linear gradient of 0 to 20 per cent ethanol in the latter buffer; and (b) 100 ml of 20 per cent ethanol in the same buffer; 2 ml of each fraction was assayed for radioactivity.

studies of Michelson are most relevant since he has found that the presence of a bromine residue in the 8 position restricts, via stearic hindrance, rotation at the glycoside bond, thus converting the nucleoside from the "anti" conformation found in double-stranded helices with Watson-Crick geometry (Donohue and Trueblood, 1960; Ward and Reich, 1968) to the "syn" conformation. Presence of the bulky AAF residue on the 8 position of guanosine would produce a similar conformational change at the glycoside bond; the construction of a space-filling model (CPK) indicates that this is the case. The presence of a single AAF residue, therefore, might introduce a gross change in the conformation of that region of the tRNA, thereby altering interaction with specific activating enzymes, codons, or ribosomes. A similar disturbance in the conformation of DNA also might account for previously described effects of AAF on certain functional properties of DNA (Troll *et al.*, 1968; Maher, Miller, Miller, and Szybalski, 1968). This hypothesis also predicts that guanosine residues in double-stranded regions of nucleic acids (which are in the "anti" conformation) will be less accessible to reaction with the drug than those in single-stranded regions, since in the former configuration the 8 position of guanosine is relatively inaccessible to attack by a bulky residue. Preliminary experiments done in collaboration with Dr. Dezider Grunberger indicate that the attachment of AAF to guanosine residues present in the triplets G_pU_pU (which normally codes for valine) or A_pA_pG (which normally codes for lysine) completely inactivates the ability of these triplets to stimulate ribosomal binding of valyl tRNA and lysyl tRNA, respectively (Grunberger and Weinstein, unpublished data). This model system provides us with an opportunity to examine in further detail the effect of a carcinogen on a triplet of nucleotides, probably the smallest functional unit of nucleic acids.

Summary

In summary, I have proposed that cancer is due to an aberration in differentiation which, in certain cases, is potentially reversible. This concept has profound implications in terms of our approach to treatment of the disease. In addition, it focuses attention on the possibility that the critical target for carcinogens may be "extragenic." I have reviewed evidence that at least two hepatic carcinogens, ethionine and acetylaminofluorene (AAF), react preferentially with rat liver tRNA. Several characteristics of the tRNA population of both normal rat liver and the Novikoff hepatoma have also been described. Model experiments employing N-acetoxy-AAF and *E. coli* tRNA indicate that this carcinogen produces

selective modifications in the amino acid acceptance, codon recognition, and chromatographic behavior of specific tRNA's. The functional modifications in nucleic acids produced by AAF can be attributed to a change in nucleoside conformation from "anti" to "syn."

We have speculated previously about mechanisms by which carcinogen-induced modifications of tRNA might produce tumors (Axel, Weinstein, and Farber, 1967; Weinstein, 1968). Proof of the validity of these speculations requires definitive evidence that tRNA's normally play an important role in cell regulation and differentiation in higher organisms. Studies along these lines are now in progress in our laboratory.

ACKNOWLEDGMENTS

The author wishes to acknowledge the invaluable contributions of Drs. Louis M. Fink, Susumu Nishimura, Tamotsu Goto, and Manjul Agarwal to this paper. He is indebted to Drs. Alfred Gellhorn, Jacob Furth, Emmanuel Farber, and James Miller for helpful discussions on several points mentioned in this paper.

This research was supported by United States Public Health Service Research Grant R10 CA-02332 from the National Cancer Institute.

The author is a Career Scientist of the Health Research Council of the City of New York (I-190).

REFERENCES

Adams, A., T. Lindahl, and J. R. Fresco. 1967. Conformational Differences Between the Biologically Active and Inactive Forms of a Transfer Ribonucleic Acid. *Proceedings of the National Academy of Sciences of the U.S.A.*, 57:1684–1691.

Agarwal, M. K., and I. B. Weinstein. 1969. *In Vivo* Binding of Acetylaminofluorene (AAF) to Rat Liver Transfer RNA. (Abstract) *Proceedings of the American Association for Cancer Research*, 10:2.

Ames, B. N., and P. E. Hartman. 1963. The Histidine Operon. *Cold Spring Harbor Symposia on Quantitative Biology*, 28:349–356.

Alpert, M. E., J. Uriel, and B. de Nechaud. 1968. Alpha$_1$ Fetoglobulin in the Diagnosis of Human Hepatoma. *New England Journal of Medicine*, 278:984–986.

Axel, R., I. B. Weinstein, and E. Farber. 1967. Patterns of Transfer RNA in Normal Rat Liver and During Hepatic Carcinogenesis. *Proceedings of the National Academy of Sciences of the U.S.A.*, 58:1255–1260.

Baliga, B. S., E. Borek, I. B. Weinstein, and P. R. Srinivasan. 1969. Differences in the Transfer RNA's of Normal Liver and Novikoff Hepatoma. *Proceedings of the National Academy of Sciences of the U.S.A.*, 62:899–905.

Bergquist, P. L., D. J. Burns, and C. A. Plinston. 1968. Participation of Redundant Transfer Ribonucleic Acids from Yeast in Protein Synthesis. *Biochemistry*, 7:1751–1761.

Bergquist, P. L., and R. E. F. Matthews. 1962. Occurrence and Distribution of Methylated Purines in the Ribonucleic Acids of Subcellular Fractions. *Biochemical Journal*, 85:305–313.

Bower, B. F., and G. S. Gordan. 1965. Hormonal Effects of Nonendocrine Tumors. *Annual Review of Medicine*, 16:83–118.

Braun, A. C., and H. N. Wood. 1961. The Plant Tumor Problem. *Advances in Cancer Research*, 6:81–109.

Brookes, P., and P. D. Lawley. 1964. Reaction of Some Mutagenic and Carcinogenic Compounds with Nucleic Acids. *Journal of Cellular and Comparative Physiology*, 64(Suppl. 1):111–127.

Caskey, C. T., A. Beaudet, and M. Nirenberg. 1968. RNA Codons and Protein Synthesis, Dissimilar Responses of Mammalian and Bacterial Transfer RNA Fractions to Messenger RNA Codons. *Journal of Molecular Biology*, 37:99–118.

Cory, S., K. A. Marcker, S. K. Dube, and B. F. C. Clark. 1968. Primary Structure of a Methionine Transfer RNA from *Escherichia coli*. *Nature*, 220:1039–1040.

Crick, F. H. C. 1966a. Codon-Anticodon Pairing: The Wobble Hypothesis. *Journal of Molecular Biology*, 19:548–555.

Crick, F. H. C. 1966b. The Genetic Code—Yesterday, Today, and Tomorrow. *Cold Spring Harbor Symposia on Quantitative Biology*, 31:1–9.

Doi, R. H., I. Kaneko, and B. Goehler. 1966. Regulation of a Serine Transfer RNA of *Bacillus subtilis* under Two Growth Conditions. *Proceedings of the National Academy of Sciences of the U.S.A.*, 56:1548–1551.

Donohue, J., and K. N. Trueblood. 1960. Base Pairing in DNA. *Journal of Molecular Biology*, 2:363–371.

Dudock, B. S., and G. Katz. 1969. Large Oligonucleotide Sequences in Wheat Germ Phenylalanine Transfer Ribonucleic Acid: Derivation of the Total Primary Structure. *Journal of Biological Chemistry*, 244:3069–3074.

Ehrenstein, G. von, and D. Dais. 1963. A Leucine Acceptor sRNA with Ambiguous Coding Properties in Polynucleotide-Stimulated Polypeptide Synthesis. *Proceedings of the National Academy of Sciences of the U.S.A.*, 50:81–86.

Everson, T. C., and W. H. Cole. 1966. *Spontaneous Regression of Cancer* (A Study and Abstract of Reports in the World Medical Literature and of Personal Communications Concerning Spontaneous Regression of Malignant Disease). Philadelphia, Pennsylvania: W. B. Saunders Co., 550 pp.

Farber, E. 1968. Biochemistry of Carcinogenesis. *Cancer Research*, 28:1859–1869.

Farber, E., J. McConomy, B. Franzen, F. Marroquin, G. A. Stewart, and P. N. Magee. 1967. Interaction Between Ethionine and Rat Liver Ribonucleic Acid and Protein in Vivo. *Cancer Research*, 27:1761–1772.

Fink, L. M., T. Goto, and I. B. Weinstein. 1969. Rat Liver Phenylalanine tRNA. (Abstract) *Federation Proceedings*, 28:409.

Fink, L. M., S. Nishimura, and I. B. Weinstein. 1968. Modification of Transfer RNA by a Derivative of Acetylaminofluorene. (Abstract.) *Proceedings of the American Association for Cancer Research*, 9:21.

Gellhorn, A. 1966. Editorial on Cancer: Facts and Theories. Clinical Physiology, Chemotherapy, Fundamental Nature and Mechanisms of Gene Control. *Seminars in Hematology*, 3:99–113.

Giege, R., J. Heinrich, J.-H. Weil, and J.-P. Ebel. 1969. Étude des Propriétés Biologiques des Acides Ribonucléiques de Transfert de Levure Ayant Incorporé du 5-Fluorouracile. *Biochimica et biophysica acta*, 174:53–70.

Gillam, I., S. Millward, D. Blew, M. von Tigerstrom, E. Wimmer, and G. M. Tener.

1967. The Separation of Soluble Ribonucleic Acids on Benzoylated Diethylamino-ethylcellulose. *Biochemistry*, 6:3043–3056.

Gold, P., and S. O. Freedman. 1965. Specific Carcinoembryonic Antigens of the Human Digestive System. *Journal of Experimental Medicine*, 122:467–481.

Gonano, F. 1967. Specificity of Serine Transfer Ribonucleic Acids in the Synthesis of Hemoglobin. *Biochemistry*, 6:977–983.

Grunberger, D., and I. B. Weinstein. Unpublished data.

Gurdon, J. B. 1967. "Nuclear Transplantation and Cell Differentiation," *Cell Differentiation* (A Ciba Foundation Symposium), A. V. S. de Reuck and J. Knight, Eds. Boston, Massachusetts: Little, Brown and Co. Pp. 65–74.

Henshaw, E. C., and H. H. Hiatt. 1963. Binding of Fluorenylacetamide to Rat Liver Ribonucleic Acid (RNA) In Vivo. (Abstract) *Proceedings of the American Association for Cancer Research*, 4:27.

Hung, P. P., and L. R. Overby. 1968. Alteration in Function of Transfer Ribonucleic Acid of *Escherichia coli* after Infection with Phage Qβ. *Journal of Biological Chemistry*, 243:5525–5531.

Ivanov, F. A., V. J. Fel, and J. M. Olenov. 1968. The Investigation of some Antigens of Zajdela Ascitic Rat Hepatoma Cells. *Cancer Research*, 28:1524–1530.

Kaiser, I. I. 1969. Studies on 5-Fluorouracil-Containing Ribonucleic Acid. I. Separation and Partial Characterization of Fluorouracil-Containing Transfer Ribonucleic Acids from *Escherichia coli*. *Biochemistry*, 8:231–238.

Kaneko, I., and R. H. Doi. 1966. Alteration of Valyl-sRNA During Sporulation of *Bacillus subtilis*. *Proceedings of the National Academy of Sciences of the U.S.A.*, 55:564–571.

Kellogg, D. A., B. P. Doctor, J. E. Loebel, and M. W. Nirenberg. 1966. RNA Codons and Protein Synthesis. IX. Synonym Codon Recognition by Multiple Species of Valine-, Alanine-, and Methionine-sRNA. *Proceedings of the National Academy of Sciences of the U.S.A.*, 55:912–919.

Kelmers, A. D., G. D. Novelli, and M. P. Stulberg. 1965. Separation of Transfer Ribonucleic Acids by Reverse Phase Chromatography. *Journal of Biological Chemistry*, 240:3979–3983.

King, C. M., and B. Phillips. 1968. Enzyme-Catalyzed Reactions of the Carcinogen N-Hydroxy-2-Fluorenylacetamide with Nucleic Acid. *Science*, 159:1351–1353.

Kistner, R. W., C. T. Griffiths, and J. M. Craig. 1965. Use of Progestational Agents in the Management of Endometrial Cancer. *Cancer*, 18:1563–1579.

Kleinsmith, L. J., and G. B. Pierce, Jr. 1964. Multipotentiality of Single Embryonal Carcinoma Cells. *Cancer Research*, 24:1544–1551.

Kriek, E. 1968. Difference in Binding of 2-Acetylaminofluorene to Rat Liver Deoxy-ribonucleic Acid and Ribosomal Ribonucleic Acid In Vivo. *Biochimica et biophysica acta*, 161:273–275.

Kriek, E., J. A. Miller, U. Juhl, and E. C. Miller. 1967. 8-(N-2-Fluorenylacetamido)-Guanosine, an Arylamidation Reaction Product of Guanosine and the Carcinogen N-Acetoxy-N-2-Fluorenylacetamide in Neutral Solution. *Biochemistry*, 6:177–182.

Lawley, P. D., and P. Brookes. 1965. Molecular Mechanisms of the Cytotoxic Action of Difunctional Alkylating Agents and of Resistance to this Action. *Nature*, 206:480–483.

Lazzarini, R. A. 1966. Differences in Lysine-sRNA from Spore and Vegetative Cells

of *Bacillus subtilis*. *Proceedings of the National Academy of Sciences of the U.S.A.*, 56:185–190.

Macpherson, I. 1965. Reversion in Hamster Cells Transformed by Rous Sarcoma Virus. *Science*, 148:1731–1733.

Magee, P. N., V. M. Craddock, and P. F. Swann. 1967. "The Possible Significance of Alkylation of Nucleic Acids in Carcinogenesis of the Liver and other Organs," *Carcinogenesis: A Broad Critique* (The University of Texas M. D. Anderson Hospital and Tumor Institute, 20th Annual Symposium on Fundamental Cancer Research, 1966). Baltimore, Maryland: The Williams & Wilkins Co. Pp. 421–439.

Maher, V. M., E. C. Miller, J. A. Miller, and W. Szybalski. 1968. Mutations and Decrease in Density of Transforming DNA Produced by Carcinogenic Esters of N-Hydroxy-2-Acetylaminofluorene and N-Hydroxy-N-Methyl-4-aminoazobenzine. (Abstract) *Federation Proceedings*, 27:645.

Marroquin, F., and E. Farber. 1965. The Binding of 2-Acetylaminofluorene to Rat Liver Ribonucleic Acid In Vivo. *Cancer Research*, 25:1262–1269.

Marshall, R. E., C. T. Caskey, and M. Nirenberg. 1967. Fine Structure of RNA Codewords Recognized by Bacterial, Amphibian, and Mammalian Transfer RNA. *Science*, 155:820–826.

Matsushima, T., S. Kawabe, M. Shibuya, and T. Sugimura. 1968. Aldolase Isozymes in Rat Tumor Cells. *Biochemical and Biophysical Research Communications*, 30: 565–570.

McKinnell, R. B., B. A. Deggins, and D. D. Labat. 1969. Transplantation of Pluripotential Nuclei from Triploid Frog Tumors. *Science*, 165:394–396.

Michelson, A. N. Personal communication.

Miller, E. C., P. D. Cooke, P. D. Lotlikar, and J. A. Miller. 1964. The Metabolism and Carcinogenicity of *N*-Hydroxy-2-Acetylaminofluorene (*N*-HO-AAF) and some of its Possible Metabolites. (Abstract) *Proceedings of the American Association for Cancer Research*, 5:45.

Miller, E. C., Y. Juhl, and J. A. Miller. 1966. Nucleic Acid Guanine: Reaction with the Carcinogen N-Acetoxy-2-Acetylaminofluorene. *Science*, 153:1125–1127.

Miller, J. A. 1968. Summary of Informal Discussion on the Mechanisms Involved in Carcinogenesis. *Cancer Research*, 28:1875–1879.

Miller, J. A., and E. C. Miller. 1967. "Activation of Carcinogenic Aromatic Amines and Amides by N-hydroxylation In Vivo," *Carcinogenesis: A Broad Critique* (The University of Texas M. D. Anderson Hospital and Tumor Institute, 20th Annual Symposium on Fundamental Cancer Research, 1966). Baltimore, Maryland: The Williams & Wilkins Co. Pp. 397–420.

Mirzabekov, A. D., D. Grünberger, A. Holy, A. A. Bayev, and F. Sorm. 1967. Recognition of Synonym Codons by Purified Yeast tRNA[Val] Fractions and Fragments from tRNA[Val]. *Biochimica et biophysica acta*, 145:845–847.

Miura, K.-I. 1967. Specificity in the Structure of Transfer RNA. *Progress in Nucleic Acid Research and Molecular Biology*, 6:39–82.

Muench, K. H. 1966. Chloroquine-Mediated Conversion of Transfer Ribonucleic Acid of *Escherichia coli* from an Inactive to an Active State. *Cold Spring Harbor Symposia on Quantitative Biology*, 31:539–542.

Mushinski, J. F., and M. Potter. 1969. Transfer RNA Variations in Mouse Plasma Cell Tumors. *Proceedings of the American Association for Cancer Research*, 10:63.

Nirenberg, M., and P. Leder. 1964. RNA Codewords and Protein Synthesis: The

Effect of Trinucleotides upon the Binding of sRNA to Ribosomes. *Science*, 145: 1399–1407.

Nishimura, S., F. Harada, U. Narushima, and T. Seno. 1967. Purification of Methionine-, Valine-, Phenylalanine- and Tyrosine-Specific tRNA from *Escherichia coli*. *Biochimica et biophysica acta*, 142:133–148.

Nishimura, S., and I. B. Weinstein. 1969. Fractionation of Rat Liver Transfer Ribonucleic Acid. Isolation of Tyrosine, Valine, Serine, and Phenylalanine Transfer Ribonucleic Acids and Their Coding Properties. *Biochemistry*, 8: 832–842.

Nordmann, Y., and F. Schapira. 1966. Action Inhibitrice de l'Adénosine Triphosphate sur l'Aldolase de l'Hépatome Humain. *Comptes Rendus Hebdomadaires des Séances de l'Académie des Sciences série D (Sciences Naturelles)*, 262:1896–1897.

Novelli, G. D., B. J. Ortwerth, U. Del Monte, and L. Rosen. 1970. "Studies on the Alkylation of Rat Liver Transfer RNA by the Hepatocarcinogen, Ethionine," *Genetic Concepts and Neoplasia* (The University of Texas M. D. Anderson Hospital and Tumor Institute at Houston, 23rd Annual Symposium on Fundamental Cancer Research, 1969). Baltimore, Maryland: The Williams & Wilkins Co. Pp. 409–426.

Pillinger, D. J., J. Hay, and E. Borek. 1969. The Effect of Hypermethylation on the Activity of tRNA. (Abstract) *Federation Proceedings*, 28:889.

Pollack, R. E., H. Green, and G. Todaro. 1968. Growth Control in Cultured Cells: Selection of Sublines with Increased Sensitivity to Contact Inhibition and Decreased Tumor-Producing Ability. *Proceedings of the National Academy of Sciences of the U.S.A.*, 60:126–133.

RajBhandary, U. L., R. D. Faulkner, and A. Stuart. 1968. Studies on Polynucleotides. LXXIX. Yeast Phenylalanine Transfer Ribonucleic Acid: Products Obtained by Degradation with Pancreatic Ribonuclease. *Journal of Biological Chemistry*, 243:575–583.

Ritossa, F. M., K. C. Atwood, and S. Spiegelman. 1966. On the Redundancy of DNA Complementary to Amino Acid Transfer RNA and its Absence from the Nucleolar Organizer Region of *Drosophila melanogaster*. *Genetics*, 54:663–676.

Sanders, F. K., and B. O. Burford. 1968. Morphological Conversion, Hyperconversion, and Reversion of Mammalian Cells Treated In Vitro with *N*-Nitrosomethylurea. *Nature*, 220:448–453.

Seno, T., M. Kobayashi, and S. Nishimura. 1968. Purification of *Escherichia coli* Methionine tRNA$_F$ and Methionine tRNA$_M$ and Studies on their Biophysical and Biochemical Properties. *Biochimica et biophysica acta*, 169:80–94.

Söll, D., J. D. Cherayil, and R. M. Bock. 1967. Studies on Polynucleotides. LXXV. Specificity of tRNA for Codon Recognition as Studied by the Ribosomal Binding Technique. *Journal of Molecular Biology*, 29:97–112.

Söll, D., J. Cherayil, D. S. Jones, R. D. Faulkner, A. Hampel, R. M. Bock, and H. G. Khorana. 1966. sRNA Specificity for Codon Recognition as Studied by the Ribosomal Binding Technique. *Cold Spring Harbor Symposia on Quantitative Biology*, 31:51–61.

Söll, D., and U. L. RajBhandary. 1967. Studies on Polynucleotides. LXXVI. Specificity of Transfer RNA for Codon Recognition as Studied by Amino Acid Incorporation. *Journal of Molecular Biology*, 29:113–124.

Staehelin, M., H. Rogg, B. C. Baguley, T. Ginsberg, and W. Wehrli. 1968. Structure of a Mammalian Serine tRNA. *Nature*, 219:1363–1365.

Stent, G. S. 1964. The Operon: On Its Third Anniversary: Modulation of Transfer RNA Species Can Provide a Workable Model of an Operator-Less Operon. *Science*, 144:816–820.

Subak-Sharpe, H., R. R. Bürk, L. V. Crawford, J. M. Morrison, J. Hay, and H. M. Keir. 1966. An Approach to Evolutionary Relationships of Mammalian DNA Viruses Through Analysis of the Pattern of Nearest Neighbor Base Sequences. *Cold Spring Harbor Symposia on Quantitative Biology*, 31:737–748.

Sueoka, N., T. Kano-Sueoka, and W. J. Gartland. 1966. Modification of sRNA and Regulation of Protein Synthesis. *Cold Spring Harbor Symposia on Quantitative Biology*, 31:571–580.

Taylor, M. W., C. A. Buck, G. A. Granger, and J. J. Holland. 1968. Chromatographic Alterations in Transfer RNA's Accompanying Speciation, Differentiation and Tumor Formation. *Journal of Molecular Biology*, 33:809–828.

Troll, W., S. Belman, E. Berkowitz, Z. F. Chmielewicz, J. L. Ambrus, and T. J. Bardos. 1968. Differential Responses of DNA and RNA Polymerase to Modifications of the Template Rat Liver DNA Caused by Action of the Carcinogen Acetylaminofluorene In Vivo and In Vitro. *Biochimica et biophysica acta*, 157:16–24.

Tsutsui, E., P. R. Srinivasan, and E. Borek. 1966. tRNA Methylases in Tumors of Animal and Human Origin. *Proceedings of the National Academy of Sciences of the U.S.A.*, 56:1003–1009.

Uriel, J., B. de Nechaud, M. S. Birencwajg, R. Masseyeff, L. Leblanc, C. Quenum, F. Loisillier, and P. Grabar. 1967. Antigènes Embryonnaires et Cancer du Foie chez l'Homme: Association de la α_1-Foetoprotéine Sérique avec l'Hépatome Primaire. *Comptes Rendus Hebdomadaires des Séances de l'Académie des Sciences série D (Sciences Naturelles)*, 265:75–78.

Viale, G. L., A. F. Restelli, and E. Viale. 1967. Basi Metilate Nei t-RNA dei Tumori Cerebrali. *Tumori*, 53:533–539.

Wainfan, E., P. R. Srinivasan, and E. Borek. 1966. Can Methylation of tRNA Serve a Regulatory Function? *Cold Spring Harbor Symposia on Quantitative Biology*, 31:525–537.

Ward, D. C., and E. Reich. 1968. Conformational Properties of Polyformycin: A Polyribonucleotide with Individual Residues in the *syn* Conformation. *Proceedings of the National Academy of Sciences of the U.S.A.*, 61:1494–1501.

Weinstein, I. B. 1963. Comparative Studies on the Genetic Code. *Cold Spring Harbor Symposia on Quantitative Biology*, 28:579–580.

————. 1968. "Genetic Code of Normal and Neoplastic Mammalian Cells," *Nucleic Acids, Proteins and Cancer* (Japanese Cancer Center Gann Monograph No. 4), Y. Yamamura, T. Aoki, and M. Muramatsu, Eds. Tokyo, Japan: Maruzen Co., Ltd. Pp. 3–16.

Weinstein, I. B., S. M. Friedman, and M. Ochoa, Jr. 1966. Fidelity During Translation of the Genetic Code. *Cold Spring Harbor Symposia on Quantitative Biology*, 31:671–681.

Weisblum, B., F. Gonano, G. von Ehrenstein, and S. Benzer. 1965. A Demonstration of Coding Degeneracy for Leucine in the Synthesis of Protein. *Proceedings of the National Academy of Sciences of the U.S.A.*, 53:328–334.

Weiss, J. F., and A. D. Kelmers. 1967. A Newer Chromatographic System for Increased Resolution of Transfer Ribonucleic Acids. *Biochemistry*, 6:2507–2513.

Weiss, J. F., R. L. Pearson, and A. D. Kelmers. 1968. Two Additional Reversed-Phase Chromatographic Systems for the Separation of Transfer Ribonucleic Acids and Their Application to the Preparation of Two Formylmethionine and a Valine Transfer Ribonucleic Acid from *Escherichia coli* B. *Biochemistry*, 7:3479–3487.

Weiss, S. B., W. T. Hsu, J. W. Foft, and N. H. Scherberg. 1968. Transfer RNA

Coded by the T4 Bacteriophage Genome. *Proceedings of the National Academy of Sciences of the U.S.A.*, 61:114–121.

Yang, W.-K., and G. D. Novelli. 1968. Isoaccepting tRNA's in Mouse Plasma Cell Tumors that Synthesize Different Myeloma Proteins. *Biochemical and Biophysical Research Communications*, 31:534–539.

Yegian, C. D., and G. S. Stent. 1969a. Differential Aminoacylation of Three Species of Isoleucine Transfer RNA from *Escherichia coli*. *Journal of Molecular Biology*, 39:59–71.

————. 1969b. An Unusual Condition of Leucine Transfer RNA Appearing During Leucine Starvation of *Escherichia coli*. *Journal of Molecular Biology*, 39:45–58.

Zachau, H. G., D. Dütting, H. Feldmann, F. Melchers, and W. Karau. 1966. Serine Specific Transfer Ribonucleic Acids. XIV. Comparison of Nucleotide Sequences and Secondary Structure Models. *Cold Spring Harbor Symposia on Quantitative Biology*, 31:417–424.

Studies on the Alkylation of Rat Liver Transfer RNA by the Hepatocarcinogen, Ethionine

G. DAVID NOVELLI, B. J. ORTWERTH,* U. DEL MONTE,† AND LAWRENCE ROSEN

Biology Division, Oak Ridge National Laboratory, Oak Ridge, Tennessee

For about the past five or six years, our laboratory, as well as several others, has been concerned with the idea that transfer ribonucleic acids (tRNA's) may play a role in metabolic regulation, in addition to their traditional function of translating the genetic code during protein synthesis. This notion grew out of the observation that many of the amino acids are aminoacylated to more than one species of tRNA and that such tRNA's interact with different codons. These are called isoaccepting species of tRNA. As the methods for the separation of tRNA improved and the genetic code unraveled, evidence for more and more isoaccepting tRNA's accumulated until there seemed to be as many tRNA's as the triplets in the genetic code, of which there are 64. These observations have strengthened the growing conviction that the tRNA's may indeed perform a regulatory role. This idea was first used by Itano (1966) to explain the different rate of synthesis of the α chains in normal hemoglobin compared to the synthesis of the α chains in sickle cell hemoglobin in heterozygous individuals. He postulated that the messenger RNA (mRNA) for sickle cell hemoglobin could contain a codon for which there was a limited supply of the specific tRNA for that codon. Ames and Hartman (1963) expanded the idea of control by tRNA and formalized it by calling such control "modulation," *i.e.*, control of the reading of mRNA by modulator tRNA's. These tRNA's would be present in small amounts or in altered forms so that they become rate-limiting (see also Stent, 1964).

The tRNA's as a class of compounds have many features that favor them as candidates for metabolic regulators. Although tRNA's are presumably synthesized on a deoxyribonucleic acid (DNA) template from

* Present address: Department of Ophthalmology, University of Missouri Medical School, Columbia, Missouri.

† Present address: Universita Degli Studi Di Firenze, Istituto Di Patologia Generale, Firenze, Italy.

the four ribonucleoside triphosphates, they subsequently undergo a series of reactions that leads to the formation in these molecules of a number of unusual nucleotides. These are listed in Table 1. These structural modifications occur after the primary gene product has been made and, most probably, are controlled by environmental factors. It is becoming increasingly clear that many of these modifications are essential for the proper functioning of tRNA.

TABLE 1. *Modified Purine and Pyrimidine Nucleosides Identified in Various RNA's*

Purine nucleosides

1-Methyladenosine	Dunn (1961)
N^6-methyladenosine	Littlefield and Dunn (1958)
2' (3')-O-Ribosyladenosine	Hall (1964a)
N^6-(aminoacyl) adenosines	Smith and Dunn (1959b)
N^6, N^6-dimethyladenosine	Littlefield and Dunn (1958)
2-Methyladenosine	Littlefield and Dunn (1958)
2'-O-Methyladenosine	Hall (1964b)
N^6-(isopentenyl) adenosine	Hall, Robins, Stasiuk, and Thedford (1966); Zachau, Dütting, and Feldmann (1966)
2-Thiomethyl-N^6 (isopentenyl) adenosine	Harada *et al.* (1968)
1-Methylguanosine	Smith and Dunn (1959b)
N^2-methylguanosine	Smith and Dunn (1959b)
N^2, N^2 dimethylguanosine	Smith and Dunn (1959a)
7-Methylguanosine	Dunn (1963)
N^2-ribosylguanosine	Hemmens (1964); Shapiro and Gordon (1964)
2'-O-Methylguanosine	Hall (1964b)
Inosine	Hall (1963b)
1-Methylinosine	Hall (1964b)

Pyrimidine nucleosides

3-Methylcytidine	Dunn (1960)
5-Methylcytidine	Hall (1963a)
2-Thiocytidine	Carbon, David, and Studier (1968)
N^4-acetylcytidine	Zachau, Dütting, and Feldmann (1966)
2'-O-Methylcytidine	Hall (1964b)
3-Methyluridine	Hall (1963a)
5-Methyluridine	Littlefield and Dunn (1958)
2'-O-Methyluridine	Hall (1964b)
1,5-Diribosyluridine	Lis and Lis (1962)
5-Methylaminomethyl-2-thiouridine	Carbon, David, and Studier (1968)
Pseudouridine	Cohn (1960)
2'-O-Methylpseudouridine	Hall (1964b)
4-Thiouridine	Lipsett (1965); Carbon, Hung, and Jones (1965)

The influence of these rare bases on the various functions of tRNA has been studied most intensively with respect to the methylated bases. There are a number of methylating enzymes or methylases which may be specific for a given base or for a specific position on a given base and, as seems likely, perhaps for a certain base in a rather definite oligonucleotide sequence (Borek and Srinivasan, 1966; Borek, 1968). Significant differences in coding response between normal and undermethylated leucine tRNA (tRNA[Leu]) and phenylalanine tRNA (tRNA[Phe]) have been observed by Capra and Peterkofsky (1966) and by Littauer, Revel, and Stern (1966). Shugart, Novelli, and Stulberg (1968) separated methylated from undermethylated tRNA[Phe] by reversed-phase column (RPC) chromatography (Kelmers, Novelli, and Stulberg, 1965; Weiss and Kelmers, 1967) and demonstrated that the degree of methylation influenced the amino acid acceptor activity remarkably. The most undermethylated species had only about 20 to 25 per cent of the activity of the fully methylated species. In subsequent work, Shugart, Chastain, Novelli, and Stulberg (1968) demonstrated that in vitro methylation of undermethylated tRNA could restore completely the amino acid-acceptor activity to some but not to all tRNA's. That the other substituent groups are also necessary for tRNA function is evident from the many chemical modifications that have been made on tRNA with subsequent loss of acceptor activity, coding response, or both (see review by Miura, 1967). Taken together, these facts suggest that there is an almost infinite variety of ways by which the function of tRNA can be altered and that many of these changes can be brought about by changes in the environment without alteration of the genetic complement of a cell.

Ethionine

It is known that feeding rats a diet containing ethionine, the ethyl analog of methionine, leads to the production of hepatomas in seven to eight months and that this effect can be reversed by increasing the level of methionine in the diet during the first five months of feeding (Farber and Ichinose, 1958). It was subsequently shown that injecting ethyl-labeled ethionine into the rats results in the appearance of ethyl groups in RNA and protein (Farber and Magee, 1960; Stekol, Mody, and Perry, 1960) with soluble RNA (sRNA) having more label than protein. Labeling of DNA also was reported by Stekol, Mody, and Perry (1960) and 7-ethylguanine was isolated as the labeled constituent. These observations suggested to us that the ethylation of tRNA by ethionine may be an underlying facet of ethionine carcinogenesis. Since, at the Oak Ridge National Laboratory, we had developed some new column chromatographic techniques capable of excellent resolution of isoaccepting tRNA's, we undertook a detailed study of the effect of ethionine on the tRNA's of rat liver. The experimental design was to place male rats of both the Sprague-Dawley and Fisher strains on an ethionine-containing diet for five months, according to the specifications of Farber (1956). We then made a detailed study of the kinetics and requirements for the incorporation of the ethyl group from [ethyl-1-^{14}C]-L-ethionine into liver nucleic acids.

Results

We first decided to study the extent of ethylation of the different fractions of liver nucleic acids. Rats were injected with 100 μc of labeled ethionine in two doses separated by 24 hours. The livers were removed and the nucleic acids were isolated by standard procedures. Table 2 compares the relative ethylation of DNA and tRNA. After denaturation of the DNA and subsequent treatment with ribonuclease, pronase, and alkaline hydrolysis, the apparent labeling of DNA was reduced to an insignificant level. This is significantly different from the finding of Stekol, Mody, and Perry (1960), who reported a much greater degree of labeling of DNA and the isolation of 7-ethylguanine from the DNA. In the absence of details on the separation of the DNA from RNA, we can only conclude that the 7-ethylguanine was isolated from contaminating tRNA. By methylated albumin-kieselguhr (MAK) chromatography, tRNA was separated from ribosomal RNA. There was little or no label in the ribosomal RNA, but as can be seen in Table 2, the tRNA fraction was highly labeled. Farber, McConomy, and Frimansky (1967) were unable to find a significant amount of label in carefully isolated DNA preparations in either normal or ethionine-fed rats. Our results agree with this report and suggest that the small amount of label associated with DNA is mainly the

TABLE 2. *Labeling of DNA and tRNA by [ethyl-1-^{14}C]-L-Ethionine**

Experiment	Count/min/A$_{260}$
1. DNA (after SDS treatment)	5.1
2. No. 1 (treated with pronase and ribonuclease)	2.4
3. No. 2 (after 0.3 N KOH, 18 hours)	0.7
4. tRNA	200.0

* DNA and tRNA were isolated from the livers of rats receiving 100 μc of [ethyl-1-^{14}C]-L-ethionine (3.9 mc/mmole) in two doses separated by 24 hours (adapted from Ortwerth and Novelli, 1969).

Abbreviations: A$_{260}$, absorbance at 260 nm; SDS, sodium dodecyl sulfate.

TABLE 3.   Effect of ^{12}C-Methionine on the In Vivo Labeling of tRNA
by [ethyl-1-^{14}C]-L-Ethionine*

Injection	Labeling time (hr)	tRNA Counts/min/liver
1. ^{14}C-ethionine	19	11,650
2. ^{14}C-ethionine $+$ ^{12}C-methionine	19	11,000
3. ^{14}C-ethionine $+$ ^{12}C-methionine	19	15,700
4. ^{14}C-ethionine	12	7,850
5. ^{14}C-ethionine $+$ ^{12}C-methionine every 3 hr	12	7,560

* All injections of ^{14}C-ethionine contained 12.8 μmoles (50 μc). Equimolar amounts of ^{12}C-methionine were injected in each case, except in experiment 3, in which a tenfold excess of methionine was injected (adapted from Ortwerth and Novelli, 1969).

result of contamination by RNA. The radioactivity that remains with the DNA after removal of RNA and protein represents one ethyl group for every 10^6 nucleotides. This is one or two orders of magnitude less than the labeling seen with polycyclic hydrocarbons of which the mode of action is thought to involve binding to the DNA (Miller and Miller, 1966).

Stekol (1965) reported that the simultaneous injection of ^{12}C-methionine in equimolar amounts with the radioactive ethionine prevented the labeling of the tRNA. Since Stekol (1965) also showed that most of the ethionine that enters the liver is quickly converted to S-adenosylethionine (SAE), this compound was assumed to be the ethyl donor, just as S-adenosylmethionine (SAM) acts as a methyl donor. To our surprise, when we conducted a similar experiment, the ^{12}C-methionine failed to dilute the label. Those data are shown in Table 3. Indeed, the simultaneous injection of a tenfold excess of methionine actually stimulated the labeling by ethionine. These data suggested to us that SAE might not be the ethyl donor for the alkylation of tRNA. We next compared the labeling of tRNA by ethionine in normal rats and in ethionine-fed rats. In this experiment, after the usual labeling period, the tRNA was isolated and fractionated by RPC chromatography to separate the individual tRNA's. The specific activity of each fraction was measured and averaged. These data are given in Table 4. Presumably, the ethionine-fed animals had a rather large pool of unlabeled SAE; however, the ^{14}C-ethionine injected into these animals was not diluted and apparently did not pass through this pool.

We then studied the kinetics of labeling liver tRNA by ethionine. These data are shown in Figure 1. In this experiment, rats were given 50 μc of [ethyl-1-^{14}C]-L-ethionine, and two rats were killed at 1, 3, 6, 12, and 24 hours after the injection. The radioactivity in tRNA was measured

TABLE 4. *Labeling of Liver tRNA with [ethyl-1-¹⁴C]-L-Ethionine in Normal and Ethionine-Fed Rats*

Rat	Average specific activity
Normal	350
Ethionine-fed	340

Adapted from Ortwerth and Novelli, 1969.

as was the acid-soluble pool. After a short lag period, the labeling of tRNA proceeded linearly during the next 11 hours, even though the acid-soluble pool changed greatly. This suggests that the rate of labeling is independent of the SAE pool. In a similar experiment, the label in the tRNA and in the acid-soluble pool was measured over a five-day period. These results, shown in Figure 2, indicate that there is no further labeling of tRNA after 24 hours; the label in tRNA was already decreasing when there were over 10^6 counts per minute in the acid-soluble pool. The half-life of the alkyl groups was about 2.5 days. This is a more rapid turnover than the value of 4.5 days calculated for normal rabbit liver by Erdos and Bessada (1966), but it is in agreement with the value determined by Hoagland (personal communication) for rat liver. Our failure to eliminate the in vivo alkylation of tRNA from ethionine by excess methionine together with the observation that the alkyl groups are turning over even when the acid-soluble pool contains a huge excess of labeled SAE forced us to conclude that, unlike normal methylation that clearly uses SAM as the methyl donor, the observed ethylation does not use SAE as the ethyl donor. The three-hour or so lag period suggested that perhaps a small amount of the injected ethionine was being metabolized to a different intermediate that becomes the active ethyl donor. The stimulation by a tenfold excess of methionine would be consistent with this idea. The excess methionine could compete for the supply of adenosine triphosphate (ATP) and thereby reduce the amount of ethionine tied up as SAE and permit more of the ethionine to pass through the unknown pool for the alkylation of tRNA.

The half-life of the alkyl group suggested that *de novo* synthesis of tRNA might be a necessary requirement for the ethylation reaction to occur. This appears to be true for the normal methylation of tRNA as studied by Fleissner and Borek (1963). Therefore, we tested the effect of actinomycin D on the ethylation reaction. The actinomycin D (1 mg/kg) level that inhibited RNA synthesis (as measured by the incorporation of orotic acid into RNA) by about 60 per cent led to the inhibition of ethylation by about 60 to 70 per cent. These data are shown in Table 5.

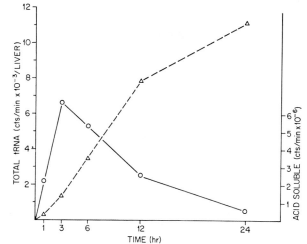

FIGURE 1. The 24-hour time course of in vivo labeling of rat liver tRNA after an injection of 50 μc [ethyl-1-^{14}C]-L-ethionine.

FIGURE 2. The time course of the loss of ^{14}C-ethyl groups from rat liver tRNA over a five-day period.

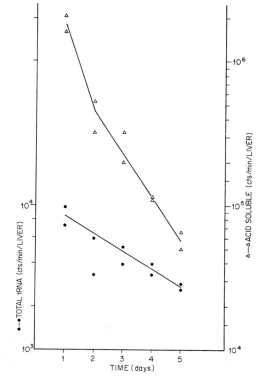

TABLE 5. *The Effect of Inhibition of RNA Synthesis by Actinomycin D on the Incorporation of [ethyl-1-^{14}C]-L-Ethionine into Rat Liver tRNA**

Injection	Counts/min in tRNA/liver
^{14}C-ethionine	10,870
^{14}C-ethionine 5 hours after actinomycin D (100 μg/kg)	16,000
^{14}C-ethionine 5 hours after actinomycin D (1 mg/kg)	4,200

* All rats received 50 μc [ethyl-1-^{14}C]-L-ethionine (3.9 μc/μmole) in a single injection and were killed 24 hours postinjection (adapted from Ortwerth and Novelli, 1969).

We made several attempts to ethylate tRNA with SAE-[ethyl-1-^{14}C] into normal rat liver tRNA, normal *Escherichia coli* tRNA, and undermethylated *E. coli* tRNA using the in vitro system of Srinivasan and Borek (1963) as modified by Shugart, Novelli, and Stulberg (1968). In all experiments, no ethylation was observed from SAE although good methylation took place using SAM-(methyl-^{14}C) under the same conditions. Successful in vitro ethylation could be achieved only with a crude homogenate. The activity is small considering the large amount of homogenate. These results are shown in Table 6. The system has a requirement for heterologous tRNA and uses SAE as the ethyl donor. These data are similar to those published by Hancock (1968) in which he observed the ethylation of *E. coli* tRNA by SAE using enzyme preparations from normal and neoplastic mouse tissues. His results were also achieved with a heterologous system and also represent quite weak alkylating activity as compared with methylating activity. It appears to be impossible to alkylate tRNA in homologous systems with SAE; this is similar to the in vitro methylation of tRNA using SAM and is consistent with our finding that *de novo* synthesis of tRNA is required for in vivo alkylation with ethionine. Most of the ethionine taken up by the liver is converted to SAE, leaving very little available to pass through our hypothetical pool. In fact, the actual ethylation amounts to less than 0.02 per cent of the injected dose. It is possible that the alkylations we were observing might have been caused by a radioactive contaminant in the commercial preparation of the ^{14}C-ethionine since variations in the specific activity of the preparations used in different experiments did not seem to cause the labeling of tRNA.

Several commercial preparations of [ethyl-1-^{14}C]-L-ethionine were checked for contaminants by paper chromatography in a number of different systems and were shown to be contaminated with ethionine sulfoxide and ethionine sulfone. Neither of these was active in the ethylation of tRNA when tested alone. A more direct test for contamination would be to dilute the radioactive ethionine with ^{12}C-ethionine since it is rather unlikely that the ^{12}C compound would have the same kind of contaminants that are likely to be present in the radioactive product. To our dismay, when we diluted the [ethyl-1-^{14}C]-L-ethionine with amounts of ^{12}C-ethionine over a concentration one- to tenfold in excess of the radioactive compound, there was no decrease in the labeling of tRNA. At first, such a result suggested a nonethionine contaminant in the radioactive ethionine. However, upon reflection, it occurred to us that we were not measuring the specific activity of the incorporated ethyl groups, but merely counting the radioactivity in the total tRNA. If the pool through which the ethionine passes on the way to alkylation of tRNA were small relative to the sites available on tRNA for ethylation, then the ^{12}C-ethyl groups also could alkylate the tRNA without influencing the alkylation by the ^{14}C-ethyl groups. If this is a correct interpretation, then the number of ethyl groups alkylated to tRNA should be directly proportional to the concentration of ethionine injected.

A sample of [ethyl-1-^{14}C]-L-ethionine was diluted with ^{12}C-ethionine to give preparations of different specific activities. These preparations then were injected into different rats in doses of about 50 μc, which necessitated injecting large amounts of total ethionine for those samples with lower specific activity. The data in Figure 3 show that the number of ethyl groups alkylated to tRNA is directly proportional to the injected

TABLE 6. *In Vitro Ethylation of tRNA**

Additions	Counts/min in total tRNA
Zero time control (ethionine 5 μc)	0
Zero time control (SAE 3 μc)	27
^{14}C-ethionine (5 μc)	0
^{14}C-ethionine (5 μc) + ATP (20 μmoles)	11
^{14}C-SAE (3 μc)	580; 1,170
^{14}C-SAE (3 μc) minus *E. coli* tRNA	56
^{14}C-methionine (5 μc) + ATP (20 μmoles)	4,520
^{14}C-SAM (5 μc)	4,320

* Complete system used 30 ml rat liver supernatant in the following buffer: 0.15 M KCl, 0.01 M Tris pH 7.5, 0.01 M MgCl$_2$, 0.001 M ethylenediaminetetraacetate (EDTA), and 0.02 per cent polyvinyl sulfate. Each reaction contained 250 μg *E. coli* undermethylated tRNA and the additions listed above (adapted from Ortwerth and Novelli, 1969).

Abbreviations: ATP, adenosine triphosphate; SAE, S-adenosylethionine; SAM, S-adenosylmethionine.

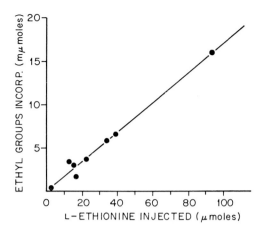

FIGURE 3. The incorporation of ethyl groups into rat liver tRNA from [ethyl-1-^{14}C]-L-ethionine as a function of the amount of ethionine injected.

dose up to 100 μmoles. Thus, even at a level of 100 μmoles of injected ethionine, the fraction that passes through the hypothetical pool is still not enough to saturate all the sites on tRNA capable of being ethylated. In another experiment using radioactive ethionine with a specific activity of 25 μc/μmole, the labeling of tRNA by a 50-μc injected dose was compared to labeling with a 1-mc dose; labeling was increased twenty- to thirtyfold, which confirms the result of the dilution experiment. Finally, we did manage to saturate the hypothetical pool by using an injected dose of almost 300 μmoles and a more than twentyfold dilution with ^{12}C-ethionine. These results, shown in Table 7, indicate a reduction of tRNA labeling by 50 per cent under the conditions employed.

In light of these data, we suggest that the active intermediate in the ethylation of tRNA is formed in very small amounts from ethionine and that this unknown compound is relatively unstable in vivo. Saturating

TABLE 7.   *The Effect of ^{12}C-L-Ethionine on the Ethylation of Rat Liver tRNA by [Ethyl-1-^{14}C]-L-Ethionine**

Injection	Acid soluble pool counts/min/liver	Incorporation into tRNA counts/min/liver
^{14}C-ethionine (13.6 μmoles)	1.74×10^6	14,100
	1.75×10^6	13,240
^{14}C-ethionine (13.6 μmoles) + ^{12}C-ethionine (272 μmoles)		6,100
		7,300

* All rats received 45 μc of [ethyl-1-^{14}C]-L-ethionine (3.3 μc/μmole) together with the ^{12}C-ethionine in a single injection and were killed 24 hours postinjection. (Adapted from Ortwerth and Novelli, 1969.)

levels of ethionine must be considered as the amount of ethionine that will ethylate all available sites on the newly synthesized tRNA. At saturating doses of injected ethionine, we are incorporating approximately 45 mμ-moles of ethyl groups into tRNA over a 12- to 24-hour period. Thus, with a few assumptions concerning (1) the amount of tRNA in the liver, (2) its molecular weight, and (3) the weight of the liver, we can calculate that at saturating doses of injected ethionine, we are incorporating less than one ethyl group per tRNA molecule. This confirms our suggestion that, at moderate doses of ethionine, the number of sites on tRNA is not limiting and indicates the reason why rather large doses of ^{12}C-ethionine do not have any effect on the incorporation of the radioactive ethyl groups.

We made a further attempt to alter the ethylation of tRNA using methionine. This experiment was suggested by results of Farber *et al.* (1964) showing that an injection of methionine at a level of 1 mg/g body weight would prevent the formation of SAE for five hours even though ethionine was injected at the same level. We, therefore, injected 1 mg methionine/g body weight into experimental rats; 10 minutes later, 50 μc [ethyl-1-^{14}C]-L-ethionine was injected into both experimental and control rats. This amounted to a thousandfold excess of methionine compared to the tracer levels of the radioactive ethionine. After 5 hours, the methionine-treated rats appeared moribund and the experiment was terminated. The comparison of the labeling of tRNA is shown in Table 8. The overwhelming amount of methionine reduced the ethylation of tRNA by 62 per cent. However, the important fact is that any tRNA was alkylated at all under conditions that prevent the formation of SAE. These results are in direct contrast to those of Stekol, Mody, and Perry (1960), who reported that an equimolar amount of unlabeled methionine injected with labeled ethionine almost completely inhibited the alkylation of RNA. In an attempt to rationalize the discrepancy between the two studies, we suggest that, in the absence of details of RNA isolation, Stekol, Mody, and Perry (1960) were measuring the competition between ethionine and methionine for aminoacylation to methionine tRNA, a reaction for which methionine is the preferred substrate.

With regard to the interpretation of the inhibition of ethylation by massive doses of methionine, one can do little more than speculate. It is possible that the huge excess of methionine has tied up so much of the cellular ATP as SAM that little is available for tRNA synthesis, which is a prerequisite for the ethylation to proceed. Conversely, Farber *et al.* (1964) reported that ethionine could inhibit the methylation of tRNA and that the inhibition could not be reversed by adenine injection. Perhaps some of the normal methylation by methionine uses the same path-

TABLE 8. *Inhibition of Ethylation by ^{12}C-Methionine**

Injection	Time	Counts/min in tRNA/liver
[Ethyl-1-^{14}C]-L-Ethionine	5 hours	4,200
[Ethyl-1-^{14}C]-L-Ethionine + ^{12}C-methionine	5 hours	1,590

* Each rat received 45 μc ^{14}C-ethionine (14 μc/μmole). The experimental rats received an injection of 1 mg ^{12}C-methionine/gram body weight (450 to 500 mg) 10 minutes before the ^{14}C-ethionine (adapted from Ortwerth and Novelli, 1969).

way we are postulating for ethionine, but in this case, ethionine is the preferred substrate and only when massive amounts of methionine are present can it compete with ethionine.

Modification of tRNA

Earlier in the paper, we pointed out that with very large doses of injected ethionine, *i.e.* saturation doses, the most alkylation we could calculate was less than one ethyl group per molecule of tRNA. This caused us to wonder whether ethylation, in place of the normal methylation, would have any effect on the amino-acceptor activity of tRNA. Accordingly, we compared the relative amino acid-acceptor activity of tRNA

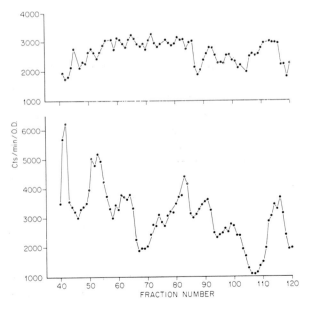

FIGURE 4. RPC-2 chromatography of in vivo labeled tRNA preparations f r o m rat liver. The top curve shows the labeling pattern obtained with an injection of 10 μc [methyl-^{14}C] - L - methionine. The l o w e r curve was obtained with an injection of 100 μc [ethyl-1-^{14}C]-L-ethionine. In each case, the labeling time was 48 hours. (Redrawn from Ortwerth and Novelli, 1969.)

isolated from normal rat liver to those isolated from animals that had been on an ethionine diet for 5 months. Typical results are shown in Table 9. Except for a few tRNA's from the livers of ethionine-fed rats that had an increased acceptor activity, most of the acceptor activities were decreased in the fed rats. Table 10 shows comparable data for an ethionine-induced hepatoma. This tumor occurred in a rat that had been fed an ethionine-containing diet for five months followed by a normal laboratory diet for seven months. In this case, most of the acceptor activities were decreased in the tRNA from the hepatoma, with the notable exception of methionine tRNA that showed almost a 50 per cent increase in the hepatoma. The reason for this increase is not readily apparent.

We next wondered if the slight ethylation of tRNA caused by the injection of [ethyl-1-^{14}C]-L-ethionine could influence the chromatographic profile of tRNA as revealed by RPC (Weiss and Kelmers, 1967). We injected separate groups of rats with 100 μc of [ethyl-1-^{14}C]-L-ethionine or [methyl-^{14}C]-methionine. After isolation of the tRNA's from the liver, they were chromatographed over RPC, system 2 (RPC-2) columns (Figure 4). It seems quite obvious that the distribution of labeled methyl groups is rather uniform throughout the chromatogram. However, the distribution of ethyl groups is not uniform at all, suggesting that some sites are better ethyl acceptors than others.

In a comparison of isoaccepting tRNA's from normal rat liver, from livers of rats fed an ethionine diet for five months, and from subsequent hepatomas, we have completed the co-chromatography of all 20 amino acids. In these studies, we have noted a number of qualitative and quantitative changes in a number of isoaccepting tRNA's, but we will not present a detailed survey of these chromatograms in this paper since we are unable to come to a meaningful conclusion as to their relevance to the cancer problem. These chromatograms will be published elsewhere as a matter of record.

A tedious and painstaking analysis (Rosen, 1968) on the identification of the alkylated nucleosides and bases that occur in tRNA after injecting [methyl-^{14}C]-methionine compared to similar derivatives following the injection of [ethyl-1-^{14}C]-L-ethionine has yielded meaningful results (Table 11). Several significant differences in alkylation were evident when the alkylation produced with methionine was compared to that resulting from ethionine. A large number of the alkylated purines were found to be 1-methyl adenine after ^{14}C-methionine injection, whereas no ethylated adenine was found after ethionine injection. A methyl uridylic acid is found after methionine injection, but this is absent after ethionine injection. The most notable difference, however, is in the alkyl-

TABLE 9. *Effect of Ethionine Feeding on Amino Acid-Acceptor Activity of Rat Liver tRNA*

Amino acid	Normal $\mu\mu$moles/A_{260}	Ethionine-fed $\mu\mu$moles/A_{260}	$\dfrac{\text{Ethionine-fed}}{\text{Normal}}$
Glycine	106.5	130.5	1.23
Isoleucine	40.4	42.8	1.07
Histidine	40.6	41.0	1.01
Tyrosine	26.5	25.7	0.97
Leucine	79.3	77.0	0.97
Methionine	47.3	45.4	0.96
Serine	75.1	71.0	0.95
Lysine	74.9	68.2	0.91
Alanine	77.8	68.4	0.88
Valine	30.8	27.0	0.88
Arginine	63.4	55.1	0.87
Threonine	58.6	45.5	0.78
Phenylalanine	42.8	29.8	0.70
Aspartic acid	82.9	52.5	0.63
Proline	67.8	42.0	0.62

Abbreviation: A_{260}, absorbance at 260 nm.

TABLE 10. *Amino Acid-Acceptor Activity of tRNA from Normal Rat Liver and from an Ethionine-Induced Hepatoma*

Amino acid	tRNA liver $\mu\mu$moles/A_{260}	tRNA hepatoma $\mu\mu$moles/A_{260}	$\dfrac{\text{Hepatoma}}{\text{Liver}}$
Glycine	123	109	0.88
Alanine	86	88	1.02
Leucine	123	107	0.87
Methionine	56	83	1.48
Isoleucine	49	40	0.82
Tyrosine	31	36	1.16
Tryptophan	95	91	0.96
Glutamic acid	98	92	0.92
Asparagine	128	123	0.96
Aspartic acid	81	69	0.85
Proline	46	47	1.02
Histidine	71	69	0.97
Serine	59	56	0.95
Valine	86	62	0.72
Phenylalanine	40	33	0.83
Arginine	91	94	1.03
Threonine	100	76	0.76

Abbreviation: A_{260}, absorbance at 260 nm.

NOVELLI *et al.* : 423

TABLE 11. *Methylated and Ethylated Bases in Rat Liver tRNA*

Bases	Alkyl = methyl* % of total	Alkyl = ethyl† % of total
N²-alkylguanine	10	23
N², N²-dialkylguanine	12	2
1-Alkyladenine	14	0
7-Alkylguanine	5	10
5-Alkylcytidylic acid	19	4
5-Alkyluridylic	14	4
Tentative identification, an alkylguanine	6	17
Alkyluridylic		0
2'-0-Alkyl pyrimidines	7	35‡

* Injection schedule: eight male rats (CD/CR) were starved 21 hours and then injected three times at 2.5-hour intervals with ¹⁴C-³H-L-methionine, 45 μc each injection (specific activity = 47.8 μc/μmole). The rats were killed 18 hours after the last injection. The final tRNA fraction had 679 A_{260} units and specific activity of 144 count/min/A_{260}. (Partly adapted from Rosen, 1968.)

† Injection schedule: two male rats (CD/CR) were starved overnight and then injected with 1 mc of (ethyl-1-¹⁴C)-L-ethionine (21 μc/μmole) each. Starvation was continued, and the animals were killed 20 hours later. The final tRNA fraction had 173 A_{260} units and a specific activity of 3,330 count/min/A_{260} unit.

‡ Probably three or four different ones.

Abbreviation: A_{260}, absorbance at 260 nm.

ated pyrimidines. After ethionine injection, 35 per cent of the total alkyl groups were found to be 2'-0-ethyl pyrimidines and a small number of these are found after methionine injection. These data clearly confirm the other work reported in this paper that the alkylation of tRNA by ethionine proceeds by a pathway different from that employed by the cell to produce normal methylation of tRNA. The relevance of the alkylations to the general process of carcinogenesis remains to be elucidated in future experimental work, but the experiments described in this paper provide a framework upon which other experimental approaches to the subject can be made.

ACKNOWLEDGMENTS

This research was sponsored jointly by the National Cancer Institute and the United States Atomic Energy Commission under contract with the Union Carbide Corporation.

ABBREVIATIONS

ATP—Adenosine triphosphate
DNA—Deoxyribonucleic acid

RNA—Ribonucleic acid
RPC-2—Reversed phase chromatography, system 2
SAE—S-Adenosylethionine
SAM—S-Adenosylmethionine
SDS—Sodium dodecyl sulfate
sRNA—Soluble ribonucleic acid
tRNA—Transfer ribonucleic acid
tRNA[Leu]—Leucine transfer ribonucleic acid
tRNA[Phe]—Phenylalanine transfer ribonucleic acid

REFERENCES

Ames, B. N., and P. E. Hartman. 1963. The Histidine Operon. *Cold Spring Harbor Symposia on Quantitative Biology*, 28:349–356.

Borek, E. 1968. "Methylation Reactions as Possible Control Factors in Protein Synthesis: A Personal Essay," *Exploitable Molecular Mechanisms and Neoplasia* (The University of Texas M. D. Anderson Hospital and Tumor Institute at Houston, 22nd Annual Symposium on Fundamental Cancer Research, 1968). Baltimore, Maryland: The Williams & Wilkins Co. Pp. 163–188.

Borek, E., and P. R. Srinivasan. 1966. The Methylation of Nucleic Acids. *Annual Review of Biochemistry*, 35:275–298.

Capra, J. D., and A. Peterkofsky. 1966. The Coding Properties of Methyl-Deficient Leucyl-Transfer RNA. *Journal of Molecular Biology*, 21:455–465.

Carbon, J., H. David, and M. H. Studier. 1968. Thiobases in *Escherichia coli* Transfer RNA. 2-Thiocytosine and 5-Methylaminomethyl-2-Thiouracil. *Science*, 161:1146–1147.

Carbon, J. A., L. Hung, and D. S. Jones. 1965. A Reversible Oxidative Inactivation of Specific Transfer RNA Species. *Proceedings of the National Academy of Sciences of the U.S.A.*, 53:979–986.

Cohn, W. E. 1960. Pseudouridine, A Carbon-Carbon Linked Ribonucleoside in Ribonucleic Acids: Isolation, Structure, and Chemical Characteristics. *Journal of Biological Chemistry*, 235:1488–1498.

Dunn, D. B. 1960. The Isolation of 5-Methylcytidine from RNA. *Biochimica et biophysica acta*, 38:176–178.

———. 1961. The Occurrence of 1-Methyl Adenine in Ribonucleic Acid. *Biochimica et biophysica acta*, 46:198–200.

———. 1963. The Isolation of 1-Methyladenylic Acid and 7-Methylguanylic Acid from Ribonucleic Acid. *Biochemical Journal*, 86:14P–15P.

Dunn, D. B., J. D. Smith, and P. F. Spahr. 1960. Nucleotide Composition of Soluble Nucleic Acid from *Escherichia coli*. *Journal of Molecular Biology*, 2:113–117.

Erdos, T., and R. Bessada. 1966. The Turnover of Ribosomal RNA and Soluble RNA in the Rabbit Uterus. *Biochimica et biophysica acta*, 129:628–631.

Farber, E. 1956. Similarities in the Sequence of Early Histological Changes Induced in the Liver of the Rat by Ethionine, 2-Acetylaminofluorene, and 3'-Methyl-4-Dimethylaminoazobenzene. *Cancer Research*, 16:142–148.

Farber, E., and H. Ichinose. 1958. The Prevention of Ethionine-induced Carcinoma of the Liver in Rats by Methionine. *Cancer Research*, 18:1209–1213.

Farber, E., and P. N. Magee. 1960. The Probable Alkylation of Liver Ribouncleic Acid by the Hepatic Carcinogens Dimethylnitrosamine and Ethionine. *Biochemical Journal*, 76:58P.

Farber, E., J. McConomy, B. Frazen, F. Marroquin, G. A. Stewart, and P. N. Magee. 1967. Interaction Between Ethionine and Rat Liver Ribonucleic Acid and Protein in Vivo. *Cancer Research,* 27:1761–1772.

Farber, E., H. Shull, S. Villa-Trevino, B. Lombardi, and M. Thomas. 1964. Biochemical Pathology of Acute Hepatic Adenosinetriphosphate Deficiency. *Nature,* 203:34–40.

Fleissner, E., and E. Borek. 1963. Studies on the Methylation of Soluble RNA. I. Methylation of the s-RNA Polymer. *Biochemistry,* 2:1093–1100.

Hall, R. H. 1963a. Isolation of 1-Methylinosine and Inosine from Yeast Soluble Ribonucleic Acid. *Biochemical and Biophysical Research Communications,* 13: 394–398.

———. 1963b. Method for Isolation of 2'-O-Methylribonucleosides and N'-Methyladenosine from Ribonucleic Acid. *Biochimica et biophysica acta,* 68:278–283.

———. 1963c. Isolation of 3-Methyluridine and 3-Methylcytidine from Soluble Ribonucleic Acid. *Biochemical and Biophysical Research Communications,* 12: 361–364.

———. 1964a. Isolation of N[6]-(Aminoacyl)adenosine from Yeast Ribonucleic Acid. *Biochemistry,* 3:769–773.

———. 1964b. On the 2'-O-Methylribonucleoside Content of Ribonucleic Acids. *Biochemistry,* 3:876–880.

Hall, R. H., M. I. Robins, L. Stasiuk, and R. Thedford. 1966. Isolation of N[6] (γ, γ-Dimethylallyl) Adenosine from Soluble Ribonucleic Acid. *Journal of the American Chemical Society,* 88:2614–2615.

Hancock, R. L. 1968. Soluble RNA Ethylase Activity of Normal and Neoplastic Mouse Tissues. *Cancer Research,* 28:1223–1230.

Harada, F., H. J. Gross, F. Kimura, S. H. Change, S. Nishimura, and U. L. RajBhandary. 1968. 2-Methylthio N[6]-(Δ^2-Isopentenyl) Adenosine: A Component of *E. coli* Tyrosine Transfer RNA. *Biochemical and Biophysical Research Communications,* 33:299–306.

Hemmens, W. F. 1964. neo-Guanylic Acid Produced by the Action of Acid on Ribonucleic Acid. *Biochimica et biophysica acta,* 91:332–334.

Hoagland, M. B. Personal communication.

Itano, H. A. 1966. Genetic Regulation of Peptide Synthesis in Hemoglobins. *Journal of Cellular Physiology,* 67 (Supplement 1):65–76.

Kelmers, A. D., G. D. Novelli, and M. P. Stulberg. 1965. Separation of Transfer Ribonucleic Acids by Reverse Phase Chromatography. *Journal of Biological Chemistry,* 240:3979–3983.

Lipsett, M. N. 1965. The Isolation of 4-Thiouridylic Acid from the Soluble Ribonucleic Acid of *Escherichia coli. Journal of Biological Chemistry,* 240:3975–3978.

Lis, A. W., and E. W. Lis. 1962. Isolation and Characterization of Presumed 3, 5-Diribosyluracil. *Biochimica et biophysica acta,* 61:799–806.

Littauer, U. Z., M. Revel, and R. Stern. 1966. Coding Properties of Methyl-Deficient Phenylalanine Transfer RNA. *Cold Spring Harbor Symposia on Quantitative Biology,* 31:501–514.

Littlefield, J. W., and D. B. Dunn. 1958. The Occurrence and Distribution of Thymine and Three Methylated-Adenine Bases in Ribonucleic Acids from Several Sources. *Journal of Biochemistry,* 70:642–651.

Madison, J. T., and R. W. Holley. 1965. The Presence of 5, 6-Dihydrouridylic Acid in Yeast "Soluble" Ribonucleic Acid. *Biochemical and Biophysical Research Communications*, 18:153–157.

Miller, J. A., and E. C. Miller. 1966. A Survey of Molecular Aspects of Chemical Carcinogenesis. *Laboratory Investigation*, 15:217–241.

Miura, K.-I. 1967. Specificity in the Structure of Transfer RNA. *Progress in Nucleic Acid Research and Molecular Biology*, 6:39–82.

Ortwerth, B. J., and G. D. Novelli. 1969. Studies on the Incorporation of L-Ethionine-Ethyl-1-^{14}C into the Transfer RNA of Rat Liver. *Cancer Research*. (in press.)

Rosen, L. 1968. Ethylation In Vivo of Purines in Rat-Liver tRNA by L-Ethionine. *Biochemical and Biophysical Research Communications*, 33:546–550.

Shapiro, R., and N. C. Gordon. 1964. On the Structure of Neoguanosine. *Biochemical and Biophysical Research Communications*, 17:160–164.

Shugart, L., B. H. Chastain, G. D. Novelli, and M. P. Stulberg. 1968. Restoration of Aminoacylation Activity of Undermethylated Transfer RNA by In Vitro Methylation. *Biochemical and Biophysical Research Communications*, 31:404–409.

Shugart, L., G. D. Novelli, and M. P. Stulberg. 1968. Isolation and Properties of Undermethylated Phenylalanine Transfer Ribonucleic Acids from a Relaxed Mutant of Escherichia coli. *Biochimica et biophysica acta*, 157:83–90.

Smith, J. D., and D. B. Dunn. 1959a. An Additional Sugar Component of Ribonucleic Acids. *Biochimica et biophysica acta*, 31:573–575.

———. 1959b. The Occurrence of Methylated Guanines in Ribonucleic Acids from Several Sources. *Biochemical Journal*, 72:294–301.

Srinivasan, P. R., and E. Borek. 1963. The Species Variation of RNA Methylase. *Proceedings of the National Academy of Sciences of the U.S.A.*, 49:529–533.

Stekol, J. A. 1965. "Formation and Metabolism of S-Adenosyl Derivations of A-Alkyl Homocysteins in the Rat and Mouse," *Transmethylation and Biosynthesis of Methionine*, S. K. Shapiro and F. Schlenk, Eds. Chicago, Illinois: Chicago University Press. Pp. 235–252.

Stekol, J. A., U. Mody, and J. Perry. 1960. The Incorporation of the Carbon of the Ethyl Group of Ethionine into Liver Nucleic Acids and the Effect of Ethionine Feeding on the Content of Nucleic Acids in Rat Liver. *Journal of Biological Chemistry*, 235:PC59–PC60.

Stent, G. S. 1964. The Operon: On its Third Anniversary: Modulation of Transfer RNA Species Can Provide a Workable Model of an Operator-less Operon. *Science*, 144:816–820.

Weiss, J. F., and A. D. Kelmers. 1967. A New Chromatographic System for Increased Resolution of Transfer Ribonucleic Acids. *Biochemistry*, 6:2507–2513.

Zachau, H. G., D. Dütting, and H. Feldmann. 1966. Nucleotide Sequences of Two Serine-Specific Transfer Ribonucleic Acids. *Angewandte Chemie* (International Edition in English), 5:422.

Panel Discussion

Session Chairman T. C. Hsu, The University of Texas M. D. Anderson Hospital and Tumor Institute at Houston, Houston, Texas: From what we have heard during this symposium and from what we have read in the literature, I cannot deny disappointment and pessimism regarding our knowledge of the structure of chromosomes and the role of chromosomes in oncogenesis. It appears that we are still with Boveri in 1914, wondering whether chromosome changes induce neoplastic transformation. We still debate, as did cytologists in the 1920's and 1930's, whether a chromatid is single or multistranded. And we are still searching for a mechanism or mechanisms for chromosome breaks, of which we know next to nothing.

If we consider that normal development could result in cell types as diversified as neurons, myeloblasts, and spermatocytes without genomic changes or chromosomal abnormalities, and if we consider cancer as a deviation of normal development or an error in development, there is no reason that carcinogenesis must require an alteration in chromosomal constitution. I was pleased to hear from Dr. Weinstein and Dr. Novelli that at least some carcinogens react primarily with transfer RNA instead of DNA. Their data suggest that carcinogenesis may originate at the translational level. Perhaps sooner or later work will be done to see if messenger ribonucleic acids (mRNA's) are also involved.

It appears, therefore, that initiation of cancer cells does not have to be accompanied by changes in the genetic apparatus. Yet drastic changes in chromosome composition have been noted repeatedly in neoplasms. As Dr. Atkins reported, even polyps and in situ carcinomas show karyotypic alterations. What do these phenomena suggest? Probably that chromosomal changes occur after transformation, but some of the chromosomal changes confer certain advantages on the neoplastic cells. One of the speculations may be that a certain selection takes place to yield a genetic background that is common to all neoplasms.

Pathologists have noted for many years that neoplasms, when compared with their normal counterparts, often display characteristic changes in nucleoli: more nucleoli, larger nucleoli, or more basophilic nucleoli. It is possible that the increase in nucleolus activity in neoplasms is a result of changes in chromosomal composition, i.e. chromosomes bearing ribosomal DNA (rDNA) segments are selected so that cancer genomes have an increase of the rDNA cistrons. In Dr. Moorhead's presentation, he noted an increase of the number of chromosomes showing secondary constrictions or nucleolus organizers. Whether all cancer cells contain a higher number of rRNA cistrons than normal cells remains to be tested, but this is at least a thought.

I would also like to make a few comments on chromosome breaks. Many of us remember the work of Fogh and Fogh on chromosome breaks induced by mycoplasma or pleuropneumonia-like organisms (PPLO). A recent paper by Freed showed that the lack of arginine induced chromosome damage in cells in tissue culture. It is interesting to note that PPLO requires rather large amounts of arginine for growth. Then, is it possible that the induction of chromosomal breaks by PPLO is secondary, i.e. a result of arginine depletion? A number of years ago T. A. McCoy selected a cell strain from a rat hepatoma which was able to grow in a medium without asparagine. I had an occasion to examine cytologically these cells during their early stages of establishment. We noted numerous chromosome breaks. However, when the resistant cells were firmly established, chromosome breaks disappeared in the mutant cell line. Could this mean that the situation is analogous to the arginine deficiency of

Freed?

I have taken enough time for opening comments. I would like to ask Dr. Novelli to start, and invite the audience to participate.

Dr. G. David Novelli, Oak Ridge National Laboratory, Oak Ridge, Tennessee: Our degree of sophistication is only now beginning to increase to the point that we know we made a mistake with tRNA. We couldn't do this before. Of all RNA's in the cell, the tRNA is the smallest, yet its synthesis is totally unknown.

Another point that I should like to mention is in connection with virus and tumor formation. There have been now two reports of viruses bringing in their own tRNA. In the case of avian myeloblastosis virus, it appears as if the virus brings in its own tRNA, whereas, in the case of herpesvirus, it appears as if the genome is coding for a new tRNA. I'd like to comment on work we are doing with T-infected *Escherichia coli* as a background for this to explain how I think it might work. We have been doing much work on T2-infected *E. coli* cells; what happens is that, immediately upon infection, a specific leucine tRNA is destroyed. I believe this is the mechanism by which all host protein synthesis is shut off. Nothing further happens until very near the end. Then, two new tRNA leucines appear; these are coded for by the phage genome. This was reported at the Twenty-Second Annual Symposium on Fundamental Cancer Research last year by Dr. Samuel B. Weiss. The leucine tRNA seems to be somehow involved in completion of virus structure. This could be a model for the way a change in tRNA could lead to tumor development.

Dr. I. Bernard Weinstein, Columbia University College of Physicians and Surgeons and Francis Delafield Hospital, New York, New York: After my talk, several objections were raised, based on the fact that the carcinogen binds to the tRNA for a limited period of time, and yet the tumor, once initiated, persists on serial transplantation for many generations, in the absence of the carcinogen. I agree that continued persistence of the carcinogen is not necessary to maintain the neoplastic state, although recent studies suggest that carcinogen does persist for longer periods of time than we realize. In addition, the hepatic carcinogens ethionine and acetylaminofluorene must be fed to rats for three to six months before tumors develop. A single exposure is not sufficient. (A different mechanism may be utilized with polycyclic hydrocarbons, since with these agents a single exposure can initiate carcinogenesis.)

How can we get around the inevitable conclusion that, eventually, maintenance of the neoplastic state does not require the presence of the carcinogen? I do not think that this type of stability is unique to cancer cells, since a similar mechanism may be responsible for normal differentiation. It is clear that once differentiation has occurred, it may be stabilized and persist, even in the absence of the original inductive forces. At the same time, destabilization occurs if the cytoplasm drastically changes.

An elegant demonstration of this is the nuclear transplantation studies of Gurdom. Intestinal epithelial cells of the adult frog have a distinctive pattern of gene expression and develop progeny cells which are always intestinal epithelial cells. However, when a nucleus of these cells is transplanted into the cytoplasm of an enucleated frog egg, this nucleus now directs the full development of a normal adult frog. We know, therefore, that the cells of higher organisms are capable of shifting into various "steady states" during normal differentiation.

I think it is useful to separate neoplasia into three stages: initiation, promotion, and maintenance. Initiation and promotion might operate via changes in tRNA and maintenance might occur via normal mechanisms which stabilize states of differentiation.

Dr. R. L. Hancock, The Jackson Laboratory, Bar Harbor, Maine: I would like to make a few comments on Dr. Novelli's presentation. As you know, I have published studies demonstrating the ethylation of soluble RNA (sRNA) using S-adenosylethionine (SAE) in vitro. However, I used *E. coli* sRNA. In support of Dr. Novelli's contention that tRNA is ethylated by a pathway other than SAE, I have done extensive studies attempting to ethylate mouse liver sRNA using mouse liver enzymes under a variety of conditions. These studies have been unsuccessful. However, if the identical studies are done with the use of S-adenosylmethionine (SAM), I can detect trace amounts of methylation. Until hearing this paper, I interpreted these results as being the result of deficiency of hypomethyl or amethyl sRNA in my mouse liver preparations of sRNA, thus the inability to demonstrate the reaction since the ethylation reaction is more feeble in general than methylation as assayed with *E. coli* sRNA. But even if I eventually demonstrate in vitro ethylation by homologous enzymes, this would not nullify the possibility of a different in vivo pathway for sRNA.

My second comment is in defense of my use of *E. coli* sRNA as substrate. Since sRNA methylates have had an ample opportunity to methylate homologous sRNA in vivo, it would not make sense to use it as a routine substrate for an assay unless one knew of methods to demethylate sRNA without other deleterious effects. Therefore, if one is interested at all in studying the basic properties of these enzymes, one must have a suitable substrate. I have not found any substitutes; sRNA methylase will not use homopolymers; interestingly, neither will it use relatively large fragments of *E. coli* sRNA. This suggests, then, that the total sRNA with its particular conformation is required for methylase activity. In fact, I have recently been able to correlate extent of methylation with induced conformation changes.

At these meetings last year, Dr. E. Borek presented some of my finding on differences between fetal liver and adult liver preparations in methylation of *E. coli* sRNA. If these differences in extent of methylation reflect differences in methylation sites, as they must, it seems that one could envisage different sites being methylated in vivo on embryonic tRNA, thus inducing changes in conformation, codon response, ribosomal binding capacities, *etc.* without the necessity of the naturally occurring tRNA being in a hypermethylated state.

Finally, I would like to report a study I have just completed on a new hepatoma that arises in 100 per cent of the males of XDBA2/WyDi F_1 hybrid mice. Neither of the parental strains has hepatomas, but multiple discrete hepatomas large enough to study biochemically occur in the hybrid mice. Some hepatomas within the same liver had normal diploid modes of chromosomes and some had, for example, hypertriploid. When compared with adjacent liver, some had normal sRNA methylase levels of activity, and others had increased activity. Furthermore, the adenosine triphosphate (ATP): L-methionine 5-adenosyl transferase activities are present only in trace amounts in some of the hepatomas and are normal in others. My preliminary work and extensive studies by Sheid and Bilik have shown that this enzyme activity is higher in minimal deviation hepatomas, thus being like liver, rather than having only trace amounts as I have showed for BW7756 mouse hepatoma and as Sheid and Bilik showed with the Novikoff rat hepatoma. Studies I have made on sRNA methylases using minimal deviation hepatomas from Dr. Van Potter's laboratory are too preliminary for comment, but I will not be surprised if the kinds of detectable sRNA methylase activities are the same as those found in liver. All of these data, including the differences in the embryonic material, suggest a correlation between the state of differentiation and the variety of sRNA methylation reactions that the cell is capable of accomplishing. This conclusion is similar to those of Dr. Weinstein and Dr. Novelli, as far as showing the tRNA as performing a critical role in differentiation.

Dr. Novelli: I would like to repeat the comment I made at this meeting last year when Dr. Borek and Dr. Hancock were making the correlation that in many tumors there is an increase in methylase activity. We did in fact look at an ethionine-induced hepatoma. We did not measure to see whether there was an increase in methylase activity. We asked whether we could methylate it, and we could. It is undermethylated with respect to normal and I wish to state again that it seems anomalous that in tumors there is an increase in methylase activity, yet the tumor tRNA is undermethylated. Using a heterologous tRNA, *e.g. E. coli* tRNA, to measure methylase activity of tumor is somewhat dangerous. The state of methylation of the tRNA of the tissue should be the question investigated.

Dr. E. H. Y. Chu, Oak Ridge National Laboratory, Oak Ridge, Tennessee: Dr. Weinstein and Dr. Novelli have presented evidence for the action of chemical carcinogens at the translational level. I would like to consider the possibility that certain chemical carcinogens may, in fact, react with the genetic material.

In a tissue culture system of Chinese hamster cells, we have developed techniques for selecting biochemical mutations and have further demonstrated the induction of mutations with chemical mutagens. In the same system, both experimental mutagenesis and carcinogenesis can now be studied. One approach is to test the mutagenicity of known carcinogens. Among other carcinogens we have tested so far, we have also included the aromatic amine AAF and its derivatives. These are the same series of compounds used by Dr. Weinstein in his work. We find that in hamster cells, N-acetoxy-AAF is highly mutagenic, N-hydroxy-AAF moderately mutagenic, and AAF non- or slightly mutagenic. We are interested in following this approach further to test the somatic mutation theory of carcinogenesis.

Dr. Weinstein: There is a good deal of work in the literature on the question of whether all carcinogens are also mutagens, and, in general, there is a correlation between the two effects. However, this correlation may be trivial because most chemical carcinogens react with nucleic acids in general, both RNA and DNA. It is not unexpected, therefore, that carcinogens reacting in certain systems with DNA are mutagenic; the critical question, however, is how do they produce tumors? Do they do so by reacting with DNA or with RNA? The mutagenesis data do not provide an answer to this question. Finally, in the specific example that you gave, AAF itself is not a mutagen because AAF does not react with nucleic acids. It must first undergo metabolic activation.

Dr. R. C. Gallo, National Cancer Institute, Bethesda, Maryland: Dr. Novelli talked about T2-infected bacteria and some of the alterations in transfer RNA that occur after T2 infection. In collaboration with Dr. Robert Ting of the National Cancer Institute, we have found that polyoma-transformed rat embryo cells have a marked increase in tRNA methylases. Both the rate and the extent of methylation increased. These observations were made with both undermethylated *E. coli* tRNA and yeast tRNA as substrates. However, whereas the difference was two- to threefold with *E. coli* as substrate, the difference with yeast tRNA as substrate was about tenfold. These findings indicate that there is not only an increase in the amount of tRNA methylases following oncogenic transformation, but also that new species of tRNA methylases may appear.

My second comment concerns a study recently completed in my laboratory. Since differences in tRNA profiles have been found in some differentiated tissues, we have been concerned that some changes in tRNA profiles found in neoplastic cells may be representative of differences between immaturity and maturity, rather than of neoplasia per se. We have compared the tRNA profiles for all 20 amino acids of human lymphoblasts, normal and leukemic, and have found about four significant differences. These cells appeared morphologically identical and had the same generation time. It could be coincidental, but I think it is interesting that in the differences Dr. Novelli showed between tRNA profiles of ethionine-fed and control animals, two differences were: an absent arginyl-tRNA peak and a markedly reduced leucyl-tRNA peak in the ethionine-fed animals. We have found identical results in leukemic *versus* normal cells.

Dr. L. M. Fink, Columbia University, New York, New York: There is increasing evidence for heterogeneity of tRNA chromatographic profiles using tRNA extracted from varying normal embryonic and neoplastic tissues. One must be very careful in interpreting these changes as having anything to do with the neoplastic process. Different tissues probably have qualitatively and quantitatively different tRNA profiles. This is inherent in comparing the Novikoff hepatoma and normal liver.

Dr. J. C. Arcos, Tulane University Medical School, New Orleans, Louisiana: It is probably not correct to say that the ability to N-hydroxylate AAF is absent in the genetic makeup of the guinea pig. Uehleke and, independently from him, Kiese and von Jagow, in Germany, have shown that isolated guinea pig liver microsomes do N-hydroxylate AAF. However, while rats excrete N-hydroxy-AAF, guinea pigs do not appear to do so. Also, from the data published, it seems that there are significant quantitative differences in the N-hydroxylation in rats and guinea pigs. Thus, we do not appear to have found the ultimate cause of the activity of AAF in the rat and its inactivity in the guinea pig. Possibly, the final answer lies in the ability to O-conjugate N-hydroxy-AAF, an ability which may be present in the first species and absent in the second. The finding in the Miller's laboratory that O-esters of AAF are more reactive and more carcinogenic than AAF itself, and the recently discovered sulfotransferase activity, are important in this respect.

Dr. Weinstein: Thank you for your comment. I probably glossed over the activation of AAF a little too quickly. As pointed out, there are at least two steps in the activation. N-hydroxylation is the first step, and conversion to an active ester is the second. It is possible that the guinea pig is defective in the second step. I wonder if you know whether AAF administered to the guinea pig is bound to guinea pig nucleic acid?

Dr. Arcos: As far as I remember, no extensive study has been carried out on this as yet.

Dr. Weinstein: It would be of interest to know whether the guinea pig is capable of forming the proximate carcinogen which binds with nucleic acids.

Dr. Hsu: I want to know whether Dr. Rapp will give some information about whether during the viral infection the tRNA is also changed. Is there any such information?

Dr. Fred Rapp, Baylor College of Medicine, Houston, Texas: Except for the comments concerning polyoma and the comments made by Dr. Novelli concerning induction of a new tRNA after herpes simplex virus infection, I know of no such information.

Dr. Novelli: There is a case in the avian myeloblastosis virus. The problem there is you do not know whether this is new tRNA or sequestering cellular tRNA. It seems to me that there are too many. There are about 10 to 14 that have been reported both in Oregon and also Czechoslovakia.

Dr. Hsu: In the electron micrographs of Dr. Cole and Dr. Brinkley, the sister chromatids seem to be sort of a cross from one to the other. I wonder if they really are crossed and, during anaphase movement, these strands will be broken and repaired afterward. Do you have any comment on this?

Dr. Arthur Cole, The University of Texas M. D. Anderson Hospital and Tumor Institute, Houston, Texas: Yes, I think this is relevant to the general discussion of deoxyribonuclease activity and ligase activity. A theory developing in popularity holds that the chromosomal genetic material is capable of repairing DNA breaks—the capability seems to be built in. After radiation treatment, some people think that essentially all DNA breakage is repaired and that DNA strand breakage per se is not involved in radiation killing effects. This leads to the possibility, and this is the suggestion of several people, including Amos Norman, that the chromatids are interlocked in metaphase structures. This interlocking may be the consequence of the chromatid replication. Hence, strand breakage and ligase activity may occur during separation in mitosis.

To test this idea, we are now trying to look at the size of the DNA molecules during metaphase, after metaphase, during anaphase, *etc.* If the theory is true, we would expect a change in the molecular weight distribution. We would expect perhaps some degradation in the distribution. That is in fact what we did observe, but the experiments so far are very coarse. The interchromatid strands are presumably not seen at the light microscope level, but are invariably observed at the electron microscope level. Although they appear continuous, we can't say yet whether they are interlocked strands from both chromatids. It is possible that they are not actually interlocked but are just stuck.

Dr. B. R. Brinkley, The University of Texas M. D. Anderson Hospital and Tumor Institute, Houston, Texas: I believe these interchromatid strands are important. Regarding our knowledge concerning the structure of the chromosome, cytologists have looked at these things for almost a hundred years now by all kinds of crude and sophisticated methods, but we are still learning new things about them. Certainly we are confused as to how the chromosome is organized. We are also confused as to how damage to the chromosome relates to the problem of cancer. I think the answer will ultimately be made in molecular terms, but in defense of morphology, they must also be observed microscopically. For instance, these interchromatid strands have not been dealt with extensively in the literature, yet they may be tremendously important. If the sister chromatids are linked and they require a mechanism in metaphase to release for anaphase movement, a malfunction in the mechanisms could lead to nondisjunction, another problem that is not fully understood. So I believe there is still some merit in looking at chromosome structure.

Dr. Rapp: I would like to give Dr. Hsu at least one possible unifying concept. He mentioned that PPLO caused depletion of arginine. It is also known that the two viruses that cause the most damage to chromosomes, adenovirus and herpes simplex virus, also require arginine for replication. I don't know whether anyone has carried out studies with the RNA viruses concerning the effect of arginine deprivation. However, it is possible that PPLO and the DNA-containing viruses break chromosomes by depriving the environment of arginine.

Dr. M. M. Cohen, State University of New York, Buffalo, New York: I was tremendously interested in the strands that were demonstrated in the electron microscope pictures, the interchromatid strands. However, until we can demonstrate that these strands are actually DNA, I think that Dr. Brinkley is not going to be able to put us out of business so easily. If these are non-DNA strands, we still may have breaks in the chromosomes which are attached by some other type of matrix, perhaps nuclear protein, and there may be a true division of the genetic material which is being attacked by some nongenetic material. In the defense of light microscopy, the fragments that we see attached to the chromosome matrix by the strands may not really be integral to the genetic code or the message encoded in the chromosome.

Dr. W. S. Sly, Washington University School of Medicine, St. Louis, Missouri: I would like to suggest that a tRNA mechanism and a genetic mechanism are not necessarily mutually exclusive as one possible cause of malignant change. Dr. Novelli suggested that induction of new tRNA species is the mechanism for switching on late genes in phage T4 infection. Similarly, appearance of a new tRNA may be essential as part of the process of triggering a new cycle of cellular DNA synthesis. If such were true, one might think of a genetic alteration which causes the gene for this tRNA to operate constitutively as a possible mechanism for unrestrained cell division. In this context, I wonder whether anyone has examined tRNA's at different stages of the cell cycle in synchronous cell populations of mammalian cells. It would be very interesting to see if a new species of tRNA appears following mitosis.

Dr. Sheldon Wolff, University of California Medical Center, San Francisco, California: I think that perhaps Cohen has a point regarding these interconnecting fibers. If these are interlocked as Amos Norman claims and they are the genetic material, following segregation you would expect that the two daughter cells would be different genetically because of such things that occur after bridge breakage-fusion cycles if you break DNA. You wouldn't always expect both daughter chromatids to be the same, yet we know that they are. This makes me think that perhaps this is not genetic material. It might have some DNA that is redundant or something of this sort, but it doesn't seem to be used to carry information from one generation to the other.

Dr. Hsu brought up something regarding the question of repair— whether chromosomes are always broken and that breaking agents don't break chromosomes but just prevent this normal repair. If you believe that the chromosome consists only of DNA, some experiments can be interpreted as evidence against this. As we study the repair after fractionated doses of radiation, we find that acrodines, which inhibit repair of DNA, and also phleomycin, which inhibits repair of double-stranded breaks in DNA, do not effect repair of radiation damage in these breaks. If the chromosome were DNA, this would indicate that this is not the type of mechanism that Dr. Hsu postulated was not occurring. I take these experiments as evidence that perhaps the chromosome does not consist only of DNA—that DNA may not be the important thing that we're looking at in the breakage-rejoining phenomenon.

Dr. Fritz Lampert, Armed Forces Institute of Pathology, Washington, D.C.: In collaboration with Dr. DuPraw and Dr. Bahr, I did whole-mount electron microscopy of unsectioned chromosomes after surface spreading and critical point drying. We found that every chromosome consists of 200- to 300-A diameter fibers and that these fibers constitute the entire mass of the chromosome. We did quantitative electron microscopy also, measuring the dry mass of entire chromosomes and of fiber segments. Interconnecting fibers have the same mass and the same density, namely about 1.3 grams per cubic inch as the fibers within the chromosome. The present hypothesis is that not only one fiber generates one chromosome, but also that one fiber could generate several chromosomes. There is no doubt that these fibers contain DNA; this can be proved by their density and by their dry mass. They contain DNA in the percentage of about 15 to 20 per cent; the rest is protein.

Dr. Jane Setlow, Oak Ridge National Laboratory, Oak Ridge, Tennessee: An amateur would like to know why you don't use radioautography with the electron microscopy to settle the question of the nature of those threads.

Dr. Cole: We have attempted to concentrate more on enzyme digestive studies to give us some hint of the structure, but I can't say that we've come to any satisfactory conclusion. Maybe Dr. Brinkley has some comments.

Dr. Brinkley: Dr. Margery Shaw of Anderson Hospital is doing autoradiography using her electron microscope technique on chromosomes from human beings. Although her results are preliminary at this time, she does see some indications that ^{3}H-thymidine label is associated with interconnecting strands.

Genetics of Somatic Cells

Weak Evidence for Bacterial-Type Regulation in Animal Cells

JOHN W. LITTLEFIELD

Genetics Unit, Children's Service, Massachusetts General Hospital, and Department of Pediatrics, Harvard Medical School, Boston, Massachusetts

Differentiation, in its simplest form, consists of a change in the activity or amount of an enzyme or other intracellular protein; embryogenesis seems to be an extraordinarily complex and interacting series of such changes in different cells. In 1961, Jacob and Monod proposed a unitary and convincing model for the regulation of protein synthesis in bacteria which subsequently has been corroborated and complicated (Epstein and Beckwith, 1968). Since 1961, the temptation to formulate the differentiation of animal cells in similar terms, with some modification of the model to allow for irreversibility, has been almost irresistible. Today there is a widespread and entrenched assumption that "the problem" of differentiation is "solved," and that embryogenesis is an understandable although elaborate program of sequential genetic activations, only the details of which remain to be put in order. A related phenomenon is the easy, glamorous employment of terms like "induction" and "repression" which no longer have clear-cut meaning. This sort of thinking not only endangers the support and self-esteem of those left with the problem, but threatens the supply of new people who must eventually solve it. We need to take a close look at the evidence for bacterial-type regulation in animal cells. Others, with different points of view, also have been concerned with this question (Pardee and Wilson, 1963; Eagle, 1965; Wright, 1966; and Harris, 1968).

Oft Proposed Examples

Variable evidence exists for regulation at several points between deoxyribonucleic acid (DNA) and finished proteins in animal cells, and there are, no doubt, many other methods of regulation yet to be discovered (Littlefield, 1968). Of course, this could be predicted from the complexity of an animal cell, as compared to bacteria, which involves such features as chromosomes, nucleolus, nuclear membrane, the ability to function without growing, the extensive and continuous turnover of cell proteins (Eagle, 1965), and the existence of redundant DNA (Britten and Kohne, 1968), giant nuclear ribonucleic acid (RNA), long-lasting template RNA (Penman, 1967), and proteins shuttling between nucleus and cytoplasm (Goldstein and Prescott, 1967). The various increases in enzyme activities caused by hormones surely involve several mechanisms. Even when specific transcription and enzyme synthesis seem to occur, as with tyrosine transaminase, the situation has become much more complex than expected at first (Granner, Hayashi, Thompson, and Tomkins, 1968). Extensive and important control of the amounts of enzymes through stabilization by substrates, co-factors, metals, *etc.*, is now accepted (Schimke, 1964c). Regulation probably can be exerted at the translational level in several ways (Harris, 1968), although none are well established or understood as yet, and the timing of transcription may be restricted in animal cells (Littlefield, 1966; Klevecz and Ruddle, 1968; Turner, Abrams, and Lieberman, 1968) as in yeast (Tauro, Halvorson, and Epstein, 1968), although this has aroused little attention so far. Furthermore, regions of autosomes, as well as of an X chromosome, seem capable of inactivation through condensation. Finally, histones may be found to have a role in cross-linking DNA to produce this condensation, but understanding of the actual mechanism involved must await a molecular model for chromosome structure in general. Currently, condensation seems a crude type of control and not specific for different types of cells (Martin, 1966; Pflueger and Yunis, 1966); in the chick erythrocyte, it is reversible and perhaps related to nuclear volume (Harris, 1968).

In addition to this multitude of other mechanisms, let us see what evidence exists in regard to the occurrence and importance of true substrate induction or end-product repression in animal cells. Reviews of the cell culture literature with which I am most familiar (Eagle, 1965; Green and Todaro, 1967) suggest the possible examples listed in Table 1. In each, a reversible change in activity of the enzyme follows a change in the concentration of substrate ("inducer") or end product ("corepressor"). However, in only one case (arginase) has the enzyme been purified and its turnover actually studied to demonstrate an increased rate of synthesis. Indeed, to illustrate the complexity of the situation, may I point out that arginase, first thought to be simply substrate inducible, was later found to be stabilized by manganese (Schimke, 1964a), and, recently, to increase nonspecifically in activity in the absence of unrelated amino acids (Eliasson, 1967). In several other instances, the inducer has been found to stabilize a rapidly turning-over enzyme (Schimke, 1964c);

TABLE 1. *Proposed Examples of Bacterial-Type Regulation in Animal Cells*

Enzyme	"Inducer"	"Corepressor"	Reference
Arginase	Arginine		Schimke, 1964c
Argininosuccinic acid synthetase		Arginine	Schimke, 1964b
Argininosuccinase		Arginine	Schimke, 1964b
Alkaline phosphatase	Phenyl phosphate		Griffin and Cox, 1967
Aspartate transcarbamylase		Uridine	Ennis and Lubin, 1963
β-glucuronidase		Glucuronic acid	Paul et al., 1964
Glutamyl transferase	Glutamic acid	Glutamine	DeMars, 1958
Phosphoglycerate dehydrogenase		Serine	Pizer, 1964

alkaline phosphatase is an example of this (Griffin and Cox, 1967). The converse possibility, that an end product might destabilize an enzyme via a structural modification or subunit dissociation rather than repress its synthesis, has received little attention. The available evidence indicates that glutamyl transferase is an unstable enzyme in cells of human beings, as well as those of mice, and does not exclude the possibility of destabilization by glutamine (DeMars, 1958; Paul and Fottrell, 1963). Incidentally, the activities of both alkaline phosphatase (Griffin and Cox, 1966) and glutamyl transferase (Moscona, Moscona, and Saenz, 1968) are also increased by steroids. For alkaline phosphatase, this now appears to result from a configurational change in preexisting enzyme (in contradistinction to tyrosine transaminase), and, despite current interpretation, the same may be true for glutamyl transferase.

The evidence most often quoted for end-product repression in animal cells concerns the urea cycle enzymes, argininosuccinic acid synthetase and argininosuccinase, which increase in activity 1.5 to 15 times in cultured mouse and human aneuploid cell lines grown in a limiting concentration of arginine (Schimke, 1964b). This example has particular appeal because the same enzymes provided one of the earliest examples of bacterial-type regulation. However, Tedesco and Mellman (1967) showed that, in diploid fibroblasts from human beings, synthetase activity showed essentially no change in growth-limiting concentrations of arginine; we have found this to be true for argininosuccinase as well (Shih and Littlefield, unpublished data). The ability to modulate the urea cycle enzymes may give a selective advantage to aneuploid cells in the artificial cell culture system; this also seems likely for the acquisition of cystathionase (Eagle, Washington, and Friedman, 1966) and cytidine deaminase (Ellem, 1968). Perhaps some bacterial-type regulation has been covered up in the differentiation of a fibroblast (Krooth, 1964; Eagle, Washington, and Friedman, 1966).

Would the other examples of possible induction and repression cited in Table 1 stand up under detailed investigation? Eagle (1965) has pointed out that, in general, the pathways involved in amino acid anabolism do not behave as if they are controlled by end-product repression. Furthermore, the deprivation of arginine (cited above), of serine, which leads to an increased phosphoglycerate dehydrogenase activity, of uridine, which leads to an increased aspartate transcarbamylase activity, and of glucuronate, which leads to an increased β-glucuronidase activity, may operate through toxic effects. Also, many enzymes change their activity in culture in response to cell contact or nutritional depletion, and it is not evident how thoroughly these parameters were controlled in the experiments cited. Finally, Green and Todaro (1967) have noted that the increases of enzyme activities cited in Table 1 are no more than fifteen-fold and often much less, which is a great deal smaller than the increases in β-galactosidase and other inducible or repressible proteins in bacteria, or, indeed, than the increases in collagen, hemoglobin, and amylase in differentiated cells. Perhaps the latter are the real examples of derepression in animal cells although they may be less immediately recognized because of irreversibility.

Clues From Disease

Soon after publication of the Jacob-Monod hypothesis (1961), it was recognized as surprising that the cells of heterozygous carriers of several inborn metabolic errors almost always contained a reduced activity of the relevant enzyme, often close to 50 per cent of the normal value (Epstein, 1964). Further examples of this "gene dosage" have since been recognized (Hsia, 1966). If the concentration of an end product usually controlled the rate of formation of a synthetic enzyme in animal cells, as it does in bacteria, the normal allele on the homologous chromosome should have been derepressed to produce more enzyme and make up the deficit. This suggests that end product repression is uncommon in human beings; but, of course, pathways may be controlled less by amounts of enzymes than by concentrations of substrates or direct feedbacks (Wright, 1966), with little difference in end-product concentrations in normal and heterozygous individuals. (Incidentally, for the newly described deficiency of adenine phosphoribosyltransferase, it has been suggested [Kelley *et al.*, 1968] that the enzyme level of less than 50 per cent in the heterozygote can be explained if the protein is a dimer and has little activity when composed of one normal and one abnormal subunit; the same might be true for carriers of orotic aciduria [Krooth, 1964]. Greater than 50 per cent activity in carriers could be explained in an analogous fashion.)

Similarly, the amounts of many serum proteins, such as the clotting factors and the lipoproteins, are reduced in heterozygous carriers of deficiencies. It has been suggested that the defective allele produces an altered molecule which directly or indirectly prevents synthesis from the normal allele. Indeed, this could be true in one family with prothrombin deficiency (Shapiro and Martinez, 1968). But, while attractive, this idea is predicated upon a new sort of feedback mechanism involving the recognition of specific proteins.

An exception to the general rule is analbuminemia, a rare autosomal recessive disorder in which the affected individuals synthesize only a trace of albumin, whereas heterozygous carriers have normal serum albumin levels (Bernhold and Kallee, 1959). In the heterozygous carriers, it seems as if the normal allele is allowed to overproduce albumin, or somehow corrects the defect in the other allele. Another exception is glucose-6-phosphatase deficiency in mice (Erickson, Gluecksohn-Waelsch, and Cori, 1968). These situations may be important and clearly need more study.

An opposite and equally mysterious abnormality, *i.e.* notable deficiency of a serum protein in a heterozygous individual, occurs in the case of the normal serum inhibitor of C'1-esterase (Donaldson and Rosen, 1964), and, occasionally, for alpha$_1$-antitrypsin (Talamo, Kowalyshyn, and Austen, 1969). Also obscure at this time is the rare occurrence of dominant inheritance of notable deficiency of immunoglobulin A (IgA) (Stocker, Ammann, and Rossi, 1968), and its occasional sporadic association with partial deletion of the long arm of only one of the two chromosomes No. 18 (Feingold *et al.*, 1969). Previously, we suspected children with the latter condition to be heterozygous for a locus controlling IgA synthesis and to have lost the active allele through the partial deletion. However, it is difficult to explain dominant inheritance of IgA deficiency in this way in the absence of consanguinity. One suspects these "mutants" may relate to the fascinating phenomena of allelic exclusion and suppression of allotype that is recognized in other immunoglobulin-producing cells (Herzenberg, McDevitt, and Herzenberg, 1968). Or, they may represent *trans* control between chromosomes of much significance for our understanding of regulation.

It has been believed that a disease can be regarded as involving disordered regulation if the protein can be both shown to be of normal structure and produced in decreased quantity. However, it is now recognized that a structural mutation in a protein with adjacent representation in DNA ("polarity mutant") can produce this same picture. Indeed, it seems possible that a base substitution which did not alter an amino acid but did change the transfer RNA (tRNA) to one in less supply might also slow synthesis. Such mutations, which can decrease synthesis without altering structure, have indicated that it will be difficult to establish the occurrence of a disorder of regulation. Meanwhile, evidence for the importance and widespread occurrence of structural mutations in man has accumulated steadily (Childs and der Kaloustian, 1968). Many amino acid substitutions occur in areas of a protein molecule which do not affect its function or stability; only the occasional substitution does so, and when it is homozygous, it causes disease. Several metabolic disorders previously regarded as caused by defective regulation are now believed to result from structural mutations, e.g. the common form of glucose-6-phosphate dehydrogenase deficiency in Negros (Yoshida, 1968), acatalasemia (Aebi et al., 1967), and citrullinemia (Tedesco and Mellman, 1967). It is instructive that the amino acid substitution in the former seems not to reduce the catalytic activity but to destabilize the enzyme, so that, on the average, there is less of it per red blood cell. Also in citrullinemia, the amino acid substitution has affected the substrate affinity of argininosuccinic acid synthetase, which still works well at high substrate concentrations, so that the enzymatic block is not complete.

Although there is now less enthusiasm to regard inborn errors as caused by disordered bacterial-type regulation, abnormalities of development are still commonly described in this way, as a delayed or absent "turning-on" of an enzyme such as phenylalanine hydroxylase, glucose-6-phosphatase, or glucuronyl transferase. In this regard, the shift in perinatal life from the production of hemoglobin F to hemoglobins A and A_2 has long been suggested as an example of such regulation, despite the fact that it remains uncertain whether the shift occurs in the individual cell. Furthermore, high hemoglobin F trait can be regarded quite adequately as a deletion of the β and δ loci, and thalassemia can be interpreted in many ways which do not involve disordered regulation (Zuckerkandl, 1964).

Finally, mention should be made of those few diseases which exhibit increased activities of enzymes. In two of these, increases are minor and likely to have trivial explanations (Loos, Prins, and Zürcher, 1968;

Nyhan *et al.*, 1969). However, the significantly increased activity of δ-aminolevulinic acid synthetase in acute intermittent porphyria (Tschudy *et al.*, 1965) is a more interesting candidate for a regulatory disorder. It is inherited as a single gene and has been compared to both an "operator-constitutive" mutant (Granick, 1966) and a "hyperinducible" state (Stanbury, Wyngaarden, and Fredrickson, 1966). But it is a mitochondrial enzyme, and we need to know that complex structural changes, such as those that occur in microsomes, do not take place in this organelle in response to phenobarbital and other agents. Further, a structural mutation causing increased enzyme stability or production, as recently described by Yoshida *et al.* (1968), or even increased catalytic activity or decreased response to a naturally occurring inhibitor can hardly be excluded.

The Hybridization Experiments

In the last analysis, the question of the occurrence of bacterial-type regulation in animal cells cannot be decided by study of protein structure or amount alone. It necessitates a method of genetic analysis in somatic cells not yet available, since the problem is to establish the presence or absence of distinct regulator genes. The technique of cell hybridization provides a step in this direction because evidence for the products of such genes, that is, diffusible repressors, can be sought.

The several experiments of this general nature performed in recent months are summarized in Table 2. These experiments involve the fusion of animal cells which are and are not performing "differentiated" functions ranging from the synthesis of specific proteins to quite complex processes. Operationally, one assumes that repressors diffuse freely in the hybrid cell and are not in such short supply as to exhibit gene dosage themselves. That is to say, a repressor, if present, would interact with related loci on any and all chromosomes. Either assumption may not be justified.

There are difficulties with almost all of the experiments in Table 2. First, with the exception of collagen synthesis, and perhaps of interferon and growth hormone, the systems studied have not been proved to involve a change in the rate of synthesis of a protein, which is a prerequisite to their consideration as possible examples of bacterial-type regulation. The first five examples (malignancy, melanin production, teratoma differentiation, heterochromatin, and contact inhibition) involve complex functions and, in some instances, interspecific hybridizations, so that the results may depend on quite unknown or perhaps trivial factors. This

TABLE 2. *Amounts of "Differentiated" Proteins or Functions in Hybrids Between "Differentiated" and "Nondifferentiated" Cells*

Specific protein or function	Less than additive	Approximately additive	More than additive	Reference
Malignancy			X	Scaletta and Ephrussi, 1965
Melanin Production	X			Davidson, Ephrussi, and Yamamoto, 1966
Teratoma Differentiation	X			Finch and Ephrussi, 1967
Heterochromatin	X			Harris, 1968
Contact inhibition			X	Weiss, Todaro, and Green, 1968
DOPA oxidase	X			Davidson and Yamamoto, 1968
Interferon			X	Carver, Seto, and Migeon, 1968
Growth hormone	X			Sonnenschein, Tashjian, and Richardson, 1968
Collagen		X		Green, Ephrussi, Yoshida and Hamerman, 1966
Folate reductase		X		Littlefield, 1969
Orotidylate pyrophosphorylase and decarboxylase		X		Silagi, Darlington, and Bruce, 1969

Abbreviation: DOPA, dihydroxyphenylalanine.

same objection, interspecific hybridization, can be raised in the next three experiments, which deal with dihydroxyphenylalanine (DOPA) oxidase, interferon, and growth hormone. Moreover, only one or very few hybrid clones have been analyzed in these studies; these results might simply represent the loss of the relevant chromosome. In fact, the increase of hamster interferon in hamster-mouse hybrids may just reflect the response of the hamster genome to foreign nucleic acids (Goldsby, 1968).

The last three experiments, which involve intraspecific crosses (mouse-mouse, hamster-hamster, or man-man), provide no evidence for diffusible repressors in animal cells. If orotic aciduria were caused by either excess repressor or a mutant repressor which no longer interacted with inducer, operator loci on the chromosomes from the normal cell might have been repressed; however, no such effect is evident in the single hybrid clone studied. In our studies on folate reductase, five mutant hamster cell lines containing up to 40 times the usual enzyme activity were fused with wild-type hamster cells; in 32 of 35 hybrids studied, the reductase activity was intermediate between the two parental lines. If, as seems likely for various reasons, the increased enzyme activity in the mutant lines is caused by overproduction, these results suggest that all five mutants are analogous to the less common "operator-constitutive" mutants in bacteria. Indeed, it may be difficult to select a "regulator-constitutive" mutant in a diploid cell; such a mutant would not be evident in the initial heterozygous step because of the production of repressor from the normal allele. Finally, in studies clearly involving overproduction of protein, Green, Ephrussi, Yoshida, and Hamerman (1966) showed that the synthesis of collagen was intermediate in six clones of hybrids between collagen-synthesizing and noncollagen-synthesizing mouse cells, suggesting that no interaction occurred in the hybrid between the genomes of the parental cells.

Conclusion

One is left with the belief that, at this point in our knowledge, the evidence for bacterial-type regulation in animal cells is small and what there is of it is not firm. Indeed, one suspects that the complexities of animal cells, let alone their ability to interact with each other, will provide many surprises before we have a true understanding of differentiation and embryogenesis. New insights and concepts seem to be needed, rather than a continued preoccupation with those already available.

ACKNOWLEDGMENT

Research mentioned in this paper was supported by United States Public Health Service grant number CA-04670.

REFERENCES

Aebi, H., E. Bossi, M. Cantz, S. Matsubara, and H. Suter. 1968. "Acatalas(em)ia in Switzerland," *Hereditary Disorders of Erythrocyte Metabolism* (City of Hope Symposium Series), E. Beutler, Ed. New York, New York: Grune and Stratton, Inc. Vol. I. Pp. 41–63.

Bennhold, H., and E. Kallee. 1959. Comparative Studies on the Half-Life of I^{131}-Labeled Albumins and Nonradioactive Human Serum Albumin in a Case of Analbuminemia. *The Journal of Clinical Investigation*, 38:863–872.

Britten, R. J., and D. E. Kohne. 1968. Repeated Sequences in DNA. *Science*, 161: 529–540.

Carver, D. H., D. S. Y. Seto, and B. R. Migeon. 1968. Interferon Production and Action in Mouse, Hamster, and Somatic Hybrid Mouse-Hamster Cells. *Science*, 160:558–559.

Childs, B., and V. M. der Kaloustian. 1968. Genetic Heterogeneity. *New England Journal of Medicine*, 279:1205–1212.

Davidson, R. L., B. Ephrussi, and K. Yamamoto. 1966. Regulation of Pigment Synthesis in Mammalian Cells, as Studied by Somatic Hybridization. *Proceedings of the National Academy of Sciences of the U.S.A.*, 56:1437–1440.

Davidson, R. L., and K. Yamamoto. 1968. Regulation of Melanin Synthesis in Mammalian Cells, as Studied by Somatic Hybridization, II. The Level of Regulation of 3,4-Dihydroxyphenylalanine Oxidase. *Proceedings of the National Academy of Sciences of the U.S.A.*, 60:894–901.

DeMars, R. 1958. The Inhibition by Glutamine of Glutamyl Transferase Formation in Cultures of Human Cells. *Biochimica et biophysica acta*, 27:435–436.

Donaldson, V. H., and F. S. Rosen. 1964. Action of Complement in Hereditary Angioneurotic Edema: The Role of C′1-Esterase. *The Journal of Clinical Investigation*, 43:2204–2213.

Eagle, H. 1965. Metabolic Controls in Cultured Mammalian Cells. *Science*, 148: 42–51.

Eagle, H., C. Washington, and S. M. Friedman. 1966. The Synthesis of Homocystine, Cystathionine, and Cystine by Cultured Diploid and Heteroploid Human Cells. *Proceedings of the National Academy of Sciences of the U.S.A.*, 56:156–163.

Eliasson, E. 1967. Repression of Arginase Synthesis in Chang Liver Cells. *Experimental Cell Research*, 48:1–17.

Ellem, K. A. O. 1968. Cytidine Aminohydrolase Activity in Intact Cultured Transformed Cells. *Journal of Cellular Physiology*, 71:17–22.

Ennis, H. L., and M. Lubin. 1963. Capacity for Synthesis of a Pyrimidine Biosynthetic Enzyme in Mammalian Cells. *Biochimica et biophysica acta*, 68:78–83.

Epstein, C. J. 1964. Structural and Control Gene Defects in Hereditary Diseases in Man. *Lancet*, 2:1066–1067.

Epstein, W., and J. R. Beckwith. 1968. Regulation of Gene Expression. *Annual Review of Biochemistry*, 37:411–436.

Erickson, R. P., S. Gluecksohn-Waelsch, and C. F. Cori. 1968. Glucose-6-Phosphatase Deficiency Caused by Radiation-Induced Alleles at the Albino Locus in the Mouse. *Proceedings of the National Academy of Sciences of the U.S.A.*, 59:437–444.

Feingold, M., R. S. Schwartz, L. Atkins, R. Anderson, C. S. Bartsocas, D. L. Page, and J. W. Littlefield. 1969. IgA Deficiency Associated with Partial Deletion of Chromosome 18. *American Journal of Diseases of Children*, 117:129–136.

Finch, B. W., and B. Ephrussi. 1967. Retention of Multiple Developmental Potentialities by Cells of a Mouse Testicular Teratocarcinoma during Prolonged Culture *in Vitro* and their Extinction upon Hybridization with Cells of Permanent Lines. *Proceedings of the National Academy of Sciences of the U.S.A.*, 57:615–621.

Goldsby, R. A. Personal communication.

Goldstein, L., and D. M. Prescott. 1967. Proteins in Nucleocytoplasmic Interactions. I. The Fundamental Characteristics of the Rapidly Migrating Proteins and the Slow

Turnover Proteins of the *Amoeba proteus* Nucleus. *The Journal of Cell Biology*, 33:637–644.

Granick, S. 1966. The Induction In Vitro of the Synthesis of δ-Aminolevulinic Acid Synthetase in Chemical Porphyria: A Response to Certain Drugs, Sex Hormones, and Foreign Chemicals. *Journal of Biological Chemistry*, 241:1359–1375.

Granner, D. K., S. Hayashi, E. B. Thompson, and G. M. Tomkins. 1968. Stimulation of Tyrosine Aminotransferase Synthesis by Dexamethasone Phosphate in Cell Culture. *Journal of Molecular Biology*, 35:291–301.

Green, H., B. Ephrussi, M. Yoshida, and D. Hamerman. 1966. Synthesis of Collagen and Hyaluronic Acid by Fibroblast Hybrids. *Proceedings of the National Academy of Sciences of the U.S.A.*, 55:41–44.

Green, H., and G. Todaro. 1967. The Mammalian Cell as Differentiated Microorganism. *Annual Review of Microbiology*, 21:573–600.

Griffin, M. J., and R. P. Cox. 1966. Studies on the Mechanism of Hormone Induction of Alkaline Phosphatase in Human Cell Cultures, II. Rate of Enzyme Synthesis and Properties of Base Level and Induced Enzymes. *Proceedings of the National Academy of Sciences of the U.S.A.*, 56:946–953.

———. 1967. Studies on the Mechanism of Substrate Induction and L-Cyst(e)ine Repression of Alkaline Phosphatase in Mammalian Cell Cultures. *Journal of Cell Science*, 2:545–555.

Harris, H. 1968. *Nucleus and Cytoplasm*. London, England: Oxford University Press, 126 pp.

Herzenberg, L. A., H. O. McDevitt, and L. A. Herzenberg. 1968. Genetics of Antibodies. *Annual Review of Genetics*, 2:209–244.

Hsia, D. Y. 1966. The Diagnosis of Carriers of Disease-Producing Genes. *Annals of the New York Academy of Sciences*, 134:946–964.

Jacob, F., and J. Monod. 1961. Genetic Regulatory Mechanisms in The Synthesis of Proteins. *Journal of Molecular Biology*, 3:318–356.

Kelley, W. N., R. I. Levy, F. M. Rosenbloom, J. F. Henderson, and J. E. Seegmiller. 1968. Adenine Phosphoribosyltransferase Deficiency: A Previously Undescribed Genetic Defect in Man. *The Journal of Clinical Investigation*, 47:2281–2289.

Klevecz, R. R., and F. H. Ruddle. 1968. Cyclic Changes in Synchronized Mammalian Cell Cultures. *Science*, 159:634–636.

Krooth, R. S. 1964. Properties of Diploid Cell Strains Developed from Patients with an Inherited Abnormality of Uridine Biosynthesis. *Cold Spring Harbor Symposia on Quantitative Biology*, 29:189–212.

Littlefield, J. W. 1966. The Periodic Synthesis of Thymidine Kinase in Mouse Fibroblasts. *Biochimica et biophysica acta*, 114:398–403.

———. 1968. Control Mechanisms in Animal Cell Cultures. *Archives of Biochemistry and Biophysics*, 125:410–415.

———. 1969. Hybridization of Hamster Cells with High and Low Folate Reductase Activity. *Proceedings of the National Academy of Sciences of the U.S.A.* (in press.)

Loos, J. A., H. K. Prins, and C. Zürcher. 1968. "Elevated ATP Levels in Human Erythrocytes," *Hereditary Disorders of Erythrocyte Metabolism* (City of Hope Symposium Series), E. Beutler, Ed. New York, New York: Grune & Stratton, Inc. Vol. I. Pp. 41–63.

Martin, P. G. 1966. The Pattern of Autosomal DNA Replication in Four Tissues of the Chinese Hamster. *Experimental Cell Research*, 45:85–95.

Moscona, A. A., M. H. Moscona, and N. Saenz. 1968. Enzyme Induction in Embryonic Retina: The Role of Transcription and Translation. *Proceedings of the National Academy of Sciences of the U.S.A.*, 61:161–167.

Nyhan, W. L., J. A. James, A. J. Teberg, L. Sweetman, and L. G. Nelson. 1969. A New Disorder of Purine Metabolism with Behavioral Manifestations. *Journal of Pediatrics*, 74:20–27.

Pardee, A. B., and A. C. Wilson. 1963. Control of Enzyme Activity in Higher Animals. *Cancer Research*, 23:1483–1490.

Paul, J., and P. F. Fottrell. 1963. Mechanism of D-Glutamyltransferase Repression in Mammalian Cells. *Biochimica et biophysica acta*, 67:334–336.

Paul, J., P. F. Fottrell, I. Freshney, W. R. Jondorf, and M. G. Struthers. 1964. "Regulation of Enzyme Synthesis in Cultured Cells," *Metabolic Control Mechanisms in Animal Cells* (National Cancer Institute Monograph 13), W. J. Rutter, Ed. U.S. Department of Health, Education, and Welfare, Public Health Service, National Cancer Institute. Pp. 219–228.

Penman, S. 1967. Ribonucleic Acid Metabolism in Mammalian Cells. *New England Journal of Medicine*, 276:502–511.

Pflueger, O. H., Jr., and J. J. Yunis. 1966. Deoxyribonucleic Acid Replication of Somatic Cells in the Chinese Hamster. *Nature*, 210:1074–1075.

Pizer, L. I. 1964. Enzymology and Regulation of Serine Biosynthesis in Cultured Human Cells. *Journal of Biological Chemistry*, 239:4219–4226.

Scaletta, L. J., and B. Ephrussi. 1965. Hybridization of Normal and Neoplastic Cells In Vitro. *Nature*, 205:1169–1171.

Schimke, R. T. 1964a. "Enzymes of Arginine Metabolism in Cell Culture: Studies on Enzyme Induction and Repression," *Metabolic Control Mechanisms in Animal Cells* (National Cancer Institute Monograph 13), W. J. Rutter, Ed. Bethesda, Maryland: U.S. Department of Health, Education and Welfare, Public Health Service, National Cancer Institute. Pp.197–217.

————. 1964b. Enzymes of Arginine Metabolism in Mammalian Cell Culture. I. Repression of Argininosuccinate Synthetase and Argininosuccinase. *Journal of Biological Chemistry*, 239:136–145.

————. 1964c. The Importance of Both Synthesis and Degradation in the Control of Arginase Levels in Rat Liver. *Journal of Biological Chemistry*, 239:3808–3817.

Shapiro, S., and J. Martinez. 1968. Congenital Dysprothrombinemia: An Inherited Structural Disorder of Human Prothrombin. (Abstract) *The Journal of Clinical Investigation*, 47:89a.

Shih, V. E., and J. W. Littlefield. Unpublished data.

Silagi, S., G. Darlington, and S. A. Bruce. 1969. Hybridization of Two Biochemically Marked Human Cell Lines. *Proceedings of the National Academy of Sciences of the U.S.A.* (in press.)

Sonnenschein, C., A. H. Tashjian, Jr., and U. I. Richardson. 1968. Somatic Cell Hybridization: Mouse-Rat Hybrid Cell Line Involving a Growth Hormone-Producing Parent. (Abstract) *Genetics*, 60 (Number 1, Part 2): 227–228.

Stanbury, J. B., J. B. Wyngaarden, and D. S. Fredrickson. 1966. "Inherited Variation and Metabolic Abnormality," *The Metabolic Basis of Inherited Disease*, J. B. Stanbury, J. B. Wyngaarden, and D. S. Fredrickson, Eds. New York, New York: McGraw-Hill Book Company. P. 9.

Stocker, F., P. Ammann, and E. Rossi. 1968. Selective γ-A-Globulin Deficiency, with

Dominant Autosomal Inheritance in a Swiss Family. *Archives of Disease in Childhood*, 43:585–588.

Talamo, R. C., T. Kowalyshyn, and K. F. Austen. 1969. Hereditary Alpha$_1$-Antitrypsin Deficiency in Childhood. *Pediatric Research*, 3:373.

Tauro, P., H. O. Halvorson, and R. L. Epstein. 1968. Time of Gene Expression in Relation to Centromere Distance During the Cell Cycle of *Saccharomyces cereviseae*. *Proceedings of the National Academy of Sciences of the U.S.A.*, 59: 277–284.

Tedesco, T. A., and W. J. Mellman. 1967. Argininosuccinate Synthetase Activity and Citrulline Metabolism in Cells Cultured from a Citrullinemic Subject. *Proceedings of the National Academy of Sciences of the U.S.A.*, 57:829–834.

Tschudy, D. P., M. G. Perlroth, H. S. Marver, A. Collins, G. Hunter, Jr., and M. Rechcigl, Jr. 1965. Acute Intermittent Porphyria: The First "Overproduction Disease" Localized to a Specific Enzyme. *Proceedings of the National Academy of Sciences of the U.S.A.*, 53:841–846.

Turner, M. K., R. Abrams, and I. Lieberman. 1968. Levels of Ribonucleotide Reductase Activity during the Division Cycle of the L cell. *Journal of Biological Chemistry*, 243:3725–3728.

Weiss, M. C., G. J. Todaro, and H. Green. 1968. Properties of a Hybrid between Lines Sensitive and Insensitive to Contact Inhibition of Cell Division. *Journal of Cellular Physiology*, 71:105–108.

Wright, B. E. 1966. Multiple Causes and Controls in Differentiation. *Science*, 153: 830–837.

Yoshida, A. 1968. "The Structure of Normal and Variant Human Glucose-6-Phosphate Dehydrogenase," *Hereditary Disorders of Erythrocyte Metabolism* (City of Hope Symposium Series), E. Beutler, Ed. New York, New York: Grune & Stratton, Inc. Vol. I. Pp. 146–162.

Yoshida, A., A. G. Motulsky, R. J. Dern, P. McCurdy, and H. Neitlich. 1968. Mechanisms of Genetically Controlled Increased Enzyme Activity in Man. *Program and Abstracts: The American Society of Human Genetics* (October 10–13, 1968, Austin, Texas). Pp. 19–20.

Zuckerkandl, E. 1964. Compensatory Effects in the Synthesis of Hemoglobin Polypeptide Chains. *Cold Spring Harbor Symposia on Quantitative Biology*, 29:357–374.

Discussion

Dr. G. David Novelli, Oak Ridge National Laboratory, Oak Ridge, Tennessee: Dr. Littlefield, may I suggest that the transfer ribonucleic acid (tRNA) profile in the hybrids be compared to those of the two parents. Dr. Yang in my laboratory has studied several lines of plasmacytomas; some make immunoglobulin G (IgG), and some make immunoglobulin A (IgA). He found a difference in the seryl-tRNA's. In the aggregate there are four tRNA's, one is missing in the IgA series, and another one is absent in the IgG series. All code differently. This could be the situation in the case you cited, *i.e.*, one of the tRNA's may be very low or absent. This would prevent or restrict the reading of the message for that protein.

Dr. John W. Littlefield, Massachusetts General Hospital, Boston, Massachu-

setts: The suggestion that the balance of tRNA in the hybrid might have a regulatory role is interesting.

Dr. W. S. Sly, Washington University School of Medicine, St. Louis, Missouri: There may be parallels in the regulation in bacterial cells. I believe there are many mechanisms of regulation in bacterial cells, both positive and negative—positive in arabinose and negative in the lactose pathway. The tRNA switch-on and switch-off mechanisms would probably be studied most efficiently in microbial systems.

Dr. Littlefield: My feeling is that there may well be regulation of the bacterial type, but I think it is not anywhere near as important as other more complicated mechanisms or as special complications of those mechanisms.

Dr. R. Bottomley, Oklahoma Medical Research Foundation, Oklahoma City, Oklahoma: Dr. Littlefield, additional support for your idea might come from some work that Dr. Martin Griffin and I have been doing on leukocyte alkaline phosphatase. Dr. Griffin has previously shown in HeLa cells that although alkaline phosphatase activity was increased in the presence of hydrocortisone, its rate of synthesis was not increased. We have recently shown that in chronic granulocytic leukemic cells which have a low level of alkaline phosphatase, the enzyme has low specific activity, and in leukemoid reactions in which there is an increased amount of enzyme activity, the enzyme has a very high specific activity. It would appear, therefore, that regulation of this enzyme occurs through changes in specific activity rather than through alterations in the amount of enzyme protein.

Dr. Littlefield: Were your compounds purified?

Dr. Bottomley: Yes.

Dr. Littlefield: Were these crosses of positive cells in a negative clone of the mothers?

Dr. R. DeMars, University of Wisconsin, Madison, Wisconsin: The vaguely positive cell in the phenotypically negative clones is not fully positive. This you can find in phenotypically negative clones which are heterozygous for the glucose-6-phosphate dehydrogenase (G-6-PD) deficiency too. I have thought for years, and we're now trying to investigate it, that the X chromosome that is "off" is not 100 per cent off, and if we treat it in the right way, we may turn these genes on. I think those vaguely positive cells are just suggestions of a limited expression. However, there may be less interesting interpretations; for example, that the radioactive hypoxanthine wasn't pure.

We would like to detect truly positive cells. Obviously, the selective system is a key to that. We have found that phenotypically positive clones grow in the absence of adenine but phenotypically negative clones do not. Mrs. Jeannette Felix and I are now trying to derepress the X chromosome in phenotypically negative clones, using the selective system and mutagenic agents.

The glutamine enzyme is unstable in HeLa cells. If the cells are put into a maintenance medium that is lacking in one or two essential amino acids, the cell population is rather stable for up to 72 hours. If you then treat such cultures with glutamic acid, the enzyme maintains its activity reasonably well. However, if even a low concentration (2×10^{-5}M) of glutamine is placed in these maintenance cultures, the level of the enzymes declines rapidly. I do not interpret this as being the result of destabilization of the enzymes by glutamine because diploid human cells have the derepressed amounts of glutamyl transferase in the presence of glutamine.

Dr. Littlefield: Can you exclude that this is the result of destabilization?

Dr. DeMars: I cannot exclude that. I say only that it's not that simple. I believe that the enzyme participated in turnover as do other proteins in the cell and, in the presence of glutamine, could not get made again. It does break down as do many other proteins.

There is another thing that should be looked for in cells from human beings and other metazoa, instead of always thinking in terms of operons. Two years ago, Jules Leroy and I discovered the "I" cells, caused by mutant genes in man. Their cytoplasm is cluttered with inclusions, which, incidentally, helped us to discover them. We believed that these were abnormal lysosomes and began looking at lysomal enzymes. He and I together, and now with Dr. John O'Brien in California, have already found four biochemically unrelated lysomal enzymes that are drastically diminished in the I cells. They are as diverse as β-glucuronidase, β-galactosidase, and neuraminidase. For a while, because these inclusions were loaded with lipids, we believed that the diminished activity of β-glucuronidase could be the result of interference with the activity of the enzyme, but it isn't that simple. Every effort made to uncover masked activity has failed (Dr. Trante Schroeder of the Human Genetics Institute in Heidelberg did this work). The kinetic properties of the enzyme are normal qualitatively. Its diminished activity is not caused simply by its association with an abnormal lysosome, but apparently a diminution occurs in the amount of enzyme protein. As to how that regulation works, I have no idea.

Dr. Selma Silagi, Cornell University Medical School, New York, New York: With regard to inactivation of the X chromosome in the same human-human hybridization that Dr. Littlefield mentioned, the orotic aciduric strain was crossed with the D98 aza-hypoxanthine-resistant strain. The latter, as Gartler had shown, is the A+ G-6-PD type, whereas the orotic aciduric strain is the B type. As you know, these are X-linked alleles.

In the hybrid cells, both X-linked alleles were active, as shown by starch gel electrophoresis.

In addition, Dr. Littlefield, you stated that all of the dihydroxyphenylalanine (DOPA) oxidase and melanin studies were interspecific. In my studies, the hybridization was between a melanoma from C57BL mice and L cells which were C3H in origin. The same was true in the Davidson and Ephrussi study; there was neither DOPA oxidase activity nor melanin production in the hybrid cells. Also, there was none in tumors, which in this case could be obtained from the hybrid cells by injecting them into F-1 mice of the appropriate genotypes. The tumors, which were carried for two years, also were completely amelanotic, both initially and in all transplant generations.

Mr. R. C. Ross, The University of Texas M. D. Anderson Hospital and Tumor Institute at Houston, Houston, Texas: It seems to me that besides just fusing of the cells, Dr. Littlefield, you might get more information by letting the two cells grow in their own cultures and then mixing the parameters that you want to measure, especially enzymatic parameters.

Dr. Littlefield: We have mixed extracts in our work.

Mr. Ross: Did you get the same answers that you do with cell fusion?

Dr. Littlefield: Yes, but perhaps this technique could be used more widely. Dr. DeMars, has hybridization work shown that an X which is inactive in one of the parents is turned on in the hybrid cell?

Dr. DeMars: I don't know that anyone has succeeded in doing that. We are trying it by using interspecific hybridizations in which the control might break down and also by using the second selectable marker in diploid cells. Extreme G-6-PD deficiency leads to a very slow growth rate in diploid cells, so we can now select for hybrids using phenotypically negative clones for the Lesch-Nyhan mutation and male G-6-PD-deficient cells. The gross difficulty of G-6-PD-deficient cells can be repaired beautifully by putting uridine in the cultures.

Dr. Littlefield: Dr. DeMars, you have said that within a year somebody will have illustrated mutagenesis in diploid fibroblasts. I would bet that might be Dr. Chu, and I wonder if he has done it yet. Dr. Chu, have you worked with diploid fibroblasts in your mutagenic system?

Dr. Ernest H. Y. Chu, Oak Ridge National Laboratory, Oak Ridge, Tennessee: Yes, we have diploid cells of human origin. We are just beginning to see if we can induce forward and back mutations in cultures of cells from human beings and if we can isolate somatic cell hybrids.

With reference to a question raised a moment ago, Dr. DeMars, we made cell hybrids between one cell type derived from a male patient with G-6-PD deficiency and another cell from a male carrier of the Lesch-Nyhan syndrome. In this hybrid, the two X chromosomes from both parental cells remained active.

Dr. DeMars: We are talking about a different experiment. You have mated two male cells and asked if one X gets turned off. Dr. Sly asked whether the X that was off gets turned on when you mate a female cell with some other cell.

Properties of Somatic Hybrid Cell Lines Between Mouse Cells and SV40-Transformed Human Cells

MARY C. WEISS

Centre de Génétique Moléculaire, 91, Gif-sur-Yvette, France

The oncogenic viruses of animals have permitted quantitative and reproducible analysis of neoplastic change in animals and in animal and human cells in vitro. The similarities between these model systems and cancers in human beings have led many workers to believe that similar agents may be responsible for the formation of certain types of tumors in man.

Workers in many laboratories have undertaken extensive and detailed studies of the processes of viral infection and transformation, and of the properties of transformed cells, in an attempt to determine: (1) the genetic properties of the viruses which render them permanent transforming agents, (2) the nature of cellular susceptibility to transformation, and (3) the genetic changes which accompany—or cause—and maintain the neoplastic state.

One of the most extensively studied of the oncogenic viruses is the small deoxyribonucleic acid (DNA)-containing papovavirus, SV40 (simian vacuolating virus 40) (Rapp and Butel, 1970, see pages 256 to 280, this volume). This virus causes the formation of tumors when injected into certain types of animals and causes transformation of many types of mammalian cells in vitro. Among the types of cells susceptible to SV40-induced transformation in vitro are both human and mouse cells.

Evidence for Retention of the SV40 Genome in Transformed Cells

SV40-transformed mouse cells produce no infectious virus. SV40-transformed human cells produce some virus for a limited time, and then usually cease to do so (Girardi, Jensen, and Koprowski, 1965). There are many lines of evidence which demonstrate that although transformed cells do not produce virus particles, the viral genome is retained in them.

The continuous presence of the viral genome was suggested by a number of observations of the properties of SV40-transformed cells, among which were: (1) the appearance and retention of two new non-species-specific antigens, thought to be products of viral genes, the tumor or T-antigen (also called the induced complement-fixing antigen [ICFA]) (Black, Rowe, Turner, and Heubner, 1963) and the surface transplantation antigen (Defendi, 1963; Habel and Eddy, 1963; Koch and Sabin, 1963; Girardi, 1965); and (2) the detection in transformed cells of messenger ribonucleic acid (mRNA) complementary to SV40 DNA (Benjamin, 1966). The persistence of the viral genome in SV40-transformed cells was directly demonstrated by the observation that most lines of such cells yield infectious SV40 after (Sendai virus-induced) fusion with susceptible indicator cells (Koprowski, Jensen, and Steplewski, 1967; Watkins and Dulbecco, 1967). Moreover, it has recently been found by the use of DNA-RNA hybridization techniques that numerous copies of the SV40 genome (five to 60) are present in DNA extracted from transformed cells (Westphal and Dulbecco, 1968).

Although it has thus been shown that SV40 genomes are retained and are expressed in transformed cells, the nature of the relationship of the viral genome to the transformed cell and the role of the virus genome in the maintenance of the transformed state remain to be explored.

Regarding the location of the virus genome in transformed cells, several hypotheses have been formulated. One is that the virus is carried in the nucleus or in the cytoplasm of the cells as a free ("episome"-like) particle, which may or may not be periodically associated with the genome of the host cell. According to another hypothesis, the virus genome may be stably integrated into the host's chromosomes.

The experiments to be described, initially undertaken in cooperation with Dr. Boris Ephrussi and Dr. Lawrence Scaletta, were designed to explore some of the problems just outlined. (A preliminary account of some of the experiments has been published [cf. Weiss, Ephrussi, and Scaletta, 1968].)

Somatic hybrid cells, which lose most or all of the chromosomes of one parental type, have been used to test the "free particle" and the "integration" hypotheses. It has been shown previously (Weiss and Green, 1967) that human × mouse somatic hybrids, in which nearly all chromosomes can be identified as to species of origin, lose most or all of the human chromosomes. In the experiments to be described, similar hybrids were made between cells of these two species, both of which are susceptible to transformation by SV40, and therefore can both maintain and express the viral genome. For these crosses, three types of mouse cells

TABLE 1. *Characteristics of Parental Cell Types*

Cross	Parent Human SV40-transformed	Mouse	Enzyme deficiency*	Survival in selective medium	Mean no. of chromo-somes	Per cent Markers†
1	SV-SD-C‡		None	+	Near tetraploid	74
		Cl 1 D+	TK	—	51.7	83
2	VA-2(Cl 12B)‡		HGPRT	—	71	90
		T6	None	+	40	100
3	VA-2(Cl 12B)‡		HGPRT	—	71	90
		3T3(4E)+	TK	—	70	100

* The enzyme deficiencies included in this column are those which render cells sensitive to selective medium containing aminopterin, and they include deficiencies for thymidine kinase (TK) and hypoxanthine guanine phosphoribosyl transferase (HGPRT).

† This column gives the per cent of chromosomes of each parent which are distinguishable from those of the other parent.

‡ Cloned populations.

have been used in combination with two different lines of SV40-transformed human cells. The hybrid cells have been isolated in pure culture, and maintained over many generations of growth. During this time, the karyotype of the cells was examined periodically. Simultaneously, the cells were tested for the presence of the SV40-induced T-antigen as an indicator of the presence of the viral genome (Table 1).

If the virus genome is carried in transformed cells as a free particle and is present in sufficient numbers to be constantly transmitted, then it should be expressed and maintained in all the SV40-transformed human × mouse hybrid cells, irrespective of loss of human chromosomes. However, if the SV40 genome is stably integrated into one or several human chromosomes, the viral genome should no longer be present in the hybrid cells which have lost these chromosomes. The number of human chromosomes which must be lost before loss of the viral genome is observed should indeed give an approximation of the number of integration sites of the viral genome. Finally, if loss of the viral genome from the hybrid cells were observed, this could not be attributed to loss of a human gene required for maintenance and expression of the viral genome since both parental species are susceptible to transformation by SV40.

Crosses and Characteristics of the Hybrid Cells

Three different lines of mouse cells (none of them deliberately exposed to SV40) and two different SV40-transformed human cell lines were used in the crosses. The karyological characteristics and the enzyme deficiencies of the parental cells are shown in Table 1. The selective isolation of hybrid cells from the crosses of SV-SD-C × cl 1 D (Cross 1) and of VA-2 × T6 (Cross 2) have been described previously (Weiss, Ephrussi, and Scaletta, 1968).

The third cross (VA-2 × 3T3) was carried out using the Sendai fusion technique (Harris and Watkins, 1965; Coon and Weiss, 1969) and Littlefield's selective system. Suspensions of parental cells were treated with ultraviolet (UV)-inactivated Sendai virus, diluted, and inoculated in selective medium (Littlefield, 1964). The selective medium kills both parental cell types but permits unhampered growth of hybrid cells. Within two weeks, numerous hybrid colonies were visible; their frequency was of the order of one per 5×10^2 to 1×10^3 parental cells.

Hybrid cells from all three crosses were isolated as pure clonal populations, and their karyotypes were examined after about 20 generations (Table 2). In all cases, even the very young hybrid cells contained many fewer than the parental number of human chromosomes (Figure 1); this has been true in all of the human × mouse hybrid cells thus far examined (Weiss and Green, 1967; Weiss, Ephrussi, and Scaletta, 1968; Matsuya and Green, 1969). Moreover, from the two crosses in which VA-2 was used as the human parental cell, the hybrids contained approximately two times the expected number of mouse chromosomes (Table 2). Karyo-

TABLE 2. *Expected and Observed Karyological Characteristics of Hybrid Cells*

Cross	Hybrid	Expected, or no. of generations when hybrids observed	Mean (and range) of no. of human chromosomes	Mean no. of mouse chromosomes
1 (SV-SD-C × cl 1D)	HM-SV	Expected	70–90	51.7
	HM-SV-cl 1	20	5.2(2–10)	53.5*
2 (VA-2 × T6)	VT	Expected	F1	40
	VT-2	22	18.0(15–20)	78.0
3 (VA-2 × 3T3)	3V	Expected	F1	70
	3V3	30	15.8(8–24)	135.7
	3V15	22	14.2(7–22)	130.0

* The number of human chromosomes is slightly underestimated, and that of mouse chromosomes overestimated because of the presence of some "nonmarker" chromosomes; these are always counted as "mouse chromosomes" (see Figure 1).

FIGURE 1: See legend on page 461.

typic analysis of 10 to 20 independently derived hybrid colonies from each of these two crosses revealed that there was an extraordinary similarity of the karyotypes of all of the hybrid colonies derived from one cross or the other.

These karyological peculiarities of human × mouse hybrid cells (extensive loss of human chromosomes in all crosses and doubling of the mouse complement in some crosses) appear to result from some form of asynchrony in the newly formed hybrid cells. Whatever the cause of this asynchrony, it appears to be limited to the first few divisions of the hybrid cells, since once the hybrid colonies contain 30 or more cells (and are readily detectable), the latter are clearly viable, and although they grow somewhat slowly at first (generation time of 30 to 48 hr), they begin to grow rapidly after about 30 to 50 generations, dividing every 20 to 28 hr.

TABLE 3. *Evolution of the Karyotype of Hybrid Clones*

Cross	Hybrid	No. of generations	Mean (and range) of no. of human chromosomes	Mean no. of mouse chromosomes
1 (SV-SD-C × cl 1 D)	HM-SV-cl 1	20	5.2 (2–10)	53.5
		80	1.9 (1–4)	52.4
2 (VA-2 × T6)	VT-2	22	18 (15–20)	78.0
		55	12.6(10–15)	74.8
		95	11.1 (9–22)	67.5
	VT-7	50	8.4 (3–23)	113.2
		100	10.1 (2–17)	104.7
		160	8.4 (6–15)	73.6
3 (VA-2 × 3T3)	3V3	30	15.8 (8–24)	135.7
		75	10.8 (8–15)	106.9
		130	8.8 (7–13)	96.8
	3V15	22	14.2 (7–22)	130.0
		75	6.9 (3–11)	102.0
		138	5.7 (4–9)	93.7

FIGURE 1. Karyogram and metaphase figure of a hybrid from Cross 1 (SV-SD-C × cl 1 D). The mouse parental line is characterized by the presence of a mean number of 52 chromosomes, including nine large metacentric and 43 telocentric chromosomes. In this hybrid metaphase, 44 telocentric chromosomes are present, as well as 11 long metacentrics (one or two of which may be of human origin) and five clearly distinguishable human chromosomes (second row of karyogram).

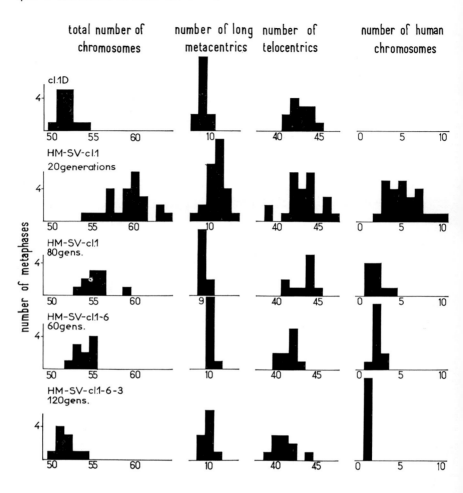

FIGURE 2. Karyotypes of mouse parental cells (cl 1 D) and a clone of HM-SV (Cross 1, SV-SD-C × cl 1 D). After 20 generations of growth, this clone contained two to 10 human chromosomes, and after 80 generations of growth, the number of human chromosomes was reduced to one to four. Two subclones are also shown: cl 1–6, containing one to three human chromosomes, and derived from it, cl 1–6–3, which contains only one human chromosome (see also Table 4). The numbers of telocentric and long metacentric chromosomes of the various hybrid populations are similar to those of the mouse parental cells, cl 1 D.

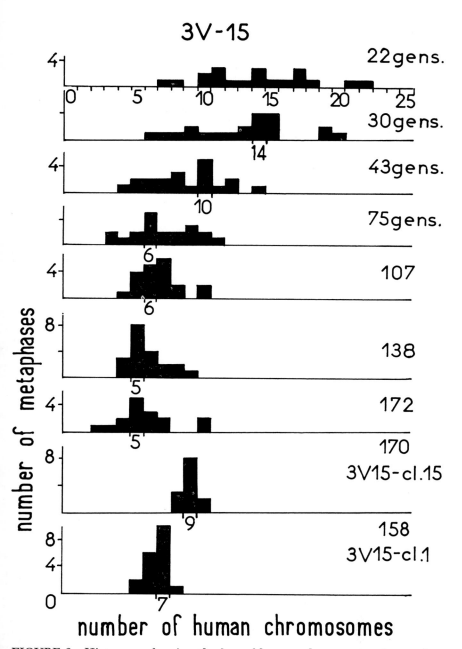

FIGURE 3. Histogram showing the loss of human chromosomes from a hybrid clone 3V-15 (Cross 3, 3T3 × VA-2). The young hybrid clone, after 22 generations of growth, contained seven to 22 human chromosomes, and this number declined progressively with continued cultivation. Two subclones (cl 15 and cl 1) contained nine and seven human chromosomes, respectively (see also Table 4).

Evolution of the Karyotype of Hybrid Cells

The hybrid cells obtained from the three crosses showed mean numbers of human chromosomes of five to 20 when they were first examined, after about 20 generations. One or two hybrid clones from each cross were chosen for further study.

The number of human chromosomes present in all hybrids declined with progressive cultivation, the most rapid loss occurring between 20 and 50 generations. Thereafter, the chromosome composition of the hybrid cell populations became more stable, but loss of human chromosomes continued to occur (Table 3).

The accompanying histograms (Figures 2 and 3) show a detailed picture of the loss of human chromosomes from two hybrid clones. The curve (Figure 4) shows the decline in mean number of human chromosomes from a hybrid population as a function of the number of cell divisions or generations. Even after hybrid populations appear to have stabilized, it is possible to isolate clones which contain substantially more or fewer human chromosomes than the mean number of the population. (Histograms show variation in chromosome numbers of populations.)

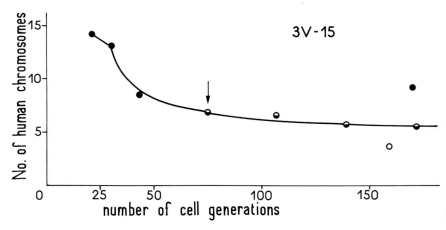

FIGURE 4. Loss of human chromosomes with growth of the hybrid cells 3V-15. The most rapid loss of human chromosomes occurred between 20 and 50 generations, after which there was some stabilization of the mean number of human chromosomes per cell. The two points which do not fall on the curve are subclones 3V15–15 (closed circle) and 3V15–9 (open circle). The closed circles designate populations containing only T-antigen-positive cells; the half-closed circles designate populations containing both T-antigen-positive and T-antigen-negative cells, and the open circle represents a population containing only T-antigen-negative cells.

TABLE 4. *Number of Human Chromosomes of T-Antigen-Positive (T-ag+)
and -Negative (T-ag⁻) Hybrid Cells*

		When T-arg⁻ first observed		Characteristics of clones		
					No. of human chromosomes	
Cross	Hybrid	No. of generations	No. of human chromosomes	No. of generations	T-ag+	T-ag⁻
1	HM-SV	30	5.2(2–10)	..	....	.....
	cl 3			60	2.9(2–4)	.....
	cl 3–8			120		1.0(1)
	cl 6			60	2.1(1–3)	
	cl 6–1			120	2.0 (2)	
	cl 6–3			120		1.0(1)
2	VT 7	100	10.1(2–17)	..	....	.....
3	3V3	102	8.6(5–11)	..	....	.....
	3V15	75	6.9(3–11)	..	....	.....
	3V15–1			158		6.5(5–7)
	3V15–9			158		5(5)
	3V15–15			170	9.0(8–10)	

Expression of and Loss of T-Antigen from Hybrid Cells

SV40-transformed cells always contain two new antigens. One of these, the T-antigen or ICFA (detected by the immunofluorescent assay), was used as an indicator of the presence (or absence) of the viral genome.

Cells were inoculated on a cover slip, allowed to grow for several days, and then fixed in cold methanol (70 per cent):acetone (30 per cent). The fixed cells were incubated for 40 minutes at 37 C in fluorescein-conjugated hamster serum against SV40 T-antigen (Flow Laboratories), washed, and examined with a fluorescent microscope. T-antigen-positive cells show a bright nuclear fluorescence (the nucleoli appearing as dark spots) against a pale green cytoplasm, while T-antigen-negative cells show pale green cytoplasmic staining, and each cell appears to have a dark hole where the nucleus lies.

Examination of the parental cells showed that none of the mouse cells were T-antigen positive, while all cells of the two (clonal) populations of SV40-transformed human parental cells were T-antigen positive.

Numerous hybrid populations have been examined in this manner. All young hybrid populations (20 to 30 generations after their formation) were found to contain only T-antigen-positive cells, with the exception of one hybrid clone (Cross 1, see below). Thus, most hybrid cells from all three crosses were found to contain and to express the viral genome.

However, after 50 to 100 generations in culture, T-antigen-negative cells began to appear in the hybrid populations, and in several cases, eventually constituted the majority of the population. Negative cells were subsequently isolated in pure culture by cloning (except from Cross 2).

The hybrid population from Cross 1 contained both positive and negative cells when it was first examined. Therefore, three T-antigen-positive clones were isolated and maintained in culture until they became heterogeneous; from them, both positive and negative subclones were isolated. Thus, we were able to demonstrate that T-antigen-negative cells clearly can and do arise from T-antigen-positive ones (Weiss, Ephrussi, and Scaletta, 1968).

One hybrid population did not give rise to T-antigen-negative cells; in two others, T-antigen-negative cells have appeared, but at too low a frequency to be readily isolated by cloning.

Karyological Characteristics of T-Antigen-Positive and -Negative Cells

It was the purpose of these experiments to determine whether a correlation exists between loss or retention of T-antigen and that of the chromosomes of the SV40-transformed parent. It is already clear that preferential and continuing loss of human chromosomes from the hybrid cells is observed and that, in most cases, loss of T-antigen occurs only after prolonged cultivation. To analyze further this apparent correlation, periodic karyotypic and T-antigen analyses have been performed on sister cultures of several hybrid populations and clones.

As shown in Table 4, for each cross there is a clear correlation between loss of T-antigen and loss of human chromosomes. In hybrid cells from the first cross, T-antigen-negative cells were observed when the number of human chromosomes was between two and 10. Pure clones of T-antigen-negative cells never contained more than two human chromosomes; more frequently, only one human chromosome was present. In hybrid populations from the third cross, however, T-antigen-negative cells appeared when the populations were characterized by the presence of three to 11 human chromosomes (Figure 4), and T-antigen-negative clones have been isolated which contain as many as five to seven human chromosomes, but never more.

From the two hybrid clones of Cross 2 and one of Cross 3, T-antigen-negative cells have not been isolated in pure culture. One of them (VT-2) has produced no T-antigen-negative cells, while the two others (VT-7 and 3V3) have been found to contain negative cells, but only at low frequency. These three hybrid populations have retained larger numbers of human chromosomes than the two which have come to be composed predominantly of T-antigen-negative cells (Table 5).

TABLE 5.   *Detection and Isolation of T-Antigen-Negative Cells from the Different Hybrid Clones*

Cross	Hybrid clone	Presence of T-antigen-negative cells detected	T-antigen-negative clones isolated	Minimum mean no. of human chromosomes*
1	HM-SV	Yes	Yes	1.9
2	VT-2	No	No	11.1
	VT-7	Yes	No	8.4
3	3V3	Yes	No	8.8
	3V15	Yes	Yes	5.6

* Minimum mean number of human chromosomes observed in hybrid clones continuously maintained in selective medium.

It was somewhat surprising to find that 90 to 97 per cent of the human chromosomes were lost before T-antigen-negative cells appeared. Since there is no clear evidence that loss of human chromosomes is not random, if loss of only one or two human chromosomes could result in loss of T-antigen, we would expect to find T-antigen-negative cells which contain a much larger number of human chromosomes, perhaps 15 or more, but none has been observed. This suggests that the viral genome is associated with more than one human chromosome (or pairs of human chromosomes).

A number of T-antigen-positive clones and T-antigen-negative subclones derived from them have been examined to determine whether there is a single human chromosome (or one of a single group of human chromosomes) which can be implicated in the conversion from T-antigen positive to negative. Although the results are not conclusive (because of the relatively small number of clones and subclones examined, and because of the possible occurrence of chromosomal rearrangements in some of them), it appears that different chromosomes are lost from the various clones when the cells become negative. For example, in hybrids from Cross 1, one or two chromosomes of Group G were common in T-antigen-positive cells (Figure 5), whereas these chromosomes were rare in negative clones derived from them. In hybrids from Cross 3, members of the same groups of human chromosomes (Groups A, C, E, and F) are present

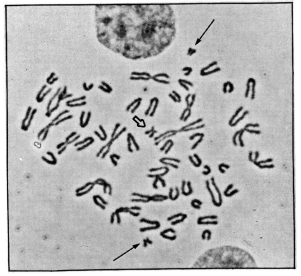

FIGURE 5. Metaphase of a cell of HM-SV1-cl 3, a highly segregated subclone from Cross 1. The cells of this clone contain three human chromosomes: one of Group E (white arrow) and two of Group G (thin black arrows). This subclone is T-antigen positive, and T-antigen-negative clones derived from it do not contain the Group G chromosomes. The Group E chromosome is present in all cells maintained in selective medium (see text), but is never present in cells which survive in 5-bromodeoxyuridine; it can therefore be concluded that it is the human chromosome which specifies thymidine kinase.

in both the positive and the negative cells, and are simply more numerous in the positive clones.

Absence of Linkage Between T-Antigen and the Human Thymidine Kinase Chromosome

The use of mouse cell lines deficient for the enzyme thymidine kinase has made it possible to test for linkage between the human chromosome which specifies this enzyme and the SV40 genome. This test is based upon the selective system described by Littlefield (1964), and its use with human × mouse hybrids has been described previously (Weiss and Green, 1967).

Two of the mouse parental lines (cl 1 D and 3T3) lack thymidine kinase activity. Growth of cells in selective medium containing hypoxanthine, thymidine, and aminopterin (which blocks the *de novo* pathway for nucleotide synthesis and makes the cells dependent upon thymidine kinase for the synthesis of thymidine monophosphate) requires thymidine kinase activity. Since the human cells we used contain this enzyme, the hybrid cells were able to grow in selective medium by virtue of complementation for this deficiency by the human enzyme. As long as the hybrid cells are maintained in selective medium, the human chromosome which specifies thymidine kinase is retained. Thus, in selective medium, hybrid cells with highly reduced numbers of human chromosomes preferentially retain at least one copy of the thymidine kinase chromosome.

The three hybrid populations from Crosses 1 and 3 have been continuously maintained in selective medium; in all of them, T-antigen-negative cells have been observed and, except in one case, isolated. In these two crosses, independently derived human transformed cells were used as the human parental line. Thus, it is clear that in the two human parental lines, the SV40 genome was not present in at least one copy of the human chromosome which specifies thymidine kinase. This suggests that there is no specific viral integration site on that chromosome.

Reinfection with SV40 of T-Antigen-Negative Hybrid Cells

T-antigen-negative hybrid cells were reinfected with SV40 for two reasons. (1) It is known that SV40-transformed cells are at least partly resistant to reinfection with virus. It could be argued that loss of T-antigen from the hybrid cell is caused by a mutation which leads to loss of expression of T-antigen, and that disappearance of this antigen does not indicate loss of the viral genome. If this were true, then such T-antigen-negative hybrid cells would be totally or partially resistant to reinfection. (2) If loss of the viral genome were caused by loss of some cellular gene (human or mouse) required for expression and maintenance of the viral genome, then no expression of viral functions would be observed after infection with SV40 of a T-antigen-negative clone of hybrid cells.

Cells of the T-antigen-negative hybrid clone 3V15-1 were infected as described by Todaro and Green (1966). Examination of T-antigen at 48 and 72 hours after virus infection has shown that 5 to 15 per cent of the cells do again produce T-antigen. There was no evidence of a cytocidal effect in the infected cells.

It is known that SV40 infection and transformation of human cells leads to extensive chromosome breakage and rearrangements (Koprowski et al., 1962; see also review by Moorhead, 1970, pages 281 to 306, this volume). However, no such chromosomal damage is observed in mouse cells infected with and transformed by SV40. The cells of the hybrid clone 3V15-1 were examined for evidence of chromosome damage after SV40 infection. Chromosome breaks and translocations were numerous in the infected cells, but not in the uninfected controls. Moreover, the chromosomal damage was not restricted to the five to seven human chromosomes present in this clone, but involved the mouse chromosomes as well. The cause of the susceptibility of cells to chromosome damage following SV40 infection is not known, but in this case it is most likely the consequence of the presence of some human chromosomes.

Growth Properties of Parental and Hybrid Cells

It has previously been shown (Weiss, Todaro, and Green, 1968) that somatic hybrids formed in crosses between parental lines which are highly sensitive and insensitive to contact inhibition of cell division behave like the sensitive parent; they reach a relatively low saturation density and cease dividing. The cell lines used in these earlier experiments were both derived from mouse tissues: 3T3, a contact-inhibited cell line which reaches a stable saturation density of 4×10^4 cells/cm², and cl 1 D, a noncontact-inhibited line derived from L cells (originally transformed by methylcholanthrene [Earle, 1943]) which reaches no stable saturation density ($>70 \times 10^4$ cells/cm² can be obtained). The hybrid cells contained most of the chromosomes of the parental lines and reached stable saturation densities of 4 to 8×10^4 cells/cm², similar to that observed for 3T3. In this case, contact inhibition of growth, characteristic only of the 3T3 parent, was expressed in the hybrid cells.

Similar measurements of saturation densities have been made for the hybrids of Cross 3, that is 3T3 × VA-2. This cross differs from the one just described in two respects. (1) Although the parental lines include a contact-inhibited and a noncontact-inhibited one, the latter parent has been transformed by SV40 and containes the complete SV40 genome (Koprowski, Jensen, and Steplewski, 1967). (2) Many or most of the chromosomes of the SV40-transformed (noncontact-inhibited) parental cell line are lost from the hybrid cells. However, since SV40 transformation originally induced loss of contact inhibition of these human cells, it is possible that retention of the SV40 genome is in some way essential for continued expression of the property of uncontrolled growth. Since all the young hybrid cells of Cross 3 contain the SV40 genome, it would be expected that if there is a viral gene which is responsible for loss of contact inhibition, and if maintenance of this change is dependent upon continuous expression of this hypothetical viral gene, then the T-antigen-positive hybrid cells should be noncontact inhibited. This expectation is strengthened by the observation that SV40 transformation of the contact-inhibited parental line 3T3 results in loss of this property (Todaro and Green, 1964).

The data of Table 6 show that the T-antigen-positive hybrids formed

TABLE 6. *Saturation Densities of Parental and Hybrid Cells*

Cell line	T-antigen	Saturation density (cells/cm²)
3T3	—	4×10^4
SV40-transformed 3T3*	+	46×10^4
VA-2	+	30×10^4
Hybrid clones (3T3 × VA-2)		
3V3	+	3×10^4
3V5	+	4.5×10^4
3V15	+	3.9×10^4
3V15–1	—	4×10^4

* Value quoted from Pollack, Green, and Todaro (1968).

between 3T3 and VA-2 show saturation densities very similar to those of the 3T3 parental cells. Moreover, the saturation densities of 3T3 and of the hybrid cells are tenfold lower than those of SV40-transformed 3T3.

These observations suggest that the loss of contact inhibition of cells observed after transformation by SV40 is not maintained by the direct action of a viral gene product. We can conclude only that the mere presence of viral genomes, integrated into human chromosomes, is not sufficient to overcome the 3T3 property of contact inhibition of growth.

Finally, change in the phenotype of these hybrid cells occurs with progessive growth, just like that previously described for the contact-inhibited hybrids of 3T3 × cl 1 D (Weiss, Todaro, and Green, 1968). Some variant clones are observed which have lost contact inhibition and grow in densely packed multilayers. However, there appears to be no correlation between this property and presence or absence of the T-antigen. The presence or absence of T-antigen cannot be predicted on the basis of growth characteristics of the cells.

Discussion

The first relevant observation of the hybrid (mouse × human SV40-transformed) cells is that, except in the one case in which extremely rapid loss of human chromosomes is observed (Cross 1), all young hybrid cells maintain and express the viral genome, as detected by the presence of the SV40-induced T-antigen. This is similar to the behavior previously described for mouse × mouse somatic hybrids, obtained from a cross in which one parental type had been transformed by polyoma virus: all hybrid cells were found to contain the polyoma T-antigen (Defendi, Ephrussi, Koprowski, and Yoshida, 1967).

The results presented above strongly support the hypothesis of chromosomal integration of SV40 genomes in transformed cells. Moreover, the integration of the genomes appears to be stable, since all hybrids begin as T-antigen-positive cells, and from all hybrid clones which have lost most of the human chromosomes, T-antigen-negative cells have evolved. If the integration were not stable, that is, if the viral genomes periodically become dissociated from one chromosome and reintegrated into another, then one would expect to find that many hybrid clones, even after loss of all human chromosomes, would remain T-antigen positive (because of reintegration of viral genomes into mouse chromosomes): this has never been observed.

That the loss of T-antigen accurately reflects loss of all viral genomes cannot be stated with certainty at the present time. Since all SV40-transformed cell lines and clones examined have been found to contain at least five copies of the viral genome (Westphal and Dulbecco, 1968), it is possible that the persistence of fewer copies would not be sufficient to cause production of detectable amounts of T-antigen. The resolution of this question awaits further experiments: attempts to reactivate infectious virus from T-antigen-negative cells, or the application of molecular hybridization techniques to T-antigen-positive and -negative clones to see if the latter retain detectable numbers of virus genomes.

However, the results of T-antigen analyses argue against the retention of small numbers of viral genomes in the hybrid cells. In particular, from Cross 1, clones which retain only two or three human chromosomes and are clearly positive appear to give rise, in a single step, to T-antigen-negative cells which contain zero to two human chromosomes. The positive cells show a clear and distinctive nuclear fluorescence, while the negative cells derived from them show no trace of nuclear fluorescence. Thus, when a positive clone has become heterogeneous, there are only two kinds of cells present: clearly positive ones, and negative ones with completely unstained nuclei; no intermediate stages are seen.

The work of Westphal and Dulbecco (1968) and of Sambrook, Westphal, Srinivasan, and Dulbecco (1968), utilizing entirely different techniques, has led to some of the same conclusions. This work involved DNA-RNA hybridization of labeled complementary RNA (cRNA) (made in vitro from purified viral DNA, which is free of contaminating cellular DNA) with nuclear DNA extracted from transformed and untransformed cells. Westphal and Dulbecco (1968) showed that the amount of molecular hybridization obtained is consistent with the presence of five to 60 SV40 genomes in transformed cells, the number of viral genomes being constant for any one clonal line of transformed cells, but varying enormously for independently transformed lines of the same and of different species.

Sambrook and his co-workers have further shown that the SV40 genomes of transformed cells are not present in the form of supercoiled circles (the form of native SV40 DNA), but are covalently linked to very large molecules of DNA, almost certainly chromosomal DNA.

These observations clearly pose the question of the number of sites of integration of SV40 DNA in the chromosomes of transformed cells. There are multiple copies of SV40 genomes which could be integrated in tandem into one chromosome or which could be randomly scattered among the chromosomes of the cells. The finding that at least 90 per cent of the human chromosomes are lost from the hybrid cells of all T-antigen-negative clones suggests that the genomes are not all integrated into one chromosome.

Marin and Littlefield (1968) have used somatic hybrids to study the stability of polyoma transformation of cells which undergo loss of chromosomes. Hybrids were made between two sublines of BHK-21/13, each resistant to a different drug. The hybrids were isolated in selective medium and subsequently transformed by polyoma virus. The transformed hybrid cells were grown in the presence of the drug to which one of the parental lines was resistant, thereby selecting for cells which had lost one or more chromosomes of the other parent. By this method, these workers were able to isolate various subclones which showed nearly normal morphology, and one of which failed to grow under the conditions which are used for selection of polyoma transformants of BHK, e.g. in soft agar. The "revertant" clone had lost slightly fewer than 20 chromosomes, contained little or no polyoma T-antigen, and was retransformable by polyoma virus (Marin and Macpherson, 1968), but at a slightly lower frequency than the hybrid cells which had never been transformed. In these experiments also, loss of an oncogenic viral genome (polyoma) appears to be associated with loss of chromosomes.

The significance of the retention of viral genomes in chromosomes of transformed cells is not fully understood at present. It is clear that the persistence of the viral genomes is responsible for the presence of at least some of the parameters of transformation, including the virus-induced T-antigen, perhaps the transplantation antigen, and the newly detected "repressor" of virus multiplication (Cassingena and Tournier, 1968) (cf. Ephrussi, 1970, pages 9 to 28, this volume). However, the characteristics of viral transformation which are perhaps of greatest interest, i.e. the acquisition of neoplasticity and loss of contact inhibition of transformed cells (Aaronson and Todaro, 1968), have not to date been positively correlated with any of these products of viral genes. In fact, there is some evidence that some of them can be absent from transformed cells (T-antigen and transplantation antigen) without loss of neoplastic potential (*cf.* Rapp and Butel, 1970, pages 256 to 280, this volume). Moreover, it has been shown by Pollack, Green, and Todaro (1968) that spontaneous variants occur in populations of virus-transformed cells. These variants are contact inhibited and possess little or no tumor-producing ability, yet retain the complete virus genome. And finally, our observations of the continued expression of contact inhibition in the 3T3 × VA-2 hybrid cells, which retain the SV40 T-antigen and, most likely, the complete virus genome, show that the presence of SV40 genomes integrated into the human (VA-2) chromosomes does not cause the same loss of contact inhibition which is observed when 3T3 itself is transformed by SV40.

Taken together, these observations suggest that the continuous presence of the viral genomes may not be the cause of the permanent change in growth properties of cells which have been transformed. It may be that there is some permanent cellular change which occurs at the time of transformation and which would remain heritable even in the absence of viral genomes, just as neoplastic conversion by chemical carcinogens is heritable in the absence of the agent which originally caused it.

ACKNOWLEDGMENTS

The author is grateful to Dr. Howard Green for supplying the 3T3-4E cells and the SV40 virus, to Dr. Boris Ephrussi for many stimulating discussions and for his critical reading of the manuscript, and to Mlle. Anne Debon for her expert technical assistance.

This work was conducted with the aid of United States Public Health Service postdoctoral fellowship F2-GM-34,679 at New York University and the Carnegie Institution of Washington, and the Centre National de la Recherche Scientifique and the Délégation Générale à la Recherche Scientifique et Technique at the Centre de Génétique Moléculaire du CNRS.

REFERENCES

Aaronson, S. A., and G. J. Todaro. 1968. Basis for the Acquisition of Malignant Potential by Mouse Cells Cultivated In Vitro. *Science*, 162:1024–1026.

Benjamin, T. L. 1966. Virus-Specific RNA in Cells Productively Infected or Transformed by Polyoma Virus. *Journal of Molecular Biology*, 16:359–373.

Black, P. H., W. P. Rowe, H. C. Turner, and R. J. Heubner. 1963. A Specific Complement-Fixing Antigen Present in SV40 Tumor and Transformed Cells. *Proceedings of the National Academy of Sciences of the U.S.A.*, 50:1148–1156.

Cassingena, R., and P. Tournier. 1968. Mise en Évidence d'un "Répresseur" Spécifique dans des Cellules d'Espèces Différentes Transformées par le Virus SV40.

Comptes Rendus Hebdomadaires des Seances de l'Académie des Sciences série D (Sciences Naturelles), 267:2251–2254.

Coon, H. G., and M. C. Weiss. 1969. A Quantitative Comparison of Formation of Spontaneous and Virus Produced Viable Hybrids. *Proceedings of the National Academy of Sciences of the U.S.A.*, 62:852–859.

Defendi, V. 1963. Effect of SV40 Virus Immunization on Growth of Transplantable SV40 and Polyoma Virus Tumors in Hamsters. *Proceedings of the Society for Experimental Biology and Medicine*, 113:12–16.

Defendi, V., B. Ephrussi, H. Koprowski, and M. C. Yoshida. 1967. Properties of Hybrids Between Polyoma-Transformed and Normal Mouse Cells. *Proceedings of the National Academy of Sciences of the U.S.A.*, 57:299–305.

Earle, W. R. 1943. Changes Induced in a Strain of Fibroblasts from a Strain C3H Mouse by the Action of 20-Methylcholanthrene. (Preliminary Report). *Journal of the National Cancer Institute*, 3:555–558.

Ephrussi, B. 1970. "Somatic Hybridization as a Tool for the Study of Normal and Abnormal Growth and Differentiation," *Genetic Concepts and Neoplasia* (The University of Texas M. D. Anderson Hospital and Tumor Institute at Houston, 23rd Annual Symposium on Fundamental Cancer Research, 1969). Baltimore, Maryland: The Williams and Wilkins Co. Pp. 9–28.

Girardi, A. J. 1965. Prevention of SV40 Virus Oncogenesis in Hamsters. I. Tumor Resistance Induced by Human Cells Transformed by SV40. *Proceedings of the National Academy of Sciences of the U.S.A.*, 54:445–451.

Girardi, A. J., F. C. Jensen, and H. Koprowski. 1965. SV40-Induced Transformation of Human Diploid Cells: Crisis and Recovery. *Journal of Cellular and Comparative Physiology*, 65:69–83.

Habel, K., and B. E. Eddy. 1963. Specificity of Resistance to Tumor Challenge of Polyoma and SV40 Virus Immune Hamsters. *Proceedings of the Society for Experimental Biology and Medicine*, 113:1–4.

Harris, H., and J. F. Watkins. 1965. Hybrid Cells Derived from Mouse and Man: Artificial Heterokaryons of Mammalian Cells from Different Species. *Nature*, 205:640–646.

Koch, M. A., and A. B. Sabin. 1963. Specificity of Virus-Induced Resistance to Transplantation of Polyoma and SV40 Tumors in Adult Animals. *Proceedings of the Society for Experimental Biology and Medicine*, 113:4–12.

Koprowski, H., F. C. Jensen, and Z. Steplewski. 1967. Activation of Production of Infectious Tumor Virus SV40 in Heterokaryon Cultures. *Proceedings of the National Academy of Sciences of the U.S.A.*, 58:127–133.

Koprowski, H., J. A. Pontén, F. Jensen, R. G. Ravdin, P. S. Moorhead, and E. Saksela. 1962. Transformation of Cultures of Human Tissue Infected with Simian Virus SV40. *Journal of Cellular and Comparative Physiology*, 59:281–292.

Littlefield, J. W. 1964. The Selection of "Mated" and Probably Recombinant Mouse Fibroblasts in Culture. *Science*, 145:709–710.

Marin, G., and J. W. Littlefield. 1968. Selection of Morphologically Normal Cell Lines from Polyoma-Transformed BHK21/13 Hamster Fibroblasts. *Journal of Virology*, 2:69–77.

Marin, G., and I. Macpherson. 1968. Studies on Reversion of Polyoma-Induced Transformation in Hamster Fibroblasts. *Excerpta Medica* (International Congress Series Number 166), 166:64.

Matsuya, Y., and H. Green. 1969. A Somatic Cell Hybrid Between the Established Human Line D98 (Presumptive HeLa) and 3T3. *Science*, 163:697–698.

Moorhead, P. A. 1970. "Virus Effects on Host Chromosomes," *Genetic Concepts and Neoplasia* (The University of Texas M. D. Anderson Hospital and Tumor Institute at Houston, 23rd Annual Symposium on Fundamental Cancer Research, 1969). Baltimore, Maryland: The Williams and Wilkins Co. Pp. 281–306.

Pollack, R. E., H. Green, and G. J. Todaro. 1968. Growth Control in Cultured Cells: Selection of Sublines with Increased Sensitivity to Contact Inhibition and Decreased Tumor-Producing Ability. *Proceedings of the National Academy of Sciences of the U.S.A.*, 60:126–133.

Rapp, F., and J. Butel. 1970. "The Virus Genome and Transformation of Mammalian Cells," *Genetic Concepts and Neoplasia* (The University of Texas M. D. Anderson Hospital and Tumor Institute at Houston, 23rd Annual Symposium on Fundamental Cancer Research, 1969). Baltimore, Maryland: The Williams and Wilkins Co. Pp. 256–280.

Sambrook, J., H. Westphal, P. R. Srinivasan, and R. Dulbecco. 1968. The Integrated State of Viral DNA in SV40-Transformed Cells. *Proceedings of the National Academy of Sciences of the U.S.A.*, 60:1288–1295.

Todaro, G. J., and H. Green. 1964. An Assay for Cellular Transformation by SV40. *Virology*, 23:117–119.

————. 1966. High Frequency of SV40 Transformation of Mouse Cell Line 3T3. *Virology*, 28:756–759.

Watkins, J. F., and R. Dulbecco. 1967. Production of SV40 Virus in Heterokaryons of Transformed and Susceptible Cells. *Proceedings of the National Academy of Sciences of the U.S.A.*, 58:1396–1403.

Weiss, M. C., B. Ephrussi, and L. J. Scaletta. 1968. Loss of T-Antigen from Somatic Hybrids Between Mouse Cells and SV40-Transformed Human Cells. *Proceedings of the National Academy of Sciences of the U.S.A.*, 59:1132–1135.

Weiss, M. C., and H. Green. 1967. Human-Mouse Hybrid Cell Lines Containing Partial Complements of Human Chromosomes and Functioning Human Genes. *Proceedings of the National Academy of Sciences of the U.S.A.*, 58:1104–1111.

Weiss, M. C., G. J. Todaro, and H. Green. 1968. Properties of a Hybrid Between Lines Sensitive and Insensitive to Contact Inhibition of Cell Division. *Journal of Cellular Physiology*, 71:105–107.

Westphal, H., and R. Dulbecco. 1968. Viral DNA in Polyoma- and SV40-Transformed Cell Lines. *Proceedings of the National Academy of Sciences of the U.S.A.*, 59:1158–1165.

Neoplasia and Gene Activity in Allophenic Mice

BEATRICE MINTZ

The Institute for Cancer Research, Fox Chase, Philadelphia, Pennsylvania

Genes must exercise critical roles in determining whether an individual will develop malignant disease. Certainly in mice, where genetically uniform strains are observable, the evidence for heritable susceptibility is overwhelming. Virtually every inbred strain has its characteristic profile of neoplasms, and some strains were in fact selectively bred for high incidence of one or another specific kind of tumor. From breeding data, it appears that susceptibility to most tumors may be polygenic (Heston, 1963). The mechanisms underlying this genetic complicity have largely eluded us, and rational progress in cancer research requires that they be ferreted out.

Genetic controls could govern many distinct facets of tumor susceptibility. Where viral agents are involved, for example, there may be an important measure of control by the target cell of viral adsorption and penetration into it, through receptors on the cell's surface; a case in point is the infection of chicken cells by Rous sarcoma virus (Rubin, 1965). There may, moreover, be hormonal, or immunologic, or other systemic factors that ultimately influence tumor cell growth and that are themselves under gene control. Inevitably, however, there must also be some intracellular genetic direction of when and how cells grow and divide, not only during normal morphogenesis, but also in response to tumorigenic stimuli capable—once they have entered cells of certain genotypes—of eliciting excessive growth and proliferation. It is with this last question of the regulation of cell-growth phenotypes in cancer-susceptible *versus* nonsusceptible genotypes that we will be primarily concerned here.

Some aspects of the malignant process, such as the nature of viral transformation, perhaps can best be explored with cells grown in vitro. But an analysis of tissue growth controls obviously requires the coherent participation of the whole, integrated organism in the experiment, so that any significant interactions between tissues or systems will be preserved. Indeed, the primary question concerning susceptibility, namely, whether it is initiated or localized in a particular tissue, cannot be answered except within the organism.

In order to establish whether loci dictating vulnerability to tumors are selectively expressing themselves in certain tissues, the relevant experiment would be a manipulation of cellular genotypes, such that high- and low-susceptibility cellular genomes were differentially distributed among tissues in a variety of ways.

In the past, investigators have partially met this requirement by the transplantation of normal, premalignant, or malignant tissues or organs between animals of different genotypes. Fruitful though those experiments have been, they possess intrinsic technical and theoretical restrictions: the surgical possibilities of exchange are limited; the transplantations always must be performed relatively late, and any gene-controlled events of importance in formative stages would already have taken place; and histocompatibility barriers between participating strains have generally required reliance upon hybrid hosts, or have necessitated immunosuppressive treatment of pure-strain hosts (by irradiation or other means) in order to prevent graft rejection. The depression of a host's immune system is manifestly a profound physiological change, perhaps favoring previously dormant resident viral populations, or engendering other serial consequences, and the course of neoplastic disease in an animal thus treated is not necessarily comparable to tumorigenesis as it ordinarily occurs. Despite the general association of increased malignancy with advancing age and its accompanying debilitations, it is a commonplace that many cancers arise in animals in good rather than poor health, immunologically competent, and often in the prime of life. Investigative attention in etiologic studies needs, therefore, to be focused upon the normal cell of a tumor-prone genotype, residing in a healthy and physiologically undisturbed individual, for it is here (not in the tumor cell, where it is a *fait accompli*) that the pivotal genetic decisions for malignancy will, at some point, first be expressed.

The experimental use of cellular genetic mosaicism, involving different intra- as well as intertissue arrangements of high- and low-susceptibility genomes, therefore ideally should be applied throughout embryonic and adult life, in the framework of an intact, healthy, and immunologically competent individual.

We have introduced a novel form of mammalian genetic manipulation in which these conditions are realized, providing us with a wide range of new in vivo possibilities for examining the bases for neoplasia. The experimental subject is a laboratory artifact, the allophenic mouse. Allophenic mice, as their name indicates (Mintz, 1967a), contain different phenotypic subpopulations of cells, because of dissimilarities in cellular genotypes. One such animal has four (or even more) parents instead of two, since it is derived by joining together two (or more) cleavage-stage embryos in vitro, each with its own set of parents and thus its own genetic constitution (Mintz, 1962a, 1962b, 1964, 1965, 1967b, 1969a). About a third of all the artificial composites, after transfer to an incubator mother, continue their development to birth and become healthy, long-lived adults. Since the birth, in this laboratory, of the first mosaic mouse (Mintz, 1965), over 1,000 quadriparental individuals have been produced and have survived. The two different cellular genotypes can be found in any or all tissues, because of the early stage at which the cells are aggregated. In addition, the total level of retained mosaicism, and the tissue distributions and proportions of the respective genotypes, vary greatly from one animal to another, even within the same paired combination (symbol $\longleftrightarrow$) of genotypes (Mintz, 1969b; Mintz and Palm, 1969).

Allophenic animals are permanently immunologically tolerant of any immunogenetic differences in their component cells and have never developed runt disease. They nevertheless possess full immunological competence to respond to and reject "foreign" antigens, such as skin grafts of another histocompatibility type (Mintz and Silvers, 1967; Mintz and Palm, 1965, 1969).

It therefore is apparent that cells from a high-tumor strain can now be made to co-exist with cells of an unrelated low-tumor strain, starting prior to cell differentiation. The permutations and combinations in tissue distributions of cellular genotypes constitute the experiment. The animals bring to light those biological relationships that are relevant to genetic control of tumor susceptibility and to the progress of malignancy and metastasis.

With the help of these quadriparental mice, we have been conducting an extensive series of studies on a number of kinds of tumors for which there is evidence of genetic predisposition. The general aims are, first, to identify whether the heredity of the potentially malignant cells, of other organs, or of the host as a whole, is responsible for susceptibility; and, ultimately, to define in molecular terms the means by which the susceptible cell phenotype is produced. The present paper will deal with mammary tumors and hepatomas, and further details concerning these and other tumors will be given in later publications (Mintz and Donnelly, in preparation).

Experimental Plan

Mammary tumors are common in females and hepatomas in males

of the C3H strain. (Hepatomas can also occur in the females [Andervont, 1950] but the age of onset is generally later than that of mammary tumors, and few hepatomas were found in our females; those hepatomas will not be discussed here.) The same kinds of tumors are found somewhat less frequently in C3Hf and relatively rarely in C57BL/6. Therefore, the C3H ⟷ C57BL/6 and C3Hf ⟷ C57BL/6 allophenic strain combinations are favorable for examining the roles of genes in mammary as well as in liver tumorigenesis. (The full designations of our sublines of these three strains are C3H/HeNIcr, C3HfB/HeNIcr, and C57BL/6JNIcr.)

Viral agents, possibly including several variants, are known to be responsible for induction of mammary tumors in mice. The viral status of sublines of a number of standard strains has been characterized; tumor incidence in our sublines is similar to patterns reported for these strains. Mammary adenocarcinoma frequency can reach 100 per cent in some strains, as in our C3H breeding females (Table 1), where the agent

TABLE 1. *Incidence and Genotypes of Mammary Tumors in Allophenic C3H(f) ⟷ C57BL/6 and Control Female Mice*

Incidence and genotype	C3Hf controls	C57BL/6 controls	C3Hf⟷ C57BL/6* allophenics	C3H controls (MTV)[†]	C57BL/6 controls (MTV)[†]	C3H⟷ C57BL/6* allophenics (MTV)[†]
No. of mice with tumors/total	6/14	0/9	5/10	16/16	6/15	23/27
% of mice with tumors	43	(Low)	50	100	40	85
Average age (mo) at tumor occurrence[‡]	15		18	10	14	10
No. of tumors	7		6	30(+3)[§]	8	42(+3)[§]
No. of tumors genotypically diagnosed			6			41
Tumor genotypes			5 C3Hf, 1 C57			33 C3H, 3 C57, 1 C3H ≅ C57, 4 C3H≫C57

* Only animals with positive evidence of genetic mosaicism, in any tissues, are included.

† C57BL/6 controls and C3H ⟷ C57BL/6 allophenics all were nursed by a C3H foster mother, to receive the milk-transmitted mammary tumor virus (MTV) carried in the C3H control strain.

‡ In cases where tumors were surgically removed and followed by recurrence, the primary-tumor age was used.

§ Numbers in parentheses are presumed recurrences of tumors surgically removed.

TABLE 2. *Incidence and Genotypes of Hepatomas in Allophenic*
C3H(f) ⟷ C57BL/6 and Control Male Mice

Incidence and genotype	C3Hf controls	C57BL/6 controls	C3Hf⟷ C57BL/6* allophenics	C3H controls (MTV)†	C57BL/6 controls (MTV)†	C3H⟷ C57BL/6* allophenics (MTV)†
No. of mice with tumors/total	3/9	1/13	3/10	9/13	0/6	13/29
% of mice with tumors	33	(Low)	30	69	(Low)	45
Average age (mo) at tumor occurrence	20	(25)	23	24		24
No. of tumors‡	3	2	4	16		26
No. of tumors genotypically diagnosed			4			23
Tumor genotypes			3 C3Hf, 1 C57			21 C3H, 1 C3H>>C57, 1 C57>>C3H

* Only animals with positive evidence of genetic mosaicism, in any tissues, are included.
† The milk-transmitted mammary tumor virus (MTV) was present; see Table 1.
‡ Separate foci, in the same or in separate lobes, were counted as individual tumors.

is the mammary tumor virus (MTV) that is ordinarily transmitted through the milk (Bittner, 1958). The C3Hf inbred strain was originally derived from C3H by foster nursing on the non-MTV C57BL strain (Heston, Deringer, Dunn, and Levillain, 1950; Heston, 1958), but apparently contains another, less virulent, form of mammary tumor virus; it has been suggested that transmission may occur through the reproductive cells (Pitelka, Bern, Nandi, and DeOme, 1964). C3Hf females do develop mammary tumors, though with considerably lower frequency and at a more advanced age than do C3H females (Heston, Deringer, Dunn, and Levillain, 1950). The C57BL/6 strain, conversely, seems to lack MTV, and has a very low incidence of mammary tumors. However, when C57BL/6 females receive the virus by foster-nursing on an MTV strain such as C3H, tumor incidence is appreciably elevated, though it remains substantially less than in C3H itself (Andervont, 1940). C57BL sublines differ in tumor incidence after MTV infection (Bittner, 1958); our subline can be readily infected, and tumor cases increase from virtually none to 40 per cent (Table 1).

Hormones are known to be required not only for normal mammary gland development and function, but also for promoting mammary tumor development. The influence of pituitary and of estrogenic hormones has been well documented, and strain differences in hormone responsiveness have been reported (Mühlbock and Boot, 1959; Nandi and Bern, 1960; Ben-David, Heston, and Rodbard, 1969).

Spontaneous hepatomas (*i.e.*, hepatomas of unknown etiology) show a similar rank order in the males of these same strains (Table 2). The incidence is highest in C3H, somewhat lower in C3Hf, and virtually nil in C57BL/6 (Burns and Schenken, 1940; Andervont, 1950; Heston, Vlahakis, and Deringer, 1960).

The experimental plan entails one study in which milk-transmitted MTV is not involved, and another in which it is present (in both females and males). In the first study, composite embryos of the C3Hf ⟷ C57BL/6 combination were assembled in vitro from blastomeres of the two donor strains, and were surgically transferred at the morula or blastocyst stage to the uterus of an ICR foster mother for further gestation and for nursing. Females of our ICR random-bred strain have few mammary tumors and lack MTV. The C3Hf and C57BL/6 controls were raised by their own mothers.

In the second study, C3H ⟷ C57BL/6 allophenic embryos were assembled by blastomere aggregation, and transferred to MTV-positive C3H foster mothers for completion of gestation and for nursing. The C3H controls were raised by their own mothers; C57BL/6 controls were given to C3H foster mothers at birth, to receive MTV. Presence of MTV in sample females of these groups, including the C3H ⟷ C57BL/6 allophenics, was kindly verified by Mr. Robert Nowinski of the Sloan-Kettering Institute, by Ouchterlony tests for viral antigen in milk.

The procedures for making allophenic mice begin with removal of cleavage-stage eggs (most conveniently at the eight-cell stage) from different donors (usually hormone-primed prepuberal females), and with explantation to a high-serum medium capable of sustaining development at the normal rate to the late blastocyst stage (Mintz, 1964, 1967b, 1969a). The enveloping egg membrane, or zona pellucida, is next dissolved with the enzyme pronase (Mintz, 1962a). After being rinsed, two entire eggs of dissimilar genotypes are then pushed into contact by means of a small glass rod, and kept motionless at 37 C, either on a microscope warm stage or in a warmed hood surrounding the microscope. This temperature was found to be the critical factor required to induce adhesion between blastomeres (Mintz, 1962b, 1964). When the paired eggs are firmly aggregated, they are incubated for 1 day, during which they reach the morula or blastocyst stage. At that time, they are surgically transferred to the uterus of a pseudopregnant female that had been mated to a sterile (vasectomized) male a day later than the matings of the egg donors. Though the in vitro aggregates and the blastocysts that develop from them are double size, regulation to normal size soon occurs in vivo (by unknown mechanisms) after implantation. Largely because of this process, some of the embryos apparently lose one of the component cell strains and are no longer genetically mosaic (Mintz, 1967a). Approximately one third of all in vitro composites eventually survive to parturition and become healthy adults (Mintz, 1965, 1967a, 1969b).

All experimental and control animals at sexual maturity were permanently mated in pairs, with same-strain mates for controls and C57BL/6 mates for allophenics. Mothers were allowed to keep litters until weaning. When an individual mouse showed evidence of a tumor, or appeared seriously ill, it was autopsied for gross pathology, and samples of pathological and normal tissues were fixed for histological study. At the same time, in the case of allophenics, pieces of tumors, normal parts of tumorous organs, and most of the remaining major organs were frozen in dry ice and stored at -57 C.

Many strain-specific markers were employed to investigate the genotypic composition of tissues in allophenics. In life, the typing procedures utilized the agouti (C3H or C3Hf) *versus* non-agouti (C57BL/6) coat color differential (Figure 1); germ cell tests, from transmission of these coat colors to progeny; erythrocyte typing for allelic differences in histocompatibility (*H-2*) antigens (Mintz and Palm, 1969); serum allotypes of γ-globulins determined by the *Ig-1* chromosomal region (Weiler and Mintz, unpublished data); grafting of skin (Mintz and Silvers, 1967) or of mammary gland tissue (Mintz and Slemmer, 1969) to pure-strain hosts, for genotypic analysis of the grafted piece; skin grafting from C3H(f) and C57BL/6 donors, for evidence of tolerance and thus of *H-2* mosaicism in the allophenic recipient (Mintz and Silvers, 1967); *etc.* At autopsy, fresh bone marrow and other tissue samples were sometimes taken for sex karyotype diagnosis of metaphase cells (Mintz, 1968; Mintz, Hungerford, and Morrow, in preparation). Various tissues frozen at autopsy were analyzed by means of strain-specific molecular variants of enzymes, detectable by starch gel electrophoretic separation; these included variants of nicotinamide adenine dinucleotide phosphate (NADP)-dependent malate dehydrogenase (*Mdh-1* locus), found in the supernatant fraction of many tissues (Henderson, 1966; Baker and Mintz, 1969); variants of glucose-6-phosphate dehydrogenase (autosomal, *Gpd-1* locus) (Ruddle, Shows, and Roderick, 1968); and some others. Test sensitivities varied among these markers: for example, a minor component could be detected down to levels of 2 per cent for *Gpd-1* phenotypes and for serum γ-globulin allotypes; 5 per cent for *Mdh-1* isozymes; 10 per cent for *H-2* antigens on erythrocytes when measured by agglutination, or 25 per cent by absorption. Sensitivity assays were based on analyses of artificial genotypic mixtures of cells. Most of the diagnostic information was obtained with measures sensitive down to at least 5 per cent (as with *Mdh-1* isozymes).

Two possible complications in the biology of allophenic mice require consideration, since one of these (loss of mosaicism) would seriously affect the problem in hand, and the other (XX ⟷ XY mosaicism) might play a role. The generalization already has been stated that some composite embryos apparently lose one or the other cell strain after implantation, even when the two strains are coisogenic with an allelic difference only at a pigmentary locus. Obviously, an experimental mouse must retain cells of both strains in order to be an appropriate subject for the question of mammary and hepatic tumorigenesis in genetic mosaics. If either cell strain has disappeared, the animal is genetically an all-C3H(f) or an all-C57BL/6 animal, and therefore a control rather than an experimental, differing from other controls only in serving as a check on any possible influence of preimplantation embryo mosaicism and of the various handling procedures. There thus far has been no evidence whatever of any influence remaining from their unusual early history, in animals that later lack mosaicism, and we can conclude that such animals are

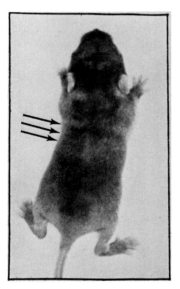

FIGURE 1. A 10-day-old C3Hf ⟷ C57BL/6 allophenic mouse, experimentally produced from aggregated blastomeres of the two separate strains. Agouti (*AA*) and non-agouti or black (*aa*) coat colors of the component strains form a regular pattern revealing the clonal basis of hair follicle (not melanocyte) development. Fine transverse bands of each genotype (arrows point to *aa*), down the full length of each side, are hair follicle clones; anteriormost head clones are beginning to slant obliquely as the face grows forward. When total non-agouti exceeds agouti, as in this mouse, non-agouti obliterates agouti in medial parts of certain head and face clones, forming a dark patch between the ears and a stellate blaze in the middle of the face.

indeed indistinguishable from other controls and should be excluded from the experimental categories. Inasmuch as quantitative levels and tissue distribution of mosaicism do vary, however, a diagnosis of "nonmosaicism" must necessarily rest upon fairly extensive tissue tests; such diagnoses usually were not made until more than six major tissues or organs had been examined and were of one genotype. The possibility cannot be excluded that some of these apparently nonmosaic animals may have a small cache of the inapparent cell genotype. On the assumption that such instances are likely to be uncommon, and therefore not to change appreciably the total picture of tumor susceptibility, we have included in the allophenic categories (Tables 1 and 2) only animals in which positive evidence of mosaicism was obtained, in any of the tissues analyzed.

In the C3Hf ⟷ C57BL/6 combination, there were 20 known mosaics (10 females and 10 males); in the C3H ⟷ C57BL/6 group with MTV, there were 56 (27 females and 29 males). These 76 allophenics comprised approximately 70 per cent of the animals of multiembryo origin that were originally in the study. Genotypic and sex distributions among the remaining presumed nonmosaics are in themselves interesting; they suggest complex processes of cell selection (Mintz, 1969b).

The other complication in the biology of allophenic mice concerns the sex phenotype. Some of the initial egg pairs would, randomly, have included a female (XX) sex chromosomal member along with a male (XY) component. Since mammary tumor incidence was tabulated in phenotypic females and hepatoma incidence in ostensible males, the question arises whether presence of cells of the opposite sex chromosomal constitution might have any bearing on the results.

As already pointed out (Mintz, 1968, 1969b), placental mammals (unlike the lower vertebrates) seem to have evolved mechanisms for stabilizing germ cell genetic sex and for minimizing the effects of sex chromosomal mosaicism. The XX ⟷ XY cellular admixture in an early mouse embryo never leads to functional sex reversal. In addition, it rarely eventuates in intersexuality (only 1 per cent of all mice of dual embryo origin are intersexes) or in sterility (less than 6 per cent are sterile). Individuals chromosomally identified as XX ⟷ XY have in fact represented virtually every morphological sex phenotype, and have included cases with normal fertility (in which the functional reproductive cells are of only one chromosomal sex). It follows that some of the allophenic females in the mammary tumor study probably contain some XY cells, and some of the males in the hepatoma survey undoubtedly have some XX cells. A minority among them have been cytologically analyzed, so that XX ⟷ XY incidence is not actually known, and consequences for tumorigenesis cannot yet be fully evaluated. Cases identified as XX ⟷ XY are indicated below.

Descriptions of mammary and liver tumor histology will be given in later publications (Mintz and Donnelly, in preparation), along with observations on metastases and on other tumors and diseases found in the present and in other genotypic populations of allophenic mice. In general, histology of tumors in allophenics was similar to that in controls, and no "new" kinds of tumors or diseases have thus far been found in the allophenics.

Mammary Tumors in Females

TUMOR INCIDENCE

The frequency of mammary tumors (Figure 2) in both C3Hf ⟷ C57BL/6 and C3H ⟷ C57BL/6 allophenic females is high, and strikingly parallels that of the high-susceptibility strains (C3Hf or C3H). The results are summarized in Table 1.

In the first study, where the high-virulence milk-transmitted MTV was absent, 43 per cent (6/14) of C3Hf control females developed mammary tumors, at an average age of 15 mo, whereas none of the C57BL/6

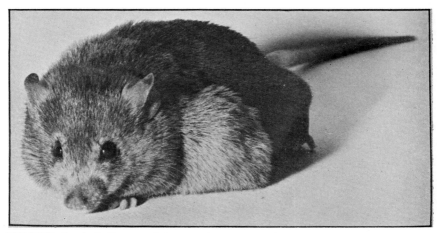

FIGURE 2. A C3H ⟷ C57BL/6 female allophenic mouse with one large mammary adenocarcinoma on the left neck and a smaller one on the right neck. The tumors were both found to be composed only of C3H cells, but many other tissues of this animal, including normal mammary tissue, contained cells of both strains.

(0/9) controls formed tumors. (A low incidence in the latter strain is not excluded, and might become apparent in a larger sample.) Of all the C3Hf ⟷ C57BL/6 experimental females (with both C3Hf and C57BL/6 cells in at least some tissues), 50 per cent (5/10) developed mammary tumors. (Among the apparently nonmosaic animals originating from C3Hf ⟷ C57BL/6 embryos but lacking evidence of one of the strains in adult life, the results were indistinguishable from those in corresponding controls: 40 per cent of the cases diagnosed as "all-C3Hf" had mammary tumors; none of the "all-C57BL/6" had any.) The slightly later average age of tumor appearance given for the mosaic C3Hf ⟷ C57BL/6 females (18 mo) as compared with the C3Hf controls (15 mo) may not be significant, since it is attributable to different quantitative standards of initial detection of tumors in the two groups by separate observers. The observer of the control group detected tumors when the average diameter was 1.0 cm; the observer of the experimental groups first reported tumors averaging 1.3 cm, suggesting delayed recognition of the experimental tumors.

In the study including milk-transmitted MTV, tumor incidence in C3H controls was much higher than among the preceding C3Hf controls: 100 per cent (16/16) of the C3H females developed mammary tumors, at an average age of 10 mo, and 40 per cent (6/15) of C57BL/6 females with MTV had mammary tumors, at an average age of 14 mo. Among the C3H ⟷ C57BL/6 allophenics (including known mosaics only), as many as 85 per cent (23/27) produced mammary tumors. (Again, the animals that had originated from allophenic embryos, but subsequently lacked evidence of mosaicism, resembled controls: 80 per cent of those presumed to be "all-C3H" and 33 per cent of the "all-C57BL/6" individuals with MTV had tumors.) The average age at tumor onset in the truly mosaic group was identical with that of the high-tumor control strain (10 mo), rather than that of the low-tumor controls (14 mo). The history of the few nontumorous mosaic females (4/27) is instructive, since it strongly suggests that the 85 per cent level of tumor occurrence among the allophenics biologically is not significantly different from the 100 per cent occurrence in the C3H controls. Among the four negative cases, two had to be killed because of other ailments at 7 to 9 mo, and therefore before the average tumor age in C3H controls (one had myelogenous leukemia plus an abdominal teratoma, and the other had anasarca and failure of delivery of fetuses at term). A third case (autopsied at 13 mo) apparently contained almost exclusively the C57BL/6 low-tumor cellular genotype; it had the fewest C3H cells of any of the allophenics and C3H was found only in the lung. In short, three of the four negatives either had few C3H cells or did not remain alive long enough to show whether their tumor-proneness resembled the high-tumor strain.

Not only are the frequency of tumor-ridden individuals and the time of tumor onset indistinguishable in the allophenics and the corresponding high-tumor strain, but the number of discrete tumor foci in C3H ←→ C57BL/6 and C3H mice also tends to be comparable and is higher than in the low-tumor C57BL/6 MTV controls. (The study lacking the milk agent simply shows similar numbers of tumors, averaging 1.2 per tumorous animal, in C3Hf ←→ C57BL/6 mosaics and C3Hf controls; no C57BL/6 controls had tumors.) For the MTV study, the figures in Table 1 include instances of surgical resection of tumors, followed by some ostensible recurrences of those resected, as well as by growth of tumors at new sites. Among the controls in this study, surgical procedures were performed in four C3H individuals (in which eight postoperative tumors, including three recurrences, appeared) and in four C3H ←→ C57BL/6 allophenics (in which seven postoperative tumors, including three recurrences, were found). If we delete all postoperative tumors from the data in Table 1, then all the remaining tumors are those that developed within a maximum of 1 mo following the earliest detection of any tumor in a given animal. Within that time period, therefore, the 16 C3H controls had a total of 25 tumors, or an average of 1.6 tumors per animal, and the 23 tumor-bearing allophenics had a total of 38 primary tumors, or an average of 1.7 each. The C57BL/6 controls with MTV, however, had only 1.3 tumors each. Multiple tumor formation is probably occurring at an even faster rate in C3H ←→ C57BL/6 and C3H (as compared with MTV-infected C57BL/6) animals than these figures would indicate, if we take into account the fact that the tumors in the former two classes have made their appearance at an earlier average age (10 months) than those in C57BL/6 (14 mo).

The evidence suggests that any undetected cases of XX ←→ XY cellular mosaicism in phenotypic females are unlikely to have exerted much influence on the total picture of mammary tumorigenesis in these experiments, even though the condition might play a physiological role in some individuals. The presence of XY cells in such females would tend, in all likelihood, to diminish rather than to increase mammary tumor frequency, at least in part through possible modifications of the hormonal picture. But, as we have seen, mammary tumor occurrence in allophenic females is already so close to the tumor-prone control strains, and therefore to 100 per cent of maximal expectation, that XY cellular contamination in allophenics cannot have significantly reduced their over-all tumor proneness. In the C3Hf ←→ C57BL/6 group, one XX ←→ XY female was identified (Mintz, 1968; Mintz, Hungerford, and Morrow, in preparation); she was sterile and had no tumor. The mammary glands in this instance contained both genotypes of cells and were less active than is usual for females, but filled the fat pads in the typical female pattern (Mintz and Slemmer, 1969). The latter fact could be accounted for by systemic estrogenic influence, to which male glands are known to respond (*e.g.*, Blair and Moretti, 1967). Two other C3Hf $\longleftrightarrow$ C57BL/6 females were sterile and had no tumors; neither had been karyologically examined. In the C3H $\longleftrightarrow$ C57BL/6 class, there were two steriles, but both had mammary tumors (at 11 mo of age); neither was chromosomally studied. It should be added that sterility is occasionally found in all strains, and one of our C3H controls also had no progeny; she had a mammary tumor at the latest age (19 mo) in that control group.

Summarizing thus far, we may conclude that the lifelong coexistence of these high- and low-mammary-tumor genetic strains of cells in individuals, starting in early cleavage on day 2 of embryonic life, leads eventually to the same degree and rate of mammary tumor formation as ordinarily characterizes the more susceptible strain. It would be of considerable interest to identify the mechanisms whereby the tendency toward mammary tumors prevails in the mosaic females, inasmuch as the same mechanisms may bear appreciable responsibility for gene-controlled susceptibility in the high-tumor strain itself.

GENOTYPES OF MAMMARY TUMORS IN ALLOPHENIC ANIMALS

The first question that arises in seeking some clue to the basis for high mammary tumor incidence in the allophenics concerns the genotypic provenance of the cells that compose these tumors.

Whether a single tumor in an allophenic mouse ever has any possibility at all of containing both high- and low-susceptibility cellular strains is of course dependent upon whether the epithelium of a single mammary gland normally develops from only one, or from more than one, genetically determined cell. In a recent study, we were able to establish that the epithelium of a single gland does in fact arise from a minimum of two cells (Mintz and Slemmer, 1969). The experimental demonstration rested upon exploitation of allelic histocompatibility (*H-2*) antigenic differences in the component cell strains of C3Hf $\longleftrightarrow$ C57BL/6 allophenic subjects. When pieces of one mammary gland were transplanted separately to recipients of each of the pure strains, acceptance or rejection by the hosts served to identify the *H-2* antigenic composition, and therefore the strain identity, of the grafted pieces. Single normal glands were found by this procedure to include cells of each of the two strains, thus demonstrating conclusively that one gland originates from at least two cells. That result, obtained under the particular circumstances of the allophenic experiment, must mean that a gland in ordinary single-genotype animals also derives from at least two genetically determined cells, although no genetic markers are present to reveal the multiclonal origin.

In an allophenic mouse, then, one mammary gland can comprise cells of both high- and low-tumor inbred strains, in actual contact with each other throughout gland development, and simultaneously exposed to common systemic influences. Will mosaic tumors be formed?

Genotypic diagnosis of malignant tissue was done for one tumor by grafting (a C3Hf tumor from a C3Hf $\longleftrightarrow$ C57BL/6 donor); the remaining tumors were typed by biochemical methods more suitable for large-scale tests. These utilized the strain-specific electrophoretic differences in molecular variants of NADP-dependent malate dehydrogenase. As shown in Table 1, 47 tumors were typed, including all six tumors from C3Hf $\longleftrightarrow$ C57BL/6 and 41 of the 45 tumors from C3H $\longleftrightarrow$ C57BL/6 animals; the remaining four tumors were small and were fixed for histological study only.

In all, five mosaic tumors (11 per cent of those analyzed) were found. Four of the five were largely C3H and had only trace amounts, or about 5 per cent, of C57BL/6. In such cases, the minor component might conceivably have been contributed by connective or vascular tissue rather than by tumor cells. The remaining case, however, had roughly equal amounts of C3H and C57BL/6 cells (Figure 3c, d) and it seems justifiable to conclude that cells of both genotypes were present in the tumor. Since C3H mammary cells become tumorous earlier (at 6 to 19 mo of age) than do C57BL/6 cells (at 10 to 20 mo of age with MTV), the odds are somewhat against obtaining tumor mosaicism in the allophenic experiment and, for this reason, the finding of any tumor mosaicism is particularly noteworthy. The mosaic tumors grossly resemble other ostensibly single tumors, and therefore also must be considered as single. Their significance remains to be clarified.

A mosaic mammary tumor produced in these experimental circumstances might mean that individual tumors in ordinary single-genotype mice originate, either some or all of the time, from more than one cell. Whether a tumor actually develops from substantially more than two cells cannot be determined here. In a human female heterozygous for enzyme variants of X-linked glucose-6-phosphate dehydrogenase (G-6-PD), with only one variant expressed in a given cell, McCurdy (1967) also found both enzymes in a breast carcinoma and concluded that it was of multicellular origin.

If a mammary tumor originates from more than one cell, we must consider the impact of this on the idea that spontaneous mutation accounts for tumor formation. The occurrence of the same "random change" in nucleotide sequence in several cells becomes highly unlikely, and mutational origin therefore becomes less likely than if a tumor arose from a single cell. However, some type of "nonspontaneous" mutation remains a possible explanation, if "mutation" is used in the broad sense to include viral genome incorporation into a host cell, or stabilized derepression of host cell loci that would normally be inactive at this time. Even if spontaneous mutation may not bear primary etiologic responsibility for mammary tumors, it is apparent that secondary mutational changes (including chromosomal aberrations), causing a host of phenotypic changes or new phenotypes, probably play a significant role in tumor progression. These could be increased by the occurrence of extended or accelerated growth and proliferation in adult cells whose physiology may be inappropriate for such activities.

If mammary tumor initiation is ever multicellular, it becomes admissible (in single-genotype animals) that the normal cells from which one tumor will arise may not be phenotypically identical, despite their identity of genotype. We have elsewhere (Mintz, 1969b) proposed the hypothesis that many or all cell types in an individual mammal may regularly include phenotypically different clonal subpopulations, produced by largely unknown genetic mechanisms. Orderly cell selection among the phenotypic variants may then constitute a major aspect of normal development, leading to a genotype-specific, total (or metaclonal) phenotype. On this hypothesis, an incipient tumor (again, in a single-genotype animal) of multicellular, and therefore possibly of multiphenotypic, origin might also progressively evolve by selection. In the present discussion, the initial phenotypic variability occurs among normal mammary cells. Here selection need not necessarily involve the same loci as might be responsible later, in the tumor itself, for clonal phenotypic variants such as the widely diverse tumor-specific antigens whose possible origin and role have been discussed by others (Old and Boyse, 1965; Prehn, 1967; Morton, Miller, and Wood, 1969).

Proceeding with the analyses of mammary tumors, we found no mosaic tumors containing hybrid enzyme. In in vivo muscle, heterokaryons of allophenic mice from two strains differing allelically at the malate dehydrogenase-1 locus, hybrid enzyme is formed, showing multinucleate muscle origin from fusion of uninucleate myoblast cells (Baker and Mintz, 1969). Absence of hybrid enzyme in mosaic tumors would have to be borne out in a larger group of such tumors in order to be conclusive. Thus far, the evidence from the limited number of mosaic tumors suggests that cell fusion or other forms of exchange of genetic information between cells are not factors in neoplastic transformation in vivo.

Despite the interest afforded by mosaic tumors, most of the mammary tumors formed in the allophenic mice were clearly pure-strain tumors (Figure 3a, b), and there was an overwhelming preponderance of tumors of the high-susceptibility genotypes (Table 1). In the C3Hf ⟷ C57BL/6 allophenics, 83 per cent (5/6) of the tumors were C3Hf. In the C3H ⟷ C57BL/6 combination, 93 per cent (38/41) of all tumors typed were substantially of the C3H strain, including 33 tumors that were apparently solely C3H. Thus the high incidence of mammary tumors in allophenic mice of these strain combinations, and the average age of tumor occurrence, are consistent with the genotypic composition of the tumors. The overriding prevalence of all-C3H(f) tumors is especially striking since not only one gland, but also one hyperplastic nodule, from

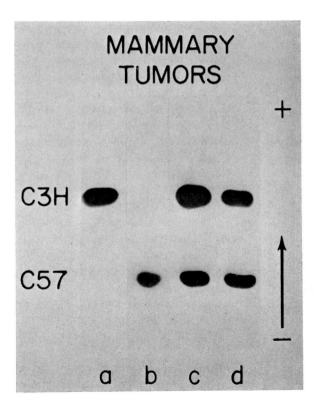

FIGURE 3. Genotypic analyses of mammary tumors from two MTV-infected C3H ⟷ C57BL/6 females, by starch gel electrophoretic separation of malate dehydrogenase (*Mdh-1*) enzyme variants found in the pure strains. With the procedures used here (Baker and Mintz, 1969), the C3H enzyme is more rapidly moving and closer to the anode. Channels a and b: C3H and C57BL/6 tumors, respectively, from separate females. Channels c and d: two samples of one genotypically mosaic tumor taken from the same animal as the all-C3H tumor in channel a.

which a tumor will arise, can easily include admixed cells of both geno-types (Mintz and Slemmer, 1969). The C57BL/6 cells in the nodule therefore must be retaining their low susceptibility, even in this intimate association with high-susceptibility cells, and remaining phenotypically normal while their C3H(f) neighbors become malignant.

Mammary tumors occurred in a similar age range in C3H ←→ C57BL/6 MTV allophenics (7 to 13 mo) and C3H controls (6 to 13 mo, except for the one sterile C3H female, who had a tumor at 19 mo). In C57BL/6 MTV controls, however, tumors arose at 10 to 20 mo. Twenty of the allophenics (including the four with previous tumor extirpations) remained alive long enough to share a 4-mo overlap period with the C57BL/6 controls, at 10 through 13 mo of age. During that time, half (3/6) of the total tumor cases among those controls occurred; i.e., 20 per cent of all 15 C57BL/6 controls (Table 1) formed tumors at 10 to 13 mo and the other half of the tumor cases in this genotype appeared at 14 to 20 mo.

If production of tumors by cells of the C57BL/6 genotype were to remain autonomous within the allophenic situation, despite the presence of C3H in many tissues including mammary gland, then 20 per cent, or four, of the 20 allophenics still alive at 10 to 13 mo should have developed mammary tumors that were largely C57BL/6-type. In point of fact, four allophenics actually did form such tumors: the three all-C57BL/6 tumors (Figure 3b) and the one half-C57BL/6 tumor (Figure 3c and d) were produced in four mosaic individuals aged 10 to 12 mo. Though there is no reason to expect that the frequency of allophenic individuals with later-appearing C57BL/6-type tumors (at 14 to 20 mo) might differ from that in C57BL/6 controls, that possibility cannot be ruled out, because tumor extirpations to prolong animals' lives were discontinued because of surgi-cal risk.

The available evidence points to an impressive retention of strain specificities in mammary gland cells of genetically mosaic animals. High-susceptibility cells remain susceptible and produce many early tumors; low susceptibility cells can be infected with MTV but still produce fewer tumors, with characteristically later onset, even when they are inter-mingled with susceptible cells in the same gland.

RELATION OF GENOTYPES IN MAMMARY TUMORS AND OTHER TISSUES

Are the susceptible-strain mammary cells producing these tumors chiefly in response to a systematically situated control? That is, is the primary expression of the "susceptibility" phenotype located in cells outside the mammary gland? If so, this should be reflected in a general predominance of the high-tumor cellular genotype in that controlling tissue, and a correlation, within individual allophenics, between genotypic composition of that system and presence or absence of mammary tumors.

Extensive tissue analyses, with many markers, strongly suggest that this is not the case. There appears to be no consistent relationship between mammary tumor presence or absence, or tumor genotype, and the genotypes of other systems studied in the same individuals.

A sample of data chosen to illustrate noncorrelation of genotypes is digrammatically represented in Figure 4. From these cases, it is evident that a C3H(f) or a C57BL/6 mammary tumor can occur in an animal whose $7S\gamma2a$ humoral antibodies or spleen cells are partly or entirely of the other genotype. To this can be added further data on lymph node analyses (with the *Gpd-1* marker). In the case designated M4 in Figure 4, for example, there were two C3Hf mammary tumors; the analyzed lymph nodes included 25 per cent C57BL/6. In another allophenic C3H ←→C57BL/6 mouse (not in Figure 4) with two all-C3H mammary tumors, the typed lymph nodes had approximately equal amounts of both genotypes; spleen and circulating γ-globulins were also of two genetic types. While hidden genotypic correlations, requiring other serological test procedures for detection, cannot be ruled out, the available evidence thus far implies that the behavior of mammary cells in the genesis of a tumor is independent of any strain-specific functional genetic information in the immunological system. Loci critically controlling high *versus* low susceptibility through different allelic substitutions in the separate inbred strains therefore presumably are not expressing themselves in the immune system. In other words, when the immune system is fully intact and competent—as it apparently is in untreated controls as well as allophenics on the eve of tumor formation—immunological functions seem not to be the most pivotal in the differential genetic susceptibility to these virally induced mammary tumors, as they ordinarily occur "spontaneously" in situ.

Other kinds of experimental investigations nevertheless have demonstrated, by means of tumor transplants, that mammary tumor viruses are capable of influencing growth of the tumor via the immune system, either positively by conferring viral tolerance in newborns exposed to virus or negatively by conferring immunity in older animals (Morton, 1969; Dezfulian, Lavrin, Shen, Blair, and Weiss, 1967). Since MTV infection normally occurs neonatally by vertical transmission in the C3H strain, acquired tolerance to MTV should also occur then and may be a major aspect of susceptibility to mammary carcinogenesis in C3H (Mor-

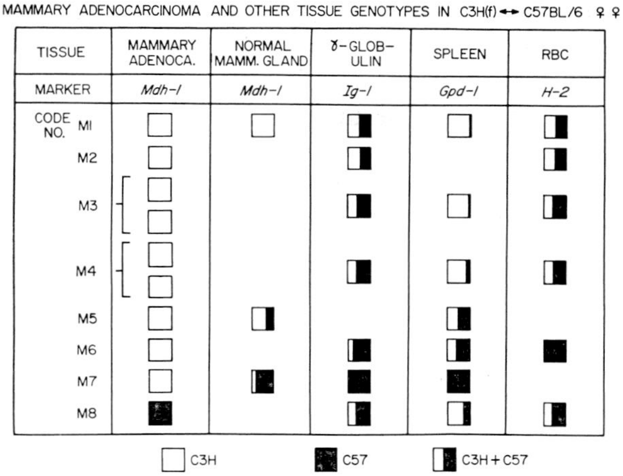

MAMMARY ADENOCARCINOMA AND OTHER TISSUE GENOTYPES IN C3H(f) ←→ C57BL/6 ♀ ♀

TISSUE	MAMMARY ADENOCA.	NORMAL MAMM. GLAND	ᵞ-GLOB-ULIN	SPLEEN	RBC
MARKER	Mdh-1	Mdh-1	Ig-1	Gpd-1	H-2
CODE NO. M1					
M2					
M3					
M4					
M5					
M6					
M7					
M8					

☐ C3H   ■ C57   ☐■ C3H+C57

FIGURE 4. Diagrammatic comparisons between genotypic composition of mammary tumors and of some other, normal, tissues in eight C3H ←→ C57BL/6 (MTV) or C3Hf ←→ C57BL/6 allophenic females (M1 to M8). Each square is partitioned to show approximate proportions of C3H or C3Hf (in white) and C57BL/6 (in black). (See text for definition of marker phenotypes and for test sensitivities. The γ-globulin results are from Weiler and Mintz [unpublished data]. The H-2 results, from Mintz and Palm [1969], were based on absorption tests except for M6, based on agglutination.) Comparisons show that mammary tumor genotype can be unrelated to the genotypes of these other tissues in the same individuals.

ton, 1969). If virus is first introduced in immunologically mature non-tolerant animals, elicitation of an immune response might be expected. These observations are not incompatible with the results in allophenic mice where viral transmission is vertical; both coexisting cellular genotypes are then infected at a young age and the animals are presumably tolerant of the virus. There as yet has been no evidence for genotype-specific differences in inducibility of tolerance to MTV, or in immunological sufficiency, as a basis for differences in tumor incidence between two strains neonatally infected with MTV. In any event, cells in one allophenic mouse share a common immune system. Thus, the mammary tumor results in allophenic mice suggest that, whatever important immune-system effects the virus may evoke, genetic differences in susceptibility operate most critically within the host's mammary cells rather than elsewhere in determining viral infectivity and/or tumorigenic response to the virus.

Surveillance against neoplasia by cells outside the immune system, as proposed in the hypothesis of "allogeneic inhibition" (Hellström and Hellström, 1966) seems not to occur in vivo in healthy animals. According to the hypothesis, neoplastic cells with variant H-2 antigens should be destroyed upon contact with other cells. As pointed out, however

(Mintz and Silvers, 1967; Mintz and Palm, 1965, 1969; Mintz and Slemmer, 1969), allophenic mice with cells of different *H-2* antigenic types remain tolerant of both. In the present study, we also see that tumor formation in them is neither prevented nor diminished.

Tumor susceptibility differences in the pure strains are likewise not decisively mediated by the erythropoietic system since, here also, the genotypic composition of erythrocytes in the allophenics may be largely or entirely of the low-tumor strain despite occurrence of tumors (Figure 4). Nandi (1967) has reported presence of MTV in red cells, and believes this to represent a phase intermediate between introduction of MTV in the milk and MTV infection of mammary tissue. He considers that inadequate production of blood-borne MTV may explain tumor resistance in his MTV-infected C57BL subline. In our experiments, however, the erythropoietic genotype appears neither to protect against nor to facilitate MTV-induced tumor production.

Not all tissues have been genotypically characterized in the allophenic mice. Endocrines are known to have supportive and stimulating roles in mammary tumorigenesis, and there are strain differences in production and response (Mühlbock and Boot, 1959; Nandi and Bern, 1960; Ben-David, Heston, and Rodbard, 1969). Hormone levels were not measured in the allophenics, and strain-specific markers for analyses of prolactin, estrogen, or other hormones are not yet available. Strain differences or differences involving XX and XY cells therefore may have contributed to the results. On the basis of quantitative studies on hormonal factors (Ben-David, Heston, and Rodbard, 1969), it seems unlikely that the high tumor incidence and the tumor genotypes obtained in allophenic mice would be ascribable solely to strain differences in genetic controls acting in the endocrines. And the presence of XY cells in some of the females should perhaps tend to diminish rather than increase tumor frequency; yet the incidence of tumors was very high.

In the general female allophenic population, C3H(f) cells did predominate in certain organs outside the mammary system, notably in the liver (to be discussed below); but since this did not necessarily occur in individuals with mammary tumors, there is no reason to believe that such organs were the primary sites of susceptibility control.

The genes responsible for susceptibility therefore appear to express themselves, or produce a phenotype, mainly in the mammary gland cells. Mammary tumors can develop in cells of susceptible strains even when cells of low-susceptibility genotype occupy various extrinsic sites; conversely, an animal can fail to develop a mammary tumor even when many of its extramammary tissues are primarily of the susceptible strain.

A number of investigators have attempted to examine this problem by grafting pure-strain mammary tissue into F_1 hybrid hosts (with or without MTV) from high- and low-susceptibility strain crosses (Prehn, 1953; Hoshino, Gardner, and Pawlikowski, 1965; Nandi et al., 1966; Dux and Mühlbock, 1968). They noted that formation of hyperplastic nodules and tumors in the grafts continued to reflect the constitution of the graft rather than that of the host. The results are consistent with localization of susceptibility factors in the gland but, as one of those investigators pointed out (Prehn, 1953), grafting is performed relatively late and such an experiment cannot disclose whether earlier systemically situated influences were more critical in determining susceptibility, because they may already have acted on the mammary gland. Moreover, an F_1 host may fail to supply some of the systemic features found in one pure strain or the other, since alleles are not necessarily codominant at all loci.

Both these difficulties are overcome in the allophenic mouse, where cell associations start in early embryonic life, and pure-strain cell genotypes are admixed (except in skeletal muscle syncytium). In addition, individual tissues or different groups of tissues can be tested when they vary from the rest of the animal in genotype; and intra- versus intercellular events can also be examined within mosaic tissues.

RELATION OF NORMAL MAMMARY GLAND DEVELOPMENT TO
TUMOR SUSCEPTIBILITY

If genetic susceptibility differences act mainly in mammary cells, what is the mechanism of action of these differences? A clue to at least one possible mechanism comes from examination of normal mammary gland development in these same experimental animals. Ostensibly normal mammary tissue was taken from an average of three separate sites, from each of 15 randomly chosen animals (10 females, five males), and genetically analyzed by means of strain variants in malate dehydrogenase isozymes. Approximately half the animals were C3Hf $\longleftrightarrow$ C57BL/6 and half C3H $\longleftrightarrow$ C57BL/6, and all had some genetic mosaicism, irrespective of mammary tissue. Despite individual differences, there was in the entire sample a marked predominance of the C3H(f) genotypes, though some of the other organs in the same group were primarily C57BL/6. Of the 15 animals tested, two had only C3H(f) in the mammary gland samples, 10 had mostly C3H(f), and only three had a larger proportion of C57BL/6 than of C3H(f).

Since mammary tumor susceptibility seems to reside chiefly in the mammary cells, the presence of more C3H(f) than C57BL/6 cells in normal mammary tissue might lead to high tumor incidence in the allophenics in one of two ways. In one instance, a population of many C3H(f) cells might provide more possibility for a tumor to form; if normal strain growth differences favor C3H(f) cells, high tumor frequency should follow, but could then be unrelated to the competitive growth advantage shown by that strain. In the other instance, genetically controlled differences in normal mammary cell growth might be intimately related to genetically controlled differences in growth response to a tumorigenic stimulus; C3H(f) normal mammary cells should then be capable of forming tumors even when they are in the minority.

The second possibility is supported by the fact that some C3H(f) tumors developed even when the neighboring normal glandular tissue was largely C57BL/6 (as in the examples in Figure 4). Of the 10 females whose normal glandular tissue was typed, seven had mammary tumors. In one of them, a C3H tumor was found, but the ostensibly normal gland samples, including one taken from a site adjacent to the tumor, all contained much more C57BL/6 than C3H. Two other females with C3H tumors had a large minority C57BL/6 glandular component. C3H(f) hyperplastic nodules were also formed in single glands that contained many C57BL/6 cells (Mintz and Slemmer, 1969).

Thus C3H(f) need not be the sole or even chief mammary genotype for tumors to appear; genetic mechanisms inclining toward tumor formation act in the C3H(f) cells whether or not those cells happen to be in the majority. That they often are in the majority, however, suggests that similar genetic mechanisms may play a role both in the normal growth of C3H(f) mammary cells and in their vigorous growth response to a tumorigenic viral stimulus. Other genes may influence viral penetration (e.g., Lilly [1966] presents evidence for gene control of mouse leukemia virus susceptibility), or response to hormones, or other variables. But it seems reasonable to suppose that cell growth and proliferation—whether during normal mammary development or tumor formation—must, to a considerable extent, be regulated by the cell's own genetic machinery. If C3H(f) normal mammary cells tend in the allophenic to outgrow C57BL/6 cells when both are exposed to common systemic influences, and when C57BL/6 cells may simultaneously be outgrowing C3H(f) in some other tissues, then tissue-specific gene expressions must be manifesting themselves. The selective advantage enjoyed by C3H(f) cells under these conditions must accrue to them by virtue of their own alleles at loci which express themselves in normal mammary cells and which dictate the rates and patterns of cellular growth and proliferation in mammary tissue. Some of these loci may also be active in other tissues; but the total battery of loci responsible for growth of mammary (or any) tissue is likely to be unique. Within that battery, allelic differences can exist between inbred strains. From the in vivo competition experiment, we infer that the sum total of allelic differences at such growth-controlling loci in the C3H(f) strains confers upon their mammary cells a greater capacity for normal growth and proliferation than exists in the C57BL/6 strain by virtue of the latter's alleles. Since the mammary gland is a complex tissue, however, this inference is not necessarily generalizable to all of its various cell types. Growth of each cell type could be governed, at least in part, by different loci. The selective advantage of C3H(f) cells therefore might be limited to certain prominent cell types. At the same time, C57BL/6 cells could be favored in some other types. Further studies of developing mosaic glands are being directed at clarifying these possibilities.

Loci controlling normal mammary cell growth and proliferation would ordinarily be expressed only during morphogenesis and during gestational and lactational changes; they would largely be silent at other times in adult life, and enzymatic and other physiological conditions in the adult cells would no longer be appropriate to sustained growth. If these loci become permantly active (or derepressed [Monod and Jacob, 1961]), possibly owing to incorporation or influence of viral genome, the cell growth and divisions that follow would not be expected to be normal. As a result, a variety of cascades of secondary and tertiary physiological changes, many irreversible, could occur. These might include chromosome aberrations, other forms of mutational change, resumption or inception of activity at other loci, etc.

We therefore propose that some of the major genetic mechanisms of tumor formation in susceptible-strain cells may be the same as the mechanisms responsible for the normal growth patterns in that genotype. The resumption of activity at the governing loci would then constitute the primary pathology. Perhaps infectible "low-susceptibility" strains in a sense are partly "slow-susceptibility" strains, with the kinds of normal-and-tumor-"growth alleles" that produce a relatively attenuated or unsustained response. Possibly even C57BL/6 MTV-infected mice might all get mammary tumors if they lived longer.

According to the preceding hypothesis, the genetic mechanisms determining the character of the growth response to a tumorigenic stimulus should be sought in the normally growing and proliferating cells rather than in tumor cells, through comparisons of strain-specific characteristics in high- and low-tumor strains. It goes without saying that the study of tumor biochemistry—already actively pursued for many kinds of tumors —requires no defense: from just such studies (along with those in viral immunology) some of the more promising practical leads for preventing or eradicating neoplasms may emerge. Our concern here is directed instead toward achieving an understanding of the etiology of neoplasms (and this also should have practical as well as theoretical implications). Though considerable attention in oncology has been given to biochemical comparisons between tumors and normal tissue, we know little about how

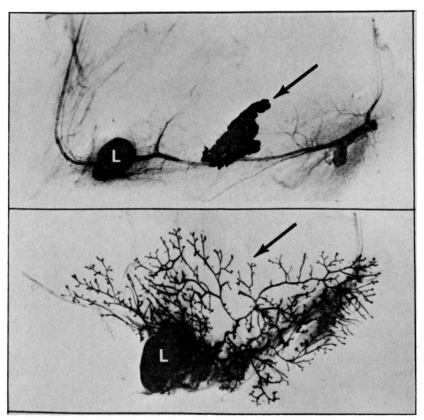

FIGURE 5. Outgrowths obtained from two halves of a single genetically mosaic hyperplastic alveolar mammary nodule of a C3Hf ⟷ C57BL/6 allophenic mouse, after transplantation to cleared fat pads of pure-strain recipients. In a C3H host (upper), surviving histocompatible cells produced hyperplastic alveolar outgrowth (arrow). In a C57BL/6 host (lower), histocompatible cells yielded entirely normal appearing outgrowth despite prolonged prior contact with the tumor-susceptible cell strain during morphogenesis and premalignancy. (A lymph node, L, is indicated in each whole mount.) (From Mintz and Slemmer, 1969.)

growth mechanisms may differ in normal cells of a high- as compared with a low-tumor genetic strain. In view of the availability of inbred strains of mice having diverse susceptibilities to specific malignant diseases, the opportunity for such studies is available. A genotype-specific disease entity (whatever the external stimulus) is a "phenotype," and genetically controlled aberrant tissue growth, irrespective of the age at which it occurs, should be subject to investigation in ways comparable to the investigation of how genes control normal growth and differentiation. One of the most powerful tools for the latter is the exploitation of genetic differences.

In normal as in abnormal development of multicellular organisms, it is necessary to know in which cells particular genes are expressing themselves. As we have seen, the answer for mammary tumor susceptibility seems to be that the mammary cells themselves are the chief site of expression of specific genetic factors that control susceptibility. The maintenance of these genotype-specific characteristics is nowhere more dramatically illustrated than in a genetically mosaic hyperplastic nodule, by the virtual indifference of admixed normal and premalignant mammary cells of different genotypes to each other. We recall that when these nodules are tested by transplant methods that selectively eliminate one genotype at a time, the tumor-susceptible cells still retain their aberrant growth character; the low-susceptibility cells, after release from entrapment in the nodule, are found unharmed and able to resume normal growth behavior (Mintz and Slemmer, 1969). Thus the high-tumor cell strain remains impervious to any ameliorating influence which might be exerted by normal neighbors. And the low-tumor strain shows no adoptive transformation or increase in susceptibility; transduction of the sort seen in bacteria (Zinder and Lederberg, 1952) is apparently not taking place, and tumor genetic information is not transferred from the C3H(f) to the C57BL/6 cells. This conclusion is further supported by the rarity of mosaic tumors from mosaic hyperplastic nodules.

Hepatomas in Males

TUMOR INCIDENCE

The investigation of hepatomas in males leads to conclusions analogous to those reached from the study of mammary tumors in females.

The incidence of spontaneous hepatomas in allophenic males (Figure 6) is high, and resembles the high-susceptibility C3Hf and C3H strains, rather than the low-susceptibility C57BL/6. Results are summarized in Table 2. In the C3Hf ⟷ C57BL/6 experiment, 30 per cent (3/10) of known mosaic males developed hepatomas; among the corresponding male controls, 33 per cent (3/9) of C3Hf and only 8 per cent or less (1/13) of C57BL/6 males had tumors. In the C3H ⟷ C57BL/6 experiment with MTV, 45 per cent (13/29) of known mosaics developed hepatomas; among controls, the incidence in C3H was 69 per cent (9/13) and was low or nil (0/6) in C57BL/6 controls with MTV. In all groups, the average age at which hepatomas were recorded was close to 2 yr; this, however, represents the time when a conspicuous external bulge was seen in the hepatic region, so that the average time of tumor onset was undoubtedly earlier than 2 yr.

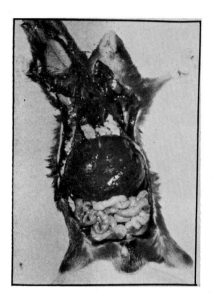

FIGURE 6. A C3H ⟷ C57BL/6 allophenic male, dissected to show the enlarged hepatomatous liver. The tumor was genotypically C3H, though C57-BL/6 as well as C3H cells occurred in various tissues.

Closer examination of the C3H ⟷ C57BL/6 males suggests that there is less of a real gap between their tumor incidence (45 per cent) and that of C3H controls (69 per cent) than these figures would suggest. This is because, in the C3H ⟷ C57BL/6 males, more animals were autopsied inadvertently for "trivial" reasons than in any other experimental or control group in the study. Six of the 29 were mistakenly diagnosed as ill, from external appearance, but were found at autopsy to lack specific disease or to have only minor ailments (*e.g.*, pneumonitis). In addition, two others of the 29 (one with lymphoblastoma and one with reticulum cell sarcoma) had livers composed entirely of C57BL/6 cells, and therefore of only the low-tumor genotype.

The higher frequency of tumorous mice in the C3H control strain than in C3Hf, and in C3H ⟷ C57BL/6 allophenics than in C3Hf ⟷

C57BL/6, is also reflected in larger numbers of tumor foci in the former instances (Table 2). If discrete foci, whether in the same or in separate lobes, are counted as individual tumors, the C3H controls averaged 1.8 tumors per tumorous animal, and the C3H $\longleftrightarrow$ C57BL/6 allophenics had an average of 2.0 tumors per affected individual; among C3Hf controls, tumor-bearing mice had 1.0 tumor each, and the affected C3Hf $\longleftrightarrow$ C57BL/6 mice averaged 1.3 tumors each. It is not known what role the mammary tumor virus, or the viral differences between C3H and C3Hf, may play.

Two phenotypically male XX $\longleftrightarrow$ XY sex chromosomal mosaics were identified in the hepatoma study (Mintz, Hungerford, and Morrow, in preparation), and they did not influence the general picture. One was a C3Hf $\longleftrightarrow$ C57BL/6 with a hepatoma, and the other a C3H $\longleftrightarrow$ C57BL/6 without a hepatoma.

Thus for hepatomas as for mammary tumors, the lifelong co-existence of genotypically high- and low-tumor cell strains within individuals, during embryonic and postnatal development, results in high frequency of tumors.

GENOTYPES OF HEPATOMAS IN ALLOPHENIC ANIMALS

We can again ask, as for mammary tumors, whether high hepatoma incidence in the allophenics is related to the genotype of cells comprising these tumors. Of 26 ostensibly discrete liver tumors, 23 were genetically analyzed by means of the strain-specific electrophoretic variants of NADP-malate dehydrogenase. Inasmuch as one normal liver lobe, in an allophenic, can contain cells of two separate genotypes, the hypothetical possibility exists that both types might occur in a tumor, if the tumor were of multicellular origin. As summarized in Table 2, two mosaic tumors were found, both in C3H $\longleftrightarrow$ C57BL/6 individuals. No hybrid enzyme was seen. In one case, the tumor was chiefly C3H with a trace (equivalent to about 5 per cent) of C57BL/6. Another animal (Figure 7d to f; and Figure 8, code No. H7) had two tumors: the one in the largest lobe was not mosaic, and was all C3H (Figure 8, upper square of code No. H7); the major hepatoma was found in the second lobe, and was chiefly C57BL/6 with a minor (approximately 14 per cent) C3H component (Figure 8, lower square of code No. H7). The latter tumor was cut into seven pieces for typing; each piece showed presence of only one strain, but six pieces were C57BL/6 (Figure 7d and f) and one was C3H (Figure 7e). Whether both cellular genotypes were tumorous in these two ostensibly mosaic tumors could not be ascertained. Possibly the

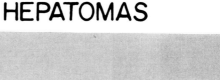

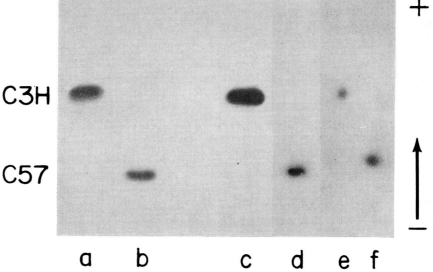

FIGURE 7. Starch gel electrophoretic analyses of hepatoma genotypes, by means of *Mdh-1* enzymatic strain differences (as in Figure 3). Channels a and b: separate C3Hf and C57BL/6 hepatomas, each from a control male of that strain. Channel c: a C3Hf hepatoma from the C3Hf ←→ C57BL/6 allophenic male listed as H1 in Figure 8. Channels d, e, f: 3 pieces of a genotypically mosaic hepatoma from the C3H ←→ C57BL/6 male listed as H7 in Figure 8. This tumor (the last of two shown for H7) was cut into seven pieces at autopsy, and was largely C57BL/6: six pieces (including channels d and f) were only C57BL/6; only one piece (channel e) was C3H. A hepatoma from another lobe of the same animal was all-C3H (diagrammed in Figure 8).

minor components may have been vascular or other tissue elements. Provisionally, the apparent mosaicism suggests the possibility that a single liver tumor in the mouse may originate from more than one cell. (A similar conclusion was reached from analysis of a hepatoma in a G-6-PD heterozygous woman [McCurdy, 1967].) In turn, the possibility remains open that spontaneous mutation thereby might become a less likely explanation of tumor origin than would be true if a tumor arose from only one cell.

From analyses of the remaining, nonmosaic, hepatomas, it is clear that they are overwhelmingly of the C3H or C3Hf genotypes. The 25 pure-strain tumors included 24 that were C3H or C3Hf (Figure 7c; and

Figure 8, code No. H1) and only one that was C57BL/6.

In summary, of 27 genetically diagnosed tumors from C3H ⟷ C57BL/6 and C3Hf ⟷ C57BL/6 allophenic mice, 93 per cent (25/27) were all or largely of the high-susceptibility genotypes. The high frequency of hepatomas in allophenics of these strain combinations is therefore consistent with the genotypic makeup of the tumors.

RELATION OF GENOTYPES IN HEPATOMAS,
NORMAL LIVER, AND OTHER TISSUES

From the sample data in Figure 8, we see that a C3H(f) liver tumor sometimes arises next to normal liver tissue (in the same lobe) that

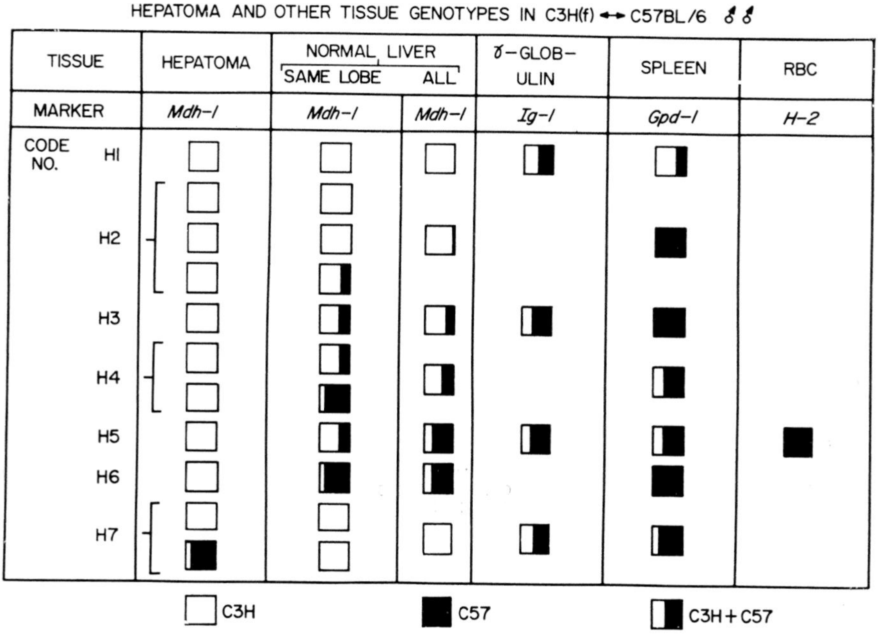

FIGURE 8. Diagrammatic comparisons between genotypic composition of hepatomas and of some other, normal, tissues in seven C3H ⟷ C57BL/6 or C3Hf ⟷ C57BL/6 allophenic males (H1 to H7). C3H(f) and C57BL/6 components are indicated as in Figure 4. (γ-Globulin results are from Weiler and Mintz (unpublished data); red blood cell analysis of H5, by the absorption test, is from Mintz and Palm (1969). See text for method of determining genotypic proportions in total normal liver.) Comparisons show that the genotypic composition of a hepatoma can differ from the prevailing genotype in normal parts of the same or other liver lobes, and also from the composition of the other tissues shown in the same individuals.

consists appreciably, or even chiefly, of C57BL/6 cells. In the animals with code numbers H2 through H6, each C3H(f) tumor is genotypically compared with the normal tissue adjacent to it in the same lobe and found to show lack of concordance; the same point is illustrated by the second (largely C57BL/6) tumor of H7, found adjacent to C3H normal cells in the same lobe. These results strikingly demonstrate genotypic autonomy of tumor changes in the transforming cells: the latter (as with tumor-prone mammary cells in mosaic nodules) seem to derive no salvation from the normal neighboring cells, nor to induce transformation in them. The results also show that prevalence of C3H(f) hepatomas in the allophenics is not simply a consequence of more C3H(f) liver cells in them: hepatomas can in fact arise where C3H(f) cells are in the minority.

Nevertheless, the composition of normal livers in the allophenic population shows a marked selective advantage favoring C3H(f) over C57BL/6 cells. Therefore, high tumor proneness in the experimentals appears to be causally and not merely coincidentally related to strain differences in normal liver growth, and to involve common genetic mechanisms to some significant extent. The population trend is seen in Figure 9, based on 41 known mosaics (21 females and 20 males), taken from a random group of C3Hf $\longleftrightarrow$ C57BL/6 and C3H $\longleftrightarrow$ C57BL/6 (plus MTV) allophenics. The analyses were of all-normal livers or of normal parts of tumorous livers. Each liver lobe was analyzed for NADP-malate dehydrogenase strain variants (which have similar specific activity in both strains), and the proportions of the two strains in the whole

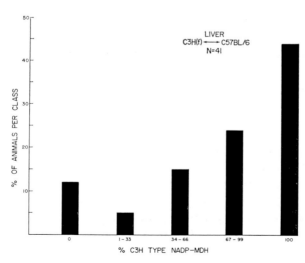

FIGURE 9. Distribution of liver genotypes in 41 C3H $\longleftrightarrow$ C57BL/6 and C3Hf $\longleftrightarrow$ C57BL/6 allophenic mice (21 ♀ ♀, 20 ♂ ♂), showing the preponderance of cases in which C3H(f) cells are favored over C57BL/6 cells in normal liver development of mosaic animals. Genotypic analyses are based on *Mdh-1* enzyme variants in the two strains.

liver were then calculated as a weighted average, according to the relative weights of the lobes. Of the 41 livers included, 44 per cent revealed only C3H(f) cells, as against 12 per cent that were only C57BL/6, and the remainder contributed to a total trend favoring C3H(f), despite trends favoring C57BL/6 in some other tissues of the same animals.

Within some (not all) individuals, the genotypic composition of the hepatoma can differ from that of serum γ-globulins from spleen cells, or from circulating erythrocytes (Figure 8). Lymph nodes (typed for *Gpd-1* alleles) also sometimes showed genotypic unrelatedness to tumor composition: H3 and H5—both animals with C3H hepatomas—averaged about equal amounts of the two cell strains in the nodes tested. Still other organs (lungs, kidneys, *etc.*) were genotypically dissimilar from the liver tumors in some of the animals.

These lines of evidence again suggest, as in the case of mammary tumors, that hepatoma susceptibility and gene activity critical for initiation and maintenance of hepatomas are determined within the liver cells of that strain, rather than at systemic foci. The genotype of the immune system, from the data thus far assembled, seems irrelevant to strain-specific tumor susceptibility in these immunologically competent subjects, so that spontaneous tumor occurrence in these strains presumably does not hinge upon immunological differences irrespective of contributory physiological roles that tolerance or immune mechanisms might indeed play in any disease where viral etiology remains a possibility, as it does for many tumors.

Once again, we find some emphasis directed toward growth control within entirely normal, but prospectively tumorous, cells. Any cell growth, whether normal or neoplastic, must require cellular genetic machinery to direct synthesis for that growth and to determine its rate and character. Resumption of cell growth and division, at a time beyond the normal growth period, would logically invoke resumption of genetic activity at loci that had governed normal growth at an earlier time in development. The specific alleles at such loci—differing to some extent in different strains—could produce many kinds of growth variation, possibly of a subtle kind, in normal development of a tissue; the differences might become highly significant if those loci are derepressed at a later stage. Presence of viral genome, and differences in adult as compared with embryonic cell physiology, could then contribute appreciably to mutations, derepression of other loci, and further chains of irrevocable errors. Of interest is the fact that rapid liver proliferation (in C3H mice) after partial hepatectomy enhances liver carcinogenesis (Hollander and Bentvelzen, 1968), as these speculations would lead us to anticipate.

There is no particular reason to expect that any tumor-specific protein that also might be found in the corresponding normal embryonic tissue (*e.g.*, the human gastrointestinal cancer antigens found in fetal but not adult gut [Gold and Freedman, 1965]) are an indication of derepression of primary growth loci causal to cancer; embryonic proteins are "phenotypes," from depressed loci, but they may be loci only secondarily depressed, by other cell aberrations, and perhaps entirely unrelated to cancer etiology.

Liver contains a number of cell types, and normal liver growth would probably depend upon many gene complexes in each cell type. These would not, as a totality, be identical with those responsible for mammary tissue growth, or for growth of other kinds of cells. Each cell type in development probably has its own proliferative kinetics, and allelic strain differences should therefore cause not only cell-type-specific growth patterns, but also genotype-specific growth patterns, in each cell type. The relation of such normal cell- and genotype-specificities to susceptibility to malignancy therefore needs to be explored further.

The Statistical Allophenic Mouse (SAM): Implications for Development and Neoplasia

When the cellular genotypes of different tissues are compared in C3H(f) $\longleftrightarrow$ C57BL/6 allophenic mice, the tissue-specific character of strain trends becomes apparent. It is this tissue specificity which suggests the genetic and developmental significance of the trends.

For each tissue thus far surveyed in a group of allophenics containing these strain combinations, the genotypic composition may vary from one individual to another. Nevertheless, each tissue exhibits its own genotypic preference in the population at large. The populational composition summarizing the diverse tendencies can be expressed as a conceptual entity, the statistical allophenic mouse (SAM). From preliminary studies of strain combinations other than C3H(f) $\longleftrightarrow$ C57BL/6, it is already apparent that each strain combination has its own populational profile of cellular genotypic components in each tissue, and therefore its own SAM. A sample of the characteristics found in the SAM for the strain confrontations involved in the present study is shown in Figure 10. While normal liver (Figure 9) and mammary gland are primarily C3H(f), the C57BL/6 strain is favored in erythropoietic tissue and γ-globulin-producing cells, and both strains have approximately equal representation in the statistical kidney. Some tissues also display statistical sex differences (Figure 10); in some instances (*e.g.*, heart) these differences may perhaps be secondary effects of sex hormone influences, but in others (*e.g.*, gonia) primary disparities in cell proliferation seem to be involved (Mintz, unpublished data).

The tissue specificities and genotypic specificities must arise from differential selective advantages enjoyed by one or the other strain by reason of genes that express themselves in the development of the tissue in question, providing it with distinctive phenotypes upon which selection can act. "Selection" here should be construed in the broadest possible sense. It may be a continuing process, as in the case of gradual loss of functional C57BL/6 spermatogonia and proportionate increase in C3H(f) spermatogonia during the reproductive life of germinal mosaic males (Mintz, 1968). Or it may occur at only restricted periods, as with mitotic selection of oogonia in females, in the embryonic day 8 to 12 time period, apparently slightly favoring C57BL/6 over C3H(f) (Figure 10, and Mintz, unpublished data). Or relative selective advantage between two genotypes within a given cell type may change from one to the other in the course of time, depending on changing kinetics in that cell population. Or the onset of genetic determination of a cell type may occur at slightly different times, affording to the earlier determined strain a head-

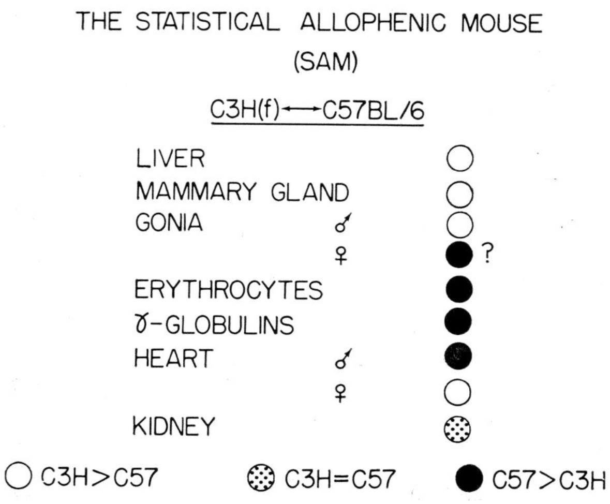

THE STATISTICAL ALLOPHENIC MOUSE
(SAM)

C3H(f) ⟷ C57BL/6

LIVER		○
MAMMARY GLAND		○
GONIA	♂	○
	♀	● ?
ERYTHROCYTES		●
𝛾-GLOBULINS		●
HEART	♂	●
	♀	○
KIDNEY		⊛

○ C3H>C57   ⊛ C3H=C57   ● C57>C3H

FIGURE 10. Examples of tissue-specific selective trends between two possible cellular genotypes differing at many loci, in normal tissues of a large population of C3H(f) ⟷ C57BL/6 allophenic mice; some tissues also show sex differences. The total populational tissue profile comprises a statistical allophenic mouse (SAM) for this particular genotypic confrontation. The results suggest tissue-specific growth phenotypes important in normal growth and development, and controlled by different batteries of gene loci in each tissue.

start in contributing cells to that tissue. These complexities, and possibly many others, may ultimately influence interpretation of the SAM results.

Nevertheless, selection—in whatever ways it occurs—must operate on phenotypes, not on genotypes, so that unequal genotypic participation in the structuring of an allophenic tissue must reflect allelic dissimilarities in phenotypes in those two strains, at specific loci responsible for directing the growth of that tissue.

It is evident that the distinction between, say, erythrocytes and melanocytes, does not lie simply in the production of hemoglobin in the former and melanin in the latter. Each kind of cell, irrespective of these specialized products, is the culmination of a long prior history of proliferation and growth. That history, in erythropoietic cells, must be quite unlike the history in melanoblasts, and must surely be governed to some important extent (even if not entirely) by different loci. Loci responsible for cell-type-specific growth patterns and kinetics must surely exist, though very little attention has been devoted to learning their identity. Perhaps many of these are regulator rather than structural genes (Jacob and Monod, 1961). Such genes may in fact be of greater importance in differentiation of cell type and fashioning of tissues than are the more widely studied genes, such as those coding for hemoglobins. Although single genes are known to be capable of marked effects on growth or even survival of cells, it would appear more likely that the complexities of growth in any cell type rest on multiple-locus gene activities.

The major differences in developing patterns of growth in liver *versus* lung, or between any other tissues, may be controlled at such hypothetical "growth-gene loci." Constellations of genes determining growth of specific cells in liver would become active in those liver-initiator cells, and constellations determining lung growth would become active in lung-initiator cells. While the respective gene batteries might include some of the same loci, a unique active-gene complex would be found in each case. In either instance, allelic differences (as in different inbred strains) would mean that alternative gene-regulatory activities would be found, or alternative structural proteins would be found, and growth phenotypes would differ quantitatively and/or qualitatively.

The high liver and mammary tumor susceptibility in C3H(f) ⟷ C57BL/6 allophenic mice seems, as already stated, to be causally related to the "dominance" of normal liver and mammary cell growth of the high-tumor strains, as exhibited in the allophenic animals. We therefore have adopted the working hypothesis that (for these tumors, and possibly for many others) the same genes that are vocal in these tissues, controlling normal cell growth in a strain-specific way, may also be heavily involved in tumorigenesis, under appropriate inciting circumstances. We are interested in characterizing the dynamically evolving phenotypic growth differences more precisely in terms of biochemical parameters and in clarifying the nature of the genetic control of these differences.

It therefore may be useful to view the problem of genetic susceptibility to tumors as being in part a developmental problem, comparable to other developmental problems, but characterized by induction (*e.g.*, viral) of "inappropriately" late expression of an otherwise normal phenotype. If genes that favor certain kinds of "vigorous" cell growth in the development of a tissue, but are less active later on, become reactivated, the phenotypic consequences may then conflict with other aspects of the cell's physiology, so that all sorts of maladjustments and errors could then occur. Other developmental hypotheses of neoplasia (which will not be reviewed in detail here) have been advanced. They have postulated: retention of an undifferentiated state in some cells, until presented with a tumorigenic stimulus; or reversion or "dedifferentiation" of cells to an embryonic state, followed by differentiation along other lines; or derepression of a specific locus producing some critical product; or built-in aberrant programming of sequences of genetic activity; *etc.* While all these views are of interest, the hypothesis presented here is directed instead toward genetic and molecular mechanisms of normal growth control, and comparison of their variant (normal) forms in cells hereditarily predisposed toward high and toward low susceptibility to malignancy. At least one major facet of the investigation would be gene control and triggering of the cell cycle and the mitotic machinery. Long recognized as a subject relevant to cancer (Schultz, 1952), newer methodologies should make cell proliferation more accessible as a genetic problem. But a wealth of other possible levels of regulation of cell growth also present themselves and may offer new insights into neoplastic processes.

Conclusions and Summary

The genetic and developmental mechanisms responsible for hereditarily determined susceptibility to neoplasia have been investigated by means of cellular genetic mosaicism in allophenic mice. In these animals (derived experimentally from aggregated blastomeres of dissimilar genotypes [Mintz, 1962b, 1965]), cells from two unrelated inbred strains, with high and low susceptibility to specific neoplastic diseases, have been made to co-exist throughout embryonic and adult life, in different proportions and in highly varied patterns of tissue distribution. Identification of the tissue localization and nature of the "susceptibility" phenotype therefore can be experimentally approached as a problem in differential gene expression.

Mammary tumors in females and hepatomas in males occur very commonly in the C3H strain (with the milk-transmitted MTV), moderately frequently in C3Hf (without milk-transmitted MTV but possibly with a less virulent form of the virus), and only rarely in C57BL/6 (without MTV); C57BL/6 can be infected with MTV, and mammary tumors then occur moderately frequently in females. The etiology of the two kinds of tumors was analyzed in 76 allophenic mice containing genotypes of either the C3H ⟷ C57BL/6 strain combination, with MTV from a C3H foster mother; or C3Hf ⟷ C57BL/6, without milk-transmitted MTV. The animals were permanently immunologically tolerant of both cell strains and showed normal immunological competence to reject antigens foreign to them.

The incidence of mammary tumors in the allophenic females and of hepatomas in the males strikingly paralleled that of the respective high-susceptibility control strain of each pair. The relatively earlier age of tumor onset and larger numbers of tumor foci, characteristic of high-tumor rather than low-tumor controls, also characterized the allophenic animals.

Genotypic analysis of the tumors, by means of strain-specific molecular variants of NADP-malate dehydrogenase (*Mdh-1* locus), revealed that the high-tumor disease history of the allophenics was consistent with the composition of their tumors: the large majority of tumors consisted of C3H or C3Hf cells, and C57BL/6 tumors were infrequent.

A few genetically mosaic mammary and liver tumors were found, of which most were largely of one genotype; one mammary adenocarcinoma had approximately equal proportions of both genotypes and no detectable hybrid cells. Mosaicism might imply multicellular tumor origin, but its real significance remains to be clarified.

Genotypic cellular composition was examined in many tissues and organs of the allophenics, by means of many markers, and evaluated in relation to presence or absence of tumors, and tumor genotype. Numerous permutations and combinations were observed. So far as available evidence indicates, the genotype of tissues extrinsic to the potentially tumorous organ is not pivotal in determining genetic susceptibility to these tumors, even though certain systemic influences, such as hormones, are known (from the work of others) to have contributing roles and to show some strain differences. Loci controlling susceptibility to mammary tumors appear to express themselves chiefly in the mammary gland cells themselves, and those controlling susceptibility to hepatomas become active mainly in liver cells. Intracellular rather than intercellular events seem paramount in the origin of these kinds of tumors in situ, since C3H(f) and C57BL/6 cells may be intimately associated (*e.g.*, intermingled in the epithelium of a single mammary gland), with no detectable consequences for genotype-specific tumor formation.

The behavior of mammary or liver cells in the genesis of a tumor also appears to be independent of any strain-specific genetic information in the immunological system, so that loci determining susceptibility through allelic substitutions in these strains are presumably not expressed in the immune system. (Immune-system responses to tumor-virus antigens, shown by others, may nevertheless contribute significantly to various aspects of tumorigenesis in all strains.)

Analyses of many normal tissues in the large population of allophenic mice disclosed tissue-specific as well as genotype-specific trends. Despite individual differences, some tissues in the population were predominantly composed of cells of one or of the other strain. The results suggest that different constellations of gene loci, each responsible for a cell-type-specific pattern of growth and proliferation, differentially express themselves in the respective cell types during development. The ensemble of dominance relations between C3H(f) and C57BL/6 alleles at all these "growth loci" would account for the collective outcome, or statistical allophenic mouse (SAM) by means of many possible kinds of selection between the component phenotypic subpopulations in each cell type during development.

In normal mammary gland and liver, C3H or C3Hf cells tend to outgrow C57BL/6 cells in the SAM, when they are in lifelong competition in vivo, in a common systemic environment. The genetically determined capacities for growth response to a tumorigenic stimulus (*e.g.*, viral) therefore similarly may differ in mammary and liver cells of these strains (apart from other possible genetic differences relevant for tumorigenesis). High tumor incidence in the allophenics does not appear to be caused simply by presence of more C3H(f) mammary and liver cells in them, since tumors can form in individuals even when the high-tumor cell strain is in the minority in these tissues.

The hypothesis therefore is advanced that the same genetic and molecular mechanisms that specifically govern normal mammary and liver cell growth during development may also be involved to a considerable degree in determining the rate and character of growth response of those cells to a tumorigenic stimulus in the adult. If loci normally controlling cell growth and division are largely inactive in adult cells, but are derepressed (*e.g.*, by virus), cell constituents and conditions may no longer be favorable for sustained growth and division; a series of genetic and physiological aberrations could then follow, further accelerated by selection for faster-growing variants. The extent and character of the initial growth response to a tumor stimulus in adult cells of different genotypes or "susceptibilities," would then depend upon their alleles at loci controlling normal growth at earlier stages. Comparisons of growth-regulatory genetic systems in normally growing mammary and liver cells in high- *versus* low-tumor strains are proposed as a means of analyzing further the basis for genetic susceptibility to tumorigenesis.

Gene control of susceptibility to viral tumors may also involve a significant measure of control of viral infectivity via the target cell itself, depending on the cellular phenotype. Allophenic mice afford new avenues for genetic analysis of this possibility in vivo under conditions in which genetically different cells are exposed to the virus within a shared set of systemic influences.

ACKNOWLEDGMENTS

All diagnoses of pathology were made by the late Dr. Andrew J. Donnelly, whose contribution formed an essential part of this program. His high professional competence, helpfulness, and enthusiasm are remembered with pleasure.

These investigations were supported by United States Public Health Service grants HD 01646, CA 06927 and FR 05539, and by an appropriation from the Commonwealth of Pennsylvania.

REFERENCES

Andervont, H. B. 1940. The Influence of Foster Nursing upon the Incidence of Spontaneous Mammary Cancer in Resistant and Susceptible Mice. *Journal of the National Cancer Institute*, 1:147–153.

———. 1950. Studies on the Occurrence of Spontaneous Hepatomas in Mice of Strains C3H and CBA. *Journal of the National Cancer Institute*, 11:581–592.

Baker, W. W., and B. Mintz. 1969. Subunit Structure and Gene Control of Mouse NADP-Malate Dehydrogenase. *Biochemical Genetics*, 2:351–360.

Ben-David, M., W. E. Heston, and D. Rodbard. 1969. Mammary Tumor Virus Potentiation of Endogenous Prolactin Effect on Mammary Gland Differentiation. *Journal of the National Cancer Institute*, 42:207–218.

Bittner, J. J. 1958. Genetic Concepts in Mammary Cancer in Mice. *Annals of the New York Academy of Sciences*, 71:943–975.

Blair, P. B., and R. L. Moretti. 1967. The Mammary Fat Pad as a Privileged Transplantation Site. *Transplantation*, 5:542–544.

Burns, E. L., and J. R. Schenken. 1940. Spontaneous Primary Hepatomas in Mice of Strain C3H: A Study of Incidence, Sex Distribution and Morbid Anatomy. *American Journal of Cancer*, 39:25–35.

Dezfulian, M., D. H. Lavrin, A. Shen, P. B. Blair, and D. W. Weiss. 1967. "Immunology of Spontaneous Mammary Carcinomas in Mice: Studies on the Nature of the Protective Antigens," *Carcinogenesis: A Broad Critique* (The University of Texas M. D. Anderson Hospital and Tumor Institute, 20th Annual Symposium on Fundamental Cancer Research, 1966). Baltimore, Maryland: The Williams and Wilkins Co. Pp. 365–393.

Dux, A., and O. Mühlbock. 1968. Susceptibility of Mammary Tissues of Different Strains of Mice to Tumor Development. *Journal of the National Cancer Institute*, 40:1259–1265.

Gold, P., and S. O. Freedman. 1965. Specific Carcinoembryonic Antigens of the Human Digestive System. *Journal of Experimental Medicine*, 122:467–481.

Hellström, I., and K. E. Hellström. 1966. Recent Studies on the Mechanisms of the Allogeneic Inhibition Phenomenon. *Annals of the New York Academy of Sciences*, 129:724–734.

Henderson, N. S. 1966. Isozymes and Genetic Control of NADP-Malate Dehydrogenase in Mice. *Archives of Biochemistry and Biophysics*, 117:28–33.

Heston, W. E. 1958. Mammary Tumors in Agent-Free Mice. *Annals of the New York Academy of Sciences*, 71:931–942.

———. 1963. "Genetics of Neoplasia," *Methodology in Mammalian Genetics*, W. J. Burdette, Ed. San Francisco, California: Holden-Day, Inc. Pp. 247–268.

Heston, W. E., M. K. Deringer, T. B. Dunn, and W. D. Levillain. 1950. Factors in the Development of Spontaneous Mammary Gland Tumors in Agent-free Strain C3Hb Mice. *Journal of the National Cancer Institute*, 10:1139–1156.

Heston, W. E., G. Vlahakis, and M. K. Deringer. 1960. High Incidence of Spontaneous Hepatomas and the Increase of this Incidence with Urethan in C3H, C3Hf, and C3He Male Mice. *Journal of the National Cancer Institute*, 24:425–435.

Hollander, C. F., and P. Bentvelzen. 1968. Enhancement of Urethan Induction of Hepatomas in Mice by Prior Partial Hepatectomy. *Journal of the National Cancer Institute*, 41:1303–1306.

Hoshino, K., W. U. Gardner, and R. A. Pawlikowski. 1965. The Incidence of Cancer in Quantitatively Transplanted Mammary Glands and its Relation to Age and Milk Agent of the Donor and Host Mice. *Cancer Research*, 25:1792–1803.

Jacob, F., and J. Monod. 1961. On the Regulation of Gene Activity. *Cold Spring Harbor Symposia on Quantitative Biology*, 26:193–211.

Lilly, F. 1966. The Inheritance of Susceptibility to the Gross Leukemia Virus in Mice. *Genetics*, 53:529–539.

McCurdy, P. R. 1967. G-6-PD as Cell Markers in the Study of Benign and Malignant Tumors. (Abstract) *Clinical Research*, 15:65.

Mintz, B. 1962a. Experimental Study of the Developing Mammalian Egg: Removal of the Zona Pellucida. *Science*, 138:594–595.

———. 1962b. Formation of Genotypically Mosaic Mouse Embryos. (Abstract) *American Zoologist*, 2:432.

———. 1964. Formation of Genetically Mosaic Mouse Embryos, and Early Development of "Lethal (t^{12}/t^{12})-Normal" Mosaics. *Journal of Experimental Zoology*, 157:273–291.

———. 1965. Genetic Mosaicism in Adult Mice of Quadriparental Lineage. *Science*, 148:1232–1233.

———. 1967a. Gene Control of Mammalian Pigmentary Differentiation. I. Clonal

Origin of Melanocytes. *Proceedings of the National Academy of Sciences of the U.S.A.*, 58:344–351.

———. 1967b. "Mammalian Embryo Culture," *Methods in Developmental Biology*, F. Wilt and N. Wessells, Eds. New York, New York: T. Y. Crowell Co. Pp. 379–400.

———. 1968. Hermaphroditism, Sex Chromosomal Mosaicism, and Germ Cell Selection in Allophenic Mice. *Journal of Animal Science*, 27: Supplement (for VIIIth (1967) Biennial Symposium on Animal Reproduction) 1:51–60.

———. 1969a. "Allophenic Mice of Multi-Embryo Origin," *Methods in Mammalian Embryology*, J. Daniel, Jr., Ed. San Francisco, California: W. H. Freeman Co. (in press.)

———. 1969b. "Developmental Mechanisms Found in Allophenic Mice with Sex Chromosomal and Pigmentary Mosaicism," *First Conference on the Clinical Delineation of Birth Defects* (Birth Defects Original Article Series), D. Bergsma and V. McKusick, Eds. New York, New York: National Foundation. Pp. 11–22.

———. Unpublished data.

Mintz, B., and A. J. Donnelly. 1969. Gene Control of Neoplasia. (in preparation.)

Mintz, B., D. Hungerford, and J. Morrow. 1969. Gene Control of Mammalian Sex Differentiation. (in preparation.)

Mintz, B., and J. Palm. 1965. Erythrocyte Mosaicism and Immunological Tolerance in Mice from Aggregated Eggs. (Abstract) *Journal of Cell Biology*, 27:66A.

———. 1969. Gene Control of Hematopoiesis. I. Erythrocyte Mosaicism and Permanent Immunological Tolerance in Allophenic Mice. *Journal of Experimental Medicine*, 129:1013–1027.

Mintz, B., and W. K. Silvers. 1967. "Intrinsic" Immunological Tolerance in Allophenic Mice. *Science*, 158:1484–1487.

Mintz, B., and G. Slemmer. 1969. Gene Control of Neoplasia. I. Genotypic Mosaicism in Normal and Preneoplastic Mammary Glands of Allophenic Mice. *Journal of the National Cancer Institute*, 43:87–95.

Monod, J., and F. Jacob. 1961. General Conclusions: Teleonomic Mechanisms in Cellular Metabolism, Growth, and Differentiation. *Cold Spring Harbor Symposia on Quantitative Biology*, 26:389–401.

Morton, D. L. 1969. Acquired Immunological Tolerance and Carcinogenesis by the Mammary Tumor Virus. I. Influence of Neonatal Infection with the Mammary Tumor Virus on the Growth of Spontaneous Mammary Adenocarcinomas. *Journal of the National Cancer Institute*, 42:311–320.

Morton, D. L., G. F. Miller, and D. A. Wood. 1969. Demonstration of Tumor-Specific Immunity Against Antigens Unrelated to the Mammary Tumor Virus in Spontaneous Mammary Adenocarcinomas. *Journal of the National Cancer Institute*, 42:289–301.

Mühlbock, O., and L. M. Boot. 1959. Induction of Mammary Cancer in Mice Without the Mammary Tumor Agent by Isografts of Hypophyses. *Cancer Research*, 19:402–412.

Nandi, S. 1967. "Host-Virus Interactions in the Mouse Mammary Tumor System," *Carcinogenesis: A Broad Critique* (The University of Texas M. D. Anderson Hospital and Tumor Institute, 20th Annual Symposium on Fundamental Cancer Research, 1966). Baltimore, Maryland: The Williams & Wilkins Co. Pp. 295–314.

Nandi, S., and H. A. Bern. 1960. Relation Between Mammary-Gland Responses to Lactogenic Hormone Combinations and Tumor Susceptibility in Various Strains of Mice. *Journal of the National Cancer Institute*, 24:907–931.

Nandi, S., M. Handin, A. Robinson, D. R. Pitelka, and L. E. Webber. 1966. Susceptibility of Mammary Tissues of "Genetically Resistant" Strains of Mice to Mammary
Tumor Virus. *Journal of the National Cancer Institute*, 36:783–801.

Old, L. J., and E. A. Boyse. 1965. Antigens of Tumors and Leukemias Induced by
Viruses. *Federation Proceedings*, 24:1009–1017.

Pitelka, D. R., H. A. Bern, S. Nandi, and K. B. DeOme. 1964. On the Significance of
Virus-Like Particles in Mammary Tissues of C3Hf Mice. *Journal of the National
Cancer Institute*, 33:867–885.

Prehn, R. T. 1953. Tumors and Hyperplastic Nodules in Transplanted Mammary
Glands. *Journal of the National Cancer Institute*, 13:859–871.

———. 1967. "Tumor Antigens," *Immunity, Cancer and Chemotherapy*. E. Mihich,
Ed. New York, New York, and London, England: Academic Press Inc. Pp. 265–279.

Rubin, H. 1965. Genetic Control of Cellular Susceptibility to Pseudotypes of Rous
Sarcoma Virus. *Virology*, 26:270–276.

Ruddle, F. H., T. B. Shows, and T. H. Roderick. 1968. Autosomal Control of an
Electrophoretic Variant of Glucose-6-Phosphate Dehydrogenase in the Mouse (*Mus
musculus*). *Genetics*, 58:599–606.

Schultz, J. 1952. The Place of Cytogenetics in Cancer Research, *Proceedings of the
Second National Cancer Conference* (American Cancer Society, Inc., National
Cancer Institute of the U.S. Public Health Service, and American Association for
Cancer Research). Vol. II. Pp. 1152–1161.

Weiler, E., and B. Mintz. Unpublished data.

Zinder, N. D., and J. Lederberg. 1952. Genetic Exchange in *Salmonella*. *Journal of
Bacteriology*, 64:679–699.

Discussion

Dr. John W. Littlefield, Massachusetts General Hospital, Boston, Massachusetts: Dr. Mintz, to what stage can you carry an embryo in culture?

Dr. Beatrice Mintz, The Institute for Cancer Research, Fox Chase, Philadelphia, Pennsylvania: Only to late blastocyst.

Dr. J. G. Kidd, Cornell University School of Medicine, New York, New York: Dr. Weiss, what happens when you put T-positive cells into animals and compare them with the T-negative cells?

Dr. Mary C. Weiss, Centre de Génétique Moléculaire, Gif-sur-Yvette, France: For two reasons, this is impossible: (1) mouse cell lines are not good tumor producers, and (2) they contain human chromosomes and they contain human surface antigens. Even if the mouse parent were highly tumorigenic, the probability of obtaining tumors in animals would be very low, and that of obtaining a significant comparison between T-antigen-positive and -negative cells would, I think, be very difficult.

Dr. Fred Rapp, Baylor College of Medicine, Houston, Texas: Dr. Weiss, do you believe that by hybridizing normal mouse cells and normal monkey cells, one could determine by chromosome loss whether any of the chromosomes were essential to the replication of the virus in that system, assuming that that hybrid were susceptible? Also in the saturation-density experiment which you described, it seems that SV40-transformed 3T3 cells should perhaps be hybridized to the SV40-transformed human cells. It may well be that the mere hybridization and perhaps the difference in cell membranes might give a different saturation density. Would this perhaps be a control for the experiments you reported?

Dr. Weiss: With respect to your second point, I agree that this is an important control that should be done. With respect to this first comment, I think something along this line is being done in Howard Green's laboratory. He is using hamster-mouse hybrids to study susceptibility to polyoma infection and transformation.

Barbara Hoffman, University of California, Davis, California: Dr. Weiss, are any experiments being done showing possible places for integration into human chromosomes of various viruses by using segregation after hybridization? In other words, if a hybrid is susceptible to something, perhaps virus attack, as certain chromosomes are lost, perhaps it is no longer susceptible. Would this allow you to map the location of susceptibility? Is this being done?

Dr. Weiss: There have been some attempts to do this. We have studied the susceptibility of human-mouse hybrids to poliovirus infection. Hybrids with 10 or 15 human chromosomes were not susceptible. Dr. Green has made other hybrids which have more human chromosomes, and some of these are susceptible. But if you remember from the histograms that I showed, the hybrid cells are highly variable in human chromosome composition, and this appears again fairly quickly after cloning. A selective marker is needed to assign linkage groups with accuracy.

Dr. Donald Ruchnagel, University of Michigan Medical School, Ann Arbor, Michigan: Dr. Mintz, Dr. Hirschhorn reminded us that absence of the radius in children with Fanconi's anemia is a common congenital malformation. Another interesting abnormality is a high level of fetal hemoglobin. Since these children usually have anemia, one cannot say whether the elevated level of fetal hemoglobin is secondary to the anemia. We have studied a family with three sisters, one of whom has Fanconi's anemia with pancytopenia; of the other two, one has only thrombocytopenia and the other has neutropenia. Neither of the latter two children have anemia. All three of the children have high fetal hemoglobins of approximately 10 per cent HbF. The implication is that the syndrome is just developing in the latter two children, *i.e.*, the events preceding the development of anemia in the Fanconi syndrome are occurring. However, to me this implies that the high fetal hemoglobin level is simply another congenital abnormality. Dr. Weinstein mentioned the immunoglobulin synthesized by hepatomas, and now you bring up the problem of differentiation and selection in tumorigenesis. Is it possible that what we have is fetal cells which are more sensitive to tumor oncogenesis, and then selection operating to favor this kind of cell?

Dr. Mintz: I have no information on fetal versus adult cells here. The investigation of other normally developing systems in allophenic mice has led us to the hypothesis that phenotypic heterogeneity among cells of a given type may be universal in development. That statement would apply to normal liver and normal mammary gland cells as well as to other types of normal cells. If there are different clonal phenotypes in a normal tissue, the possibility for selection among them is automatically present. This may indeed become a particularly significant factor in tumor etiology.

Dr. Arthur Cole, The University of Texas M. D. Anderson Hospital and Tumor Institute at Houston, Houston, Texas: The lymphoma patterns in the C3H and the C57BL/6 mice vary significantly. Have the lymphomas or reticulum cell tumors in these mosaics been studied? If so, which of the parent types do they resemble?

Dr. Mintz: We have obtained many reticulum cell sarcomas and lymphomas from these animals but the genetic analyses are incomplete. We don't have the answer yet.

Dr. I. Bernard Weinstein, Columbia University College of Physicians and Surgeons, New York, New York: Dr. Mintz, you emphasized the likelihood that exogenous carcinogen plus genetic susceptibility is required. Is it also possible that the exogenous carcinogen operates in clonal selection, since you observed predominance of C3H cells in the mammary gland? Is that a function of whether mice were foster-nursed on mothers which contained mammary agents? Can one force the clonal selection to go in various directions by known carcinogens?

Dr. Mintz: In this particular case, the answer was no; the relative extent to which C3H cells predominated in normal mammary tissue was the same in the two experimental groups, despite their differences in tumor incidence and viral status. As for the forcing situation you suggest, that is indeed a possible approach.

Dr. M. J. Markham, Montefiore Hospital, Bronx, New York: Dr. Mintz, I would like to ask about a different aspect of phenotypic expression. The C3H strain of mice has larger quantities of estrogen to maintain a normal estrus cycle as compared to other strains. But the breast tissue of most strains is equally susceptible to the effects of the estrogen. It seems that it would be important to know something about the hormonal constitution of the mosaics that you obtained and the variations in their endocrine constitutions in order to make further comment on this phenotypic expression.

Dr. Mintz: I quite agree. Hormone dependence of these tumors is well known and is very important. We have not directly examined hormone levels. I believe it is doubtful that our results turned critically on the hormonal picture, and perhaps I can give you a rather dramatic example of why I think so. Among our animals, we have found some XX $\longleftrightarrow$ XY mosaics. For example, in one mouse known to have both XX and XY cells, the mammary tissue was less active than usual for a female, but the growth pattern was characteristic of the female. Mammary tumors occurred in the allophenic females at virtually 100 per cent of maximal expectation, in comparison with the high-tumor controls, despite the presence of male (XY) cells in some of these allophenics. One would expect that the XY cells may have diminished estrogen production in some cases, yet tumor incidence was very high.

Dr. A. A. Saadi, University of Michigan School of Medicine, Ann Arbor, Michigan: Dr. Weiss, did you find any selection for or against any specific group or number of human chromosomes?

Dr. Weiss: We have no real evidence on that, but as far as we can tell, no. Some of the chromosomes are difficult to identify. For example, we see group D chromosomes only rarely. This may be because we fail to identify them, or they may be lost preferentially.

Dr. Saadi: Just because they look like mouse chromosomes?

Dr. Weiss: Yes. Among the others, those most commonly retained are the small, relatively metacentric chromosomes such as those of groups C, E, and F, and sometimes A.

Dr. Saadi: It seems difficult to assume that you are losing human chromosomes or to assume that you have recombinations of two acrocentric mouse chromosomes forming the metacentric chromosome similar to the human one. Do you have any evidence that these are not human chromosomes?

Dr. Weiss: Most mouse chromosomes are telocentric. Some of our permanent lines have some metacentric chromosomes. The human chromosomes are almost entirely metacentric and submetacentric; those are the ones which are lost. If the mechanisms which you propose were operative, then we would appear to have more human chromosomes than are really there.

Repair of Genetic Defects

Enhancement of Tumor Response to X Ray and Alkylating Agents by the Excision Repair Inhibitors, Caffeine and Chloroquine

K. L. YIELDING AND DAVID GAUDIN

Laboratory of Molecular Biology, University of Alabama in Birmingham, The Medical Center, Birmingham, Alabama

The capacity to excise and repair various types of damage to deoxyribonucleic acid (DNA) is probably a general property of living cells. This is of considerable pertinence to the problem of cancer because it provides a mechanism by which the rate of genetic damage induced by a variety of agents may be modified. Thus, the rate of mutation resulting from environmental insults depends not only on the frequency and severity of these insults, but also on the capacity of the host to repair them. It is also possible that some environmental carcinogens (or co-carcinogens) may act by modifying this mechanism so that otherwise ineffective insults may result in permanent damage. The recent report (Cleaver, 1968) that fibroblasts cultured from the skin of patients with xeroderma pigmentosum do not have excision repair capabilities may well account for the extraordinary sensitivity of these individuals to the carcinogenic effects of sunlight. This finding also emphasizes the general importance of the repair system to cancer.

Cancer therapy in many instances is aimed at producing severe damage to the DNA of the neoplastic cell. We have become interested, therefore, in a possible role for the excision-repair process in determining the responsiveness of a tumor cell to such damaging agents, and in particular, whether development of tumor resistance might be accounted for by an increased capacity to effect repair. Thus, with such a mechanism, even if an agent were penetrating a cell and producing damage in the expected manner, its biological effects might be minimized by the repair enzymes.

If this is the case, it should be possible to increase the effectiveness of such treatment by inhibiting the excision repair system. Both alkylating agents and X rays produce repairable lesions in DNA. Tumors often show cross-resistance to both types of agents. Accordingly, we have chosen to explore a possible role of excision repair in determining the effectiveness of these two types of cancer treatment by using drugs to inhibit the repair enzymes.

We have conducted experiments with a transplantable hamster plasmacytoma furnished by Dr. Glynn Wheeler of the Southern Research Institute, Birmingham, Alabama. The plasmacytoma had been shown to be highly resistant to both alkylating agents and X rays (Wheeler and Alexander, 1964). We have employed caffeine, which previously was reported to inhibit excision repair in bacteria and in mammalian cells (Rauth, 1967), and chloroquine, a 4-aminoquinoline antimalarial compound, which we have found to be an effective repair inhibitor in *Escherichia coli* at concentrations around 1×10^{-4} M.

Methods

Subcutaneous implantations of plasmacytoma were made into groups of hamsters. At about 12 to 14 days, when the transplants were easily palpable and growing rapidly, appropriate treatment schedules were started. Chloroquine was administered as a single daily intraperitoneal injection of 29 mg/kg body weight and caffeine was given as a 1 per cent solution in the drinking water. Cytoxan injections were made intraperitoneally using drug doses of 25 mg/kg. For X-irradiation, the animals were anesthetized with ether. A skin flap containing the tumor was pulled well out from the animal and the X-ray cone was placed directly over the tumor mass to minimize radiation to the animal. The progress of tumor growth was followed by direct measurements of tumor size.

Result

EFFECTS OF CHLOROQUINE AND CAFFEINE ON THE RESPONSE OF PLASMACYTOMA 'RESISTANT' TO ALKYLATING AGENTS

Figure 1 illustrates an experiment with the resistant tumor in which Cytoxan was administered with and without treatment of the animals with chloroquine or caffeine. With Cytoxan alone (curve A), there was no significant response of the tumors, indicating their characteristic resistance to alkylating agents. Cytoxan treatment in conjunction with the repair inhibitors resulted in substantial tumor regression (curve B: chloroquine + Cytoxan; curve C: caffeine + Cytoxan). Administration of the repair inhibitors alone failed to produce this response. Similar experiments with nitrogen mustard treatment of plasmacytoma and with phenylalanine mustard treatment of a transplantable hamster melanoma showed the same enhancing effects of caffeine and chloroquine.

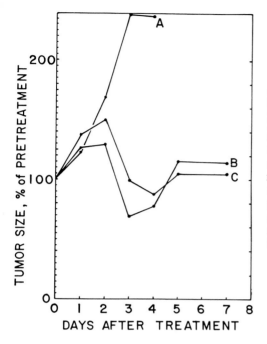

FIGURE 1. The effect of single large doses of Cytoxan in conjunction with caffeine and chloroquine on growth of Cytoxan-resistant plasmacytomas. a—Cytoxan alone, 25 mg/kg. b—Cytoxan plus chloroquine, 29 mg/kg. c—Cytoxan plus caffeine, 1 per cent in drinking water. Each point represents the average size of six tumors within that group.

EFFECTS OF CHLOROQUINE AND CAFFEINE ON THE RESPONSE OF TUMOR 'RESISTANT' TO X RAY

Because of the cross-resistance to alkylating agents and X ray and because both types of agents produce lesions in DNA which appear to share a common repair mechanism, the repair inhibitors were also tested for their effects on the X-ray response of tumors. Figure 2 presents the results of a set of such experiments with the "resistant" plasmacytoma. Curve A shows the characteristic lack of tumor response to X ray alone, while curve B, illustrating animals treated with caffeine, and curve C, for animals receiving both chloroquine and caffeine, reveal that tumor regression resulted from X ray in conjunction with the repair inhibitors.

Preliminary experiments have also been done with transplantable melanoma employing the repair inhibitors with X ray. There was considerable enhancement of X ray effect following administration of chloroquine and caffeine.

Discussion

The results of these preliminary experiments, showing that drugs

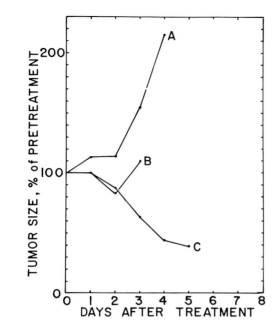

FIGURE 2. The effect of repair inhibitors when used in conjunction with X-ray treatment (800 r). *a*—X ray alone. *b*—X rays plus caffeine (1 per cent in drinking water). *c*—X rays plus both caffeine and chloroquine (29 mg/kg).

capable of inhibiting repair increased tumor sensitivity to alkylation and X ray, suggest that specific modification of the repair process may prove useful in enhancing the response of neoplasms to specific therapy. Although the present experiments do not definitely establish that the observed enhanced therapeutic response resulted from inhibition of excision repair, the implication is clear and warrants further exploration. Based on our experiments with two resistant tumor lines, we suggest that an active excision-repair mechanism could account for the resistance of some neoplasms to alkylating agents and X ray. We propose, therefore, that study of repair inhibitors may prove fruitful in developing effective adjuncts to cancer therapy. This may be accomplished by agents which act directly to inhibit repair, or by agents which modify the cell cycle in such a manner as to minimize the opportunity for repair in the interval between DNA damage and DNA replication. Both approaches are under study in our laboratories.

ADDENDUM

In addition to the experiments reported above, we have also found evidence that the dose response of a Cytoxan-sensitive plasmacytoma is also enhanced by the concomitant administration of caffeine or chloroquine to the tumor-bearing hamster. The question of whether normal tissues are also more sensitive to Cytoxan is, of course, a critical issue. In preliminary experiments, it was observed that chloroquine did not increase the extent to which Cytoxan at a dose of 40 mg/kg depressed the peripheral white cell count in mice, suggesting that the chloroquine-sensitive process is less critical in bone marrow than in the tumor.

ACKNOWLEDGMENT

This work was supported by a grant from the American Cancer Society.

REFERENCES

Cleaver, J. E.   1968.   Defective Repair Replication of DNA in Xeroderma Pigmentosum. *Nature*, 218:652–656.

Rauth, A. M.   1967.   Evidence for Dark-Reactivation of Ultraviolet Light Damage in Mouse L Cells. *Radiation Research*, 31:121–138.

Wheeler, G. P., and J. A. Alexander.   1964.   Studies with Mustards. V. In Vivo Fixation of C^{14} of Labeled Alkylating Agents by Bilaterally Grown Sensitive and Resistant Tumors. *Cancer Research*, 24:1331–1337.

Repair Replication of Damaged DNA In Vivo

PHILIP C. HANAWALT

Department of Biological Sciences and Biophysics Program, Stanford University, Palo Alto, California

In the course of evolution, living systems have developed a variety of mechanisms for dealing with potentially lethal damage in their genetic material. Some of these mechanisms involve the substitution of functional genetic substance for damaged sections of the genome by the process of genetic recombination. This type of repair is often fortuitous, however, and may not occur in direct response to the presence of a lesion in deoxyribonucleic acid (DNA). For the specific case of ultraviolet light (UV)-induced damage to DNA, there exists a photoreactivating enzyme in many cell types. However, this enzyme is very specific for the reversal of pyrimidine dimers in DNA and it does not appear to operate upon any other type of damage. The most versatile and ubiquitous of the presently known repair mechanisms is the excision-repair scheme.

Although genetic evidence for the presence of dark repair mechanisms for ultraviolet damage to DNA had been accumulating for a long time, it was not until recently that the actual nature of the excision-repair process became understood. This enlightenment began with the studies of Setlow and Carrier (1964) and of Boyce and Howard-Flanders (1964) who discovered that UV-induced thymine dimers were preferentially released from the DNA of certain UV-resistant strains of bacteria. These workers postulated that this might represent an early step in a repair process that involved the excision of damaged regions from one strand of DNA and the subsequent reconstruction of these regions with normal nucleotides, utilizing the complementary base-pairing information in the intact strand. This original interpretation has now been confirmed through the application of several additional approaches. One of these is the direct measurement of repair replication of DNA in vivo, as we will consider in detail and as first demonstrated by Pettijohn and Hanawalt (1963, 1964). Another is the demonstration that breaks appear in parental DNA strands shortly after the UV-irradiation of bacteria, and that these breaks are subsequently repaired during continued growth (Setlow,

1968). Many of the enzymic activities predicted for the steps in the excision-repair process have now been demonstrated in the extracts of cells. We will refer to some of these studies in the present discussion; however, for a more comprehensive account of the current understanding of DNA repair processes, the reader is referred to several review articles (Hanawalt, 1968; Haynes, Baker, and Jones, 1968; Howard-Flanders, 1968; Setlow, 1968; Strauss, 1968).

Repair replication of damaged DNA has now been observed in a variety of cell types, from the simplest living cells, the mycoplasmas, to complex eukaryotic cells such as the protozoans and even mammalian cells. This mode of replication has also been shown to occur in cells after a variety of treatments that lead to structural damage to DNA. A low level of repair replication or "turnover" is even seen in the DNA of cells that have not been intentionally mistreated. It is likely that the repair replication of DNA has an important general significance in the maintenance of genetic stability in all types of cells and that it may account for the ubiquity of double-stranded DNA in living systems.

Steps in the Excision-Repair Process

The postulated sequence of steps in the excision-repair scheme is illustrated in Figure 1. The process must beg'n with the recognition of the damage in the DNA. An alteration such as a UV-induced pyrimidine dimer distorts the phosphodiester backbone of the DNA since the interchain hydrogen bonds are broken in that region. However, a simple mispairing of bases (*i.e.*, transition mutation) may not result in sufficient distortion of the structure to activate the repair system. Although the photoreactivating enzyme has been shown to specifically recognize pyrimidine dimers in the DNA and to bind to DNA containing dimers, there are no indications that this enzyme is concerned with the recognition step in the excision-repair process and it may, in fact, operate in competition with the latter process. It is quite possible that the same enzyme that recognizes the altered DNA is also responsible for the first incision in the damaged strand. An endonuclease activity that appears to be specific for UV-damaged DNA has been isolated and partially purified from *Micrococcus lysodeikticus* (Nakayama, Okubo, Sekiguchi, and Takagi, 1967; Miller, Dolbeare, Mahler, and Grossman, 1967). In less purified extracts, Carrier and Setlow (1966) have observed the excision of dimers as well. The processes of incision and excision appear to be dependent upon the presence of an energy source in intact bacterial systems, and this is also true for the repair replication step. There would seem to be some additional degradation of the DNA beyond the immediate region of the damage. Such degradation has made it difficult to obtain reliable estimates for the size of the repair region. It is evident that extensive degradation in a few severely damaged cells would weight such an estimate to the high side and that the reincorporation of some of the released nucleotides would lead to an underestimate. The situation is further complicated in that, following inhibition of DNA synthesis in bacteria by UV, there is a selective degradation of the newly replicated, growing-point region in the DNA that is probably not related to the repair process (Hanawalt and Brempelis, 1967).

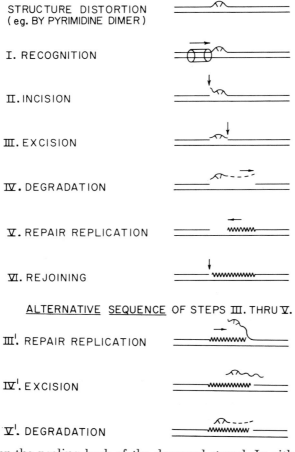

STRUCTURE DISTORTION
(eg. BY PYRIMIDINE DIMER)

I. RECOGNITION

II. INCISION

III. EXCISION

IV. DEGRADATION

V. REPAIR REPLICATION

VI. REJOINING

ALTERNATIVE SEQUENCE OF STEPS III. THRU V.

III'. REPAIR REPLICATION

IV'. EXCISION

V'. DEGRADATION

FIGURE 1. Diagrammatic representation of the p o s t u l a t e d sequence of e n z y m i c steps in the excision-repair of d a m a g e d DNA. The p r o c e s s must begin with the detection of some alteration in the secondary structure of the double-stranded DNA molecule. Steps II through VI have all been demonstrated individually as enzymic activities in the extracts from various bacterial strains. However, the complete sequence of steps has not been reconstituted in vitro. It is quite likely, as shown in alternative steps III′ through V′, that the repair replication begins as soon as the single strand incision has been made, with the concurrent release of damaged nucleotides or the peeling back of the damaged strand. In either model, the final step must involve the rejoining of the repaired section to the contiguous DNA of the original parental strand.

The repair replication step has been termed nonconservative DNA replication since parental material is replaced without net increase in the amount of DNA. It is also semiconservative in the sense that the undamaged parental strand opposite the repaired region is conserved. The repair replication might not begin until the excision has been completed, or, alternatively, the repair step might begin as soon as the incision is made, and the damaged strand could be peeled back and cut off later. The latter model is attractive because the repair could be accomplished by an enzyme complex that always moves in the same direction along the DNA, and because it does not leave exposed lengths of single-stranded DNA. In bacterial systems, the released nucleotides are found as tri- and tetra-nucleotides although exonuclease digestion of larger segments may be responsible for this product. Kelly, Cozzarelli, and Kornberg (1969) have reported that their purified preparation of the DNA polymerase from *Escherichia coli* performs a gap-translation effect in double-stranded DNA in which a 5' exonuclease activity sequentially releases nucleotides from a strand at the site of a single strand nick as the polymerase activity adds nucleotides to the 3' hydroxyl end at the nick. Furthermore, a pyrimidine dimer in the path of the advancing enzyme (or enzymes) is released as a trinucleotide. Thus, the DNA polymerase with associated exonuclease is a very likely candidate for the combined excision and repair replication steps and this would be strong evidence for the alternative model shown in Figure 1.

The final step in the repair process is the rejoining of the repaired segment to the contiguous parental DNA strand, and the likely candidate for this step is the polynucleotide ligase recently isolated and characterized in several laboratories (see Gellert, Little, Oshinsky, and Zimmerman, 1970, pages 548–554, this volume). This enzyme joins abutting ends of DNA strands at a single strand break in a double-stranded DNA, if no nucleotides are missing and if the ends are, respectively, 3' hydroxyl and 5' phosphate. This final step then restores the DNA to its functional integrity.

Experimental Detection of Repair Replication

The method for demonstrating repair replication is essentially that of Meselson and Stahl (1958) as first used to prove the normal semiconservative mode of DNA replication. A density label is used to follow the synthesis of new DNA. In the normal semiconservative mode of replication, a very short period of such labeling results in the production of "hybrid" DNA fragments that contain the parental strand hydrogen-

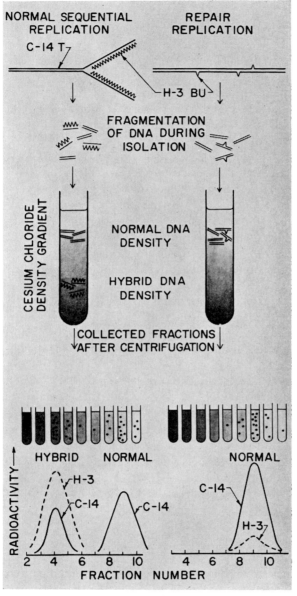

FIGURE 2. The basic protocol for the demonstration of normal repplication and repair replication of DNA in growing cells. The DNA is first radioactively labeled (*e.g.* by the incorporation of ^{14}C-labeled thymine as a specific precursor for DNA). After several generations of this prelabeling, the cells are washed to remove the unincorporated ^{14}C and they are then transferred to a new growth medium that contains both a radioactive label (*e.g.* [3]H) and also a density label (*e.g.* 5-BU to replace thymine) so that the newly synthesized DNA can be identified in the subsequent equilibrium sedimentation in a CsCl gradient. The large DNA molecules are fragmented by shearing forces during the process of isolation from the cells. Some of these fragments may contain only the parental ^{14}C label. Others that have replicated in the presence of the density label will contain both ^{14}C and ^{3}H, and the density label will have the effect of increasing the density of these fragments to the position in the gradient called "hybrid." (Such fragments contain roughly as much thymine as 5-BU.) After another

(*Continued on page 533*)

bonded to the complementary daughter strand. The unreplicated parental DNA fragments can be physically separated from these hybrid fragments by their different bouyant densities in an equilibrium density gradient of cesium chloride. For the case of repair replication, the newly synthesized regions of DNA are very short relative to the size of the fragments of DNA that are recovered from such a gradient. Thus, in general, these fragments will contain too little density label to appreciably shift the density from that of the unreplicated parental DNA. The combination of a radioactive label with the density label is useful for improving the resolution of the procedure in subsequent analysis. A useful density label is the thymine-analogue 5-bromouracil (5-BU), which, when incorporated into one strand of an *E. coli* DNA molecule, shifts the density in cesium chloride from 1.71 to 1.75 g/cc. (At considerably greater expense, a similar density shift can be achieved through the combined use of ^{13}C, ^{15}N, and ^{2}H as density labels.)

The procedure for observing repair replication is outlined in Figure 2 and the protocol is described in the figure legend essentially as in the experiments of Pettijohn and Hanawalt (1963, 1964) in which this non-conservative mode was first observed in *E. coli* strain TAU-bar. In those studies, a number of control experiments confirmed that the 5-BU label had been incorporated into parental DNA strands. Acid hydrolysis of the isolated DNA and subsequent paper chromatography of the products showed that the radioactive label was still in 5-BU and, thus, that the DNA appearing at the normal density position contained 5-BU. Extensive shearing of the DNA by sonication did not change the density distribution of DNA fragments in the gradient; this showed that the 5-BU was in very short segments of large molecules. Thermal denaturation of the DNA prior to gradient analysis indicated that the short 5-BU-containing segments were covalently joined to contiguous parental DNA strands.

As an indication that this phenomenon was related to a repair process, it was shown that bacteria that were illuminated with visible light

---

(Continued from page 532)

generation of growth, some fragments with 5-BU in both strands would be expected and these would appear at a still denser position called "heavy." Parental DNA fragments that contain short regions of repair should differ little in density from those that contain no 5-BU. Thus, repair would be indicated by the appearance of ^{3}H label near the normal density position in the gradient. The presence of ^{14}C and ^{3}H in the same sample from the centrifuge tube can be assayed at the same time in the scintillation counter, which distinguishes the two on the basis of the different energies of their emitted radiation. (Adapted from Hanawalt and Haynes, 1967.)

(to facilitate photoreactivation after the UV-irradiation) performed a reduced amount of this nonconservative mode of replication. This result was as expected if photoreactivation had split the pyrimidine dimers in situ, thus obviating the need for excision and repair (Pettijohn and Hanawalt, 1964). A thymine-requiring derivative of the UV-sensitive *E. coli* B_{s-1} that could not excise thymine dimers (Setlow and Carrier, 1964) was shown not to perform repair replication after UV-irradiation (Hanawalt and Pettijohn, 1965).

However, a serious objection remained to the unambiguous interpretation of the observed pattern of 5-BU incorporation as repair replication. Since the UV-irradiated cells were known to contain degradation products of DNA, there existed the problem that the released thymidine could be reincorporated in competition with the 5-BU in the normal mode of replication. If sufficient thymidine were present, this could result in the appearance of DNA fragments with the observed physical properties. Hybrid DNA fragments would be produced that contained thymine in the parental strand, but a mixture of thymine and 5-BU in the daughter strand. The problem was especially serious because of the known preference of bacteria for thymine over 5-BU when both are present in the growth medium (Hackett and Hanawalt, 1966). A subsequent detailed analysis of the incorporation of 5-BU by the normal and repair modes has shown that the repair system exhibits an even greater selectivity for thymine over the analogue than does the normal replication mode (Kanner and Hanawalt, 1968). These studies and others to be described below also rule out the explanation of "repair replication" as an artifact caused by an intracellular pool of thymidine.

It was important to demonstrate that the DNA fragments that had incorporated 5-BU by the nonconservative mode were then capable of normal replication. After heavy UV doses, it was seen that prolonged incubation of the bacterial cultures in 5-BU medium led to broad bands of intermediate density DNA (between normal and hybrid densities), presumably because of the presence of the large pools of thymidine degradation products. The complication of continuing normal synthesis could be eliminated, however, by subjecting the cultures to a preliminary period of protein-synthesis inhibition. This procedure results in the eventual termination of DNA replication (Maaløe and Hanawalt, 1961) at a unique point on the bacterial chromosome (Lark, Repko, and Hoffman, 1963). A culture of *E. coli* strain TAU-bar was starved for four required amino acids for 90 minutes, by which time DNA synthesis had ceased. UV-irradiation of this culture was found to stimulate the nonconservative mode of DNA replication (Hanawalt, 1967). Thus, the repair system enzymes must have been present in the cells already and their synthesis had not been induced by the presence of the damage in DNA. The culture was allowed to incorporate radioactively labeled 5-BU for 20 minutes still in the absence of the amino acids. No label appeared at the hybrid density position. When the culture was then transferred to fresh growth medium containing nonradioactive 5-BU and the amino acids, the normal replication mode resumed and a hybrid band appeared. The radioactive 5-BU label was transferred to the hybrid density position at the same rate as the prelabel in the parental DNA. Thus, the repaired DNA was shown to be capable of normal replication and there was evidently no selection against the replication of the repaired DNA in the subsequent pattern of replication (Hanawalt, 1967).

The normal semiconservative mode of replication can also be suppressed selectively in certain temperature-sensitive DNA replication-deficient mutants of bacterial strains $E.$ $coli$ TAU-bar and CR 34. Under incubation conditions at the restrictive temperature, the nonconservative repair mode of replication is stimulated by UV-irradiation. In fact, the amount of repair replication was found to be similar at the normal growth temperature as compared to that at the restrictive temperature (42 C) after a UV dose that led to a 2.5 per cent survival of colony-forming ability (Couch and Hanawalt, 1967). Thus, the repair mode of replication can be activated in the absence of normal sequential replication of the bacterial chromosome.

So far, all of the examples we have described have made use of 5-BU as the density label for indicating repair. Yet it is well known that 5-BU is pathogenic for bacteria and one might worry that the observed phenomena are related to the deleterious effects of 5-BU itself. This criticism can be answered by the use of density labels that are not deleterious to the cells. Repair replication after UV-irradiation of bacteria was measured by Billen, Hewitt, Lapthisophon, and Achey (1967) through the use of ^{13}C-glucose, ^{15}N (as NH_4Cl) and ^2H (as H_2O) as combined density labels. Hanawalt et $al.$ (1969) have also measured repair through the use of combined ^{15}N and ^2H as density labels. It was of special interest that one of the strains tested was $E.$ $coli$ JC 1553 which had been shown to be deficient in the process of genetic recombination (Clark and Margulies, 1965). The amount of repair measured in the mutant after a given UV dose was similar to that seen in the parental strain (JC 411). Thus, the genetic deficiency in the recombination-deficient strain was not part of the excision-repair sequence, at least through the step of repair replication. More recent evidence has indicated that these recombination-deficient and UV-sensitive strains are unable to perform another type of dark repair process, one that involves genetic recombination and that is distinct from the excision-repair scheme.

It has been possible to compare the amount of repair for a given UV dose and time of incubation using either thymine or labeled 5-BU in the temperature-sensitive DNA replication-deficient bacterial mutants at the restrictive temperature. The same amount of UV-stimulated DNA replication was observed whether thymine or 5-BU was being incorporated. Thus, we conclude that 5-BU incorporation into DNA can be taken as a reasonable quantitative measure of repair replication in the *E. coli* system.

The extent of repair as a function of dose and of time has been more difficult to study. An early approach to this problem by Hanawalt and Haynes (as quoted in Haynes, Baker, and Jones, 1968) involved the measurement of the amount of repair replication by 30 minutes after different UV doses to bacterial cultures that had been starved for required amino acids to block normal DNA replication. The amount of repair quickly rose to a plateau (at a dose of 750 ergs/mm^2, 2537 A) but then declined at higher doses. Both ^{32}P- and ^{3}H-labeled 5-BU were used simultaneously to measure repair—hopefully to assess the problem of competing nucleotide pools; (*i.e.* one would expect a different pattern of relative labeling of repaired DNA segments with 5-BU and with inorganic phosphate as the amount of competing degradation products was varied by changing the UV dose). The ^{32}P and ^{3}H labels indicated equivalent dose-response effects for repair. The decline at higher doses could have been caused by the saturation of the repair system or possibly by the inactivation of the repair system. However, a more serious complication is that the actual amount of repair after a given dose appears to be less under amino acid starvation conditions than under normal growth conditions. Thus, any meaningful quantitative measurement of the extent of repair should be carried out on exponentially growing cultures of cells. Billen (1968) has studied both the time course of repair and the dose-response relationship for repair using the ^{13}C, ^{15}N, ^{2}H labeling system, and his results are in agreement with those of Couch and Hanawalt (1967).

Thus far, we have been considering only the repair replication of DNA that has not yet replicated again by the normal mode. It is possible, after low UV doses, to examine the relative amount of repair replication in parental DNA strands both ahead of and behind the normal growing point. The method is outlined in the schematic illustration of the bacterial chromosome in Figure 3. If one allows growth for a prolonged time after the irradiation, then it is possible to isolate the hybrid DNA and subject it to a second CsCl gradient banding, but under alkaline conditions so that the strands will be separated. Then the amount of label in the parental strands that have replicated normally can be assessed. This method has the advantage that one is looking at DNA that is functional with respect to normal replication. Presumably the repair process has been completed in such strands, so this should be the optimum method for the determination of a dose-response curve for the repair process.

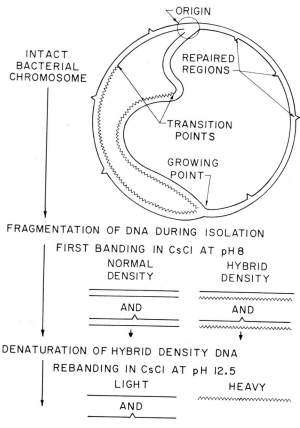

FIGURE 3. Schematic representation of the replicating bacterial chromosome, illustrating the different major classes of DNA fragments expected upon isolation of the DNA in a CsCl density gradient. It is assumed that the thymine analogue 5-BU was substituted for thymine in the culture medium at the time that the growing point was at the "transition points." The strands containing 5-BU instead of thymine are indicated, as in Figure 2, by the wavy lines. Some short repaired regions are indicated in parental DNA strands both ahead of and behind the normal growing point. The first banding in a neutral CsCl gradient permits the physical separation of the normally replicated and unreplicated DNA fragments. Repair ahead of the growing point is indicated by 5-BU label in the normal density band. The rebanding of the hybrid density DNA fragments in an alkaline CsCl density gradient separates the parental and daughter strands and facilitates the determination of the amount of repair in regions of the chromosome behind the normal growing point. This method has the advantage that one is always looking at DNA that is functionally normal with respect to normal replication. Presumably these DNA fragments have been replicated normally after being repaired, although it is also possible that some repair has occurred after the replication of damaged segments.

Repair Replication in Different Systems

Although repair replication was first seen in bacterial systems, and most of our understanding of the process still derives from the study of these systems, it has also been shown in a number of other systems. Table 1 summarizes the systems and conditions under which repair replication has been observed. Of particular interest was the demonstration of repair replication in the simplest living cells, the mycoplasmas (Smith and Hanawalt, 1969). An example of the determination of repair in *Mycoplasma laidlawii* B is given in Figure 4. For a UV dose of 85 ergs/mm² yielding a 70 per cent survival level, the kinetics for repair replication appeared to be linear to apparent saturation after about half a generation period. The repair amounted to a 1.2 per cent replacement of the chromosome and this permitted a rough estimate to be made of the size of the repair region. The 80 to 150 nucleotide repair regions would not be expected to shift appreciably the densities of the high molecular weight fragments of DNA in the CsCl gradients, as illustrated in Figure 4. The same amount of repair was seen in parental strands ahead of and behind the normal growing point in the chromosome. As with *E. coli*, visible light illumination after UV irradiation was shown to reduce the amount of subsequent repair replication.

TABLE 1. *Repair Replication of DNA as Assayed by the Density Labeling Method*

Organism	Treatment	Density label	Reference
E. coli TAU-bar	UV	5-BU	Pettijohn and Hanawalt, 1964
E. coli TAU-bar	HN2	5-BU	Hanawalt and Haynes, 1965
E. coli TAU-bar	Thymine starvation	5-BU	Pauling and Hanawalt, 1965
E. coli TAU-bar	Nitrosoguanidine	5-BU	Cerdá-Olmedo and Hanawalt, 1967
E. coli B/r	UV, X rays	^{13}C-^{15}N-D$_2$O	Billen, Hewitt, Lapthisophon, and Achey, 1967
E. coli JC 1553 rec⁻	UV	^{15}N-D$_2$O	Hanawalt *et al.*, 1969
E. coli CR 34/43 T$_s$DNA	UV	5-BU	Couch and Hanawalt, 1967
Mycoplasma laidlawii B	UV	5-BU	Smith and Hanawalt, 1969
Tetrahymena pyriformis	UV	5-BU	Brunk and Hanawalt, 1967
HeLa cells	UV	5-BU	Rasmussen and Painter, 1966
HeLa cells	X rays	5-BU	Painter and Cleaver, 1967
Normal human skin fibroblasts	UV	5-BU	Cleaver, 1968

Abbreviations: 5-BU, 5-bromouracil; HN2, nitrogen mustard; UV, ultraviolet light.

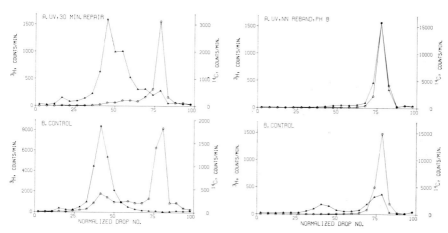

FIGURE 4. Demonstration of repair replication in *M. laidlawii* B, one of the simplest types of living cells. The DNA was prelabeled with ¹⁴C-thymidine. Then the culture was incubated in medium containing nonradioactive 5-BU for a short period so that thymidine pools would be exhausted and so that the "transition point" fragments of DNA would contain only the ¹⁴C label. The culture was split into equal portions and one of these received a UV dose of 85 ergs/mm² from a germicidal UV lamp. (This dose leads to a survival level of about 70 per cent by the assay of colony-forming units.) Both control and irradiated portions of the culture were then incubated for 30 minutes in the presence of ³H-labeled 5-bromodeoxyuridine (BUdR). The DNA was extracted and the density distribution of the fragments was examined by equilibrium sedimentation in CsCl as illustrated. Note the relative amount of hybrid DNA that has been synthesized by control and by irradiated cultures. The hybrid band is on the left. The ¹⁴C label is indicated by the circles and the ³H label by the triangles in these computer-drawn plots of the data. The tail from the hybrid band into the region of the normal density band makes it difficult to quantitatively assess the amount of repair. A rebanding of the normal density region of the gradient in a second neutral CsCl gradient, as shown on the right, eliminates this problem. Note that some "repair" is evident in parental DNA from the unirradiated control culture. (From Smith and Hanawalt, 1969.)

    The discovery of the v-gene in T4 phage indicated that even phage systems of the complexity of the T-even type also carried the genetic information for dark repair of their damaged DNA. Setlow (1968) showed that the v-gene was responsible for the excision of UV-induced pyrimidine dimers from the phage DNA. The demonstration of repair replication in this system has been complicated by the extensive genetic recombination that also occurs in the phage-infected cell. Tiny pieces of 5-BU-containing daughter DNA strands appear in parental DNA fragments by

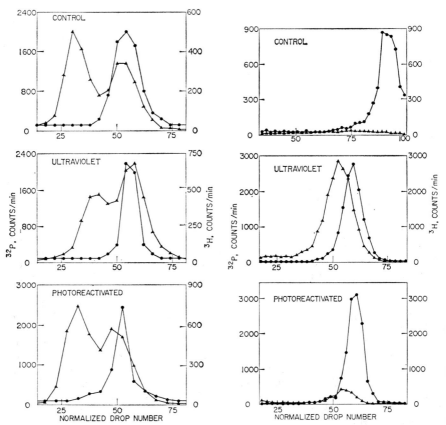

FIGURE 5. Demonstration of repair replication in *Tetrahymena pyriformis*, a eukaryotic cell type. Cultures of this protozoan were grown for several generations in medium containing ³H-labeled thymidine to prelabel the DNA. Portions of the culture were irradiated with a UV dose of about 250 ergs/mm² which causes little detectable loss in viable cells. One irradiated portion was also exposed to visible light to facilitate the photoreactivation of the pyrimidine dimers produced by the UV. Then ³²P (as inorganic phosphate) and 5-bromodeoxyuridine (BUdR) were added to all three cultures. After more than one generation of growth, the cells were harvested by centrifugation and the isolated DNA was examined in CsCl gradients. The ³H prelabel is indicated by the circles and the ³²P label by the triangles in these computer drawn plots. The plots on the left are the result of the first banding in neutral CsCl. The bands on the right in these gradients represent the hybrid DNA; all of the original parental DNA has replicated at least once, so there is no band corresponding to unreplicated parental DNA. The bands on the left represent twice-replicated DNA that contains only the ³²P label.

(Continued on page 541)

the process of genetic recombination, and this process is indistinguishable from repair, when the density labeling approach is used. The situation is complicated further by the fact that UV stimulates genetic recombination in the phage. Attempts to eliminate this problem have involved the use of mutant phage that are deficient in genetic recombination.

What about the eukaryotic cell systems of much greater complexity than the bacterial types? Brunk and Hanawalt (1967) examined the protozoan *Tetrahymena pyriformis* for evidence of repair replication after UV-irradiation. The nonconservative pattern was seen, as illustrated in Figure 5. Also, as predicted, the amount of this synthesis was reduced by conditions that promoted photoreactivation. However, there appeared to be an important difference in comparison with the simpler systems so far discussed. Note that the repair label is shifted significantly in density from that of the parental DNA strands that do not contain 5-BU. Two facts are evident: (1) only a small fraction of the parental DNA strands contain appreciable amounts of 5-BU label, and (2) strands that do contain the label contain a sufficient amount to increase detectably the density of these strands. The actual amount of 5-BU can be determined by measuring this density shift in CsCl gradients and by a determination of the molecular size of these DNA fragments by zone sedimentation in a sucrose gradient (Brunk and Hanawalt, 1969). This approach has led to an estimate of about 5,000 nucleotides replaced per repaired lesion in the DNA. An alternative model to consider assumes that most of the 5-BU in these long segments came from sister-chromatid exchanges with normally replicated homologous DNA. As with the T4 system, these recombinational events would be difficult to distinguish from repair replication.

The most exciting application of the 5-BU-labeling method for

---

(Continued from page 540)

Again, note the relative amount of DNA synthesis that has occurred in the same period in control, irradiated, and photoreactivated cultures. The hybrid density fractions from each of the gradients on the left were pooled and rebanded, respectively, in the alkaline gradients shown on the right to permit the determination of repair replication in parental strands. The gradients on the right actually are from a second alkaline rebanding so that the heavily labeled daughter strands are not present. (That is, the light parental DNA from the alkaline rebanding was pooled and then subjected to the second alkaline rebanding.) Note that photoreactivation has reduced the amount of repair replication. Note also that the repair peak is shifted slightly toward higher density than the bulk of the parental DNA. (From Brunk and Hanawalt, 1967.)

measuring repair, especially for those interested in the genetic aspects of neoplasia, was the recent demonstration by Cleaver (1968) that normal skin fibroblasts from human beings were capable of repair replication after UV treatment. Yet, fibroblasts from patients with the rare hereditary skin disease xeroderma pigmentosum exhibited much reduced levels of repair replication. It was concluded that the failure of DNA repair must somehow be related to the fatal skin cancers that these patients generally develop upon exposure to sunlight. This is the first experimental evidence for the possible significance of the excision-repair process in the protection from or recovery from a carcinogenic transformation in cells of man.

Repairable Damage

In bacterial systems, a variety of deleterious agents have been shown to stimulate repair replication. Some of these are listed in Table 1. Since the bifunctional alkylating agent, nitrogen mustard, primarily attacks the 7-nitrogen position of guanine, the resulting defect bears little resemblance to the pyrimidine dimer produced by UV. Nevertheless, repair replication was observed by Hanawalt and Haynes (1965) in *E. coli* strain TAU-bar following treatment of the cells with this reagent. The detailed operation of the excision-repair process is a bit obscure in this case, however, since the predominant product in the DNA so treated involves an interstrand cross-link between guanines in complementary strands.

The powerful mutagen and carcinogen, nitrosoguanidine, has been shown to stimulate repair replication (Cerdá-Olmedo and Hanawalt, 1967). One might wonder whether the repair system deals with any of the mutagenic effects of this reagent. However, the sensitivity to mutagenesis by nitrosoguanidine in the repair-deficient bacterial strain *E. coli* B_{s-1} was similar to that in the parental wild-type strain. Thus, it would appear that the mutagenic damage produced by nitrosoguanidine is not recognizable by the excision-repair system. The demonstration of repair replication after treatment of cells with X-irradiation has been complicated by the much more extensive degradation of DNA that normally accompanies such treatment. Indirect evidence that still other types of damage to DNA can be repaired by the excision-repair system has come from studies on the breakdown of DNA in UV-resistant strains of bacteria after treatment with mitomycin C (*cf.* Howard-Flanders, 1968).

Relationships to Normal Nucleic Acid Metabolism

There is some rather indirect evidence that repair replication may be coupled to the process of transcription in bacteria. It was shown by Pauling and Hanawalt (1965) that thymine starvation in the thymine-requiring *E. coli* strain TAU-bar stimulated the nonconservative repair mode of DNA replication. Yet, no defect in DNA is known to be produced by the absence of thymine. Previous studies had implicated the synthesis of messenger ribonucleic acid (mRNA) in the phenomenon of thymineless death (Hanawalt, 1963). Also it had long been known that thymine deprivation led to loss in viability (*i.e.*, thyminelesss death) and that the effects of thymine starvation were synergistic with those of UV. It was suggested that transcription might occasionally introduce breaks in the DNA (either to facilitate free rotation of a portion of the chromosome or perhaps as a regulatory mechanism) and that in the absence of thymine an exonuclease might enlarge the resulting gaps. This hypothesis was consistent with our observation of repair replication following a period of thymine starvation (Pauling and Hanawalt, 1965). A prediction of this model is that a repair-deficient bacterium should be unusually sensitive to thymine starvation as well as to UV. Such a mutant has recently been isolated by Pauling and Hamm (1968). The deficiency in this mutant appears to be in the level of polynucleotide ligase. Thus, the chromosome in this strain may contain an unusually large number of unrepaired single strand breaks during normal growth and the additional imposition of repairable damage by UV soon overtaxes the ligase function in the excision-repair system.

It is possible that breaks in parental DNA strands may also be a normal consequence of the sequential replication of the chromosome. Again, the breaks might be necessary to provide for the free rotation of a portion of the chromosome (Hanawalt, 1968). Of course, a simple break in the phosphodiester backbone of the DNA would not necessarily result in the observation of the incorporation of labeled nucleotides (as essential for the detection of repair replication) or even ^{32}P for that matter, since the ligase can rejoin a 3' hydroxyl terminus to a 5' phosphate terminus without any phosphate exchange. In studies on the amount of repair replication (turnover) during normal growth in the DNA of *E. coli* strain TAU-bar, Hanawalt (1966) found that after 30 minutes of growth in 5-BU medium with high specific activity ^{32}P, there was from three to five times more ^{32}P associated with parental strands that had replicated (isolated from hybrid band) than with those that had not (isolated from normal density band). However, the studies of Smith and Hanawalt

(1969) did not resolve any difference in the amount of turnover ahead of, and behind, the normal growing point in the DNA of *M. laidlawii* B.

Finally, it is of interest to consider the DNA polymerase that performs the repair replication function. Is it the same one that participates in normal replication? The question might be easily answered if there existed any conditionally lethal mutant bacterial strain that was deficient in the DNA polymerase for normal replication, but unfortunately no such mutant is yet available. Several indirect lines of evidence suggest that different enzyme systems are involved in the normal semiconservative mode and in the nonconservative mode of DNA synthesis in *E. coli*. First, this idea is supported by the finding that the amount of repair replication is not affected by placing a temperature-sensitive DNA synthesis-deficient mutant at the restrictive temperature (Couch and Hanawalt, 1967). Second, the observation of different selectivities for thymine over 5-BU in the normal and repair modes of synthesis is also suggestive that the two enzyme systems are not identical (Kanner and Hanawalt, 1968). Of course, there is no indication that the polymerase enzyme itself is responsible for this difference, even though it may be presumed that the normal and repair modes operate with precursors from the same intracellular pool. The next important step in our understanding of the excision-repair scheme must involve the purification of the entire repair-enzyme complex and the in vitro demonstration of its stepwise or coordinated operation. The process may utilize as few as three enzymes, (1) the recognition-excision enzymes, (2) the excision-repair enzyme, and (3) the polynucleotide ligase.

ADDENDUM

It has recently been shown by R. Setlow, J. Regan, J. German, and W. Carrier (*Proceedings of the National Academy of Sciences of the U.S.A.*, 64: 1035–1041, 1969) that *Xeroderma pigmentosum* cells do not perform the dimer-excision step in the excision-repair sequence.

A bacterial mutant has been isolated by P. de Lucia and J. Cairns (*Nature*, 224:1164, 1969) that is deficient in extracts in the Kornberg DNA polymerase. This mutant is UV-sensitive and seems to be deficient in DNA repair, as evidenced by a lower single-strand DNA molecular weight than in the parent strain during the growth period following UV irradiation. However, we have been unable to demonstrate a reduced level of repair replication in the mutant. We suggest that the defective polymerase is functional in vivo, but that it interferes with the ligase-catalyzed rejoining step in repair.

ACKNOWLEDGMENTS

Our studies on repair replication have been supported by research contract AT(04–3)326–7 with the United States Atomic Energy Commission and grant GM 09901 from the United States Public Health Service. This work was begun in collaboration with a graduate student, David Pettijohn, and the continuing study is largely the result of the efforts of graduate students; Clifford Brunk, John Couch, and Douglas Smith; postdoctoral associates, Crellin Pauling, Lee Kanner, and Harold Bendigkeit; and research assistants, Jean Evoy, Keiko Imamoto, Ilga Brempelis, and Julie Spranza. We have benefitted from helpful discussions with many colleagues, particularly Robert Haynes and Kendric Smith.

REFERENCES

Billen, D. 1968. "Comparison of the Rate and Extent of Deoxyribonucleic Acid Repair and Semiconservative Synthesis in Bacteria Exposed to Ultraviolet Light," *Effects of Radiation on Cellular Proliferation and Differentiation.* Vienna, Austria: International Atomic Energy Agency. Pp. 103–114.

Billen, D., R. R. Hewitt, T. Lapthisophon, and P. M. Achey. 1967. Deoxyribonucleic Acid Repair Replication After Ultraviolet Light or X-Ray Exposure of Bacteria. *Journal of Bacteriology*, 94:1538–1545.

Boyce, R. P., and P. Howard-Flanders. 1964. Release of Ultraviolet Light Induced Thymine Dimers From DNA in *E. coli* K-12. *Proceedings of the National Academy of Sciences of the U.S.A.*, 51:293–300.

Brunk, C., and P. Hanawalt. 1967. Repair of Damaged DNA in a Eucaryotic Cell: *Tetrahymena pyriformis. Science*, 158:663–664.

———. 1969. The Nature of the Excision-Repair Region in the DNA from a Eucaryotic Organism, *Tetrahymena pyriformis. Radiation Research*, 38:285–295.

Carrier, W. L., and R. B. Setlow. 1966. Excision of Pyrimidine Dimers from Irradiated Deoxyribonucleic Acid In Vitro. *Biochimica et biophysica acta*, 129:318–325.

Cerdá-Olmedo, E., and P. Hanawalt. 1967. Repair of DNA Damaged by N-methyl-N'-nitro-N-nitrosoguanidine in *E. coli. Mutation Research*, 4:369–371.

Clark, A. J., and A. D. Margulies. 1965. Isolation and Characterization of Recombination-Deficient Mutants of *Escherichia coli* K12. *Proceedings of the National Academy of Sciences of the U.S.A.*, 53:451–459.

Cleaver, J. E. 1968. Defective Repair Replication of DNA in *Xeroderma pigmentosum. Nature*, 218:652–656.

Couch, J., and P. C. Hanawalt. 1967. DNA Repair Replication in Temperature-Sensitive DNA Synthesis Deficient Bacteria. *Biochemical and Biophysical Research Communications*, 29:779–784.

Gellert, M., J. W. Little, C. K. Oshinsky, and S. B. Zimmerman. 1970. "Studies on the Enzymatic Joining of DNA Strands," *Genetic Concepts and Neoplasia* (The University of Texas M. D. Anderson Hospital and Tumor Institute at Houston, 23rd Annual Symposium on Fundamental Cancer Research, 1969). Baltimore, Maryland: The Williams & Wilkins Co. Pp. 548–554.

Hackett, P., and P. Hanawalt. 1966. Selectivity for Thymine Over 5-Bromouracil in a Thymine-Requiring Bacterium. *Biochimica et biophysica acta*, 123:356–363.

Hanawalt, P. 1963. Involvement of Synthesis of RNA in Thymineless Death. *Nature*, 198:286–288.

———. 1966. "Repair Replication in the Bacterial Genome," *Genetical Aspect of*

Radiosensitivity: Mechanisms of Repair. Vienna, Austria: International Atomic Energy Agency. Pp. 97–104.

———. 1967. Normal Replication of DNA Following Repair Replication in Bacteria. *Nature*, 214:269–270.

———. 1968. "Cellular Recovery From Photochemical Damage," *Photophysiology*, A. C. Giese, Ed. New York, New York: Academic Press, Inc. Vol. IV. Pp. 203–251.

Hanawalt, P., and I. Brempelis. 1967. "Selective Degradation of Newly Replicated DNA After Inhibition of DNA Synthesis in *E. coli*." (Abstract) *Proceedings of the Seventh International Congress of Biochemistry* (Tokyo, Japan, August 19–26, 1967). P. 650.

Hanawalt, P., and R. H. Haynes. 1965. Repair Replication of DNA in Bacteria: Irrelevance of Chemical Nature of Base Defect, *Biochemical and Biophysical Research Communications*, 19:462–464.

———. 1967. Repair of DNA. *Scientific American*, 216:36–43.

Hanawalt, P., and D. Pettijohn. 1965. In N. E. Gillies: "Discussion Secretary's Report," *Recent Progress in Photobiology* (The Proceedings of an International Congress held at Oxford, July, 1964, under the auspices of the Comité Internationale de Photo biologie), E. J. Bowen, Ed. New York, New York: Academic Press, Inc. P. 82.

Hanawalt, P., D. Pettijohn, E. C. Pauling, C. F. Brunk, D. W. Smith, L. C. Kanner, and J. L. Couch. 1969. Repair Replication of DNA In Vivo. *Cold Spring Harbor Symposia on Quantitative Biology*, 33:187–194.

Hanawalt, P., and D. Ray. 1964. Isolation of the Growing Point in the Bacterial Chromosome. *Proceedings of the National Academy of Sciences of the U.S.A.*, 52:125–132.

Haynes, R. H., R. M. Baker, and G. E. Jones. 1968. "Genetic Implications of DNA Repair," *Energetics and Mechanisms in Radiation Biology*, Glyn O. Phillips, Ed. New York, New York: Academic Press. Pp. 425–465.

Hewitt, R., and D. Billen. 1965. Reorientation of Chromosome Replication After Exposure to Ultraviolet Light of *Escherichia coli*. *Journal of Molecular Biology*, 13:40–53.

Howard-Flanders, P. 1968. DNA Repair. *Annual Review of Biochemistry*, 37: 175–200.

Kanner, L., and P. Hanawalt. 1968. Efficiency of Utilization of Thymine and 5-Bromouracil for Normal and Repair DNA Synthesis in Bacteria. *Biochimica et biophysica acta*, 157:532–545.

Kelly, R. B., N. R. Cozzarelli, and A. Kornberg. 1969. Mechanism Action of *E. coli* DNA Polymerase. *Biophysical Journal (Society Abstracts*, Thirteenth Annual Meeting, February 26–March 1, 1969, Los Angeles, California), 9:A-16.

Lark, K. G., T. Repko, and E. J. Hoffman. 1963. The Effect of Amino Acid Deprivation on Subsequent Deoxyribonucleic Acid Replication. *Biochimica et biophysica acta*, 76:9–24.

Maaløe, O., and P. Hanawalt. 1961. Thymine Deficiency and the Normal DNA Replication Cycle. I. *Journal of Molecular Biology*, 3:144–156.

Meselson, M., and F. W. Stahl. 1958. The Replication of DNA in *Escherichia coli*. *Proceedings of the National Academy of Sciences of the U.S.A.*, 44:671–682.

Miller, D. S., F. A. Dolbeare, I. Mahler, and L. Grossman. 1967. Endonuclease I of *Micrococcus lysodeikticus. Abstracts: Biophysical Society, Eleventh Annual Meeting* (February 22–24, 1967, Houston, Texas). P. 123.

Nakayama, H., S. Okubo, M. Sekiguchi, and M. Takagi. 1967. A Deoxyribonuclease Activity Specific for Ultraviolet-Irradiated DNA: A Chromatographic Analysis. *Biochemical and Biophysical Research Communications,* 27:217–223.

Painter, R. B., and J. E. Cleaver. 1967. Repair Replication in HeLa Cells After Large Doses of X-Irradiation. *Nature,* 216:369–370.

Pauling, C., and L. Hamm. 1968. Properties of a Temperature-Sensitive Radiation-Sensitive Mutant of *Escherichia coli. Proceedings of the National Academy of Sciences of the U.S.A.,* 60:1495–1502.

Pauling, C., and P. Hanawalt. 1965. Nonconservative DNA Replication Following Thymine Starvation in Bacteria. *Proceedings of the National Academy of Sciences of the U.S.A.,* 54:1728–1735.

Pettijohn, D., and P. Hanawalt. 1963. Deoxyribonucleic Acid Replication in Bacteria Following Ultraviolet Irradiation. *Biochimica et biophysica acta,* 72:127–129.

———. 1964. Evidence for Repair-Replication of Ultraviolet Damaged DNA in Bacteria. *Journal of Molecular Biology,* 9:395–410.

Rasmussen, R. E., and R. B. Painter. 1966. Radiation-Stimulated DNA Synthesis in Cultured Mammalian Cells. *The Journal of Cell Biology,* 29:11–19.

Setlow, R. B. 1967. "Repair of DNA," *Regulation of Nucleic Acid and Protein Biosynthesis,* V. V. Koningsberger and L. Bosch, Eds. Amsterdam, The Netherlands: Elsevier Publishing Co.; New York, New York: American Elsevier Publishing Co., Inc.; and London, England: Elsevier Publishing Co., Ltd. Pp. 51–62.

Setlow, R. B., and W. L. Carrier. 1964. The Disappearance of Thymine Dimers from DNA: An Error-Correcting Mechanism. *Proceedings of the National Academy of Sciences of the U.S.A.,* 51:226–231.

Smith, D. W., and P. Hanawalt. 1969. Repair Replication of DNA in Ultraviolet Irradiated *Mycoplasma laidlawii* B. *Journal of Molecular Biology,* 46:57–72.

Strauss, B. 1968. "DNA Repair," *Current Topics in Microbiology and Immunology,* Heidelberg, Germany: Springer-Verlag. Vol. 44. Pp. 1–85.

Studies on the Enzymatic Joining of DNA Strands

MARTIN GELLERT, JOHN W. LITTLE,
CAROL K. OSHINSKY, AND STEVEN B. ZIMMERMAN

Laboratory of Molecular Biology, National Institute of Arthritis and Metabolic Diseases, National Institutes of Health, Bethesda, Maryland

It will be useful to put our work in the context of this session on the repair of genetic damage. Chromosomal damage produced by ultraviolet radiation, or by treatment with alkylating agents, is repaired mainly by a process involving excision and repair of the damaged portion. More explicitly, the damaged bases and some surrounding nucleotides on the same deoxyribonucleic acid (DNA) strand are removed by the action of nucleases and the missing stretch is then resynthesized, using the undamaged strand as template. Finally, to restore the covalent continuity of the DNA structure, the newly synthesized segment must be rejoined to the undamaged part of its strand. The outlines of this process in bacterial systems have been well documented (for review see Howard-Flanders and Boyce, 1966), and similar repair has been shown recently to occur in mammalian cells (Lett, Caldwell, Dean, and Alexander, 1967; Painter and Cleaver, 1967).

In this paper, we shall discuss a family of enzymes which are capable of carrying out the final rejoining step of the repair process. Such enzymes (variously called polynucleotide ligase, polynucleotide-joining enzyme, and, by us, DNA ligase) have been purified from *Escherichia coli* infected with bacteriophage T4 (Weiss and Richardson, 1967a; Becker, Lyn, Gefter, and Hurwitz, 1967; Cozzarelli, Melechen, Jovin, and Kornberg, 1967), from uninfected *E. coli* (Olivera and Lehman, 1967b; Zimmerman, Little, Oshinsky, and Gellert, 1967; Gefter, Becker, and Hurwitz, 1967), and from mammalian tissues (Lindahl and Edelman, 1968). While concentrating our discussion on the *E. coli* enzyme, we shall draw frequent comparisons with ligases from other sources.

The DNA-Joining Reaction

The reaction catalyzed by DNA ligases is briefly described as the closure of single strand breaks ("nicks") in double-helical DNA (Figure 1). In other words, the substrate differs locally from intact DNA only in the rupture of an internucleotide bond on one of the strands. The reaction restores the intactness of this strand, forming a 3′–5′ phosphodiester bond identical to the normal internucleotide linkage. The reaction appears to be unspecific with regard to the base of the nucleotide residue on either side of the break; formation of most of the 16 possible internucleotide links has by now been reported (*e.g.* Gefter, Becker, and Hurwitz, 1967; Gupta *et al.*, 1968).

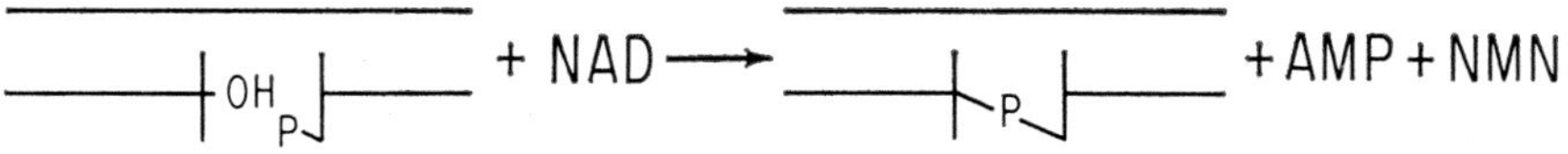

FIGURE 1. Schematic representation of the joining of a broken DNA strand by *E. coli* DNA ligase. AMP, adenylate; NAD, nicotinamide adenine dinucleotide; NMN, nicotinamide mononucleotide.

Other requirements on the substrate structure are exacting: (1) The apposed ends must be held in register by base-pairing to the complementary strand. If the strands are separated by denaturation, or if the complementary strand is also broken at the same point (double strand break), no joining is possible. Similarly, joining is blocked by removal of a few nucleotides between the apposed ends (Gefter, Becker, and Hurwitz, 1967). (2) The juxtaposed strands must end in 5′-phosphoryl and 3′-hydroxyl groups. Dephosphorylated ends, or those with 3′-phosphoryl groups, cannot be sealed. (3) Both strands must be deoxyribonucleotide polymers. No joining of breaks in double-stranded polyribonucleotides has been detected, nor can breaks in a polydeoxyribonucleotide strand be sealed if it is base-paired to a polyribonucleotide strand (Olivera and Lehman, 1968).

The high specificity of the ligase reaction implies that breaks which are directly produced by irradiation, as with X rays, generally will not be repairable by DNA ligase alone, since only a small fraction can be expected to have the proper chemical structure. Rather, one may expect that the full process of excision, resynthesis, and rejoining will be needed in this case as well.

What are typical substrates for DNA ligase? Perhaps the conceptually simplest substrate is made by limited digestion of native DNA with pancreatic deoxyribonuclease, which creates single strand breaks of the correct chemical structure. Their sealing by DNA ligase can then be followed by the increase in single strand molecular weight or, as worked out by Weiss and Richardson, by the resulting insusceptibility of the phosphoryl group at the break to phosphomonoesterases (Weiss and Richardson, 1967a).

Another kind of substrate is made by mixing long strands of polydeoxyadenylic acid (dA) with shorter strands of polydeoxythymidylic acid (dT). The two polymers hydrogen-bond to each other and, under suitable conditions, the dT chains take up adjoining positions on the dA backbone, so that the ends of neighboring dT chains can be joined. Once again, the reaction can be followed by the disappearance of phosphatase-susceptible phosphoryl groups, here located at the 5′-termini of dT chains (Olivera and Lehman, 1967b).

A naturally occurring substrate is available in the DNA of bacteriophage λ (and related phages). At its ends, this viral DNA has short single-stranded regions whose base-sequences are complementary and can cohere to form either circular molecules or intermolecular aggregates. In the hydrogen-bonded circular configuration, the ends can be joined by DNA ligase to form double-stranded covalent circles, easily recognized by their very rapid sedimentation in alkali (Gellert, 1967). We have also devised a more rapid assay based on covalent joining of intermolecular aggregates of λ DNA (Zimmerman, Little, Oshinsky, and Gellert, 1967).

Characterization of DNA Ligase

The *E. coli* DNA ligase has been purified 1,300-fold (Zimmerman and Oshinsky, 1969). At this stage, it is perhaps 25 per cent pure, as judged by polyacrylamide gel electrophoresis (Gellert and Oshinsky, unpublished data). Its molecular weight is about 100,000 daltons, and there is evidence for the presence of subunits, which may or may not be identical (Zimmerman and Oshinsky, 1969).

The *E. coli* enzyme requires nicotinamide adenine dinucleotide (NAD) as cofactor, and consumes it stoichiometrically in the DNA-joining reaction; one molecule of NAD is cleaved (to adenylate and nicotinamide mononucleotide) for each DNA break that is sealed (Zimmerman, Little, Oshinsky, and Gellert, 1967; Olivera and Lehman, 1967a). Thus, the phosphodiester bond is made at the expense of the pyrophosphoryl linkage of NAD. This surprising reaction is an exception to the customary use of NAD as an oxidative cofactor, in which the pyrophosphoryl linkage, of course, remains intact.

The T4-induced and mammalian ligases utilize adenosine triphosphate (ATP) in a similar manner, the breakdown products being adenylate and pyrophosphate. The specificity of both groups of enzymes is strict; there is no perceptible stimulation of *E. coli* DNA ligase by ATP or of the T4 and mammalian enzymes by NAD.

Except for this distinction, though, both types of ligase work by remarkably similar mechanisms. In the first step, which can take place in the absence of DNA, a covalent ligase-adenylate complex is formed, releasing nicotinamide mononucleotide or pyrophosphate (Little, Zimmerman, Oshinsky, and Gellert, 1967; Weiss and Richardson, 1967b; Lindahl and Edelman, 1968). This complex is stable, can be isolated, and is competent to carry out the DNA-joining reaction without additional cofactor. The exact chemical nature of the complex is not yet known, but it probably involves linkage through the phosphoryl group of adenosine monophosphate (AMP).

In the next step of the reaction, the adenylyl moiety is transferred to the 5′-phosphoryl end at the DNA single strand break (Olivera, Hall, and Lehman, 1968), forming an adenylyl-5′-phosphoryl group which has the pyrophosphoryl linkage characteristic of the original cofactor and thus retains its "activated" character. Finally, the DNA internucleotide bond is formed, with elimination of adenylate. Thus the steps in the overall reaction can be written as shown below.

$$\left. \begin{array}{l} \text{NAD} \\ \text{or} \\ \text{ATP} \end{array} \right\} + \text{ligase} \rightleftarrows \text{AMP-ligase} + \left\{ \begin{array}{l} \text{Nicotinamide mononucleotide (NMN)} \\ \text{or} \\ \text{Pyrophosphate (PP)} \end{array} \right.$$

$$\text{AMP-ligase} + \text{nicked DNA} \longrightarrow \text{AMP-DNA} + \text{ligase}$$

$$\text{AMP-DNA} \xrightarrow{\text{ligase}} \text{joined DNA} + \text{AMP}$$

$$\left. \begin{array}{l} \text{NAD} \\ \text{or} \\ \text{ATP} \end{array} \right\} + \text{nicked DNA} \xrightarrow{\text{ligase}} \text{joined DNA} + \text{AMP} + \left\{ \begin{array}{l} \text{NMN} \\ \text{or} \\ \text{PP} \end{array} \right.$$

Cellular Function of DNA Ligase

The mechanism of DNA ligase action is thus quite well understood. The physiological role of DNA ligase in the cell is much less clear.

In trying to understand the function of an enzyme, it is often useful to alter its intracellular activity either with specific inhibitors or by mutational means. Unfortunately, no specific inhibitors of DNA ligases are yet known. Mutant strains of phage T4 which make a defective DNA ligase are known (Fareed and Richardson, 1967). The most obvious phenotypic defect in such phage-infected cells is an early cessation of DNA synthesis. This indication of a direct role for DNA ligase in DNA synthesis can be correlated with the studies of Okazaki *et al.* (1968) which suggest that DNA is made in fragments which are later linked into a continuous chromosomal structure, presumably by the action of DNA ligase. In agreement with this scheme, in cells infected with a temperature-sensitive T4 ligase mutant at the restrictive temperature, the newly made DNA retains its original low molecular weight, whereas with wild-type phage, the DNA is rapidly converted to a high molecular weight form (Sugimoto, Okazaki, and Okazaki, 1968; Newman and Hanawalt, 1968; Hosoda and Mathews, 1968).

On closer investigation, unfortunately, this conclusion is not entirely straightforward. T4 infection also induces the synthesis of several powerful endonucleases. If the level of DNA ligase is normal, the resealing of endonucleolytic breaks is able to maintain the integrity of the DNA. In infection with a ligase-defective mutant, however, both parental and newly synthesized DNA are rapidly degraded (Masamune and Richardson, 1968). Thus, the conclusion that DNA ligase is directly involved in DNA synthesis must remain suspect.

Similar mutant studies in uninfected *E. coli*, in which the endonuclease problem is far less severe, would clearly be valuable. Unfortunately, ligase-defective mutants of *E. coli* have not yet been found (with the possible exception of one strain of complex properties [Pauling and Hamm, 1968]). In looking for such mutants in our laboratory, we first assayed DNA ligase activity in extracts of representative ultraviolet-sensitive, X-ray-sensitive, and recombination-deficient strains, thinking that a ligase defect could lead to one of these phenotypes. When all these strains proved to have normal ligase levels, we then surmised that, as in T4, a ligase deficiency could lead to cessation of DNA synthesis. Accordingly, we measured DNA ligase levels in more than 20 *E. coli* mutants (isolated by Dr. F. Bonhoeffer) in which DNA synthesis is temperature sensitive, being arrested at 42 C. In none of these strains was the DNA ligase activity temperature sensitive; we thus concluded that none of them was a ligase mutant (Gellert, Little, Oshinsky, and Zimmerman, 1968). We are now looking for ligase mutants with other techniques.

Our understanding of the cellular function of DNA ligase remains in an unsettled and paradoxical state. The search for this enzyme began because such a function seems to be required for genetic repair and recombination. But if DNA ligase is also needed for an essential function, such as DNA synthesis, then this requirement masks any role in repair or recombination, since a ligase-defective cell will not be merely deficient in repair or recombination, but inviable. The existing evidence for the in vivo role of DNA ligase, even if not entirely satisfying, suggests that it is involved in DNA synthesis. The theory is most plausible that DNA ligase also functions in repair of damaged DNA—so plausible as to be almost convincing—but there is as yet no direct evidence in support of this idea.

REFERENCES

Becker, A., G. Lyn, M. Gefter, and J. Hurwitz. 1967. The Enzymatic Repair of DNA. II. Characterization of Phage-Induced Sealase. *Proceedings of the National Academy of Sciences of the U.S.A.*, 58:1996–2003.

Cozzarelli, N. R., N. E. Melechen, T. M. Jovin, and A. Kornberg. 1967. Polynucleotide Cellulose as a Substrate for a Polynucleotide Ligase Induced by Phage T4. *Biochemical and Biophysical Research Communications*, 28:578–586.

Fareed, G. C., and C. C. Richardson. 1967. Enzymatic Breakage and Joining of Deoxyribonucleic Acid. II. The Structural Gene for Polynucleotide Ligase in Bacteriophage T4. *Proceedings of the National Academy of Sciences of the U.S.A.*, 58:665–672.

Gefter, M. L., A. Becker, and J. Hurwitz. 1967. The Enzymatic Repair of DNA. I. Formation of Circular λDNA. *Proceedings of the National Academy of Sciences of the U.S.A.*, 58:240–247.

Gellert, M. 1967. Formation of Covalent Circles of λDNA by *E. coli* Extracts. *Proceedings of the National Academy of Sciences of the U.S.A.*, 57:148–155.

Gellert, M., and C. K. Oshinsky. Unpublished data.

Gupta, N. K., E. Ohtsuka, H. Weber, S. H. Chang, and H. G. Khorana. 1968. Studies on Polynucleotides. LXXXVII. The Joining of Short Deoxyribopolynucleotides by DNA-Joining Enzymes. *Proceedings of the National Academy of Sciences of the U.S.A.*, 60:285–292.

Hosoda, J., and E. Mathews. 1968. DNA Replication In Vivo by a Temperature-Sensitive Polynucleotide Ligase Mutant of T4. *Proceedings of the National Academy of Sciences of the U.S.A.*, 61:997–1004.

Howard-Flanders, P., and R. P. Boyce. 1966. DNA Repair and Genetic Recombination: Studies on Mutants of *Escherichia coli* Defective in These Processes. *Radiation Research*, (Suppl. 6):156–181.

Lett, J. T., I. Caldwell, C. J. Dean, and P. Alexander. 1967. Rejoining of X-Ray Induced Breaks in the DNA of Leukaemia Cells. *Nature*, 214:790–792.

Lindahl, T., and G. M. Edelman. 1968. Polynucleotide Ligase from Myeloid and Lymphoid Tissues. *Proceedings of the National Academy of Sciences of the U.S.A.*, 61:680–687.

Little, J. W., S. B. Zimmerman, C. K. Oshinsky, and M. Gellert. 1967. Enzymatic Joining of DNA Strands. II. An Enzyme-Adenylate Intermediate in the DPN-Dependent DNA Ligase Reaction. *Proceedings of the National Academy of Sciences of the U.S.A.*, 58:2004–2011.

Masamune, Y., and C. C. Richardson. 1968. Enzymatic Breakage and Joining of Deoxyribonucleic Acid. IV. DNA Synthesis in E. coli Infected with Ligase-Negative Mutants of Phage T4. *Proceedings of the National Academy of Sciences of the U.S.A.*, 61:1328–1335.

Newman, J., and P. Hanawalt. 1968. Role of Polynucleotide Ligase in T4 DNA Replication. *Journal of Molecular Biology*, 35:639–642.

Okazaki, R., T. Okazaki, K. Sakabe, K. Sugimoto, and A. Sugino. 1968. Mechanism of DNA Chain Growth. I. Possible Discontinuity and Unusual Secondary Structure of Newly Synthesized Chains. *Proceedings of the National Academy of Sciences of the U.S.A.*, 59:598–605.

Olivera, B. M., Z. W. Hall, and I. R. Lehman. 1968. Enzymatic Joining of Polynucleotides. V. A DNA-Adenylate Intermediate in the Polynucleotide-Joining Reaction. *Proceedings of the National Academy of Sciences of the U.S.A.*, 61:237–244.

Olivera, B. M., and I. R. Lehman. 1967a. Diphosphopyridine Nucleotide: A Cofactor for the Polynucleotide-Joining Enzyme from Escherichia coli. *Proceedings of the National Academy of Sciences of the U.S.A.*, 57:1700–1704.

———. 1967b. Linkage of Polynucleotides Through Phosphodiester Bonds by an Enzyme from *Escherichia coli*. *Proceedings of the National Academy of Sciences of the U.S.A.*, 57:1426–1433.

———. 1968. Enzymic Joining of Polynucleotides. III. The Polydeoxyadenylate-Polydeoxythymidylate Homopolymer Pair. *Journal of Molecular Biology*. 36:261–274.

Painter, R. B., and J. E. Cleaver. 1967. Repair Replication in HeLa Cells After Large Doses of X-Irradiation. *Nature*, 216:369–370.

Pauling, C., and L. Hamm. 1968. Properties of a Temperature-Sensitive Radiation-Sensitive Mutant of Escherichia coli. *Proceedings of the National Academy of Sciences of the U.S.A.*, 60:1495–1502.

Sugimoto, K., T. Okazaki, and R. Okazaki. 1968. Mechanism of DNA Chain Growth. II. Accumulation of Newly Synthesized Short Chains in E. coli Infected with Ligase-Defective T4 Phages. *Proceedings of the National Academy of Sciences of the U.S.A.*, 60:1356–1362.

Weiss, B., and C. C. Richardson. 1967a. Enzymatic Breakage and Joining of Deoxyribonucleic Acid. I. Repair of Single-Strand Breaks in DNA by an Enzyme System from Escherichia coli Infected with T4 Bacteriophage. *Proceedings of the National Academy of Sciences of the U.S.A.*, 57:1021–1028.

———. 1967b. Enzymatic Breakage and Joining of Deoxyribonucleic Acid. III. An Enzyme-Adenylate Intermediate in the Polynucleotide Ligase Reaction. *Journal of Biological Chemistry*, 242:4270–4272.

Zimmerman, S. B., J. W. Little, C. K. Oshinsky, and M. Gellert. 1967. Enzymatic Joining of DNA Strands: A Novel Reaction of Diphosphopyridine Nucleotide. *Proceedings of the National Academy of Sciences of the U.S.A.*, 57:1841–1848.

Zimmerman, S. B., and C. K. Oshinsky. 1969. Enzymatic Joining of DNA Strands. III. Further Purification of the DNA Ligase from *E. coli* and Multiple Forms of the Purified Enzyme. *Journal of Biological Chemistry*, 244:4689–4695.

Repair of DNA in Haemophilus influenzae. III. Excision and Recombination Defects and the Site of Repair of Ultraviolet-Irradiated Transforming DNA

JANE K. SETLOW, M. E. BOLING, AND K. L. BEATTIE

Biology Division, Oak Ridge National Laboratory, Oak Ridge, Tennessee

Four questions frequently asked concerning the effects of radiation on cells are: (1) What is the radiation-sensitive part of the cell? (2) What is the nature of the primary damage? (3) How does this damage result in the biological effects? (4) What, if anything, can the cell do about such damage? One of the curious aspects of the field of radiation biology is that experiments concerning the fourth question have been able to provide some of the best evidence for answers to the other questions, although logically one might expect the questions to be answered more or less in the order given here. The outstanding example is the set of experiments showing that ultraviolet (UV)-resistant *Escherichia coli* can excise UV-induced pyrimidine dimers from its deoxyribonucleic acid (DNA) and resume DNA synthesis after a time, whereas UV-sensitive *E. coli* cannot (R. B. Setlow and Carrier, 1964; R. B. Setlow, Swenson, and Carrier, 1963). The answers to the four questions suggested by this result are: (1) DNA, (2) pyrimidine dimers, (3) inhibition of DNA synthesis, and (4) excision of damaged parts.

The sufficient reason for studing repair of DNA in another organism, *Haemophilus influenzae*, is that it can do something *E. coli* cannot do very well, namely undergo genetic transformation. Mutants of this microorganism have been isolated which have various defects in their ability to repair DNA (J. K. Setlow *et al.*, 1968a, b). Three types of DNA are known to be repaired in the *H. influenzae* cell: (1) the cell's own DNA, (2) the DNA of *H. influenzae* bacteriophage, and (3) the DNA from other *H. influenzae* cells (transforming DNA) which is taken up by the competent cell from the medium. For UV irradiation, the presence or absence of a mechanism for excising pyrimidine dimers is important in the survival of irradiated *H. influenzae* cells, bacteriophage, and transforming DNA (J. K. Setlow *et al.*, 1968a, b). The rapid rejoining of single strand breaks in the DNA caused by dimer excision also is important for survival of the three types of DNA (J. K. Setlow *et al.*, 1968b). In the case of the direct effect of ionizing radiation, there is strong evidence that X ray-induced single strand breaks in *H. influenzae* DNA contribute to the decrease in the ability of this DNA to transform cells. This evidence consists in the correlation between the resistance of irradiated transforming DNA to inactivation as a function of the recipient cell and the recipient cell's ability to rejoin rapidly the single strand breaks in its own DNA (J. K. Setlow *et al.*, 1968b). The sensitivity or resistance of the cells themselves to ionizing radiation, however, seems to depend on the presence of a strand-rejoining mechanism rather than on the rate of rejoining (Randolph and J. K. Setlow, 1969).

When and Where Is Ultraviolet-Irradiated Transforming DNA Repaired by the Cell?

It was shown earlier that pyrimidine dimers induced in transforming DNA by UV radiation may become incorporated into the recipient cell genome (J. K. Setlow *et al.*, 1968b). Therefore, repair of damaged transforming DNA could take place either before or after integration. An experiment designed to distinguish between these possibilities is outlined in Figure 1. If repair of UV-irradiated transforming DNA occurs only after integration, then we would expect to find specific competition for repair enzymes only in DNA which itself is able to pair with or integrate into the recipient's genome. Various types of DNA will enter the competent cell, but only DNA from *H. influenzae* (or a close relative) will integrate (Steinhart and Herriott, 1968). Specific competition may be measured by observing a decrease in survival of UV-irradiated transforming DNA resulting from the presence of other irradiated DNA in the competent cell. The results of the experiment are summarized in Figures 2, 3, and 4. In these figures, the greater the slope, the higher the sensitivity. Figure 2 shows that the survival of UV-irradiated DNA in wild-type cells is higher in the presence of calf thymus DNA, regardless of whether the nonhomologous DNA has been irradiated. The same effect was observed with DNA from *E. coli*. Similar results were obtained when UV-sensitive mutants lacking the excision mechanism were used as recipient cells. Figures 3 and 4 show that the survival of irradiated transforming DNA is also higher in the presence of unirradiated homologous DNA, but survival is decreased by irradiated homologous DNA (Figure 3) except when the recipient cell is unable to excise pyrimidine dimers from its DNA (Figure 4). In the latter case, irradiated homologous DNA has the same effect as unirradiated homologous DNA.

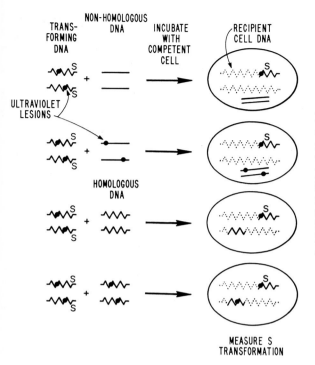

FIGURE 1. Schematic diagram of an experiment to determine whether repair takes place before or after integration. S, streptomycin marker. Only the homologous DNA integrates into the DNA of the recipient cell.

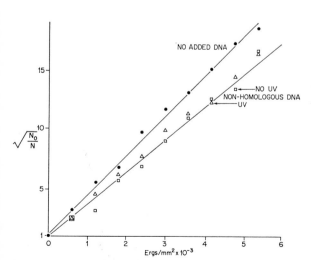

FIGURE 2. UV inactivation of transforming DNA (streptomycin marker) at 254 nm assayed on wild-type cells in the presence and absence of calf thymus DNA. UV dose to calf thymus DNA: 3×10^4 ergs/mm^2 at 254 nm. Concentration of DNA's with competent cells: 1.5 μg/ml calf thymus DNA; 0.03 μg/ml transforming DNA. N_0 and N are the number of transformants resulting from unirradiated and irradiated transforming DNA, respectively. Similar results were obtained with the cathomycin marker, except that the sensitivities were all proportionately lower.

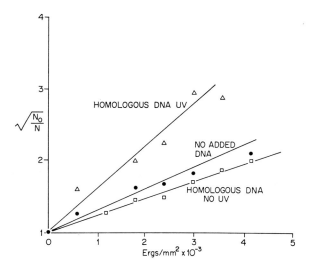

FIGURE 3. UV inactivation of transforming DNA (cathomycin marker) at 254 nm assayed on wild-type cells in the presence and absence of *H. influenzae* DNA which did not contain this marker. UV dose to the homologous DNA: 3×10^4 ergs/mm^2 at 254 nm. Concentration of DNA's with competent cells: 1.5 μg/ml homologous DNA; 0.03 μg/ml transforming DNA. N_0 and N are the number of transformants resulting from unirradiated and irradiated transforming DNA, respectively. Similar results were obtained with the streptomycin marker, except that the sensitivities were all proportionately higher.

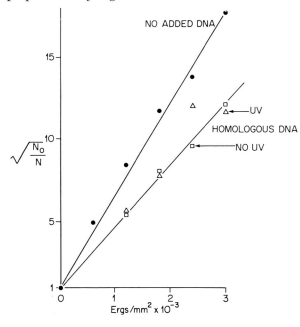

FIGURE 4. UV inactivation of transforming DNA (streptomycin marker) at 254 nm assayed on the sensitive mutant DB112 in the presence and absence of *H. influenzae* DNA which did not contain this marker. UV dose to the homologous DNA: 3×10^4 ergs/mm^2 at 254 nm. Concentration of DNA's with competent cells: 1.5 μg/ml homologous DNA; 0.03 μg/ml transforming DNA. N_0 and N are the number of transformants resulting from unirradiated and irradiated transforming DNA, respectively. Similar results were obtained with the cathomycin marker, except that the sensitivities were all proportionately lower.

The increase in survival caused by nonhomologous DNA or unirradiated homologous DNA in wild-type cells or by irradiated homologous DNA in excisionless mutants is probably caused by competition for an enzyme that breaks down irradiated transforming DNA before the marker on the DNA can be integrated. We believe that the decrease in survival caused by irradiated homologous DNA in cells with an excision mechanism is the result of specific competition for repair enzymes. In mutants lacking such enzyme systems, there is no such specific competition. Because there is apparently no specific competition from nonhomologous DNA, which does not integrate, we can conclude that all, or almost all, of the repair of transforming DNA takes place after integration.

The Effect of Repair of Ultraviolet Damage on Transcription

The expression of a marker on transforming DNA requires a time for transcription and translation of the information contained in this DNA. It is of interest to determine whether the expression time varies with dose of UV-radiation to the transforming DNA, and whether there are marked differences in this respect when strains which contain different defects in repair are used as recipient cells. In the case of all but one of the strains, there is little or no UV-induced increase in expression time beyond the usual two hours. The presence or absence of an excision mechanism apparently does not affect the kinetics of transcription of markers on UV-irradiated DNA (Table 1). This suggests that the normal repair process does not markedly delay transcription. Similarly, the presence of unrepaired UV-induced lesions may prevent transcription, but does not delay it.

DB115, the strain in which there is a lengthening of expression time resulting from irradiation of the transforming DNA, is a UV-sensitive mutant which can, however, excise pyrimidine dimers from its DNA. It is slow in rejoining the gaps in its DNA made by excision (J. K. Setlow *et al.*, 1968b). It can be seen from Table 1 that the number of transformations in this strain resulting from irradiated transforming DNA about doubles if the expression time is considerably longer than the usual two-hour period, whereas no such change can be seen in the case of wild-type cells and the very UV-sensitive DB112. One could imagine that gaps in the DNA decrease the amount of messenger ribonucleic acid (mRNA) to be transcribed after the gap (shown schematically in Figure 5), much as nonsense mutations cause a smaller amount of mRNA to be made (Baker and Yanofsky, 1968; Imamoto and Yanofsky, 1967). Eventually, the gaps in DB115 may be closed and transcription can proceed. In the

TABLE 1. *Transformations to Drug Resistance Resulting from UV-Irradiated DNA as a Function of Time of Adding the Drug*

Recipient cell	Dose (ergs/mm² at 254 nm)	Time (hours)	Per cent of unirradiated control	
			Streptomycin	Cathomycin
Wild-type	3,600	2.0	0.77	15.0
		3.0	0.75	14.0
		4.0	. . .	17.0
	5,400	2.0	0.37	11.0
		3.0	0.38	10.0
		4.0	. . .	10.0
DB112*	2,400	2.0	0.30	1.40
		3.0	0.26	1.60
	5,400	2.0	0.06	0.45
		3.0	0.05	0.58
DB115†	3,600	2.0	0.25	4.40
		3.0	0.43	7.00
		4.0	0.48	9.20
	5,400	2.0	0.10	3.20
		2.5	. . .	3.80
		3.0	0.24	4.40
		3.5	0.28	5.20
		4.0	0.27	. . .

* Nonexcising.
† Excises dimers, but is slow at rejoining single strand gaps.
Abbreviation: nm, nanometer.

INTEGRATED TRANSFORMING DNA

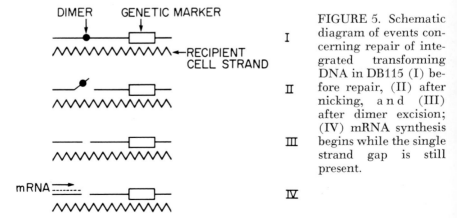

FIGURE 5. Schematic diagram of events concerning repair of integrated transforming DNA in DB115 (I) before repair, (II) after nicking, and (III) after dimer excision; (IV) mRNA synthesis begins while the single strand gap is still present.

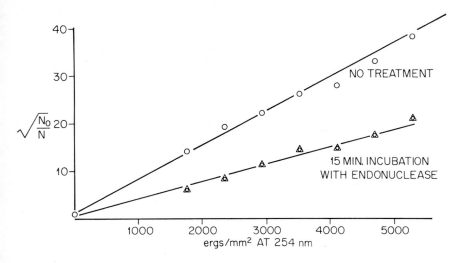

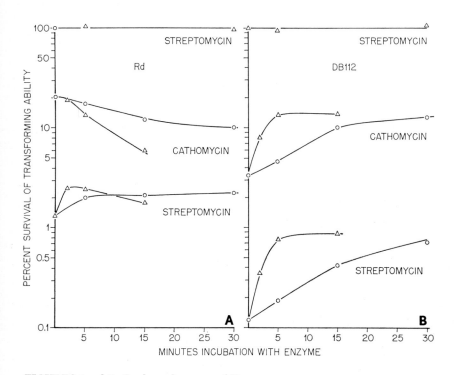

FIGURES 6 and 7: See legends on page 562.

case of wild-type cells, there are many fewer gaps than UV-induced lesions at any one time during the repair period (J. K. Setlow *et al.*, 1968b), so that even if mRNA synthesis begins during the repair period, there are relatively few gaps present to interfere with transcription. Similarly, in the case of strains which do not excise dimers, there are also few gaps.

Defective Excision of Pyrimidine Dimers in Two Ultraviolet-Sensitive Mutants

It was concluded from earlier work that the two excisionless mutants are defective in two different cistrons because of the frequency with which they may be crossed by transformation to produce a recombinant with normal excision properties (J. K. Setlow *et al.*, 1968b). The particular defect in one of these mutants, DB112, has become apparent from an enzymological study done in collaboration with R. B. Setlow and W. L. Carrier. A purified endonuclease from *Micrococcus luteus* is specific for damaged DNA (Carrier and R. B. Setlow, 1970; R. B. Setlow, J. K. Setlow, and Carrier, 1970). This enzyme makes single strand nicks in UV-irradiated DNA without excising pyrimidine dimers, but does not affect the biological activity of unirradiated DNA (see Figure 7) and, therefore, can be assumed to be free of nonspecific deoxyribonuclease. UV-irradiated transforming DNA treated with this enzyme and assayed on the excisionless mutant, DB112, shows a large increase in survival of transforming ability (Figures 6 and 7B). The same DNA assayed on wild-type cells, however, is not remarkably reactivated by enzyme treat-

FIGURE 6. UV-irradiated transforming DNA (1 μg/ml) containing the streptomycin marker incubated at 37 C for 15 minutes with a purified endonuclease from *M. luteus* (protein concentration 6 μg/ml) and assayed on the UV-sensitive mutant DB112. N_0 and N are the number of transformants resulting from unirradiated and irradiated DNA, respectively (R. B. Setlow, J. K. Setlow, and Carrier, 1970).

FIGURE 7. Transforming DNA (1 μg/ml) containing cathomycin and streptomycin markers incubated at 37 C for various times with a purified endonuclease from *M. luteus* (protein concentration: $\triangle$ 6 μg/ml, $\bigcirc$ 2 μg/ml) and assayed on (A) Rd (wild-type *H. influenzae*) or (B) the UV-sensitive mutant, DB112. UV dose to transforming DNA: 0 (no inactivation) or 2,400 ergs/mm². (Note the greater sensitivity in the case of the streptomycin marker.) (From R. B. Setlow, J. K. Setlow, and Carrier, 1970.)

ment (Figure 7A) and, in the case of the cathomycin marker, is inactivated.

Two conclusions may be drawn from these data: (1) The specific endonuclease supplies a function missing in DB112, namely, the ability to make the first cut next to the pyrimidine dimer, the first step in excision. After these cuts are made in the transforming DNA, DB112 is able to continue with the excision process by making the second cut. (2) The relative rate of the various sequential steps in repair must be important for the survival of transforming DNA. For cells which can themselves excise pyrimidine dimers, the usual pattern in time is disrupted when the transforming DNA enters the cell with nicks already present. Since the subsequent steps take time, breakdown of some of the transforming DNA can result from exonuclease action at the site of the single strand nicks. A schematic outline of these possibilities is given in Figure 8.

In the case of the other excisionless mutant, DB116, the enzyme-treated transforming DNA appears to be reactivated to a small degree. We might suppose that this mutant is able to carry out the first step in excision, but is blocked in some later step.

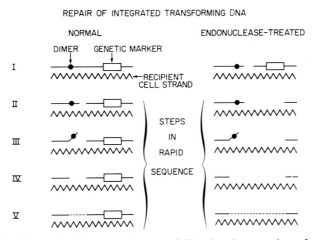

FIGURE 8. Schematic diagram of events following integration of normal and endonuclease-treated transforming DNA which was first subjected to UV-irradiation (I) before the cell has altered the integrated DNA, (II) after one nick (breakdown has occurred in the case of the previously endonuclease-treated transforming DNA), (III) just before dimer excision, (IV) just after dimer excision, and (V) after repair replication.

Defective Recombination in an Ultraviolet-Sensitive Mutant

The importance of recombination-defective *H. influenzae* is that such mutants may yield information on the mechanism of recombination. One of the UV-sensitive mutants, DB117, has what appears to be a defect in recombination, in that this mutant is transformed with an efficiency less than 10^{-4} times that of the other strains, although its ability to take up DNA from the medium is normal (J. K. Setlow *et al.*, 1968b).

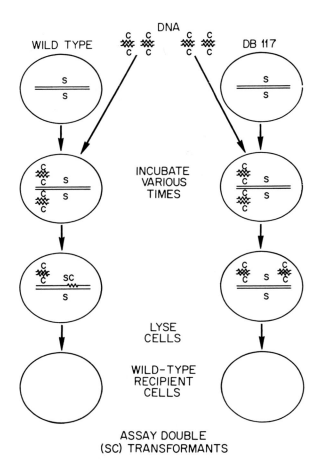

FIGURE 9. Schematic diagram of events when either wild-type or DB117 cells resistant to streptomycin (S) are exposed to DNA carrying a cathomycin (C) marker. These two markers are linked when they are on the same DNA and can transform cells to resistance against both drugs at once (SC). Data obtained from such an experiment are shown in Table 2.

TABLE 2. *Number of Transformations (per 0.1 ml) from Lysates Made from Streptomycin (S)-Resistant Cells Exposed to Cathomycin (C) DNA**

Incubation time (minutes)	Wild-type cells			DB117		
	S ($\times 10^{-3}$)	C	SC	S ($\times 10^{-3}$)	C	SC
10	176	138	9	228	103	<0.1
20	227	192	34	230	217	<0.1
40	200	253	49	235	235	<0.1

* Experiment shown schematically in Figure 9.

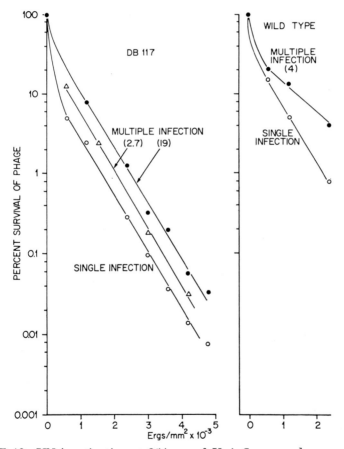

FIGURE 10. UV inactivation at 254 nm of *H. influenzae* phage assayed in two different hosts under conditions of multiple and single infection. The numbers in parentheses are the ratios of input virus to bacteria.

An experiment described schematically in Figure 9 provides evidence that the transformation defect is a failure of the incoming DNA to integrate with the recipient cell genome. DNA bearing one marker (resistance to cathomycin) is incubated with competent cells which are either wild-type or DB117 and which contain another marker (resistance to streptomycin). At intervals, the cells are lysed and the lysate's ability to transform other wild-type cells to both streptomycin and cathomycin resistance is measured. The number of double (streptomycin and cathomycin) transformants is a measure of the amount of integration that took place in the first set of cells. It can be seen from the data of Table 2 that there are considerable numbers of double transformations from the wild-type lysate, but no evidence of any from the DB117 lysate. It is also apparent that the time course of the number of transformations from the original marker on the DNA (cathomycin resistance) is not remarkably different in the two lysates, showing that the lack of transformation in DB117 cannot be explained on the basis of increased nuclease activity in these cells.

If there is indeed something wrong with the recombination mechanism in DB117, it should be possible to show a difference between wild type and DB117 with respect to other types of recombination. *H. influenzae* phage is a DNA-containing temperate virus (Harm and Rupert. 1963). Following extracellular ultraviolet irradiation of these phages, the phage DNA may be repaired in wild-type *H. influenzae* as well as in DB117 (J. K. Setlow *et al.*, 1968a). One way to assess recombination in phage DNA is to measure multiplicity reactivation, a phenomenon in which viable phages are produced by multiple infection with phages that are nonviable in single infection (Luria, 1947). Multiplicity reactivation is usually considered to result from recombination of undamaged parts of nonviable phage (Dulbecco, 1952).

The survival of UV-irradiated phage on single infection is approximately the same in wild-type cells and in DB117 (Figure 10) (J. K. Setlow *et al.*, 1968a). However, the multiple infection survival is different in the two strains. There is little or no evidence of multiplicity reactivation in DB117 since the final slopes of the survival curves are very similar (Figure 10). However, the final slopes in the case of the wild-type hosts differ by about a factor of two, a situation similar to that in T4 phage (Harm, 1956).

Two conclusions may be drawn from this experiment: (1) *H. influenzae* phage makes use of the recombination mechanism belonging to the host cell, and (2) DB117 does indeed have a defective recombination mechanism.

It is of interest to determine whether there are other biological or biochemical properties that are altered in DB117. For example, it is reasonable to suppose that a defect in a rejoining enzyme such as polynucleotide ligase (Gellert, Little, Oshinsky, and Zimmerman, 1970, see pages 548 to 554, this volume) could be responsible for the lack of recombination. However, if this is true, the ligase must be a special one, since the rejoining of single strand breaks made by excision of pyrimidine dimers in DB117 is normal, even though the mutant is defective in rejoining X ray-induced single strand breaks (J. K. Setlow *et al.*, 1968b). Thus, there may be a special ligase that joins together pieces of DNA in recombination as well as X ray-induced breaks.

ACKNOWLEDGMENTS

This research was sponsored by the United States Atomic Energy Commission under contract with the Union Carbide Corporation. We thank Miss Alice Mattingly for competent technical assistance in the early phases of some of the experiments.

REFERENCES

Baker, R. F., and C. Yanofsky. 1968. The Periodicity of RNA Polymerase Initiations: A New Regulatory Feature of Transcription. *Proceedings of the National Academy of Sciences of the U.S.A.*, 60:313–320.

Carrier, W. L., and R. B. Setlow. 1970. Endonuclease from *Micrococcus luteus* which has Activity toward Ultraviolet-Irradiated DNA: Purification and Properties. *Journal of Bacteriology*, 102:178–186.

Dulbecco, R. 1952. A Critical Test for the Recombination Theory of Multiplicity Reactivation. *Journal of Bacteriology*, 63:199–207.

Gellert, M., J. W. Little, C. K. Oshinsky, and S. B. Zimmerman. 1970. "Studies on the Enzymatic Joining of DNA Strands," *Genetic Concepts and Neoplasia* (The University of Texas M. D. Anderson Hospital and Tumor Institute at Houston, 23rd Annual Symposium on Fundamental Cancer Research, 1969). Baltimore, Maryland: The Williams & Wilkins Company. Pp. 548–554.

Harm, W. 1956. On the Mechanism of Multiplicity Reactivation in Bacteriophage. *Virology*, 2:559–564.

Harm, W., and C. S. Rupert. 1963. Infection of Transformable Cells of *Haemophilus influenzae* by Bacteriophage and Bacteriophage DNA. *Zeitschrift für Vererbungslehre*, 94:336–348.

Imamoto, F., and C. Yanofsky. 1967. Transcription of the Tryptophan Operon in Polarity Mutants of *Escherichia coli*. I. Characterization of the Tryptophan Messenger RNA of Polar Mutants. *Journal of Molecular Biology*, 28:1–23.

Luria, S. E. 1947. Reactivation of Irradiated Bacteriophage by Transfer of Self-Reproducing Units. *Proceedings of the National Academy of Sciences of the U.S.A.*, 33:253–264.

Randolph, M. L., and J. K. Setlow. 1969. X-Ray Damage to the DNA of *Haemophilus influenzae* and its Repair. *Biophysical Journal* (Society Abstracts, Thirteenth Annual Meeting, February 26–March 1, 1969, Los Angeles, California), 9:A-56.

Setlow, J. K., D. C. Brown, M. E. Boling, A. Mattingly, and M. P. Gordon. 1968a. Repair of Deoxyribonucleic Acid in *Haemophilus influenzae*. I. X-Ray Sensitivity of Ultraviolet-Sensitive Mutants and their Behavior as Hosts to Ultraviolet-Irradiated Bacteriophage and Transforming Deoxyribonucleic Acid. *Journal of Bacteriology*, 95:546–558.

Setlow, J. K., M. L. Randolph, M. E. Boling, A. Mattingly, G. Price, and M. P. Gordon. 1968b. Repair of DNA in Haemophilus influenzae. II. Excision, Repair of Single-Strand Breaks, Defects in Transformation, and Host Cell Modification in UV-Sensitive Mutants. *Cold Spring Harbor Symposia on Quantitative Biology*, 33: 209–218.

Setlow, R. B., and W. L. Carrier. 1964. The Disappearance of Thymine Dimers from DNA: An Error-Correcting Mechanism. *Proceedings of the National Academy of Sciences of the U.S.A.*, 51:226–231.

Setlow, R. B., J. K. Setlow, and W. L. Carrier. 1970. Endonuclease from *Micrococcus luteus* which has Activity toward Ultraviolet-Irradiated Deoxyribonucleic Acid: Its Action on Transforming Deoxyribonucleic Acid. *Journal of Bacteriology*, 102: 187–192.

Setlow, R. B., P. A. Swenson, and W. L. Carrier. 1963. Thymine Dimers and Inhibition of DNA Synthesis by Ultraviolet Irradiation of Cells. *Science*, 142: 1464–1466.

Steinhart, W. L., and R. M. Herriott. 1968. Fate of Recipient Deoxyribonucleic Acid During Transformation in *Haemophilus influenzae*. *Journal of Bacteriology*, 96: 1718–1724.

Discussion

Dr. Martin Gellert, National Institute of Arthritis and Metabolic Diseases, National Institutes of Health, Bethesda, Maryland: I have a comment for Dr. Hanawalt about repair of nitrogen mustard-produced cross-links. We get 10 or 20 molecules of nitrogen mustard bound by just one end for every one which actually produces a cross-link. I suggest that, in this case, repair replication may be largely repair of those lesions in which there is only a monofunctional reaction. I don't doubt that there is repair of cross-links to some extent. I think the biological data show this, but when you look at it chemically, you may be seeing mainly the repair of single events instead of doubles.

Dr. Jane K. Setlow, Oak Ridge National Laboratory, Oak Ridge, Tennessee: Dr. Gellert, I don't believe the relationship between sensitivity to X rays in *Escherichia coli* mutants and the ability to rejoin X-ray-induced breaks is clear. When screening for polynucleotide ligase in the mutants, was it clear that all of them failed to rejoin X-ray-induced breaks?

Dr. Gellert: No. They were just X-ray sensitive. They were not screened for anything except that.

Dr. Philip C. Hanawalt, Stanford University, Palo Alto, California: Dr. Setlow, if the repair of transforming deoxyribonucleic acid (DNA) occurs after integration and if integration involves incorporation of a single strand, and that would appear to be the damaged strand, wouldn't you expect to observe cases in which the repair may involve the reversion to the untransformed states, since it would be using the host DNA as template for the repair?

Dr. Setlow: Absolutely. I suspect that is one of the causes of the decrease in the transforming ability of DNA. However, we know that it doesn't happen all the time because we can measure some survival. In other words, even though the dimer is chopped out of the offending piece, the marker is still intact because it is on the rest of the transforming DNA.

Dr. R. B. Painter, University of California Medical Center, San Francisco, California: Regarding the X-ray-induced single strand breaks, Dr. Smith at Stanford has already shown that X-ray-induced breaks, *i.e.* X-irradiated DNA, are not repaired by ligase alone. Also, he has data indicating that most damage does not occur in the phosphate backbone, but probably in the sugar.

Dr. Setlow: There is, in some strains, a correlation between single strand rejoining in X-ray-treated cells and survival. The correlation has not been established well in a number of *E. coli* strains, but it has in some and it certainly has been established well in *Haemophilus* by Randolph.

Dr. Hanawalt: Yes. However, the level of rejoining may not reflect anything about the level of ligase activity, but rather what is going on in the preceding steps.

DNA Strand Scission and Rejoining in Mammalian Cells

RONALD M. HUMPHREY, D. L. STEWARD, AND B. A. SEDITA

Section of Cellular Studies, Department of Physics, The University of Texas M. D. Anderson Hospital and Tumor Institute at Houston, Houston, Texas

The repair of damage to a critical cellular molecule(s) may determine whether a given cell lives or dies. It is not surprising then that cells of all types appear to have the capacity to modify damage induced by chemicals and radiation. At the molecular level, a great deal has been learned about the lesion(s) induced by exposure to radiation (especially ultraviolet light [UV]) and about the biochemical steps leading to the modification of damage (see review by Hanawalt, 1969).

Ionizing radiation produces single and double strand breaks in a critical target molecule, deoxyribonucleic acid (DNA), and it has been reported that radiation resistant bacterial cells have the capability of rejoining the single strand breaks (McGrath and Williams, 1966; Kaplan, 1966). This rejoining process was demonstrated by the use of zone-sedimentation analysis in alkaline-sucrose gradients. In this way the sedimentation coefficient of the DNA was measured in control and irradiated cells and the molecular weight calculated (Burgi and Hershey, 1963; Studier, 1965) when cells labeled with tritiated thymidine (^{3}H-TdR) were gently lysed on top of an alkaline sucrose gradient. The single strand breaks produced in the irradiated DNA resulted in a molecular weight significantly lower than the unirradiated control DNA. However, if irradiated cells were incubated in normal growth medium following irradiation, a return of molecular weight to the control level was observed, and this change has been interpreted as evidence of a rejoining process. Shortly thereafter, a similar response was demonstrated in mouse leukemic cells (Lett, Caldwell, Dean, and Alexander, 1967) with the DNA rejoining mechanism appearing to be analogous to that of bacterial cells.

These discoveries have led us and several other laboratories to investigate the nature of the DNA rejoining process in several lines of mammalian cells by the use of alkaline sucrose gradients. Some of the specific questions which have been investigated are: (1) What is the influence of the stage of the mammalian cell cycle [The cell cycle consists of the pre-DNA synthesis period, G_1; the DNA synthesis period, S; the post-DNA synthesis period, G_2; the mitotic period, M (Howard and Pelc, 1953).] on the induction and rejoining of single strand breaks? (2) Is the rejoining process enzymatic in nature? (3) Is there a requirement for synthesis of DNA, ribonucleic acid (RNA), or protein for the rejoining of single strand breaks in mammalian cells? (4) What is the effect on the rejoining process when a known radiation sensitizer, 5-bromodeoxyuridine (BUdR) is present in the DNA?

Experimental Protocol

CELL LINES AND SYNCHRONY TECHNIQUES

The cell lines used in the present study were the human kidney T cells (Bootsma, 1965), Chinese hamster strain (Don) (Hsu and Zenses, 1964), and Chinese hamster ovary (CHO) (Tjio and Puck, 1958). The stock cultures were maintained as monolayers in McCoy's 5a medium supplemented with 20 per cent fetal calf serum.

The technique for synchronizing Don hamster cells labeled with ³H-TdR in large rotating glass cylinders has been previously described (Humphrey, Steward, and Sedita, 1968). Briefly, labeled cells were collected in metaphase by the addition of Colcemid to the medium 2 hr

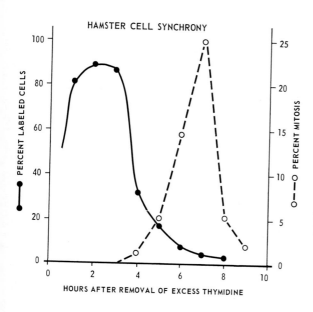

FIGURE 1. CHO cells synchronized by excess TdR (8 mM). The number of S-phase cells was determined by 10-min pulse label with ³H-TdR. The per cent mitosis was determined by counting number mitotic figures per 1,000 cells.

prior to selective detachment of the mitotic cells (Stubblefield and Klevecz, 1965). For CHO and T cells the cell cultures were grown for 15 hr
in ^{3}H-TdR medium (0.5 μc/ml, 1.9 Ci/mM) and were then synchronized
with excess thymidine (TdR) (Petersen and Anderson, 1964; Galavazi,
Schenk, and Bootsma, 1966). With this technique a large population of
cells was obtained at the G_1-S boundary when the excess TdR was washed
from the cultures.

The movement of synchronized cells was determined by scoring
labeled S-phase cells and mitotic index. Figure 1 shows the results for
CHO cells. The response of S-phase cells was determined beginning at
1 hr after washing out excess TdR. To obtain mitotic cells, Colcemid was
added after 3 hr incubation and the culture was incubated for an additional 2 hr. Gentle shaking of the monolayer yielded a cell suspension
with about 95 per cent metaphase arrested cells.

T cells were used to obtain data on response of G_1 phase and the G_1
population was obtained 13 hr after washing out excess TdR.

The treatment of cells (gamma irradiation procedure), lysing technique, centrifugation technique, assay procedure for radioactivity in the
gradient, and calculation for molecular weight determinations have all
been reported in detail (Humphrey, Steward, and Sedita, 1968). An
outline of the experimental protocol is given in Figure 2. Cells suspended
in saline were lysed in a solution of 2 per cent tri-iso-propylnaphthalene
sulfonic acid (Eastman Organic Chemical) and 1 per cent p-amino-
salicylic acid (Sigma) adjusted to pH 12.5. All gradients were the constant velocity, exponential type (Noll, 1967) and the sucrose solutions
were adjusted to pH 12.5 with NaOH. Centrifugation was carried out in
a Spinco Model L preparative ultracentrifuge at 22,500 rpm for 4½ hr,

TABLE 1. *The Efficiency of Single Strand Break Induction by Ionizing Radiation
at Different Phases of the Cell Cycle*

Phase of cell cycle	B/g/rad*
Asynchronous	2.05×10^{12}
S phase	1.9×10^{12}
Mitosis	2.05×10^{12}

* Calculations based on the relationship of:

$$\text{B/g/rad} = N \left(\frac{\dfrac{1}{\text{mol wt}_i} - \dfrac{1}{\text{mol wt}_c}}{\text{dose (rads)}} \right)$$

where N is Avogadro's number, mol wt$_i$ is the
number average molecular weight of DNA of irradiated cells, and mol wt$_c$ is from unirradiated controls.

Abbreviation: B, breaks.

EXPERIMENTAL PROTOCOL

Cells grown 15 Hr. with 0.5 μc/ml
H^{3}TdR (1.9 Ci/mM)

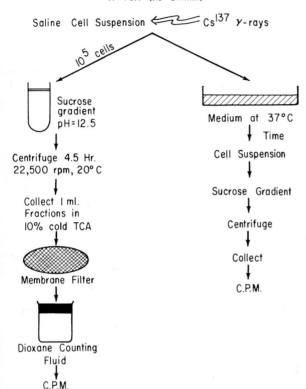

FIGURE 2. Diagram showing the experimental protocol for determining the molecular weight of DNA. Details are given in text.

20 C, using an SW 25.1 rotor. Fractions (1 ml) were precipitated with cold 10 per cent trichloroacetic acid (TCA), collected on 0.45 μ cellulose nitrate filters and assayed for radioactivity in a liquid scintillation spectrometer.

Modifications introduced for temperature changes, drug treatment, UV exposure, and pulse labeling were as follows: (1) For temperature changes the cells were incubated either at room temperature (22 C) or in an ice bath (2 C) for the given time period; (2) Freshly prepared drug dilutions in water were introduced to the culture medium just prior to addition of the cells; (3) For UV experiments the cells were grown on plastic Petri dishes in medium containing 0.5 μc/ml tritiated bromodeoxyuridine (^{3}H-BUdR) and 5.0 μg/ml BUdR for 15 to 18 hr. Calculations for the percentage of TdR replacement were done according to Dewey and Humphrey (1965). Cells around the edge of the dish were removed by scraping with a cotton swab; the dish was washed twice with saline and exposed to UV. The UV source and calibration have been described elsewhere (Humphrey, Dewey, and Cork, 1963); (4) For pulse experiments, exponentially growing cultures were labeled with 10 μc/ml of ³H-TdR (6.0 Ci/mM) for 1 min at 37 C. Immediately the culture was washed three times with cold (2 C) medium containing 10 μg/ml TdR. In both (3) and (4), cells were removed from the surface by a rubber policeman and treated as shown in Figure 2.

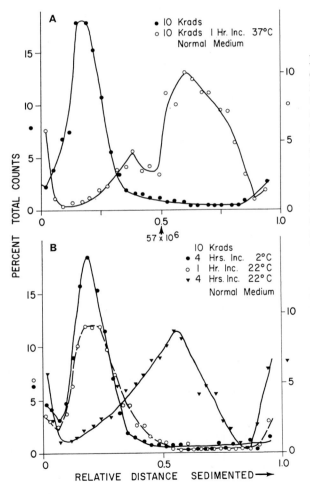

FIGURE 3. The profile of radioactive material in terms of per cent total counts versus the distance sedimented in the centrifuge tube. Centrifugation was at 22,500 rpm for 4.5 hr at 20 C on constant velocity alkaline sucrose gradient. Panel A, cells received 10,000 rads and were lysed immediately (●), incubated for 1 hr at 37 C (○); Panel B, incubated 1 hr at 22 C (○), 4 hr at 22 C (▼), or 4 hr at 2 C (●). The molecular weight is indicated at the mid-point of the centrifuge tube for orientation purposes. In each of these graphs the molecular weight at 0.25 was 10.5×10^6 and 160×10^6 at 0.75.

Results and Discussion

EFFICIENCY OF BREAK PRODUCTION

It has been shown that for mammalian cells the yield of single strand breaks in the DNA is proportional to the X-ray dose (Lett, Caldwell,

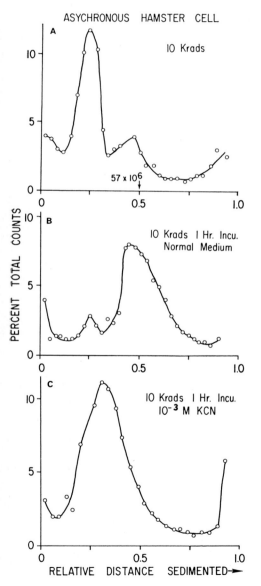

FIGURE 4. Radioactivity profile of DNA from asynchronous hamster cells irradiated with 10,000 rads and lysed immediately (A); incubated one hour at 37 C in normal medium (B); or incubated 1 hr in medium plus 10^{-3} M KCN (C).

Dean, and Alexander, 1967; Lohman, 1968). By use of synchronized populations it was possible to obtain data on the efficiency of break production at different phases of the cell cycle. The data shown in Table 1 indicate that the number of single strand breaks induced per rad is uniform through the cell cycle. In terms of cell killing and chromosomal damage, Chinese hamster cells are most sensitive to X ray while in the G_2 and mitotic phases, and most resistant in the S phase (Sinclair and Morton, 1965; Dewey, 1967). However, the data presented here clearly demonstrate that the DNA sustained the same amount of damage per molecule whether the cells were in the most sensitive (G_2 and mitosis) or the most resistant (S) phase.

THE ENZYMATIC NATURE OF THE REJOINING PROCESS

Studies on the effect of low temperature on the repair of sub-lethal damage have been interpreted as indicating that the repair process may be a passive, physical chemical reaction in the cell (Elkind et al., 1965). However, other data on effects of both low temperature and oxidative metabolism on repair of sub-lethal damage and restitution of chromosomal damage indicate the repair process could be enzymatic in nature (Wolff and Luippold, 1954; Savage, Neary, and Evans, 1960; Hall and Lajtha, 1963; Berry and Oliver, 1964; Berry, 1966). We have examined the effect of low temperature and potassium cyanide (KCN) on rejoining of single strand breaks and the data are illustrated in Figures 3 and 4.

Figure 3 shows the effect of different post-irradiation temperatures on the process of rejoining single strand breaks. In these experiments asychronous populations of hamster cells were used. Following a dose of 10,000 rads, the weight average molecular weight (the weight average molecular weight was calculated from the distribution of the radioactivity in the centrifuge tube based on the relationship of sedimentation coefficient and molecular weight derived for alkaline-treated DNA [Studier, 1965]) was 20×10^6. Incubation for 1 hr at 37 C after irradiation resulted in a molecular weight of about 80×10^6 (Figure 3A). From Figure 3B it can be seen that at 22 C the rejoining process was slowed but not completely inhibited and after 4 hr the molecular weight was similar to that at 37 C. Incubation times of 4 hr or longer at 2 C failed to give any evidence of strand rejoining. However, if the temperature inhibited cells were returned to 37 C the rejoining process was complete within 1 hr giving a molecular weight distribution similar to that shown in Figure 3A. A marked inhibitory effect by 10^{-3} M KCN on the rejoining process is seen from the data of Figure 4. These data strongly suggest that the DNA rejoining process is enzymatic in nature, having an optimal temperature of around 37 C and a requirement for an active oxidative metabolism.

EFFECT OF CELL CYCLE AND METABOLIC INHIBITORS ON
THE REJOINING PROCESS

Although the age-dependent radiation response of mammalian cells

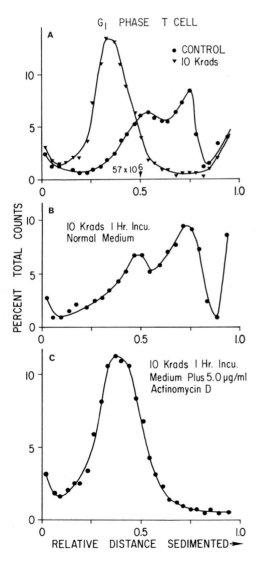

FIGURE 5. Radioactivity profile of DNA from synchronized T cells irradiated during the G_1 phase. (A) unirradiated control (●) and 10,000 rads lysed immediately (▼); (B) 1 hr incubation in normal medium; and (C) 1 hr incubation in medium plus 5.0 μg/ml AD.

is well documented both for chromosomal damage and cell killing (see reviews by Wolff, 1968, and Sinclair, 1968), the explanation for this phenomenon has not been elucidated. Some of the explanations advanced

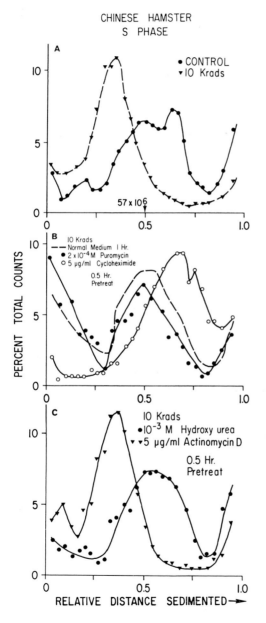

FIGURE 6. Radioactivity profile of DNA from synchronized CHO cells irradiated during the S phase. (A) (●) unirradiated control and (▼) 10,000 rads lyse immediately; (B) 10,000 rads and 1 hr incubation in normal medium (- - -), (●) 1 hr incubation in medium plus 2×10^{-4} M puromycin and (○) 1 hr incubation in medium plus 5 μg/ml cycloheximide; (C) 10,000 rads and 1 hr incubation in medium plus 10^{-3} M HU (●), and (▼) 1 hr incubation in medium containing 5 μg/ml AD. The cell cultures also received a 0.5 hr pre-treatment with drug prior to irradiation.

TABLE 2. *The Molecular Weight (Weight Average)* of Denatured DNA Obtained from Unirradiated Control Cells, Irradiated Cells (10,000 rads), and Irradiated Cells Following a 1- to 2-Hr Postirradiation Incubation During Different Phases of the Cell Cycle in Normal Medium or Medium Containing Inhibitor*

			Treatment (post-incubation)				
Cell cycle period	Control	Irradiated	Normal medium	Medium plus AD†	Medium plus HU‡	Medium plus FUdR§	Medium plus puro-mycin#
Asynchronous	57 ± 12	20 ± 5	60 ± 17	——	——	——	——
Mitosis							
(metaphase)	56 ± 18	25 ± 5	48 ± 10	——	——	——	——
S	61 ± 18	26 ± 7	72 ± 11	33 ± 13	68 ± 6	72 ± 15	70 ± 18

* The standard deviation is indicated.
† AD $= 5.0$ μg/ml.
‡ HU $= 10^{-3}$ M.
§ FUdR $= 0.1$ μg/ml.
# Puromycin $= 2 \times 10^{-4}$ M.

are: (1) a quantitative difference in the amount of damage produced in critical-target molecules by a given dose of irradiation; (2) a change in the number of critical-target molecules; (3) a change in the nature of the critical-target molecule; (4) fluctuations during the cycle of molecules such as oxygen or -SH groups which alter radiation response; and (5) qualitative or quantitative differences in cellular repair capability.

As a working model for our experiments we have assumed that DNA is the critical target molecule and we have attempted to measure the ability of cells to rejoin single strand breaks in the DNA under different conditions during various phases of the cell cycle.

The data given in Figures 5, 6, and 7 show that the rejoining process is functional when the cells are in G_1, S, and mitosis. Data (not shown) for G_2 phase cells are also in agreement with this observation. These data (Lohman, 1968; Humphrey, Steward, and Sedita, 1968) confirm previous observations on this important finding, and indicate that single strand breaks are rejoined in all phases of the cell cycle.

Since cells in metaphase are not engaged in DNA synthesis and have a very low rate of ribonucleic acid (RNA) or protein synthesis (Taylor, 1960; Prescott and Bender, 1962; Terasima and Tolmach, 1963), we have interpreted these results as indicating that extensive DNA, RNA, or protein synthesis is probably not required for rejoining of DNA strands. We have conducted corollary experiments with metabolic inhibitors such as puromycin, cycloheximide, hydroxyurea (HU), fluorodeoxyuridine

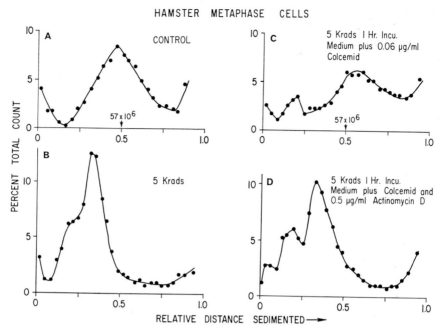

FIGURE 7. Radioactivity profile of DNA from synchronized CHO cells irradiated during metaphase (95 per cent mitotic index at beginning and end of experiment). (A) unirradiated control; (B) 5,000 rads and lyse immediately; (C) 5,000 rads and 1 hr incubation in medium plus 0.06 μg/ml Colcemid; (D) 5,000 rads and 1 hr incubation in medium plus Colcemid and 5.0 μg/ml AD (not 0.5 μg/ml AD, as stated in picture).

(FUdR), actinomycin D (AD), and 2-mercapto-1-(β-4-pyridethyl) benzimidazole (MPB), with both asynchronous and synchronous populations (Figures 5, 6, 7, and Tables 1 and 2). It can be seen that the inhibition of protein synthesis (puromycin and cycloheximide) and DNA synthesis (FUdR and HU) did not diminish the rejoining process. However, a marked effect of AD was observed, *i.e.*, the molecular weight of post-incubated cells (33×10^6) remained very close to that of the irradiated control (25×10^6). It is interesting to note that a similar pattern of drug response has been observed by Elkind and associates when measuring the repair of sub-lethal damage by X-ray dose fractionation survival experiments (Elkind, Moses, and Sutton-Gilbert, 1967; Elkind, 1967; Elkind, Kamper, Moses, and Sutton-Gilbert, 1967).

The mechanism of AD inhibition of rejoining of single strand breaks may be caused by either (1) a requirement for RNA synthesis caused by the inhibition of DNA-dependent RNA synthesis (Goldberg and Rabino-witz, 1962; Hurwitz, Furth, Malamy, and Alexander, 1962), or (2) a steric hindrance between the site to be repaired and the enzyme system caused by the binding property of AD to the DNA (Kersten, 1961; Ding-man and Sporn, 1965). We have performed a series of experiments with the RNA synthesis inhibitor, MPB, which apparently does not bind to the DNA, to distinguish between these two possibilities (Summers and Mueller, 1968). RNA synthesis was reduced to about 15 per cent of the control level within 0.5 hr after the addition of 50 μg/ml of MPB.

Asynchronous cultures were treated in the following manner. The inhibitor MPB was present during 0.5 hr pre-irradiation incubation, dur-ing irradiation, and during the 1 hr post-irradiation incubation. In a series

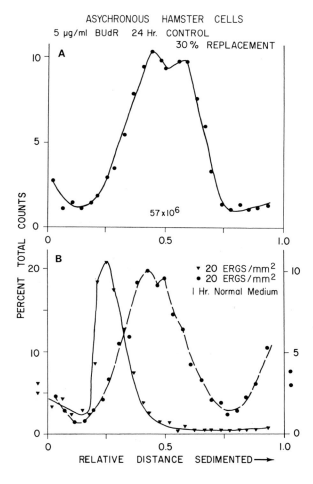

FIGURE 8. Radioactiv-ity profile of DNA from asynchronous CHO cells grown for 24 hr on medium con-taining BUdR and ^{3}H-BUdR with 30 per cent TdR replacement. (A) unirradiated control; (B) (▼) 20 ergs/mm^2 lyse immediately and (●) 20 ergs/mm^2 plus 1 hr incubation in nor-mal medium.

of experiments there was no evidence of any repression of rejoining of single strand breaks. These experiments therefore lend support to the argument that extensive RNA synthesis is not required for rejoining of DNA breaks. However, we cannot rule out the possibility that the residual capacity for RNA synthesis (15 per cent) might be involved in the rejoining process.

The lack of a requirement for DNA and protein synthesis has also been reported in other cellular repair phenomena. For example, it has been shown that the DNA synthesis inhibitors, HU and cytosine arabinoside, had no effect on repair replication in HeLa cells (Cleaver, 1968). The argument was advanced that these inhibitors act mainly at the level of nucleotide precursors. Since only small numbers of nucleotides would be required for repair replication there probably were sufficient quantities available to complete the process without continued synthesis. It is entirely feasible that this argument might also explain the lack of effect on rejoining of single strand breaks by FUdR and HU. Several investigators (Berry, 1966; Humphrey, Steward, and Sedita, 1968; Hanawalt, 1969) as well as the present data, have shown that the repair enzymes are present and functional at all times in the life of the cell. Therefore, the requirement for *de novo* synthesis of repair enzymes in response to radiation induced damage would not be necessary; hence the lack of effect of the protein synthesis inhibitors, puromycin and cycloheximide, on rejoining of single strand breaks.

THE EFFECT OF BUDR INCORPORATION ON THE INDUCTION
AND REJOINING OF SINGLE STRAND BREAKS

Incorporation of the halogenated pyrimidine, BUdR, into the DNA of virus, bacteria, or mammalian cells results in an increased response to radiation. However, the mechanism of action is not yet clear (Szybalski and Opara-Kubinska, 1965). Even though the presence of BUdR in the DNA appears to have no influence on the quantitative yield of single strand breaks in the DNA chain, the repair capacity of bacterial cells is altered (Szybalski, 1966) and more DNA-protein cross-links are formed than in normal DNA (Smith, 1964). However, for mammalian cells, the presence of BUdR at sensitizing levels does not affect the ability of HeLa cells to repair sub-lethal damage (Kim, Eidinoff, Delihas, and Laughlin, 1964). Also, we have observed that, at non-toxic levels of BUdR incorporation (30 per cent TdR replacement) in Chinese hamster cells, there is no effect on the rejoining of single strand breaks, whether induced by gamma rays or UV (Figure 8). A similar response has been observed in T cells at low levels of incorporation, but at high levels (65 per cent TdR replace-ment) there appears to be an inhibition of rejoining (Lohman, personal communication).

THE INDUCTION OF SINGLE STRAND BREAKS BY ULTRAVIOLET LIGHT

UV does not ordinarily induce single strand breaks in normal DNA. However, DNA which contains a halogenated pyrimidine such as BUdR has a lower molecular weight following exposure to UV when analyzed on alkaline sucrose gradients (Hutchinson and Koehnlein, 1967). The exact nature of the damage which results in a lower molecular weight may be caused either by direct breaks in the phosphodiester bond of the DNA or by changes in the base or sugar moiety which results in alkali-unstable bonds. Evidence that the former case is probably correct, *i.e.*, UV induces single strand breaks, recently has been discovered (Hewitt, Marburger, and Lapthisophon, 1969).

We also have observed single strand breaks in mammalian cell DNA following UV exposure as shown in Figure 9. Since the sensitizing effect of BUdR is dependent on the percentage of BUdR in the DNA prior to the onset of drug-induced toxicity (Dewey and Humphrey, 1966), we reasoned that it might be possible to measure the production of single strand breaks and their repair in BUdR-treated cells in the range of 10 to 50 per cent survival.

Cell cultures (Don) were incubated in medium containing 5.0 μg/ml of BUdR + 0.5 μc/ml ^{3}H-BUdR (0.57 Ci/mM) for 16 hr to label the DNA prior to exposure to UV. The D_0 dose obtained from colony forming ex-periments was determined to be about 10 ergs/mm^2. The reduction in weight average molecular weight was essentially proportional to the ex-posure dose up to about 20 ergs/mm^2 with a significant decrease in molec-ular weight at 10 ergs/mm^2 (Figure 9). It was of interest to determine

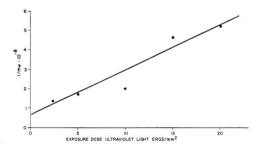

FIGURE 9. Plot of the recipro-cal of the weight average mo-lecular weight of DNA from CHO cells grown in the pres-ence of BUdR as a function of UV exposure dose.

if strand rejoining occurred under these conditions; the data are presented in Figure 8. It can be seen that at a TdR replacement value of 30 per cent, single strand breaks were rejoined during the 1-hr postirradiation incubation period. Thus, these data indicate that breaks are rejoined regardless of the method of induction (gamma rays or UV) and that BUdR incorporation at levels below drug-induced toxicity does not affect strand rejoining.

THE EFFECT OF VARIOUS AGENTS ON DISCONTINUOUS DNA SYNTHESIS IN MAMMALIAN CELLS

Several investigators have described the phenomenon of discontinuous synthesis of DNA in bacteriophage infected *Escherichia coli* (Okazaki *et al.*, 1968) and in normal *E. coli* (Yudelevich, Ginsberg, and Hurwitz, 1968) in which a series of short segments of DNA are synthesized and eventually covalently joined together by the action of the enzyme, polynucleotide ligase (Gellert, 1967; Weiss and Richardson, 1967). It also has been demonstrated that in alkaline conditions the newly synthesized ^{3}H-DNA sedimented independently of the parental ^{14}C-DNA and at a much slower rate indicating a lower molecular weight than the parental DNA (Yudelevich, Ginsberg, and Hurwitz, 1968). In mammalian cells the occurrence of small segments of newly synthesized DNA defined by a short pulse of ^{3}H-TdR has been reported (Schandl and Taylor, 1969). Furthermore, the ligase enzyme has been purified and its properties demonstrated in a variety of mammalian tissue (Lindahl and Edelman, 1968).

To further characterize the rejoining process in mammalian cells we have performed pulse-chase experiments with CHO cells in which cultures were given various treatments between a 1-min pulse and a subsequent incubation period. In our experiments, log phase cultures were exposed to 10 μc/ml (6.0 Ci/m$_M$) of ^{3}H-TdR for 1 min at 37 C. Following two washes in saline containing 10 μg/ml TdR the cells were either (1) lysed immediately, (2) incubated in medium (10 μg/ml TdR) for 30 min, (3) exposed to ultraviolet light and then incubated in medium (10 μg/ml TdR), or (4) incubated in medium supplemented with a metabolic inhibitor. In the FUdR part of the experiment TdR was not added to the medium. The molecular weight of the ^{3}H-TdR-labeled single-stranded DNA of pulsed cells was then determined on alkaline sucrose gradients. The radioactivity profiles of such an experiment are shown in Figure 10. The majority of the newly synthesized DNA sedimented in a peak corresponding to a molecular weight of about 10×10^6 (Figure 10a). During a subsequent 30-min incubation period in normal medium the ³H-DNA sedimented at a faster rate with a peak molecular weight of 30×10^6 (Figure 10b). A further incubation period of 30 min yielded the unit size of DNA characteristically observed in our gradients (Figures 5 and 6). Although the rate of DNA synthesis is markedly reduced at 50 ergs/mm² (Bootsma and Humphrey, 1968) there appeared to be very

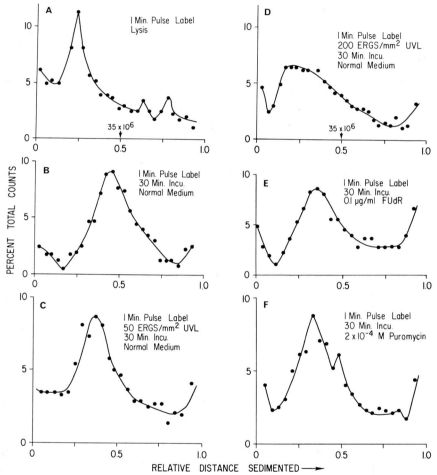

FIGURE 10. Radioactivity profile of DNA from asynchronous CHO cells following a 1-min pulse label with ³H-TdR. A—lysed immediately; B—incubated 30 min in normal medium; C—irradiated with 50 ergs/mm² UV and then incubated 30 min; D—the same as in C except 200 ergs/mm²; E—incubated 30 min in medium containing 0.1 μg/ml FUdR; F—incubated 30 min in medium containing 2×10^{-4} M puromycin.

little effect on the movement of the lower to higher molecular weight material (Figure 10). However, at much higher doses (200 ergs/mm²) there was considerable delay in movement of ³H-DNA to a higher molecular weight (Figure 10d). Other data indicate that an incubation period of about 2 hr was required to achieve a molecular weight distribution equivalent to that for unirradiated cultures. Therefore, at sufficiently high UV doses, it is possible that enough damage (pyrimidine dimers and DNA-protein cross-links) is induced so that the rate of joining up the DNA segments was reduced.

If FUdR and puromycin were present during the 30-min incubation period there was an indication of some inhibition of the movement of the lower to higher molecular weight material, but from Figures 10e and 10f it can be seen that the inhibition was not extensive. We interpret these data to mean that continued DNA or protein synthesis is not required for the formation of the phosphodiester bonds. Other experiments at low incubation temperatures (2 C) have shown a complete inhibition of the joining process.

THE SIZE OF MAMMALIAN CHROMOSOME DNA

The technique of autoradiography has been used by several investigators to measure the length of DNA fibers in mammalian cell chromosomes. It appears that the DNA of a chromosome may exist as a long fiber of several centimeters with a molecular weight between 10^{10} and 10^{11} (Cairns, 1966; Sasaki and Norman, 1966; Huberman and Riggs. 1966). Speculation (see Taylor, 1963; DuPraw, 1965, for proposed models) on how this DNA is packaged ranges from one long continuous single DNA molecule to a series of smaller units linked together by some molecule which is labile to high salt, alkaline, or detergent conditions (McGrath and Williams, 1967; Humphrey, Steward, and Sedita, 1968; Corry and Cole, 1968).

Using a 30-min labeling period with ³H-TdR and autoradiography (Huberman and Riggs, 1968), replicating sections of DNA pieces, varying from 7 to 30 μm and about 15 to 50×10^6 mol wt, were found. An additional incubation of cells for 45 min in a pulse-chase experiment gave evidence for DNA pieces of 100 μ in length (200×10^6 mol wt). For single strand DNA this is a close approximation to the size of the apparent sub-unit of 50 to 100×10^6 mol wt which is observed in our gradients (Table 2 for summary of molecular weight).

In an attempt to correlate the autoradiographic and sedimentation data (long-term label and short pulse), we have proposed the scheme outlined in Figure 11 for the arrangement of DNA in the chromosome. Recently sedimentation data have been presented which support the hypothesis that mammalian cell DNA is synthesized in small segments as defined by 15 sec to 1 min pulse labels with ^{3}H-TdR (Figure 10) (Painter, 1968; Taylor, Straubing, and Schandl, 1968; Schandl and Taylor, 1969). These would be the 15 sec to 1 min pulse units of Figure 11 and probably are below the limits of detection by ordinary autoradiographic techniques. A series of these small fragments may be joined together after 30 min incubation resulting in larger units with a higher molecular weight (intermediate unit). The size of this intermediate unit (mol wt = 50 to 60×10^6 double-stranded DNA) corresponds to the replicating sections

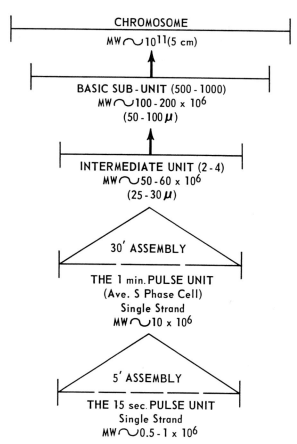

FIGURE 11. A possible scheme for the assembly of DNA sub-units in the mammalian cell chromosome.

observed (Huberman and Riggs, 1968) and to the size of the "replicon" unit described for mouse leukemic cells (Okada, 1968).

As stated earlier in this paper a subsequent incubation period (total 1 hr) of pulse-labeled (1 min) cells resulted in molecular weight distributions of DNA similar to cells which had been uniformly labeled by a 15- to 18-hr incorporation period. This observation lends further support to the hypothesis that the chromosomal DNA is arranged in a series of subunits (Cairns, 1966; McGrath and Williams, 1967; Huberman and Riggs, 1968; Okada, 1968; Humphrey, Steward, and Sedita, 1968; Corry and Cole, 1968; Taylor, 1960) held together by linker molecules which are labile to high salt or alkaline conditions.

Summary

The data on radiation-induced single strand breaks and rejoining in mammalian cell DNA support the following conclusions: (1) the processes which are responsible for the rejoining of broken pieces of DNA are present and functional during all phases of the cell cycle; (2) the DNA rejoining process in mammalian cells is enzymatic in nature and does not require an extensive synthesis of DNA, RNA, or protein; (3) the presence of BUdR in the DNA at sensitizing, but non-toxic levels, does not inhibit the rejoining process; (4) the chromosomal DNA of mammalian cells appears to be replicated as small units which are subsequently joined by a polynucleotide joining enzyme into the larger sub-units composing the long DNA fiber of the chromosome. Therefore, these data support the hypothesis that the mammalian cell chromosomal DNA is arranged in a series of small units held together by molecules which are labile to high salt alkaline, or detergent conditions.

Although there is as yet no direct proof for a relationship among the phenomena of DNA-strand rejoining, repair replication, recovery of sub-lethal damage, restitution of chromosomal damage, and cell survival in mammalian cells, we submit that the weight of evidence, thus far obtained, supports the hypothesis that these phenomena are related manifestations of cellular repair processes.

ACKNOWLEDGMENTS

Special appreciation is expressed to Mrs. V. Willingham and Mrs. J. Winston, and Mr. Joe Allred for the synchronization of many cultures and for the collection of several hundred sucrose gradients, and to Mrs. Beverly Whitesel for editorial assistance.

The authors would like to thank Dr. Paul Lohman (Medical Biological Laboratory, Rijswijk, The Netherlands) for making some of his data available prior to publication. Computations were performed by the Common Research Computer Facility supported by United States Public Health Service grant FR-00254. Supported in part by grant CA-04484 from the National Cancer Institute.

REFERENCES

Berry, R. J. 1966. Effects of Some Metabolic Inhibitors on X-ray Dose-Response Curves for the Survival of Mammalian Cells In Vitro, and on Early Recovery Between Fractionated X-ray Doses. *British Journal of Radiology*, 39:458–463.

Berry, R. J., and R. Oliver. 1964. Effect of Post-Irradiation Incubation Conditions on Recovery Between Fractionated Doses of X-ray. *Nature*, 201:94–96.

Bootsma, D. 1965. Changes Induced in the First Post-Irradiation Generation Cycle of Human Cells Studied by Double Labeling. *Experimental Cell Research*, 38: 429–431.

Bootsma, D., and R. M. Humphrey. 1968. The Progression of Mammalian Cells Through the Division Cycle Following Ultraviolet Irradiation. *Mutation Research*, 5:289–298.

Burgi, E., and A. D. Hershey. 1963. Sedimentation Rate as a Measure of Molecular Weight of DNA. *Biophysical Journal*, 3:309–321.

Cairns, J. 1966. Autoradiography of HeLa Cell DNA. *Journal of Molecular Biology*, 15:372–373.

Cleaver, J. E. 1968. Repair Replication and Degradation of Bromouracil Substituted DNA in Mammalian Cells After Ultraviolet Irradiation. *Biophysical Journal*, 8: 775–791.

Corry, P. M., and A. Cole. 1968. Radiation-Induced Double-Strand Scission of the DNA of Mammalian Metaphase Chromosomes. *Radiation Research*, 36:528–543.

Dewey, W. C. 1967. Comparison of Chromosomal Damage and Lethality in Synchronized Chinese Hamster Cells. *Radiation Research*, 31:577.

Dewey, W. C., and R. M. Humphrey. 1962. Relative Radiosensitivity of Different Phases in the Life Cycle of L-P59 Mouse Fibroblasts and Ascites Tumor Cells. *Radiation Research*, 16:503–530.

———. 1965. Increase in Radiosensitivity to Ionizing Radiation Related to Replacement of Thymidine in Mammalian Cells with 5-Bromodeoxyuridine. *Radiation Research*, 26:538–553.

Dingman, C. W., and M. B. Sporn. 1965. Actinomycin D and Hydrocortisone: Intracellular Binding in Rat Liver. *Science*, 149:1251–1254.

DuPraw, E. J. 1965. Macromolecular Organization of Nuclei and Chromosomes: A Folded Fibre Model Based on Whole-Mount Electron Microscopy. *Nature*, 206: 338–343.

Elkind, M. M. 1967. "Sublethal X-ray Damage and Its Repair in Mammalian Cells," *Radiation Research 1966*, G. Silini, Ed. Amsterdam, The Netherlands: North-Holland Publishing Company. Pp. 558–586.

Elkind, M. M., C. Kamper, W. B. Moses, and H. Sutton-Gilbert. 1967. "Sub-Lethal Radiation Damage and Repair in Mammalian Cells," *Recovery and Repair Mechanisms in Radiobiology* (Brookhaven Symposia in Biology). Upton, New York: Brookhaven National Laboratory. No. 20. Pp. 134–157.

Elkind, M. M., W. B. Moses, and H. Sutton-Gilbert. 1967. Radiation Response of

Mammalian Cells Grown in Culture. VI. Protein, DNA, and RNA Inhibition During the Repair of X-Ray Damage. *Radiation Research*, 31:156–173.

Elkind, M. M., H. Sutton-Gilbert, W. B. Moses, T. Alescio, and R. W. Swain. 1965. Radiation Response of Mammalian Cells Grown in Culture. V. Temperature Dependence of the Repair of X-Ray Damage in Surviving Cells (Aerobic and Hypoxic). *Radiation Research*, 25:359–376.

Galavazi, G., H. Schenk, and D. Bootsma. 1966. Synchronization of Mammalian Cells In Vitro by Inhibition of the DNA Synthesis. *Experimental Cell Research*, 41:428–437.

Gellert, M. 1967. Formation of Covalent Circles of Lambda DNA by *E. coli* Extracts. *Proceedings of the National Academy of Sciences of the U.S.A.*, 57:148–155.

Goldberg, I. H., and M. Rabinowitz. 1962. Actinomycin D Inhibition of Deoxyribonucleic Acid Dependent Synthesis of Ribonucleic Acid. *Science*, 136:315–316.

Hall, E. J., and Z. G. Lajtha. 1963. The Recovery of *Vicia faba* Meristem Cells From X-Radiation. *Radiation Research*, 20:187–194.

Hanawalt, P. 1968. "Cellular Recovery from Photochemical Damage," *Recent Progress in Photochemistry*, A. C. Giese, Ed. New York, New York: Academic Press, Inc. Vol. IV. P. 203.

Hewitt, R., K. Marburger, and T. Lapthisophon. 1969. A Mechanism for 5-Bromouracial Sensitization of Some Biological Systems to Ultraviolet Light. (Abstract) *Radiation Research*. (in press.)

Howard, A., and S. R. Pelc. 1953. Synthesis of Deoxyribonucleic Acid in Normal and Irradiated Cells and Its Relation to Chromosome Breakage. *Heredity*, 6:261–273.

Hsu, T. C., and M. T. Zenses. 1964. Mammalian Chromosomes In Vitro. XVII. Idiogram of the Chinese Hamster. *Journal of the National Cancer Institute*, 32:857–869.

Huberman, J. A., and A. D. Riggs. 1966. Autoradiography of Chromosomal DNA Fibers from Chinese Hamster Cells. *Proceedings of the National Academy of Sciences of the U.S.A.*, 55:599–606.

———. 1968. On the Mechanism of DNA Replication in Mammalian Chromosomes. *Journal of Molecular Biology*, 32:327–341.

Humphrey, R. M., W. C. Dewey, and A. Cork. 1963. Relative Ultraviolet Sensitivity of Different Phases in the Cell Cycle of Chinese Hamster Cells Grown In Vitro. *Radiation Research*, 19:247–260.

Humphrey, R. M., D. L. Steward, and B. A. Sedita. 1968. DNA-Strand Breaks and Rejoining Following Exposure of Synchronized Chinese Hamster Cells to Ionizing Radiation. *Mutation Research*, 6:459–465.

Hurwitz, J., J. J. Furth, M. Malamy, and M. Alexander. 1962. The Role of DNA and RNA Synthesis. III. The Inhibition of Enzymatic Synthesis of RNA and DNA by Actinomycin D and Proflavine. *Proceedings of the National Academy of Sciences of the U.S.A.*, 48:1222–1229.

Hutchinson, F., and W. Koehnlein. 1967. The Mechanism by Which Bromouracil Sensitizes DNA to Ultraviolet. (Abstract) *Radiation Research*, 31:547.

Kaplan, H. S. 1966. DNA-Strand Scission and Loss of Viability after X Irradiation of Normal and Sensitized Bacterial Cells. *Proceedings of the National Academy of Sciences of the U.S.A.*, 55:1442–1446.

Kersten, W. 1961. Interaction of Actinomycin C with Constituents of Nucleic Acids. *Biochimica et biophysica acta*, 47:610–611.

Kim, J. H., M. L. Eidinoff, N. Delihas, and J. S. Laughlin. 1964. The Effect of 5-Bromodeoxyuridine on the Recovery Phenomenon in Sublethally Irradiated Cells. *Experimental Cell Research*, 36:411–438.

Lett, J. T., I. Caldwell, C. J. Dean, and P. Alexander. 1967. Rejoining of X-Ray Induced Breaks in the DNA of Leukaemia Cells. *Nature*, 214:790–792.

Lindahl, T., and G. M. Edelman. 1968. Polynucleotide Ligase from Myeloid and Lymphoid Tissues. *Proceedings of the National Academy of Sciences of the U.S.A.*, 61:680–687.

Lohman, P. H. M. 1968. Induction and Rejoining of Breaks in the Deoxyribonucleic Acid of Human Cells Irradiated at Various Phases of the Cell Cycle. *Mutation Research*, 6:449–458.

———. Personal Communication.

McGrath, R. A., and R. W. Williams. 1966. Reconstruction In Vivo of Irradiated *Escherichia coli* Deoxyribonucleic Acid; the Rejoining of Broken Pieces. *Nature*, 212:534–535.

———. 1967. Interruptions in Single Strands of the DNA in Slime Mold and Other Organisms. *Biophysical Journal*, 7:309–317.

Noll, H. 1967. Characterization of Macromolecules by Constant Velocity Sedimentation. *Nature*, 215:360–363.

Okada, S. 1968. Replicating Units (Replicons) of DNA in Cultured Mammalian Cells. *Biophysical Journal*, 8:650–664.

Okazaki, R., T. Okazaki, K. Sakabe, K. Sugimoto, and A. Sugino. 1968. Mechanism of DNA Chain Growth. I. Possible Discontinuity and Unusual Secondary Structure of Newly Synthesized Chains. *Proceedings of the National Academy of Sciences of the U.S.A.*, 59:598–605.

Painter, R. B., and A. Schaefer. 1969. State of Newly Synthesized HeLa DNA. *Nature*, 221:1215–1217.

Petersen, D. F., and E. C. Anderson. 1964. Quantity Production of Synchronized Mammalian Cells in Suspension Culture. *Nature*, 203:642–643.

Prescott, D. M., and M. A. Bender. 1962. Synthesis of RNA and Protein During Mitosis in Mammalian Tissue Culture Cells. *Experimental Cell Research*, 26:260–268.

Sasaki, M. S., and A. Norman. 1966. DNA Fibres from Human Lymphocyte Nuclei. *Experimental Cell Research*, 44:642–645.

Savage, J. R. K., G. J. Neary, and H. J. Evans. 1960. The Rejoining Time of Chromatid Breaks Induced by Gamma Radiation in *Vicia faba* Root Tips at 3°C. *Journal of Biophysical and Biochemical Cytology*, 7:79–85.

Schandl, E. K., and J. H. Taylor. 1969. Early Events in the Replication and Integration of DNA Into Mammalian Chromosomes. *Biochemical and Biophysical Research Communications*, 34:291–300.

Sinclair, W. K., and R. A. Morton. 1965. X-Ray and Ultraviolet Sensitivity of Synchronized Chinese Hamster Cells at Various Stages of the Cell Cycle. *Biophysical Journal*, 5:1–25.

Sinclair, W. K. 1968. Cyclic X-Ray Responses in Mammalian Cells In Vitro. *Radiation Research*, 33:620–643.

Smith, K. 1964. "Photochemistry of the Nucleic Acids," *Photophysiology*, A. C. Giese, Ed. New York, New York: Academic Press, Inc. Vol. II. Pp. 329–388.

Stubblefield, E., and R. Klevecz. 1965. Synchronization of Chinese Hamster Cells by Reversal of Colcemid Inhibition. *Experimental Cell Research*, 40:660–664.

Studier, F. W. 1965. Sedimentation Studies of the Size and Shape of DNA. *Journal of Molecular Biology*, 11:373–390.

Summers, W. P., and G. C. Mueller. 1968. A Study of Factors Regulating RNA Synthesis in HeLa Cells Using MPB, A Reversible Inhibitor of RNA Synthesis. *Biochemical and Biophysical Research Communications*, 30:350–355.

Szybalski, W. 1966. Molecular Events Resulting in Radiation Injury, Repair, and Sensitization of DNA. *Journal of the Arkansas Medical Society*, 62:488–494.

Szybalski, W., and Z. Opara-Kubinska. 1965. "Radiobiological and Physicochemical Properties of 5-Bromodeoxyuridine-Labeled Transforming DNA as Related to the Nature of the Critical Radiosensitive Structures," *Cellular Radiation Biology*, (The University of Texas M. D. Anderson Hospital and Tumor Institute at Houston, 18th Annual Symposium on Fundamental Cancer Research, 1964). Baltimore, Maryland: The Williams and Wilkins Co. Pp. 223–240.

Taylor, J. H. 1960. Nucleic Acid Synthesis in Relation to the Cell Division Cycle. *Annals of the New York Academy of Sciences*, 90:409–421.

————, Editor. 1963. *Molecular Genetics.* New York, New York: Academic Press, Inc., 46 pp.

Taylor, J. H., N. Straubing, and E. Schandl. 1968. Units and Patterns of Replication in Mammalian Chromosomes. (Abstract) *The Journal of Cell Biology*, 39:134a.

Terasima, T., and L. J. Tolmach. 1963. Growth and Nucleic Acid Synthesis in Synchronously Dividing Populations of HeLa Cells. *Experimental Cell Research*, 30:344–362.

Tjio, J. H., and T. T. Puck. 1958. Genetics of Somatic Mammalian Cells. II. Chromosomal Constitution of Cells in Tissue Culture. *Journal of Experimental Medicine*, 108:259–268.

Weiss, B., and C. C. Richardson. 1967. Enzymatic Breakage and Joining of Deoxyribonucleic Acid. I. Repair of Single-Strand Breaks in DNA by an Enzyme System from *Escherichia coli* Infected with T_4 Bacteriophage. *Proceedings of the National Academy of Sciences of the U.S.A.*, 57:1021–1028.

Wolff, S. 1968. Chromosome Aberrations and the Cell Cycle. *Radiation Research*, 33:609–619.

Wolff, S., and H. E. Luippold. 1954. Metabolism and Chromosome Break Rejoining. *Science*, 122:231–232.

Yudelevich, A., B. Ginsberg, and J. Hurwitz. 1968. Discontinuous Synthesis of DNA during Replication. *Proceedings of the National Academy of Sciences of the U.S.A.*, 61:1129–1136.

Nonconservative Replication of Damaged DNA in Mammalian Cells

R. B. PAINTER

Laboratory of Radiobiology, University of California Medical Center, San Francisco, California

For some time, our laboratory has been engaged in attempts to demonstrate repair of mammalian deoxyribonucleic acid (DNA). Specifically, we have demonstrated that "repair replication," as first described in bacteria by Pettijohn and Hanawalt (1964), occurs in mammalian cells after ultraviolet (UV)-irradiation (Rasmussen and Painter, 1966; Cleaver, 1967, 1968a; Cleaver and Painter, 1968) and large doses of X-irradiation (Painter and Cleaver, 1967; Painter, 1968). Repair replication apparently occurs in mammalian cells also after treatment with nitrogen mustard (Roberts, Crathorn, and Brent, 1968) and after illumination of cells in which the DNA contains a base analogue (Painter and Cleaver, 1969). In this paper, I shall review the results of our studies on repair replication after lower doses of ionizing radiation and discuss characteristics of the product of repair replication.

Materials and Methods

HeLa S3 monolayer cultures were grown in Eagle's minimal essential medium (MEM) supplemented with 15 per cent calf serum. The protocol for CsCl equilibrium density gradient (isopycnic) experiments was as follows: Cultures were grown exponentially in Eagle's MEM which was changed to Eagle's MEM containing 10^{-6} M 5-fluorodeoxyuridine (FUdR) and 1.6×10^{-5} M 5-bromodeoxyuridine (BUdR) and incubation was continued for one hour. This medium was removed and replaced with Leibovitz medium containing 10^{-6} M FUdR and 1.6×10^{-5} M ³H-BUdR (20 μc/ml, Schwarz BioResearch) just prior to irradiation. The cultures were irradiated at 1,200 R per minute with 300 kvp X rays at a half-value layer (HVL) of 0.36 mm Cu. Incubation in radioactive medium for three hours after the irradiation was followed by washing and incubation for one more hour in 10^{-6} M FUdR plus 1.6×10^{-5} M non-radioactive BUdR. The cells were then washed with 0.15 M saline-0.015 M sodium citrate (SSC), scraped into SSC, centrifuged, and resuspended in 0.5 ml SSC. Three drops of 1 per cent sodium dodecyl sulfate were added and the cells subjected to three rapid freeze-thaw (-80 C to 60 C) cycles to assure complete lysis. To this suspension, ribonuclease (K + K Chemicals) was added to a final concentration of 50 μg/ml and incubation continued at 37 C for one hour. Pronase (Calbiochem) was then added to a final concentration of 500 μg/ml and incubation continued for one more hour. The mixture was extracted vigorously twice with an equal volume of chloroform-amyl alcohol (24:1), dialyzed against three or more changes of SSC, diluted with SSC to 4.50 ml, and added to 5.8 g CsCl. The preparations were placed in polyallomer tubes and spun at 37,000 rev/min for 36 or more hours in the 40 rotor of a Model L (Beckman Spinco) ultracentrifuge. Fractions were collected from the bottom of each tube using an automatic fraction collector behind a continuous flow cell in a PMQ II (Zeiss Instruments) to record the absorption of light at 260 nm. Aliquots (10 or 50 μl) from each fraction were placed onto Whatman 3 MM circular (1-inch diameter) filter papers, which were immersed in 5 per cent trichloroacetic acid (TCA), then in alcohol, and finally in acetone, dried, placed in toluene containing 4 g/l PPO and 50 mg/l POPOP and counted in a scintillation spectrometer (Packard Instrument Company).

Venom phosphodiesterase (Calbiochem) was purified according to the method of Keller (1964). Terminally labeled DNA was prepared by Dr. Newton Hayes, Los Alamos Laboratory, using purified terminal nucleotidyl transferase (addase) from calf thymus. Some preparations were made from HeLa DNA from our laboratory while others were made from calf thymus DNA (Calbiochem). The end addition with ^{14}C-deoxyadenosine triphosphate (Schwarz BioResearch) amounted to about 2 per cent of the total DNA.

Uniformly labeled HeLa DNA was prepared by growing the cells for four days with 0.01 μg/ml ^{14}C-labeled thymidine. The "repair DNA" was obtained from cells which were irradiated with 10^5 R and incubated with ^{3}H-BUdR; this material was purified by rebanding samples of the "repair peak." All DNA samples were extracted three or more times with phenol and then exhaustively dialyzed to remove the phenol.

To determine the kinetics of release of radioactivity from DNA, 0.1 ml DNA (8 to 9 μg labeled with ^{3}H or ^{14}C) was incubated with 0.1 ml 10^{-1} M NaCl, 0.1 ml 10^{-2} M MgCl$_2$, 0.6 ml 0.1 M Tris (pH 9.3), and 0.06 ml (31.2 units [one unit is defined as the amount of enzyme that produces a change of 0.01 in optical density (OD) at 400 nm in 15 minutes when incubated at pH 9.3 with 0.006 M p-nitrophenylphosphothymidine]) of phosphodiesterase. The release of radioactivity was monitored by removing 0.1-ml aliquots every 10 to 15 minutes and adding to them 0.1 ml of 1 mg/ml herring sperm DNA (Calbiochem) and 0.8 ml ice cold 4 per cent perchloric acid (PCA). The aliquots were then centrifuged, and in 0.5 ml of the supernatants, radioactivity was counted. Two aliquots were removed before addition of enzyme. One was used for the zero time point; the other was hydrolyzed by heating at 100 C for 10 minutes with 4 per cent PCA to determine the total radioactivity in the DNA sample.

Results

HeLa cells irradiated with 0, 10^2, 10^3, and 10^4 R and incubated according to the protocol outlined in the section on Materials and Methods were analyzed isopycnically. The first centrifugations yielded patterns indistinguishable from one another, $i.e.$ no evidence for repair replication was observed in any of the gradients. From each gradient, the fractions that contained the normal and intermediate density regions were combined and analyzed isopycnically again. The results of this first rebanding op-

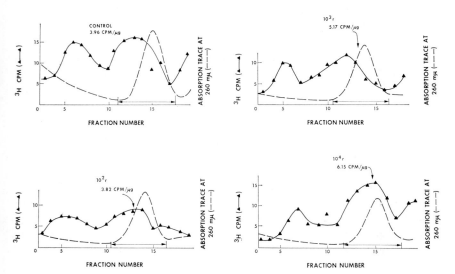

FIGURE 1. Plots of second reband of equilibrium density gradients from cells irradiated with 0, 10^2, 10^3, and 10^4 R and incubated with ^{3}H-BUdR, as indicated in the text. Arrows show fractions from each gradient from which the final measurements of specific activity were made.

eration also failed to show clear evidence for repair replication, so the rebanding operation was repeated. The results of the second rebanding (third gradient) show evidence for nonconservative synthesis (Figure 1). All gradients, including control, show a peak of radioactivity to the heavy side of normal density, as well as at the hybrid density (the hybrid density still reflects the presence of DNA which was replicated by the semiconservative mode). The regions of normal and intermediate density of each gradient were combined, their OD at 260 nm measured, and their radioactivity determined. Using 1 OD unit $= 48$ μg/ml, the specific activities, as count/min/μg,were: control, 3.96; 10^2 R, 3.82; 10^3 R, 5.17; 10^4 R, 6.15. When measured in this way, there appears to be a weak dose response; however, the results from control cultures and from those irradiated with 100 R are not different.

The results of the solubilization of DNA by phosphodiesterase, which is an exonuclease, are shown in Figure 2. Almost all of the radioactivity of terminally labeled DNA was released within the first 10 minutes, whereas the radioactivity of both the uniformly labeled DNA and the "repaired" DNA was not completely released for 60 to 90 minutes after addition of the enzyme. This experiment was repeated several times. It was also performed with heat-denatured DNA, which yielded essentially the same results (Figure 3). The cause of the slower release from single-stranded DNA is uncertain; however, the enzyme had been stored for a longer time than when used with double-stranded DNA.

Discussion

The difficulty of showing repair replication after ionizing radiation

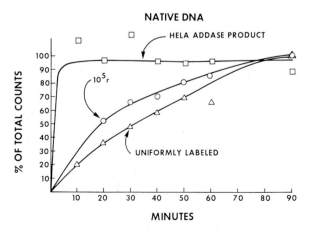

FIGURE 2. Time course of release of radioactivity from various preparations of labeled native DNA by venom phosphodiesterase.

DENATURED DNA

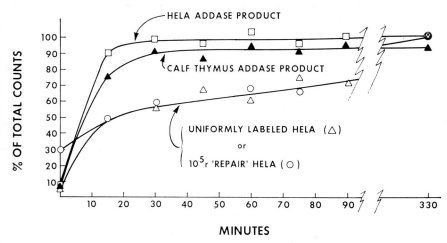

FIGURE 3. Time course of release of radioactivity from various preparations of labeled denatured DNA by venom phosphodiesterase.

is clearly illustrated by this experiment. We have shown previously (Painter and Cleaver, 1967; Painter, 1968) that a clear "repair" peak occurs on the first isopycnic analysis after 10^5 R. Results with phosphodiesterase show that this synthesis does not result from end addition. This enzyme releases radioactivity from "repaired" DNA in almost the same manner as from uniformly labeled DNA; the kinetics of release of radioactivity from the terminal addition product, however, are completely different.

The nature of the nonconservative synthesis that occurs in unirradiated cells is unknown. If radioactive segments formed by semiconservative replication were adjacent to normal density DNA, fragmentation would sometimes occur, such that only a small amount of ^{3}H-BUdR is attached to the end of a normal density fragment. The resulting labeled DNA might band near to or at normal density (Figure 4). We think we eliminated this possibility by incubating the cells with unlabeled BUdR before and after the ^{3}H-BUdR treatment, so that all ^{3}H-labeled DNA formed by semiconservative replication will be contiguous with hybrid segments. This nonconservative replication may be a repair-like synthesis that occurs normally in these cells as a result of nonspecific (*e.g.* thermal) damage or because it may have a normal function in DNA synthesis.

Evidence for the latter in bacteria has been presented and discussed by Hanawalt (1966). Thus, the presence of this synthesis in controls obviously contributes to the difficulty of showing a specific repair response after a low dose of X rays.

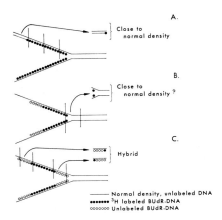

FIGURE 4. Models of DNA labeled by various procedures and of the kinds of labeled fragments possibly generated upon DNA extraction.

a—Molecule in which normal density DNA is immediately adjacent to ^{3}H-BUdR-labeled segment. Upon extraction, some fragments containing ^{3}H-BUdR at the ends of otherwise normal density DNA are generated. These could have so little of the density label that their buoyant density is unaffected but enough ^{3}H to be detected, and thus be confused with DNA labeled by the "repair replication" mode.

b—Molecule in which ^{3}H-BUdR is adjacent to nonradioactive BUdR-containing segment. No fragments of the kind illustrated in a can be generated, but there exists the possibility of fragments being generated which contain the growing point and only a small amount of a newly replicated, ^{3}H-BUdR-labeled, "four-stranded" region. The density of this kind of fragment may also be close to normal.

c—Molecule in which ^{3}H-BUdR is between two nonradioactive BUdR-containing segments. All ^{3}H-labeled fragments generated will have nonradioactive BUdR adjacent to them and, therefore, will band as hybrid.

Consideration of the amount of base damage that occurs in DNA also sheds light on the reasons for difficulties in demonstrating repair replication after X-irradiation. Repair replication is believed to be stimulated by those kinds of injuries, exemplified by base damage, that result in deformation of DNA secondary structure (Hanawalt and Haynes, 1967). The G value for DNA base damage in vivo is not known; for in vitro irradiation, it appears to be 0.2 to 0.7 (Bacq and Alexander, 1961).

The HeLa cell contains an average of 17×10^{-12} g, or 10^{13} daltons, of DNA (Lee and Puck, 1960). One rad $= 100$ ergs/g $= 6 \times 10^{13}$ ev/g, so that the DNA of each HeLa cell absorbs $(17 \cdot 10^{-12} \times 6 \cdot 10^{13})$ about 1,000 ev/rad, which probably results in no more than 10 damaged bases per rad ($G \leq 1$). Therefore, a HeLa cell irradiated with 10^5 R will contain less than 10^6 damaged bases.

Consider now the damage that occurs following UV-irradiation. Trosko, Chu, and Carrier (1965) found that the yield of dimers was about 0.05 per cent per 100 ergs/mm^2 in Chinese hamsters; the yield is not appreciably different in cells of human beings (Regan, Trosko, and Carrier, 1968). Thymine makes up about 0.3 of the bases in mammalian DNA, so there are approximately 10^{10} thymines per HeLa cell. Thus, 100 ergs/mm^2 will yield about 5×10^6 thymine dimers per cell. Thymine-cytosine dimers, cytosine-cytosine dimers, and other kinds of base damage increase the total yield so it is probable that 100 ergs/mm^2 of UV produce at least 10 times as much base damage as do 10^5 R. DNA degradation does not occur in mammalian cells in the first several hours after UV- or X-irradiation (Rasmussen and Painter, 1964; Cleaver, 1968b; Little, 1968; Painter, 1968) and, therefore, amplification of the lesion by extensive excision does not occur as it apparently does in bacteria. Repair replication is difficult to demonstrate in HeLa cells at doses less than 200 ergs/mm^2 and at least one rebanding is necessary to show the repair peak clearly (Cleaver and Painter, 1968). Therefore, it is hardly surprising that it is difficult to demonstrate repair replication after low doses of X rays. And, unfortunately, the question of whether repair replication actually plays a role in enhancing reproductive integrity of mammalian cells still remains unanswered.

ACKNOWLEDGMENTS

I am most grateful to Dr. Newton Hayes for preparing the terminally labeled DNA; I thank Mrs. Beatrice Abrams and Miss Barbara Reisner for their excellent assistance in performing these experiments.

The work was performed under the auspices of the U. S. Atomic Energy Commission.

REFERENCES

Bacq, Z. M., and P. Alexander. 1961. *Fundamentals of Radiobiology*. Oxford, England: Pergamon Press, 2nd Edition. P. 201.

Cleaver, J. E. 1967. The Relationship Between the Rate of DNA Synthesis and its Inhibition by Ultraviolet Light in Mammalian Cells. *Radiation Research*, 30:795–810.

———. 1968a. Defective Repair Replication of DNA in Xeroderma Pigmentosum. *Nature*, 218:652–656.

———. 1968b. Repair Replication and Degradation of Bromouracil-Substituted DNA in Mammalian Cells After Irradiation with Ultraviolet Light. *Biophysical Journal*, 8:775–791.

Cleaver, J. E., and R. B. Painter. 1968. Evidence for Repair Replication of HeLa Cell DNA Damaged by Ultraviolet Light. *Biochimica et biophysica acta*, 161:552–554.

Hanawalt, P. C. 1966. "Repair Replication in the Bacterial Genome," *Genetical Aspects of Radiosensitivity: Mechanisms of Repair*. Vienna, Austria: International Atomic Energy Agency. Pp. 97–104.

Hanawalt, P. C., and R. H. Haynes. 1967. The Repair of DNA. *Scientific American*, 216:36–43.

Keller, E. 1964. The Hydrolysis of "Soluble" Ribonucleic Acid by Snake Venom Phosphodiesterase. *Biochemical and Biophysical Research Communications*, 17: 412–415.

Lee, H. H., and T. T. Puck. 1960. The Action of Ultraviolet Radiation on Mammalian Cells as Studied by Single-Cell Techniques. *Radiation Research*, 12:340–348.

Little, J. B. 1968. Radiation-Induced DNA Degradation in Human Cells: Lack of Evidence Following Moderate Doses of X-rays. *International Journal of Radiation Biology*, 13:591–595.

Painter, R. B. 1968. "Mechanisms of DNA Repair in Mammalian Cells," *Effects of Radiation on Cellular Proliferation and Differentiation*. Vienna, Austria: International Atomic Energy Agency. Pp. 91–102.

Painter, R. B., and J. E. Cleaver. 1967. Repair Replication in HeLa Cells after Large Doses of X-Irradiation. *Nature*, 216:369–370.

———. 1969. Repair Replication, Unscheduled DNA Synthesis and the Repair of Mammalian DNA. *Radiation Research*, 37:451–466.

Pettijohn, D., and P. Hanawalt. 1964. Evidence for Repair-Replication of Ultraviolet Damaged DNA in Bacteria. *Journal of Molecular Biology*, 9:395–410.

Rasmussen, R. E., and R. B. Painter. 1964. Evidence for Repair of Ultra-Violet Damaged Deoxyribonucleic Acid in Cultured Mammalian Cells. *Nature*, 203: 1360–1362.

———. 1966. Radiation-Stimulated DNA Synthesis in Cultured Mammalian Cells. *The Journal of Cell Biology*, 29:11–19.

Regan, J. D., J. E. Trosko, and W. L. Carrier. 1968. Evidence for Excision of Ultraviolet-Induced Pyrimidine Dimers from the DNA of Human Cells in vitro. *Biophysical Journal*, 8:319–325.

Roberts, J. J., A. R. Crathorn, and T. P. Brent. 1968. Repair of Alkylated DNA in Mammalian Cells. *Nature*, 218:970–972.

Trosko, J. E., E. H. Y. Chu, and W. L. Carrier. 1965. The Induction of Thymine Dimers in Ultraviolet-Irradiated Mammalian Cells. *Radiation Research*, 24:667–672.

Discussion

Dr. Jane K. Setlow, Oak Ridge National Laboratory, Oak Ridge, Tennessee: May I introduce a note of caution on the subject of bromouracil (BU) after ultraviolet (UV) treatment. Namely, the UV-treated deoxyribonucleic acid (DNA) containing bromouracil has single-stranded breaks in it. When this DNA is put into alkaline solution, it has single strand breaks. It may just have alkaline-labeled bonds in it.

Dr. R. R. Hewitt, The University of Texas M. D. Anderson Hospital and Tumor Institute at Houston, Houston, Texas: We have just completed a series of experiments in which BU-labeled λ phage infected lysogenic *Escherichia coli* C cells to form the supercircular form of the virus. This provides a means of examining whether irradiated BU-containing DNA is broken by UV irradiation. In this case, the critical test is the comparison of the breakage frequency of supercircular BU-labeled DNA in an alkaline sucrose gradient and in a cesium chloride gradient containing ethidium bromide. There is nearly one-to-one correspondence between the two. The breaks are real. One further demonstration that is needed is an analysis in neutral sucrose gradients; we are now doing this.

Dr. M. M. Elkind, National Institutes of Health, Bethesda, Maryland: Aside from the question of the role bromodeoxyuridine (BUdR) is playing after UV irradiation, apparently the effect of about 10 ergs/mm² was to reduce the average molecular size to about the same region as would 10 kilorads in your X-ray experiments. As you said, 10 ergs/mm² is about the D_0 dose, and is in the measurable range of survival, say 10 to 100 per cent, and yet 10 kilorads produces a very low level of survival with or without BUdR. Further, you pointed out that it looked as if breaks produced by both kinds of radiation were repaired. Are you suggesting perhaps that that repair process might be pertinent to the biological question or the biologically measured repair when, for example, something like colony formation is the point? Do these things fit together well?

Dr. R. B. Painter, University of California Medical Center, San Francisco, California: I will answer this in terms of whether what you see going on in these so-called molecular techniques means anything in terms of repair. After all, the first demonstrations of single strand rejoining in mammalian cells were done at approximately 3,000 R. Thus, there is a process for repair of the strands, but I don't think it means a thing in relation to whether they survive. We don't know what the last couple of steps are.

Dr. Elkind: So perhaps those processes are not related to biological function, at least in terms of cell division. Do you agree with that, Dr. Humphrey?

Dr. Ronald M. Humphrey, The University of Texas M. D. Anderson Hospital and Tumor Institute at Houston, Houston, Texas: Until we can get a biophysical technique which will allow us to use doses in the range of biological interest, the X-ray data are certainly suspect. I am encouraged by the UV data showing a correlation between DNA strand breakage, repair, and survival. That this still required bromouracil in the DNA does not allow too much optimism. I think that with the X-ray data, we must get much lower doses in order to say anything real about survival.

Dr. Daniel Billen, University of Florida, Gainesville, Florida: We have just completed some experiments on correlating repair synthesis and survival. By repair synthesis, I mean what Dr. Hanawalt described, incorporation of tritiated thymidine (^{3}H-TdR) into parental DNA. We starve cells for required amino acids and they become very resistant to UV. Aligned cells which are resistant are compared to actively growing cells. We have found, for example, that after a dose in which we get less than 2 per cent survivors with growing cells, we have roughly the same amount of repair synthesis as in the population of resistant cells that have 40 or 50 per cent survivors. I am not going to interpret this. I just want to say that in looking at these parameters, one must be extremely careful in trying to extrapolate to survival, because here there is no relationship.

In his methodology, Dr. Painter stated that what he was looking at was mostly the strand which was not opposite the BU label. Then he proceeded to show that he had to reband or repurify, and he finally ended up with a fraction of a per cent of what he started out with. Therefore, I believe he must entertain some kind of aberration, in regard to breakdown of that label incorporation, to some very extreme small piece. One must be cautious about concluding anything from this.

Dr. Painter: That's a good point. This particular experiment was done at low counts because we didn't start with as much DNA as we would have liked. In other experiments, we went up to as much as five times this DNA concentration. There is a possibility of breakdown in reutilization, but I don't know how to avoid that with this low level.

Dr. L. D. Samuels, Children's Hospital, Columbus, Ohio: I think your observation, Dr. Painter, about the lack of DNA damage in mammalian cells as compared to bacterial cells is puzzling. Might it relate to the persisting integrity of the histone framework which would minimize the size of the lesion to be repaired in mammalian cells and perhaps give them an advantage in this respect? The possibility that such agents as hydrocortisone have a stabilizing effect on the histone backbone suggests treating the cells with hydrocortisone to see what radiation response modification might occur. Do you think this is worth trying?

Dr. Painter: I don't know what hydrocortisone does. If what we see is non-conservative synthesis reflecting the repair replication mode, if it is the same thing that bacteria are doing, then it is obvious that degradation of the kind that goes on in bacteria isn't occurring. The problem is that nobody knows why degradation after excision occurs in bacteria, so we don't know why it doesn't happen in mammalian cells. I didn't mean to imply the damage was less.

Dr. A. Quiroz-Gutierrez, City of Hope Medical Center, Duarte, California:

In 1962 at the Oncology Hospital in the Mexican Institute of Social Security, animals with an induced plasmacytoma received chloroquine concomitantly with cyclophosphamide. These animals showed a dramatic response in one week. We are now beginning to study patients with these tumors, some of whom are receiving chloroquine for autoimmune disease.

Session Chairman K. Lemone Yielding, University of Alabama in Birmingham, Birmingham, Alabama: I've also been told that Burkitt's lymphoma shows good response to alkylating agents, and many in this patient population are receiving chloroquine at the time they are treated for Burkitt's lymphoma.

Index

Index

Major outhors and co-authors are listed in boldface; names of discussants are listed alphabetically under the major entry, DISCUSSANTS.

A